# Practical Management Science

VSB 2008

Fourth Edition

Wayne L.Winston | S. Christian Albright

with Cases by: Mark Broadie | Lawrence L. Lapin | William D.Whisler

CENGAGE
Learning·

Australia • Brazil • Japan • Korea • Mexico • Singapore • Spain • United Kingdom • United States

CENGAGE
Learning·

**Practical Management Science: VSB 2008,
Fourth Edition**

Practical Management Science, Fourth Edition
Wayne L. Winston | S. Christian Albright

© 2012, 2009 South-Western, Cengage Learning. All rights reserved.
Library of Congress Control Number: 2011922240

ExamView® is a registered trademark of eInstruction Corp. Windows
is a registered trademark of the Microsoft Corporation used herein
under license. Macintosh and Power Macintosh are registered
trademarks of Apple Computer, Inc. used herein under license.

Executive Editors:
 Maureen Staudt
 Michael Stranz

Senior Project Development Manager:
 Linda deStefano

Marketing Specialist:
 Courtney Sheldon

Senior Production/Manufacturing Manager:
 Donna M. Brown

Production Editorial Manager:
 Kim Frv

Sr. Rights Acquisition Account Manager:
 Todd Osborne

For product information and technology assistance, contact us at
**Cengage Learning Customer & Sales Support, 1-800-354-9706**

For permission to use material from this text or product,
submit all requests online at **cengage.com/permissions**
Further permissions questions can be emailed to
**permissionrequest@cengage.com**

This book contains select works from existing Cengage Learning resources and
was produced by Cengage Learning Custom Solutions for collegiate use. As such,
those adopting and/or contributing to this work are responsible for editorial
content accuracy, continuity and completeness.

**Compilation © 2012 Cengage Learning**
ISBN-13: 978-1-285-13943-2

ISBN-10: 1-285-13943-7
**Cengage Learning**
5191 Natorp Boulevard
Mason, Ohio 45040
USA

Cengage Learning is a leading provider of customized learning solutions with
office locations around the globe, including Singapore, the United Kingdom,
Australia, Mexico, Brazil, and Japan. Locate your local office at:
**international.cengage.com/region.**
Cengage Learning products are represented in Canada by Nelson Education, Ltd.
For your lifelong learning solutions, visit **www.cengage.com/custom.**
Visit our corporate website at **www.cengage.com.**

# Brief Contents

Insert:
*Analytics: The New Path to Value*
MIT Sloan Management Review and the IBM Institute for Business Value

Excerpted from:
*Practical Management Science*
Fourth Edition
Winston and Albright

| 2 | Introduction to Spreadsheet Modeling | 1 |
|---|---|---|
| 3 | Introduction to Optimization Modeling | 47 |
| 4 | Linear Programming Models | 113 |
| 6 | Optimization Models with Integer Variables | 207 |
| 8 | Evolutionary Solver:  An Alternative Optimization Procedure | 267 |
| 9 | Decision Making Under Uncertainty | 321 |
| 10 | Introduction to Simulation Modeling | 397 |

**Online Chapters**

| 15 | Project Management | I 5-1 |
|---|---|---|
| 16 | Multiobjective Decision Making | I 6-1 |

# MITSloan
## Management Review

## RESEARCH REPORT
## FALL 2010

In collaboration with
IBM Institute for Business Value

FINDINGS FROM THE 2010 NEW INTELLIGENT ENTERPRISE
GLOBAL EXECUTIVE STUDY AND RESEARCH PROJECT

# Analytics: The New Path to Value

How the Smartest Organizations Are
Embedding Analytics to Transform
Insights Into Action

By *MIT Sloan Management Review* and
the IBM Institute for Business Value

## AUTHORS

**STEVE LAVALLE** is the global strategy leader for IBM's Business Analytics and Optimization service line, where he leads a global team of consultants and practitioners focused on helping clients optimize their results through the application of insights, analytics and business process improvements. He can be contacted at steve.lavalle@us.ibm.com.

**MICHAEL S. HOPKINS** is editor-in-chief of *MIT Sloan Management Review*, which brings ideas from the world of thinkers to the executives and managers who use them to build businesses. He can be reached at mhopkins@mit.edu.

**ERIC LESSER** is the research director and North American leader of the IBM Institute for Business Value, where he oversees the fact-based research IBM undertakes to develop its thought leadership. He can be contacted at elesser@us.ibm.com.

**REBECCA SHOCKLEY** is the business analytics and optimization global lead for the IBM Institute for Business Value, where she conducts fact-based research to develop thought leadership for senior executives. She can be reached at rshock@us.ibm.com.

**NINA KRUSCHWITZ** is an editor and the special projects manager at *MIT Sloan Management Review*, where she coordinates the publication's editorial and innovation hub activities. She can be reached at ninakru@mit.edu.

## CONTRIBUTORS

**Fred Balboni**, GBS Global Leader: Business Analytics and Optimization (BAO), IBM
**Dr. Michael Haydock**, GBS Global Leader: Customer Analytics, IBM
**Deborah Kasdan**, Writer: GBS Strategic Communications, IBM
**Christine Kinser**, Global Leader: GBS Strategic Communications, IBM
**Katharyn White,** Vice President of Marketing, IBM

For more information or permission to reprint, please contact MIT SMR at:
E-mail: mitsmr@pubservice.com
Fax: +1 818-487-4550, attention MIT SMR/Permissions
Phone: 818-487-2064
Mail: MIT Sloan Management Review
    PO Box 15955
    North Hollywood, CA 91615

SPONSORS

# CONTENTS

## Chapter 1: Findings of The New Intelligent Enterprise Study

**3** The competitive push for analytics-driven management
**4** Top performers say analytics is a differentiator
**5** Three levels of capabilities have emerged, each with distinct opportunities
**6** Data is not the biggest obstacle
**6** Information must become easier to understand and act upon
**CASE:** Analytics, not best guesses, drive ad decisions
**7** What leaders can do to make analytics pay off — a new methodology

## Chapter 2: The Five Recommendations

**7** Recommendation 1: **Focus on the biggest and highest value opportunities**
**CASE:** Tackling healthcare fraud leads to sweeping reforms
**FOCUS:** Introducing the PADIE technique for operationalizing analytics

**9** Recommendation 2: **Within each opportunity, start with questions, not data**
**CASE:** Shifting gears from vehicle-centric to customer-centric marketing

**10** Recommendation 3: **Embed insights to drive actions and deliver value**
**CASE:** A beverage company makes the case

**12** Recommendation 4: **Keep existing capabilities while adding new ones**
**CASE:** Bridging business and analytics skills across the organization

**13** Recommendation 5: **Use an information agenda to plan for the future**
**CASE:** Insurer limits risk by establishing an agenda for today and tomorrow
**FOCUS:** How analytics propagates across functions

## Chapter 3: How to Set Yourself Up for Success

**15** Techniques to get started
**16** Make analytics pay off

## Chapter 4: The Survey — Questions and Responses

**17** Questionnaire and overall results of the 2010 New Intelligent Enterprise
Global Executive Survey

**2** Executive
Summary

**17** About the
Research

**22** Acknowledgments &
Related Publications

# Executive Summary

As the well-documented "data deluge" deepens, many executives have shifted from feeling overwhelmed (60% say they "have more information than we can effectively use") to recognizing that the smartest organizations are already capitalizing on increased information richness and analytics to gain competitive advantage.

To understand better how all organizations are attempting to capitalize on information and apply analytics today and in the future, *MIT Sloan Management Review* in collaboration with the IBM Institute for Business Value conducted a study that included a survey of nearly 3,000 executive managers worldwide, as well as in-depth interviews with leading researchers.

## Among the top-line survey findings:

**Top performers view analytics as a differentiator:** Top-performing companies are three times more likely than lower performers to be sophisticated users of analytics, and are two times more likely to say that their analytics use is a competitive differentiator.

**The biggest obstacle is not the data:** Despite the enormous challenge felt by most organizations to "get the data right," that's not what executives name as the key barrier to achieving the competitive advantage that "big data" can offer — the top two barriers are "lack of understanding of how to use analytics to improve the business" and "lack of management bandwidth."

**Where are the leaders headed? Toward making information "come alive":** Over the next 24 months, executives say they will focus on supplementing standard historical reporting of data with emerging approaches that convert information into scenarios and simulations that make insights easier to understand and to act on.

Based on data from our survey, case studies and interviews with experts, we have identified a new, five-point methodology for successfully implementing analytics-driven management and for rapidly creating value. This report describes that emerging methodology and its five critical recommendations.

▶ **Focus on the biggest opportunities first.** Attack one big important problem that can demonstrate value and catalyze the organization toward action.

▶ **Start with questions, not data.** Understand the problem — and the insights needed to solve it — before working on the data that will yield the insights.

▶ **Embed insights to drive action.** Ensure end-result impact by making information come to life, articulating use cases and expressing data-driven insights in ways that even nonexperts can understand and act upon.

▶ **Keep existing capabilities while adding new ones.** Even as centralized analytics oversight grows, keep distributed, localized capabilities in place.

▶ **Build the analytics foundation according to an information agenda.** Opportunistic application of analytics can create value fast, but it must be part of an enterprise-wide information-and-analytics plan.

# Analytics:
# The New Path to Value

How the smartest organizations are embedding analytics to transform insights into action

*The combination of an increasingly complex world, the vast proliferation of data and the pressing need to stay one step ahead of the competition has sharpened focus on using analytics within organizations. To understand better how organizations are applying analytics today, prioritizing their future investments and transforming insights into action,* MIT Sloan Management Review *in collaboration with the IBM Institute for Business Value surveyed a global sample of nearly 3,000 executives, managers and analysts. Based on our analysis of survey results, combined with interviews with academic and subject matter experts, this study offers recommendations on how organizations can bolster their analytics capabilities to achieve long-term advantage.*

At organizations in every industry, in every part of the world, senior leaders wonder whether they are getting full value from the massive amounts of information they already have within their organizations. New technologies are collecting more data than ever before, yet many organizations are still looking for better ways to obtain value from their data and compete in the marketplace. Their questions about how best to achieve value persist.

Are competitors obtaining sharper, more timely insights? Are they able to regain market advantage neglected while focusing on expenses during the past two years? Are they correctly interpreting new signals from the global economy — and adequately assessing the impact on their customers and partners? Knowing what happened and why it happened are no longer adequate. Organizations need to know what is happening now, what is likely to happen next and what actions should be taken to get the optimal results.

To help organizations understand the opportunity provided by information and advanced analytics, *MIT Sloan Management Review* partnered with the IBM Institute for Business Value to conduct a survey of nearly 3,000 executives, managers and analysts working across more than 30 industries and 100 countries (see "About the Research").

Among our key findings: Top-performing organizations use analytics five times more than lower performers (see Figure 1). Overall, our survey found widespread belief that analytics offers value. Half of our respondents said that *improvement of information and analytics was a top*

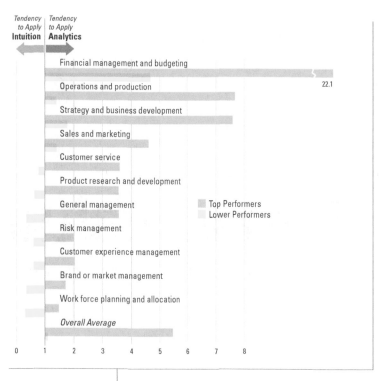

Tendency to Apply **Intuition** | Tendency to Apply **Analytics**

Financial management and budgeting

Operations and production 22.1

Strategy and business development

Sales and marketing

Customer service

Product research and development

General management

Risk management

Customer experience management

Brand or market management

Work force planning and allocation

*Overall Average*

■ Top Performers
■ Lower Performers

0  1  2  3  4  5  6  7  8

**FIGURE 1**
**The tendency for top-performing organizations to apply analytics to particular activities across the organization, as compared to lower performers. A likelihood of 1.0 indicates an equal likelihood that the organizations will use either analytics or intuition.**

*priority in their organizations.* And more than one in five said they were under intense or significant pressure to *adopt advanced information and analytics approaches.*

The source of the pressure is not hard to ascertain. Six out of 10 respondents cited *innovating to achieve competitive differentiation* as a top business challenge. The same percentage also agreed that their *organization has more data than it can use effectively.* Organizational leaders want analytics to exploit their growing data and computational power to get smart, and get ahead, in ways they never could before.

Senior executives now want businesses run on data-driven decisions. They want scenarios and simulations that provide immediate guidance on the best actions to take when disruptions occur — disruptions ranging from unexpected competitors or an earthquake in a supply zone to a customer signaling it may switch providers. Executives want to understand optimal solutions based on complex business parameters or new information, and they want to take action quickly.

These expectations can be met — but with a caveat. For analytics-driven insights to be *consumed* — that is, to trigger new actions across the organization —

they must be closely linked to business strategy, easy for end users to understand and embedded into organizational processes in order to take action at the right time. That's no small task. It requires painstaking focus on the way insights are infused into everything from manufacturing and new product development to credit approvals and call center interactions.

## Top Performers Say Analytics Is a Differentiator

Our study clearly connects performance and the competitive value of analytics. We asked respondents to assess their organization's competitive position. Those who selected "substantially outperform industry peers" were identified as top performers, while those who selected "somewhat or substantially underperforming industry peers" were grouped as lower performers.[1]

We found that organizations that strongly agreed that the use of *business information and analytics differentiates them within their industry* were twice as likely to be top performers as lower performers.

Top performers approach business operations differently from their peers. Specifically, they put analytics to use in the widest possible range of decisions, large and small. They were twice as likely to use analytics to *guide future strategies and twice as likely to use insights to guide day-to-day operations* (see Figure 2). They make decisions based on rigorous analysis at more than double the rate of lower performers. The correlation between performance

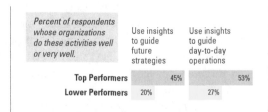

| Percent of respondents whose organizations do these activities well or very well. | Use insights to guide future strategies | Use insights to guide day-to-day operations |
|---|---|---|
| **Top Performers** | 45% | 53% |
| **Lower Performers** | 20% | 27% |

**FIGURE 2**
**Top performing organizations were twice as likely to use analytics to guide day-to-day operations and future strategies as lower performers.**

and analytics-driven management has important implications to organizations whether they are seeking growth, efficiency or competitive differentiation.

## Three Levels of Capabilities Emerged, Each with Distinct Opportunities

Organizations that know where they are in terms of analytics adoption are better prepared to turn challenges into opportunities. We segmented respondents based on how they rated their organization's analytics prowess, specifically how thoroughly their organizations had been transformed by better uses of analytics and information. Three levels of analytics capability emerged — Aspirational, Experienced and Transformed — each with clear distinctions (see Figure 3).

Aspirational. These organizations are the farthest from achieving their desired analytical goals.

Often they are focusing on efficiency or automation of existing processes, and searching for ways to cut costs. Aspirational organizations currently have few of the necessary building blocks — people, processes or tools — to collect, understand, incorporate or act on analytic insights.

Experienced. Having gained some analytic experience — often through successes with efficiencies at the Aspirational phase — these organizations are looking to go beyond cost management. Experienced organizations are developing better ways to effectively collect, incorporate and act on analytics so they can begin to optimize their organizations.

Transformed. These organizations have substantial experience using analytics across a broad range of functions. They use analytics as a competitive differentiator and are already adept at organizing people, processes and tools to optimize and differentiate. Transformed organizations are less focused on cutting costs than Aspirational and Experienced

FIGURE 3
**Three capability levels — Aspirational, Experienced, and Transformed — were based on how respondents rated their organization's analytic prowess.**

| | ASPIRATIONAL | EXPERIENCED | TRANSFORMED |
|---|---|---|---|
| Motive | •Use analytics to justify actions | •Use analytics to guide actions | •Use analytics to prescribe actions |
| Functional proficiency | •Financial management and budgeting<br>•Operations and production<br>•Sales and marketing | •All Aspirational functions<br>•Strategy / business development<br>•Customer service<br>•Product research / development | •All Aspirational and Experienced functions<br>•Risk management<br>•Customer experience<br>•Work force planning / allocation<br>•General management<br>•Brand and market management |
| Business challenges | •Competitive differentiation through innovation<br>•Cost efficiency (primary)<br>•Revenue growth (secondary) | •Competitive differentiation through innovation<br>•Revenue growth (primary)<br>•Cost efficiency (secondary) | •Competitive differentiation through innovation<br>•Revenue growth (primary)<br>•Profitability acquiring / retaining customers (targeted focus) |
| Key obstacles | •Lack of understanding how to leverage analytics for business value<br>•Executive sponsorship<br>•Culture does not encourage sharing information | •Lack of understanding how to leverage analytics for business value<br>•Skills within line of business<br>•Ownership of data is unclear or governance is ineffective | •Lack of understanding how to leverage analytics for business value<br>•Management bandwidth due to competing priorities<br>•Accessibility of the data |
| Data management | •Limited ability to capture, aggregate, analyze or share information and insights | •Moderate ability to capture, aggregate and analyze data<br>•Limited ability to share information and insights | •Strong ability to capture, aggregate and analyze data<br>•Effective at sharing information and insights |
| Analytics in action | •Rarely use rigorous approaches to make decisions<br>•Limited use of insights to guide future strategies or guide day-to-day operations | •Some use of rigorous approaches to make decisions<br>•Growing use of insights to guide future strategies, but still limited use of insights to guide day-to-day operations | •Most use rigorous approaches to make decisions<br>•Almost all use insights to guide future strategies, and most use insights to guide day-to-day operations |

organizations, possibly having already automated their operations through effective use of insights. They are most focused on driving customer profitability and making targeted investments in niche analytics as they keep pushing the organizational envelope.

Transformed organizations were three times more likely than Aspirational organizations to indicate they *substantially outperform their industry peers*. This performance advantage illustrates the potential rewards of higher levels of analytics adoption.

While our findings showed that organizations tend to wait until they have gained some experience before they apply analytics to growth objectives, this may be more a common practice than a "best practice." Our experience indicates that analytics, applied wisely to an organization's operational capabilities, can be used to accelerate a broad range of business objectives, even at the earliest stages of analytics adoption.

## Data Is Not the Biggest Obstacle

Despite popular opinion, getting the data right is not a top challenge organizations face when adopting analytics. Only about one out of five respondents in our survey cited *concern with data quality or ineffective data governance* as a primary obstacle (see Figure 4).

The adoption barriers organizations face most are related to management and culture rather than being related to data and technology. The leading obstacle to widespread analytics adoption is *lack of understanding of how to use analytics to improve the business*, according to almost four of 10 respondents. More than one in three cite lack of *management bandwidth due to competing priorities*. Organizations that use analytics to tackle their biggest challenges are able to overcome seemingly intractable cultural challenges and, at the same time, refine their data and governance approaches.

## Information Must Become Easier to Understand and Act Upon

Executives want better ways to communicate complex insights so they can quickly absorb the meaning of the data and take action on it. Over the next two years, executives say they will focus on supplementing standard historical reporting with emerging approaches that make information come alive. These include data visualization and process simulation, as well as text and voice analytics, social media analysis, and other predictive and prescriptive techniques.

New tools like these can make insights easier to understand and to act on at every point in the organization, and at every skill level. They transform numbers into information and insights that can be readily put to use instead of relying on further interpretation or leaving them to languish due to uncertainty about how to act.

---

## IBM CASE STUDY: Analytics, Not Best Guess, Drive Ad Decisions

Executives have long been accustomed to a degree of imprecision and uncertainty when making decisions critical to their growth — and survival. For some companies, like consumer electronics retailer Best Buy, their "best guess" was no longer good enough; hard facts were needed.

In an industry where the optimal allocation of advertising dollars is top of mind, and

in a time when new digital media outlets are emerging almost daily, Best Buy decided to augment its traditional advertising-mix assessment with a new analytical approach — exploiting widely sourced customer data and new models for predicting behavior.

The answers Best Buy discovered were surprising. The one medium that everyone knew was waning — televi-

sion — turned out to be an important one for its target customers. As a result, the company ended up shifting its investment from newspaper inserts to television — a decision that paid off handsomely.

Executives at Best Buy acted on new insights that defied their initial expectations. "We already have 80 to 90 percent of what we need to know about a customer somewhere in the

system," Bill Hoffman, senior vice president for customer insight, told us. It was important, however, to get analytics-driven insights out to where they were needed. "The power plants were up, but the lines were down."

No longer. Adopting an analytic approach to decisions, Best Buy exemplifies the new data-driven management practices emerging in leading organizations.

## What Leaders Can Do to Make Analytics Pay Off — A New Methodology

It takes big plans followed by discrete actions to gain the benefits of analytics. But it also takes some very specific management approaches. Based on data from our survey, our engagement experience, case studies and interviews with experts, we have been able to identify a new, five-point methodology for successfully implementing analytics-driven management and for rapidly creating value. The recommendations in the following pages are designed to help organizations understand this "new path to value" and how to travel it. While each recommendation presents different pieces of the information-and-analytics value puzzle, each one meets all of these three critical management needs:

**Reduced time to value.** Value creation can be achieved early in an organization's progress to analytics sophistication. Contrary to common assumptions, it doesn't require the presence of perfect data or a full-scale transformation to be complete.

**Increased likelihood of transformation that's both significant and enduring.** The emerging methodology we've identified enables and inspires lasting change (strategic and cultural) by tactically overcoming the most significant organizational impediments.

**Greater focus on achievable steps.** The approach being used by the smartest companies is powerful in part because each step enables leaders to focus their efforts and resources narrowly, rather than implementing universal changes. This makes every step easier to accomplish with an attractive return on investment.

Whether pursuing the best channel strategy, the best customer experience, the best portfolio or the best process innovation, organizations embracing this approach will be first in line to gain business advantage from analytics.

## Recommendation 1
## Focus on the Biggest and Highest Value Opportunities

Does attacking the biggest challenge carry the biggest risk of failure? Paradoxically, no — because big problems command attention and incite action. And as survey participants told us, management bandwidth is a top obstacle. When the stakes are high, the best talent will leap at the opportunity to get involved.

It's extraordinarily hard for people to change from making decisions based on personal experience to making them from data — especially when that data counters the prevailing common wisdom. But upsetting the status quo is much easier when everyone can see how it could contribute to a major goal. With a potential big reward in sight, a significant effort is easier to justify, and people across functions and levels are better able to support it.

A sharp focus on major opportunities can excite an organization with new possibilities. "Where are the best places to advertise to get consumers into our store?" was the looming, time-critical challenge for Best Buy. "How can we reduce the fraud and abuse that are draining scarce money and resources?" is a common refrain among government agencies around the globe.

Conversely, don't start doing analytics without strategic business direction, as these efforts are likely to stall. Not only does it waste resources, it risks creating widespread skepticism about the real value of analytics.

In our discussions with business executives, we have repeatedly heard that analytics aligned to a sig-

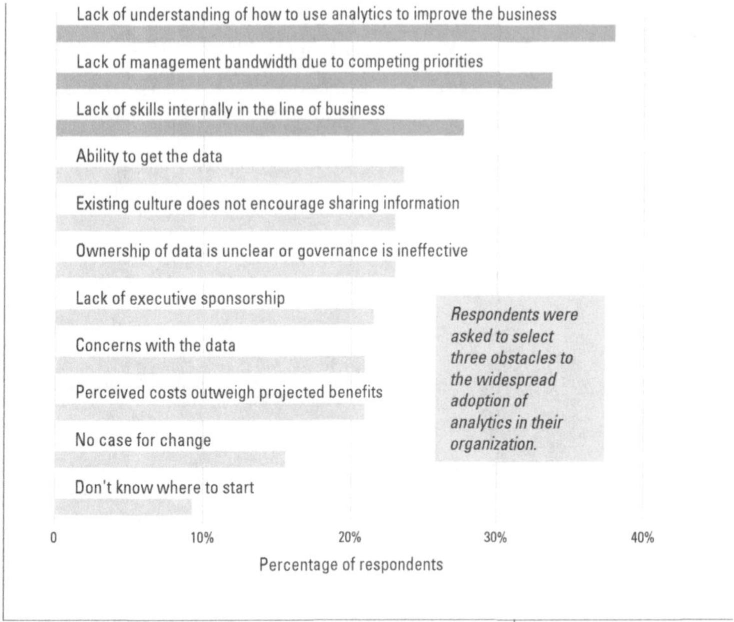

Lack of understanding of how to use analytics to improve the business

Lack of management bandwidth due to competing priorities

Lack of skills internally in the line of business

Ability to get the data

Existing culture does not encourage sharing information

Ownership of data is unclear or governance is ineffective

Lack of executive sponsorship

Concerns with the data

Perceived costs outweigh projected benefits

No case for change

Don't know where to start

*Respondents were asked to select three obstacles to the widespread adoption of analytics in their organization.*

Percentage of respondents

0    10%    20%    30%    40%

**FIGURE 4**
**The adoption barriers organizations face most are managerial and cultural rather than related to data and technology.**

## Introducing the PADIE Technique for Operationalizing Analytics

The PADIE (process-application-data-insight-embed) technique is a simple means by which a company can operationalize insights drawn from data. It's a three-step process: First, document the processes and the applications that automate them; second, use analytics techniques — descriptive, predictive, prescriptive — to gain insights from data; third, select the most appropriate approaches to embed insights into your operations.

This PADIE example from the insurance industry addresses a major partnership challenge: the need to revitalize the role of independent insurance agents who had lost large portions of their business when customers began going directly to the company's Web site to buy policies.

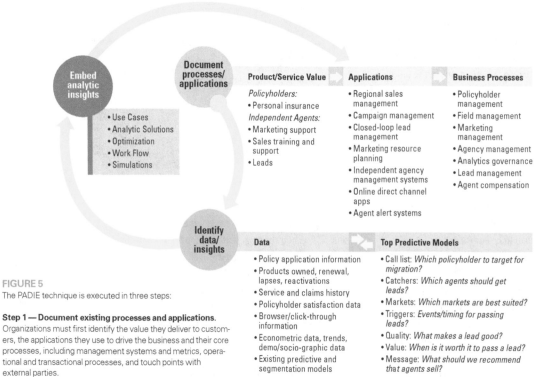

**FIGURE 5**

The PADIE technique is executed in three steps:

**Step 1 — Document existing processes and applications.**
Organizations must first identify the value they deliver to customers, the applications they use to drive the business and their core processes, including management systems and metrics, operational and transactional processes, and touch points with external parties.

**Step 2 — Identify data and insights that can solve pain points and create value.** Next, the organization must identify the questions — who, what, where, when, why and how — that will address pain points and create revenue, cost or margin value. The goal here is to give business direction to the modelers to drive their analytic inquiries into your data. Organizations also need to identify the sources of data that will be used during the analysis.

**Step 3 — Embed analytic insights.** Lastly, but most importantly for value creation, the organization needs to determine its best approach to embedding the insights into its operations. Organizations have multiple options, including use cases that describe how applications should be enhanced, new analytic solutions that can be introduced, optimization logic added to rules engines, new work flows and simulations to help management understand varying scenarios. Success with embedding insights into processes determines the ultimate success of the initiative.

nificant organizational challenge makes it easier to overcome a wide range of obstacles. Respondents cited many challenges, and none can be discounted or minimized: Executive sponsorship of analytics projects, data quality and access, governance, skills and culture all matter and need to be addressed in time. But when overtaken by the momentum of a single big idea and potentially game-changing in-

sight, obstacles like these get swept into the wake of change rather than drowning the effort.

**A process for inspiring change** Despite analytics opportunities that are as close as the nearest data warehouse, the inability to understand how analytics can solve business challenges is the most daunting obstacle to adoption. And with management attention focused on other priorities, valuable analytics opportunities can be crowded out by business as usual.

The single greatest opportunity — and challenge — to speed adoption of analytics is to embed them into daily operations. Organizations that use analytics to answer big, make-it-or-break-it challenges have the greatest opportunity to meet their business goals. The answer needs to be simple and unambiguous to work for time-pressed managers. Based on our analysis, we recommend the process-application-data-insight-embed technique (see Figure 5). It is a simple means by which an organization can operationalize insights drawn from data.

The PADIE technique helps users across the organization understand from the start the full initiative as it applies to a specific business challenge. This technique enables business and analytic teams to work together to create analytic models based on use cases that show analytics in action.

## Recommendation 2
## Within Each Opportunity, Start With Questions, Not Data

Traditionally, organizations are tempted to start by gathering all available data before beginning their analysis. Too often, this leads to an all-encompassing focus on data management — collecting, cleansing and converting data — that leaves little time, energy or resources to understand its potential uses. Actions they do take, if any, might not be the most valuable ones (see Figure 6). Instead, organizations should implement analytics by first defining the insights and questions needed to meet the big business objective and then identify those pieces of data needed for answers.

By defining the desired insights first, organizations can target specific subject areas, and use readily avail-

able data in the initial analytic models. The insights delivered through these initial models will illuminate gaps in the data infrastructure and business processes. Time that would have been spent cleaning up all data can be redirected toward targeted data needs and specific process improvements identified by the insights, enabling iterations with increasing levels of value.

Companies that make data their overriding priority often lose momentum long before the first insight is delivered. By narrowing the scope of these tasks to the specific subject areas needed to answer key questions, value can be realized more quickly, while the insights are still relevant.

Organizations that start with the data or process change first often end up with unintended consequences — such as data that is not extensible or processes that are ultimately eliminated — that require rework and additional resources to solve.

### Speeding insights into business operations
Compared with other respondents, Transformed organizations are good at data capture (see Figure 7).

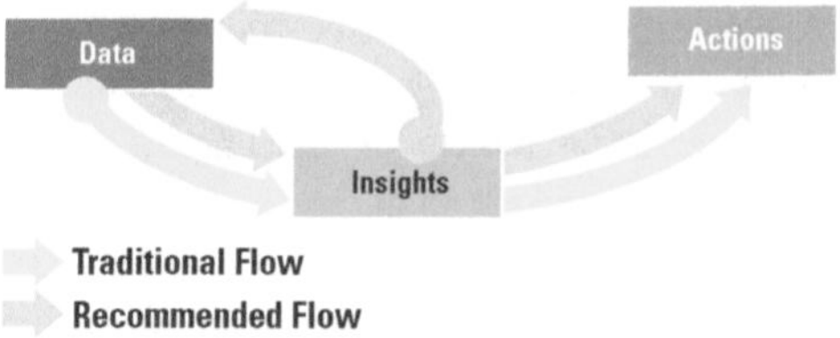

---

### IBM CASE STUDY: Tackling Health Care Fraud Leads to Sweeping Reforms

With healthcare costs spiraling, the North Carolina Department of health and human services resolved to curb suspected fraud and abuse. After an analytics pilot of the state's Medicaid records revealed numerous anomalies, the state moved quickly to deploy an advanced mathematical model to detect Medicaid problems within its system of two million users.[2] A new "Medicaid SWAT team" of special investigators is beginning to review cases flagged as suspicious by the analytic models.[3]

Legislative budget officials estimated that the state could recoup $37 million in the program's first year, which easily offset its initial investment several times over. While most of the money would be reimbursed to Medicaid, the penalties would add needed dollars to North Carolina public schools.[4]

The state is now mobilizing resources to pursue the unexpectedly large volume of fraud and abuse cases uncovered. Prompted by the results, the governor announced plans for a full suite of anti-fraud moves, including tougher laws, a public awareness campaign to encourage people to report fraud and abuse, and funding to increase the state's staff of investigators.[5]

---

Data

Actions

Insights

Traditional Flow
Recommended Flow

FIGURE 6

Organizations should start by pinpointing the insights to be leveraged, then use readily available data to test the analytic models. Actions based on those insights will help define the next set of insights and data needed. The traditional approach of starting with a comprehensive data program creates too much lag time before insights can be put into action.

## IBM CASE STUDY: Shifting Gears From Vehicle-centric to Customer-centric Marketing

As turbulence struck the auto industry, a small group of executives at one automotive company decided to focus its attention on orphaned owners — customers whose current car brands were being discontinued. They determined to use analytics to try to salvage these customers, who were at risk for significant attrition.

A marketing approach focused more on the life cycle of the vehicle — service reminders, warranty notices and upgrade reminders — meant that the company knew very little about what could impact these customers' future buying decisions. In a tough market environment and constrained by competing priorities, the company quickly fielded a new analytics approach. Instead of organizing and sifting through the terabytes of data across the organization, it quickly identified a relatively small number of key data needs, created a customer sample, then used analytic algorithms to forecast attrition probabilities, pinpoint at-risk customers and recommend precise retention strategies. Analysts uncovered a double-digit retention opportunity within a single brand worth hundreds of millions of dollars.

This prototype, initiated to uncover a specific customer insight, set off an analytics revolution. Brand managers across the organization quickly signed on to an enterprise effort to leverage analytics to shift from vehicle-based life cycle marketing to a customer-centric approach, targeted at improving both loyalty and retention.

---

Additionally, Transformed organizations are much more adept at data management. In these areas, they outpaced Aspirational organizations up to 10-fold in their ability to execute.

Enterprise processes have many points where analytic insights can boost business value. The operational challenge is to understand where to apply those insights in a particular industry and organization. When a bank customer stops automatic payroll deposits or remittance transfers, for example, who in the organization should be alerted and tasked with finding out whether the customer is changing jobs or planning to switch banks? Where customer satisfaction is low, what insights are needed and how should they be delivered to prevent defections?

To keep the three gears moving together — data, insights and timely actions — the overriding business purpose must always be in view. That way, as models, processes and data are tested, priorities for the next investigation become clear. Data and models get accepted, rejected or improved based on business need. New analytic insights — descriptive, predictive and prescriptive — are embedded into increasing numbers of applications and processes, and a virtuous cycle of feedback and improvement takes hold.

## Recommendation 3
### Embed Insights to Drive Actions and Deliver Value

New methods and tools to embed information into business processes — use cases, analytics solutions, optimization, work flows and simulations — are making insights more understandable and actionable. Respondents identified trend analysis, forecasting and standardized reporting as the most important tools they use today. However, they also identified tools that will have greater value in 24 months. The downswings in "as-is" methods accompanied by corresponding upswings in "to-be" methods were dramatic (see Figure 8).

Today's staples are expected to be surpassed in the next 24 months by:

1. Data visualization, such as dashboards and scorecards
2. Simulations and scenario development
3. Analytics applied within business processes
4. Advanced statistical techniques, such as regression analysis, discrete choice modeling and mathematical optimization.

Organizations expect the value from these emerging techniques to soar, making it possible for

FIGURE 7
**Transformed organizations felt more confident in their ability to manage data tasks than Aspirational organizations, which seldom felt their organizations performed those tasks "very well."**

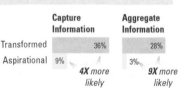

*Percent of respondents whose organizations perform these tasks very well.*

| | Capture Information | Aggregate Information | Analyze Information | Disseminate Information and Insights |
|---|---|---|---|---|
| Transformed | 36% | 28% | 34% | 21% |
| Aspirational | 9% | 3% | 4% | 2% |
| | **4X** more likely | **9X** more likely | **8.5X** more likely | **10X** more likely |

FIGURE 8
**Organizations expect that the ability to visualize data differently will be the most valuable technique in two years. Other techniques and activities that are currently delivering the most value today will still be done, but will be of less value.**

| Today | In 24 Months |
| --- | --- |
| Historic trend analysis and forecasting | Data visualization |
| Standardized reporting | Simulations and scenario development |
| Data visualization | Analytics applied within business processes |
| Analytics applied within business processes | Regression analysis, discrete choice modeling and mathematical optimization |
| Simulations and scenario development | Historic trend analysis and forecasting |
| Clustering and segmentation | Clustering and segmentation |
| Regression analysis, discrete choice modeling and mathematical optimization | Standardized reporting |

*Respondents were asked to identify the top three analytic techniques creating value for the organization, and predict which three would be creating the most value in 24 months.*

data-driven insights to be used at all levels of the organization. Innovative uses of this type of information layering will continue to grow as a means to help individuals across the organization consume and act upon insights derived through complex analytics that would otherwise be hard to piece together. For example, GPS-enabled navigation devices can superimpose real-time traffic patterns and alerts onto navigation maps and suggest the best routes to drivers.

Similarly, in oil exploration, three-dimensional renderings combine data from sensors in the field with collaborative and analytical resources accessible across the enterprise. Production engineers can incorporate geological, production and pipeline information into their drilling decisions.

Beyond 3D, animated maps and charts can simulate critical changes in distribution flow, or projected changes in consumption and resource availability. In the emerging area of analytics for unstructured data, patterns can be visualized through verbal maps that pictorially represent word frequency, allowing marketers to see how their brands are perceived.

**New techniques and approaches transform insights into actions** New techniques to embed insights will gain in value by generating results that can be readily understood and acted upon:

▶ Dashboards that now reflect actual last quarter sales will also show what sales could be next quarter under a variety of different conditions — a new media mix, a price change, a larger sales team, even a major weather or sporting event.

▶ Simulations evaluating alternative scenarios will automatically recommend optimal approaches—such

## IBM CASE STUDY: A Beverage Company Makes the Case

After fast growth through acquisitions and mergers, executives in a global beverage company were hampered by a complex array of data sets that limited their ability to make timely and fact-based decisions. Solving this problem required a standardized platform that would enable a global view of information while supporting their rules-driven, exception-based process for making decisions.

But executives knew that they needed more than just the facts; they needed to model scenarios to understand the impact of prospective decisions. The organization settled on a global key performance indicator dashboard to help users visualize relevant data and model decisions, based on key dimensions like geography, unit, brand, profitability, costs or channel. But first, to attain funding for the new platform and drive adoption, the dashboard needed wide support within the executive ranks.

To make the business case for the new approach, organization executives threw out the customary spreadsheets and instead gave executives an interactive prototype that mimicked the visual displays and functionality of the proposed dashboard. The prototype depicted the key elements of the business case, including business value and technology requirements. But, most importantly, it gave executives a taste for the proposed user experience. Executives then rallied to support the new interactive dashboard, which when implemented became a strategic part of how decisions were modeled and made in the company.

as which is the best media mix to introduce a specific product to a particular segment, or what is the ideal number of sales professionals to assign to a particular new territory.

▶ Use cases will illustrate how to embed insights into business applications and processes. For the direct-channel to agent-channel migration illustrated in Figure 5, automated work flows include initial communication with prospective insurance policyholders, timed to take place before leads are sent to the agent. In that way, permission is secured before the agent makes a call, helping to ensure a smooth channel transition and a superior customer experience.

New methods will also make it possible for decision makers more fully to *see* their customers' purchases, payments and interactions. Businesses will be able to *listen* to customers' unique wants and needs about channel and product preferences. In fact, making customers, as well as information, come to life within complex organizational systems may well become the biggest benefit of making data-driven insights real to those who need to use them.

## Recommendation 4
## Keep Existing Capabilities While Adding New Ones

When executives first realize their need for analytics, they tend to turn to those closest to them for answers. Over time, these point-of-need resources come together in local line of business units to enable sharing of insights. Ultimately, centralized units emerge to bring a shared enterprise perspective — governance, tools, methods — and specialized expertise. As executives use analytics more frequently to *inform day-to day decisions and actions*, this increasing demand for insights keeps resources at each level engaged, expanding analytic capabilities even as activities are shifted for efficiencies (see Figure 9).

Sophisticated modeling and visualization tools, as we have noted, will soon provide greater business value than ever before. But that does not mean that spreadsheets and charts should go away. On the contrary: New tools should supplement earlier ones, or continue to be used side by side, as needed.

There are other ways that capabilities grow and deepen within an organization. Disciplines like finance and supply chain are inherently data intensive, and are often where analytics first take root. Encouraged by early successes, organizations begin expanding analytic decision making to more disciplines. (See "How Analytics Propagates Across Functions.") In Transformed organizations, reusability creates a snowball effect as models from one function are repurposed into another with minimal modifications.

Over time, data-driven decision making branches out across the organization. As experience and usage grow, the value of analytics increases, which enables business benefits to accrue more quickly.

**Add value with an enterprise analytics unit** Organizations that first experience the value of analytics in discrete business units or functions are

---

## IBM CASE STUDY: Bridging Business and Analytics Skills Across the Organization

As is often the case, analytics success raises the bar to do more. As demand for useful insights has grown, a leading big-box retailer developed a sophisticated analytics environment, in which each layer — enterprise, business unit and point of need — complements rather than duplicates the specialized skills each location delivers.

Determined to leverage the structures already in place, but push them to the next level, the retailer set out to strengthen both the analytics and business skills of its practitioners. Already, analysts were working within the lines of business, knowledgeable enough to supply timely answers to ad hoc queries raised by business executives. An enterprise-wide unit also provided complex computational skills as needed, created common data definitions and crafted analytics approaches that could be duplicated across the business units.

The central unit housed the advanced analytics skills, but it was the analysts in the business units who had the advanced business knowledge and a deep understanding of the operations, objectives and economic levers required to run the business. Still lacking was the ability to bridge these two domains.

Business unit analysts now rotate into the enterprise unit, partnering with high-tech analysts to provide the business knowledge that fuels new analytics models and working collaboratively to analyze and interpret results that will be meaningful to business. At the end of the rotation, business unit analysts return with a standardized tool kit to create consistency and rigor in analysis and facilitate sharing.

likely soon to seek a wider range of capabilities —
and more advanced use of existing ones. A
centralized analytics unit, often called either a "center of excellence" or "center of competency," makes
it possible to share analytic resources efficiently and
effectively. It does not, however, replace distributed
and localized capabilities; rather, the central unit is
additive, built upon existing capabilities that may
have already developed in functions, departments
and lines of business.

We found that 63 percent more Transformed organizations than Aspirational organizations use a
*centralized enterprise unit as the primary source of
analytics*. A centralized analytics unit can provide a
home for more advanced skills to come together
within the organization, providing both advanced
models and enterprise governance by establishing
priorities and standards by:

▶ Advancing standard methods for identifying
business problems to be solved with analytics
▶ Facilitating identification of analytic business
needs while driving rigor into methods for embedding insights into end-to-end processes
▶ Promoting enterprise-level governance on priori-
tization, master data sources and reuse to capture
enterprise efficiencies
▶ Standardizing tools and analytic platforms to enable resource sharing, streamline maintenance
and reduce licensing expenses.

In three distinct areas — application of analytic
tools, functional use of analytics and location of
skills — we found that adding capabilities without
detracting from existing ones offers a fast path to
full benefits from analytics-driven management.

## Recommendation 5
## Use an Information Agenda
## to Plan for the Future

Big data is getting bigger. Information is
coming from instrumented, intercon-
nected supply chains transmitting
real-time data about fluctuations in everything from market demand to the weather.
Additionally, strategic information has started ar-
riving through unstructured digital channels: social

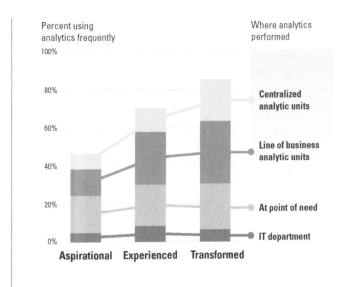

media, smart phone applications and an ever-in-
creasing stream of emerging Internet-based
gadgets. It's no wonder six out of 10 respondents
said the organization *has more data than it knows
how to use effectively*.

All this data must be molded into an information foundation that is *integrated*, *consistent* and
*trustworthy*, which were the leading data priorities
cited by our respondents (see Figure 10). Every
phase of implementation needs to align the data
foundation to an overall information agenda. The
information agenda accelerates the organization's
ability to share and deliver trusted information
across all applications and processes. It sets up information to serve as a strategic asset for the
organization.

The information agenda identifies foundational
information practices and tools while aligning IT
and business goals through enterprise information
plans and financially justified deployment road
maps. This agenda helps establish necessary links
between those who drive the priorities of the organization by line of business and set the strategy, and
those who manage data and information.

A comprehensive agenda also enables analytics
to keep pace with changing business goals. An executive at one company, for example, told us it
had it down to a science when it came to understanding the impact of price changes on single
products and single channels. But the company

FIGURE 9
The frequency with
which analytics is
used to support
decisions increases
as organizations
transition from
one level of analytic
capability to the
next. At the same
time, analytics mi-
grate toward more
centralized units,
first at the local line
of business level and
then at the enter-
prise level, while the
portion of analytics
performed at points-
of-need and with IT
remain stable.

## IBM CASE STUDY:
## Insurer Limits Risk by Establishing an Agenda for Today and Tomorrow

Under pressure from increasing competition, a financial firm recognized that growth — and survival — depended upon gaining a better understanding of its business quickly. For this, it needed an analytic foundation for strategic subject areas — first finance, then operations, then customers.

The firm completed a series of tightly scoped projects to increase analytic capabilities over

time, with each wave realizing value to help fund the next. Business needs determined the order in which enterprise data would be reported to the analytic warehouse. To speed the efforts and time to value, business users assessed precisely which data elements were needed most. Common data definitions were negotiated to create a language across product lines and business units.

The organization took a phased approach to building its data environment. For finance and operations, this meant selecting data that supported an enterprise-wide set of KPIs. All other data was put on hold. To decide which customer data was most important, the organization determined which questions they most needed to answer, first by business unit and

then across the enterprise — to find those with the greatest organizational overlap. Again, all other data would have to wait.

In this way, the organization was able to fast-track development of a robust data warehouse. As early projects produced a return on their investments and more resources became available, the data warehouse could grow.

---

was blindsided when it shifted to a customer-centric strategy, restructuring around bundled products and dynamic pricing across channels. Because its data marts had been developed de facto over time, the company found itself struggling to understand which tools and information were needed to go forward.

Lastly, building the analytic foundation under the guidance of a forward-looking information agenda enables organizations to keep pace with advances in mathematical sciences and technology. Without an enterprise-wide information agenda,

units are likely to explore these new developments independently and adopt them inconsistently, a difficult path for gaining full business benefits from analytics.

**Outline for an information agenda** The information agenda provides a vision and high-level road map for information that aligns business needs to growth in analytics sophistication with the underlying technology and processes spanning:

▶ Information governance policies and tool kits — from little oversight to fully implemented policies and practices
▶ Data architecture — from ad hoc to optimal physical and logical views of structured and unstructured information and databases
▶ Data currency — from only historical data to a real-time view of all information
▶ Data management, integration and middleware — from subject area data and content in silos to enterprise information that is fully embedded into business processes with master content and master data management
▶ Analytical tool kits based upon user needs — from basic search, query and reporting to advanced analytics and visualization.

The information agenda is a key enabler of analytic initiatives by providing the right information and tools at the right times based upon business-driven priorities.

**FIGURE 10**
**Organizations want data that is integrated, consistent and trustworthy, which were the leading data priorities cited by our respondents.**

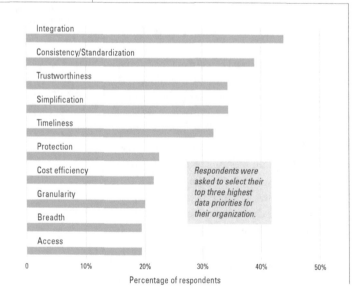

Integration
Consistency/Standardization
Trustworthiness
Simplification
Timeliness
Protection
Cost efficiency
Granularity
Breadth
Access

*Respondents were asked to select their top three highest data priorities for their organization.*

0    10%    20%    30%    40%    50%
Percentage of respondents

## Set Yourself up for Success

Aware that analytics-driven opportunities are central to growth and success, organizations seek to capture the value. They want to find the best place to begin, but for many, that entry point is elusive.

**If you are Aspirational:** Assemble the best people and resources to make the case for investments in analytics. To get sponsorship for initial projects, identify the big business challenges that can be addressed by analytics and find the data you have that fits the challenge.

**If you are Experienced:** Make the move to enterprise analytics and manage it by keeping focus on the big issues that everyone recognizes. Collaborate to drive enterprise opportunities without compromising departmental needs while preventing governance from becoming an objective unto itself.

**If you are Transformed:** Discover and champion improvements in how you are using analytics. You've accomplished a lot already with analytics, but are feeling increased pressure to do more. Focus your analytics and management bandwidth to go deeper rather than broader, but recognize it will be critical to continue to demonstrate new ways of how analytics can move the business toward its goals.

## Techniques to Get Started

**Pick your spots.** Search for your organization's biggest and highest priority challenge, and create a PADIE diagram to describe it. Show available data sources, models to be built, and processes and applications where analytics will have an impact.

## How Analytics Propagates Across Functions

Typically, organizations begin with efficiency goals, then address growth objectives, and lastly, design finely tuned approaches to the most complex business challenges. As this occurs, adoption both spreads and deepens. This contributes to a predictable pattern of analytics adoption by function (see Figure 11). Specifically, we found the following:

**Aspirational.** About one-half used analytics for financial management, about one-third each for operations, and sales and marketing. These selections reflect the traditional path of adopting analytics in inherently data-intensive areas.

**Experienced.** Analytics used for all of the above, and at greater levels. For example, the proportion of respondents likely to use it for finance increased from one-half to two-thirds. New functions, such as strategy, product research and customer service, emerged. Growth and efficiency were both met with analytics approaches.

**Transformed.** Analytics was used for all the same functions as above — and more, as the branching pattern spread within organizations. Fine-grained revenue and efficiency usage of analytics emerged, such as customer experience, to build on customer service and marketing capabilities.

These patterns suggest that success in one area stimulates adoption where analytics had not previously been considered or attempted. That is, in fact, how organizations increase their level of sophistication. Successful initiatives in supply chain functions, for example, encourage the human resources function to institute a pilot for data-driven work force planning and allocation.

While these findings describe the typical path, they are not necessarily the best or only one. Analytic leaders may want to advance their organization's capabilities more quickly using nontraditional routes.

Percent who stated their organization performs these functional analytics "well" and "very well."

■ Aspirational ■ Experienced ■ Transformed

FIGURE 11

**Analytic adoption spreads through organizations in a predictable pattern, as all respondents gained proficiency with functional analytics in the same order. The rate of adoption, as shown through proficiency, increases steadily and threshold levels support the analytic capability tiers.**

Create multiple diagrams if you're selecting from a strong list of possible initiatives. Keep in mind that your biggest problems, such as customer retention, anti-fraud efforts or advertising mix, are also your biggest opportunities. Change is hard for most, so select an initiative worthy of sustained focus that can make the biggest difference in meeting your most important business goals. Remember that focus is critical during these initial efforts. Do not get distracted once the targeted area is identified.

**Prove the value.** With your PADIE diagram in hand, use reason and benchmarks for initial executive sponsorship, but use a proof-of-value pilot to keep sponsors engaged. Estimate how much revenue can be gained, how much money can be saved and how much margins can be improved. Employ techniques to embed analytics to illustrate and prioritize the types of organizational changes that are needed to achieve the value. Pull it all together using an implementation road map with a clear starting point and a range of options for future opportunities.

**Roll it out for the long haul.** The challenge should be big, the model insightful and the business vision complete. However, the first implementation steps can be small, as long as they fit your agenda. Reduce your rework by using business analytic and process management tools that you have selected for the long haul — information governance, business analytics and business rules. As you make progress, don't forget to analyze feedback and business outcomes to determine where your analytics model and business vision can be improved.

## Make Analytics Pay Off

It takes big plans followed by discrete actions to gain the benefits of analytics. But it also takes some very specific management approaches. Each of our recommendations meets three critical management needs:

▶ Reduced time to value
▶ Increased likelihood of transformation that's both significant and enduring
▶ Greater focus on achievable steps.

To start on the fastest path to value, keep everyone focused on the big business issues and select the challenges that analytics can solve today within an agenda for the future. Build on the capabilities you already have. And always keep pressing to embed the insights you've gained into business operations.

### REFERENCES

**1.** In the performance self-assessment, other respondent options included "somewhat outperforming industry peers" and "on par with industry peers."

**2.** R. Christenson, "N.C. and IBM Team up to Ferret out Medicaid Fraud," March 25, 2010, http://www.newsobserver.com/2010/03/25/405666/nc-and-ibm-team-up-to-ferret-out.html.

**3.** "Perdue Begins Medicaid Fraud, Waste Prevention Effort," March 24, 2010, http://www.wral.com/news/state/story/7291729/.

**4.** B. Balfour, "Ten Recommendations for North Carolina's Budget Reform and Advisory Commission (BRAC)," John W Pope Civitas Institute, February 10, 2010, http://www.nccivitas.org/media/publication-archive/policy-brief/ten-recommendations-north-carolinas-budget-reform-and-advisor

**5.** "Perdue Begins Medicaid Fraud, Waste Prevention Effort."

For more information about this study, The New Intelligent Enterprise initiative and additional interviews, you may contact *MIT Sloan Management Review* at smrfeedback@mit.edu or visit the MIT SMR Web site: **sloanreview.mit.edu/tnie**

For more information about this study, you may contact the IBM Institute for Business Value at iibv@us.ibm.com, or visit the IBM IBV Web site: **ibm.com/gbs/bao**

# The Survey: Questions and Responses

How are organizations using information and analytics? (Results from the 2010 New Intelligent Enterprise Global Executive Survey.)

**Q1. What are the primary challenges facing your organization in the next two years?**
(Please select your top three.)

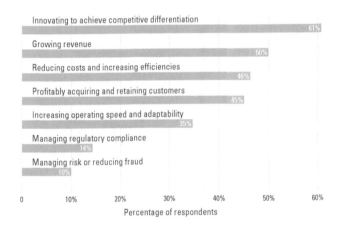

Innovating to achieve competitive differentiation — 61%
Growing revenue — 50%
Reducing costs and increasing efficiencies — 46%
Profitably acquiring and retaining customers — 45%
Increasing operating speed and adaptability — 35%
Managing regulatory compliance — 14%
Managing risk or reducing fraud — 10%

Percentage of respondents

**Q2. How well do the following statements describe your organization?**
(Please rate on a scale of 1 to 5, where 1 = Strongly disagree and 5 = Strongly agree)

The organization predicts and prepares for the future by proactively evaluating scenarios or potential trade-offs
7% 23% 27% 30% 13%

The organization makes decisions based on rigorous analytic approaches (e.g., quantitative modeling, simulation)
15% 30% 27% 19% 9%

The organization manages data to enable the ability to share and aggregate data across departments or business units
9% 24% 30% 25% 12%

Business information and analytics differentiate us within the industry
12% 25% 26% 23% 14%

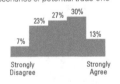

Improving our information and analytics capability is a top priority in our organization
5% 18% 27% 29% 21%

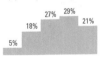

Employees are encouraged to challenge current practices and approaches
7% 18% 24% 32% 19%

The organization has more data than it knows how to use effectively
6% 14% 19% 29% 31%

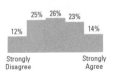

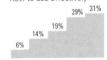

## About the Research

To understand the challenges and opportunities associated with the use of business analytics, *MIT Sloan Management Review*, in collaboration with the IBM Institute for Business Value, conducted a survey of more than 3,000 business executives, managers and analysts from organizations located around the world. The survey captured insights from individuals in 108 countries and more than 30 industries, and involved organizations of various sizes. The sample was drawn from a number of different sources, including MIT alumni and *MIT Sloan Management Review* subscribers, IBM clients and other interested parties.

In addition to these survey results, we also interviewed academic experts and subject matter experts from a number of industries and disciplines to understand the practical issues facing organizations today. Their insights contributed to a richer understanding of the data, and the development of recommendations that respond to strategic and tactical questions senior executives address as they operationalize analytics within their organizations. We also drew upon a number of IBM case studies to illustrate further how organizations are leveraging business analytics and illuminate how real organizations are putting our recommendations into action in different organizational settings.

## Q3. To what extent does your organization apply analytics to the following activities?

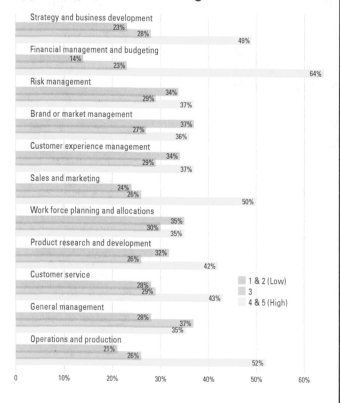

Strategy and business development
23%
28%
49%

Financial management and budgeting
14%
23%
64%

Risk management
34%
29%
37%

Brand or market management
37%
27%
36%

Customer experience management
34%
29%
37%

Sales and marketing
24%
26%
50%

Work force planning and allocations
35%
30%
35%

Product research and development
32%
26%
42%

Customer service
28%
29%
43%

General management
28%
37%
35%

Operations and production
21%
26%
52%

■ 1 & 2 (Low)
■ 3
■ 4 & 5 (High)

0    10%    20%    30%    40%    50%    60%

## Q4. How well does your business unit or department perform the following information and analytic tasks?
**(Please rate on a scale of 1 to 5, where 1 = Poorly and 5 = Very well)**

**Ability to perform data management functions**

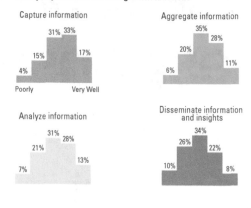

Capture information
4%
15%
31% 33%
17%
Poorly    Very Well

Aggregate information
6%
20%
35%
28%
11%

Analyze information
7%
21%
31%
28%
13%

Disseminate information and insights
10%
26%
34%
22%
8%

**Ability to apply insights**

Use insights to guide day-to-day operations
9%
26%
34%
23%
8%
Poorly    Very Well

Use insights to guide future strategies
9%
23%
29% 28%
11%

## Q5. What are the highest data priorities for your organization?
**(Please select up to three.)**

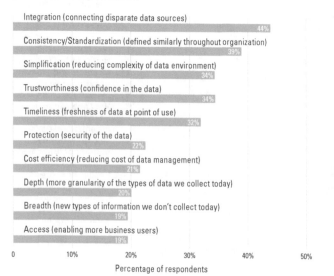

Integration (connecting disparate data sources)
44%

Consistency/Standardization (defined similarly throughout organization)
39%

Simplification (reducing complexity of data environment)
34%

Trustworthiness (confidence in the data)
34%

Timeliness (freshness of data at point of use)
32%

Protection (security of the data)
22%

Cost efficiency (reducing cost of data management)
21%

Depth (more granularity of the types of data we collect today)
20%

Breadth (new types of information we don't collect today)
19%

Access (enabling more business users)
19%

0    10%    20%    30%    40%    50%

Percentage of respondents

## Q6. Where are analytics primarily performed within your organization?
**(Please select one.)**

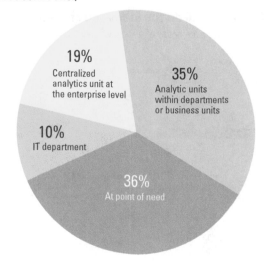

19% Centralized analytics unit at the enterprise level

35% Analytic units within departments or business units

10% IT department

36% At point of need

## Q7. Select the type of analytics creating the most value in your organization today and in 24 months.

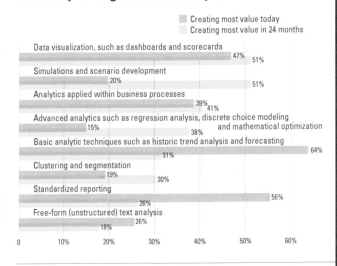

- Creating most value today
- Creating most value in 24 months

Data visualization, such as dashboards and scorecards — 47% / 51%

Simulations and scenario development — 20% / 51%

Analytics applied within business processes — 39% / 41%

Advanced analytics such as regression analysis, discrete choice modeling and mathematical optimization — 15% / 38%

Basic analytic techniques such as historic trend analysis and forecasting — 64% / 31%

Clustering and segmentation — 19% / 30%

Standardized reporting — 26% / 56%

Free-form (unstructured) text analysis — 18% / 26%

## Q8. How often do you use information and analytics to inform your actions and support decision making in your day-to-day role?

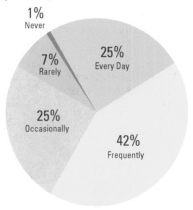

- 1% Never
- 7% Rarely
- 25% Every Day
- 25% Occasionally
- 42% Frequently

## Q9. How would you rate your personal analytic skill level?

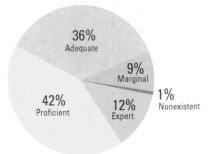

- 36% Adequate
- 9% Marginal
- 1% Nonexistent
- 12% Expert
- 42% Proficient

## Q10. How is your organization most likely to explore new uses of analytics? (Please select up to two.)

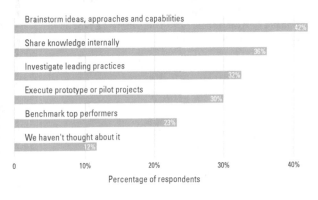

- Brainstorm ideas, approaches and capabilities — 42%
- Share knowledge internally — 36%
- Investigate leading practices — 32%
- Execute prototype or pilot projects — 30%
- Benchmark top performers — 23%
- We haven't thought about it — 12%

Percentage of respondents

## Q11. To what extent is your business unit or department under pressure to adopt new/advanced information and analytics approaches?

- Intense pressure 3%
- Significant pressure 18%
- No pressure 14%
- Very little pressure 27%
- Some pressure 38%

## Q12. What are the primary obstacles to widespread adoption and use of information and analytics in your organization? (Please select up to three.)

- Lack of understanding of how to use analytics to improve the business — 39%
- Lack of management bandwidth due to competing priorities — 34%
- Lack of skills internally in the line of business — 28%
- Existing culture does not encourage sharing information — 24%
- Ownership of data is unclear or governance is ineffective (i.e., too hard to resolve conflicts across silos) — 23%
- Lack of executive sponsorship — 23%
- Ability to get the data (e.g., inaccessible) — 22%
- Concerns with the data (e.g., untimely, untrustworthy, incomplete) — 21%
- Perceived costs outweigh projected benefits — 21%
- No case for change or no consequence of inaction — 15%
- Don't know where to start — 9%

Percentage of respondents

**Q13.** Imagine an organization transformed by better ways to collect, analyze and be prescriptively guided by information. How close are you to that ideal?
(Please rate on a scale of 1 to 10, where 1 = Not at all close and 10 = Very close)

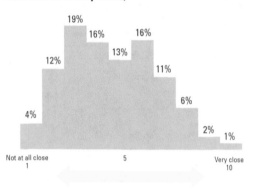

**(TEXT RESPONSES)**
**Q14.** Where do you think the greatest opportunities with analytics lie for your function, organization or industry?

**Q15.** May we contact you further about your answer to this question? (If yes, you'll be asked to give us your contact information at the end of the survey.)

**Q16.** Which of the following best describes your role?

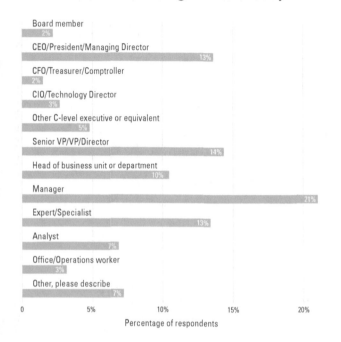

Percentage of respondents

**Q17.** What is your main functional area?

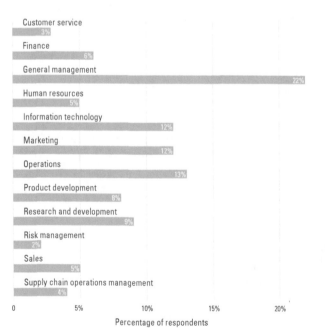

Percentage of respondents

**Q18.** Which of the following best describes the activities involved in your day-to-day role?

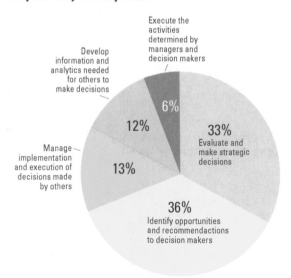

## Q19. What is your primary industry?

| Industry | % |
|---|---|
| Aerospace and Defense | 3% |
| Agriculture and Agribusiness | 1% |
| Automotive | 2% |
| Chemicals | 2% |
| Construction and Real Estate | 3% |
| Consumer Goods | 4% |
| Education | 0% |
| Energy and Natural Resources | 5% |
| Entertainment, Media and Publishing | 4% |
| Financial Services – Banking | 5% |
| Financial Services – Insurance | 2% |
| Financial Services – Investment Management | 3% |
| Government/Public Sector – Federal/Central | 4% |
| Government/Public Sector – City/Local | 1% |
| Health Care Services – Payer | 1% |
| Health Care Services – Provider | 4% |
| IT and Technology | 16% |
| Logistics and Distribution | 2% |
| Manufacturing | 10% |
| Pharmaceuticals and Biotechnology | 3% |
| Professional Services | 16% |
| Retailing | 3% |
| Telecommunications | 3% |
| Transportation, Travel and Tourism | 2% |

Percentage of respondents

## Q20. What is your organization's global annual revenue in U.S. dollars?

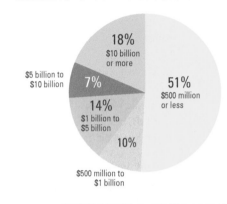

- 18% $10 billion or more
- 7% $5 billion to $10 billion
- 14% $1 billion to $5 billion
- 10% $500 million to $1 billion
- 51% $500 million or less

## Q21. How would your describe your organization's competitive position?

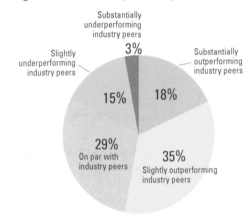

- 3% Substantially underperforming industry peers
- 15% Slightly underperforming industry peers
- 29% On par with industry peers
- 35% Slightly outperforming industry peers
- 18% Substantially outperforming industry peers

## Q22. In which geographic region are you personally located?

- 2% Eastern Europe
- Latin America
- 7% Middle East and Africa
- 13% Western Europe
- 16% Asia-Pacific
- 57% North America

## ACKNOWLEDGMENTS

John Armstrong, IBM; Marc Berson, IBM; Eric Brynjolfsson, MIT; Dr. Steve Buckley, IBM; William Fuessler, IBM; Bill Hoffman, Best Buy; Christer Johnson, IBM; Richard Lawrence, IBM; Thomas W. Malone, MIT; Andrew McAfee, MIT; Dwight McNeill, IBM; Chris Moore, IBM; Mychelle Mollot, IBM; Mark Ramsey, IBM; Will Reilly, IBM; Jeanne W. Ross, MIT; Michael Schrage, MIT; Michael Schroeck, IBM; Marc Teerlink, IBM; David Turner, IBM; Bruce Tyler, IBM; Andy Warzecha, IBM; Peter Weill, MIT; and Katharyn White, IBM.

### Additional support for this study was provided by:

**Attivio, Inc.** Attivio's unified information access software combines enterprise search, BI, data warehousing and analytic capabilities for an integrated view of content and data, regardless of source or format. http://www.attivio.com/.

**Dassault Systèmes.** Dassault Systèmes, a leader in 3D and product lifecycle management solutions, enables everyone — from designers to consumers and their communities — to create, share and experience in 3D. http://www.3ds.com/.

## RELATED PUBLICATIONS

M.S. Hopkins, S. Lavalle, and F. Balboni, "10 Insights: A First Look at the New Intelligent Enterprise Survey on Winning with Data," *MIT Sloan Management Review* 52, no.1 (fall 2010), http://sloanreview.mit.edu/x/52115.

N. Kruschwitz and R. Shockley, "10 Data Points: Information and Analytics at Work," *MIT Sloan Management* Review 52, no. 1 (fall 2010), http://sloanreview.mit.edu/x/52115.

M.S. Hopkins, "The Four Ways IT Is Revolutionizing Innovation: An Interview with Erik Brynjolfsson," *MIT Sloan Management Review* 51, no. 3 (spring 2010), http://sloanreview.mit.edu/x/51330.

M.S. Hopkins, "Putting the Science in Management Science: An Interview with Andrew McAfee," *MIT Sloan Management Review* 51, no. 4 (summer 2010), http://sloanreview.mit.edu/x/51414.

IBM Corporation, "Capitalizing on Complexity: Insights from the Global CEO Study," IBM Institute for Business Value, May 2010, www.ibm.com/gbs/ceostudy.

S. LaValle, "Breaking Away with Business Analytics and Optimization: New Intelligence Meets Enterprise Operations," IBM Institute for Business Value, November 2009, ftp://public.dhe.ibm.com/common/ssi/ecm/en/gbe03263usen/GBE03263USEN.PDF.

S. LaValle, "Business Analytics and Optimiziation for the Intelligent Enterprise," IBM Institute for Business Value, December 2009, ftp://public.dhe.ibm.com/common/ssi/ecm/en/gbe03211usen/GBE03211USEN.PDF.

# Preface

*Practical Management Science* provides a spreadsheet-based, example-driven approach to management science. Our initial objective in writing the book was to reverse negative attitudes about the course by making the subject relevant to students. We intended to do this by imparting valuable modeling skills that students can appreciate and take with them into their careers. We are very gratified by the success of the first three editions. The book has exceeded our initial objectives. We are especially pleased to hear about the success of the book at many other colleges and universities around the world. The acceptance and excitement that has been generated has motivated us to revise the book and make the fourth edition even better.

When we wrote the first edition, management science courses were regarded as irrelevant or uninteresting to many business students, and the use of spreadsheets in management science was in its early stages of development. Much has changed since the first edition was published in 1996, and we believe that these changes are for the better. We have learned a lot about the best practices of spreadsheet modeling for clarity and communication. We have also developed better ways of teaching the materials, and we understand more about where students tend to have difficulty with the concepts. Finally, we have had the opportunity to teach this material at several Fortune 500 companies (including Eli Lilly, Price Waterhouse Coopers, General Motors, Tomkins, Microsoft, and Intel). These companies, through their enthusiastic support, have further enhanced the realism of the examples included in this book.

Our objective in writing the first edition was very simple—we wanted to make management science relevant and practical to students and professionals. This book continues to distinguish itself in the market in four fundamental ways:

- **Teach by Example.** The best way to learn modeling concepts is by working through examples and solving an abundance of problems. This active learning approach is not new, but our text has more fully developed this approach than any book in the field. The feedback we have received from many of you has confirmed the success of this pedagogical approach for management science.

- **Integrate Modeling with Finance, Marketing, and Operations Management.** We integrate modeling into all functional areas of business. This is an important feature because the majority of business students major in finance and marketing. Almost all competing textbooks emphasize operations management–related examples. Although these examples are important, and many are included in the book, the application of modeling to problems in finance and marketing is too important to ignore. Throughout the book, we use real examples from all functional areas of business to illustrate the power of spreadsheet modeling to all of these areas. At Indiana University, this has led to the development of two advanced MBA electives in finance and marketing that build upon the content in this book. The inside front cover of the book illustrates the integrative applications contained in the book.

- **Teach Modeling, Not Just Models.** Poor attitudes among students in past management science courses can be attributed to the way in which they were taught: emphasis on algebraic formulations and memorization of models. Students gain more insight into the power of management science by developing skills in modeling. Throughout the book, we stress the logic associated with model development, and we discuss solutions in this context. Because real problems and real models often include limitations or alternatives, we include many "Modeling Issues" sections to discuss these important matters. Finally, we include "Modeling Problems" in most chapters to help develop these skills.

- **Provide Numerous Problems and Cases.** Whereas all textbooks contain problem sets for students to practice, we have carefully and judiciously crafted the problems and cases contained in this book. Each chapter contains four types of problems: Skill-Building Problems, Skill-Extending Problems, Modeling Problems, and Cases. Most of the problems following sections of chapters ask students to extend the examples in the preceding section. The end-of-chapter problems then ask students to explore new models. Selected solutions are available to students who purchase the Student Solution Files online and are denoted by the second-color numbering of the problem. Solutions for all of the problems and cases are provided to adopting instructors. In addition, shell files (templates) are available for most of the problems for adopting instructors. The shell files contain the basic structure of the problem with the relevant formulas omitted. By adding or omitting hints in individual solutions, instructors can tailor these shell files to best meet the individual/specific needs of their students.

## New to the Fourth Edition

The main reason for the fourth edition was the introduction of Excel 2010. Admittedly, this is not nearly as much a game changer as Excel 2007, but it does provide new features that ought to be addressed. In addition, once we were motivated by Excel 2010 to revise the book, we saw the possibility for a lot of other changes that will hopefully improve the book. Important changes to the fourth edition include the following:

- Undoubtedly, the biggest change in Excel 2010, the one that affects our book the most, is the new Solver add-in. Frontline Systems, the develop of Solver, swapped the previous version of Solver for what we used to provide separately: Premium Solver. Now all Excel 2010 users have essentially the old Premium Solver. (Therefore, we no longer provide an academic version of Premium Solver with the book.) As discussed in detail in the optimization chapters, the new Solver provides several important enhancements: (1) It has a nicer, more compact user interface; (2) it appears to work better, giving many fewer "conditions for linear model not satisfied" messages for models that are indeed linear; and (3) it includes Evolutionary Solver, which we continue to use for difficult *non-smooth* models in Chapter 8.

- To make the book somewhat shorter, we moved the old chapters 9 (Multiobjective Decision Making) and 15 (Project Management) online, renumbering the former as 16. Based on user reports, these are two of the less-covered chapters in the book, but they are still available online if you want to use them. Of course, the remaining chapters have been renumbered accordingly. (Both chapters are found on the Instructor web site and the students' Essential

Resource Web site. Instructions for access to these sites are described later in this preface.)

- In the first optimization chapter, Chapter 3, we replaced the introductory two-variable diet model with a simpler two-variable product mix model. Then we follow it up with a larger version of the same basic product mix model. We believe this should make the introduction to optimization easier for instructors to teach and for students to follow.

- In the regression and forecasting chapter, now numbered Chapter 14, we discontinued the use of the Analysis Toolpak and jumped directly into the Palisade StatTools add-in. We believe that StatTools is vastly superior to Analysis Toolpak, so we decided to take full advantage of it.

- One of the main strengths of this book has always been its numerous problems. However, some of these had been around for over a decade and were either totally out of date or required better data. Therefore, we deleted some problems, added some brand new ones, and changed the input data for many others. We have included a file for instructors, PMS4e Problem Database.xlsx, that lists all of the changes.

- One last change didn't make it into the book, but we are offering it on a limited trial basis to instructors. Specifically, we have added several large optimization models (more changing cells than Solver can handle) to the instructor materials. (They are under Extra subfolders in the Example Files folders.) The motivation for these additions is to let students experience what it is like for managers who do not have access to optimization software. What kinds of heuristics might they use? Will these heuristics get anywhere near optimality? For comparison, we have provided optimal solutions. If nothing else, we believe these examples might make students appreciate the true power of optimization software such as Solver.

## The Essential Resource Web Site for Students

The tools offered with the fourth edition of *Practical Management Science* extend beyond the textbook. Students purchasing a new textbook receive access to the Essential Resource Web site that accompanies this book. For students who do not purchase a new textbook, there are other access and product options available at CengageBrain.com.

## Software

We continue to be very excited about offering the most comprehensive suite of software ever available with a management science textbook. The commercial value of the software available with this text exceeds $1000 if purchased directly. This software is available free with *new* copies of the fourth edition. The following Palisade software is available from a link that is provided on the Essential Resource Web site:

* Palisade's **DecisionTools™ Suite,** including the award-winning **@RISK, PrecisionTree, StatTools, TopRank, RISKOptimizer, NeuralTools,** and **Evolver.** This software is not available with any competing textbook and comes in an educational version that is only slightly scaled down from the expensive commercial version. (StatTools replaces Albright's StatPro add-in that came with the second edition. If you are interested, StatPro is still freely available from http://www.kelley.iu.edu/albrightbooks, although it will not be updated for Excel 2007 or 2010.) For more information about the Palisade Corporation and the DecisionTools Suite, visit Palisade's Web site at http://www.palisade.com.

* To make sensitivity analysis useful and intuitive, we continue to provide Albright's **SolverTable** add-in (which is also freely available from http://www.kelley.iu.edu/albrightbooks). SolverTable provides data table–like sensitivity output for optimization models that is easy to interpret.

## Example Files, Data Sets, Problem Files, and Cases

Also on the Essential Resource Web site are the Excel files for all of the examples in the book, as well as many data files required for problems and cases. As in previous editions, there are two versions of the example files: a completed version and a template to get students started. Because this book is so example- and problem-oriented, these files are absolutely essential. For instructors, there is a third *annotated* version of each example file that provides even more insights into the model.

## How to Access the Essential Resource Web Site

**Student Access:** Students are given access instructions to the Essential Resource Web site via the bind-in card in new editions of their book. Go to http://login.cengagebrain.com, click on "Create an Account," and then, in the space provided, enter the unique access code found on the access card bound in your new book. Students who do not buy a new, printed textbook may search CengageBrain.com for other purchase options, such as CourseMate, which offers an eBook format of the book with access to the Essential Resource Web site.

**Instructor Access:** Go to http://login.cengage.com. Use your current user account to sign in. If you do not have an account, follow the screen instructions to create one. Verification of instructor status takes 24 to 48 hours for new accounts. Once you are logged in, type this textbook's ISBN number in the search box. (The ISBN is found on the back of your textbook.) You are then presented with selection options to add to your "Bookshelf," such as the Instructor Web site, Student Essentials Resource Web site, and CourseMate (if applicable to your class). Your selections will show up on your account home page for access to instructor and student materials.

## Ancillaries

### Instructor Materials

Adopting instructors can obtain the Instructors' Resource CD (IRCD) from your regional Cengage Learning sales representative. The IRCD includes:

* PMS4e Problem Database.xlsx file, which contains information about all problems in the book and the correspondence between them and those in the previous edition
* Solution files (in Excel format) for all of the problems and cases in the book and solution shells (templates) for selected problems in the modeling chapters
* PowerPoint® presentation files
* Test Bank in Word format and now also in ExamView Testing Software

Instructor ancillaries are also posted on the Instructor Web site. Access instructions are described in the previous section. Albright also maintains his own Web site at http://www.kelley.iu.edu/albrightbooks. Among other things, this site includes errata for each edition.

### Student Solutions

Student Solutions for many of the odd-numbered problems (indicated in the text with a colored box on the problem number) are available in Excel format. Students can purchase access to Student Solutions Files on CengageBrain.com. In the search window of this Web site, type in this book's ISBN number (found on the back cover of your book) and hit enter. A product page will show you "Related Products" you can purchase, including the Student Solutions.

## Companion VBA Book

Soon after the first edition appeared, we began using Visual Basic for Applications (VBA), the programming language for Excel, in some of our management science courses. VBA allows you to develop decision support systems around the spreadsheet models. (An example appears at the end of Chapter 3.) This use of VBA has been popular with our students, and many instructors have expressed interest in learning how to do it. For additional support on this topic, a companion book, *VBA for Modelers, 3e* (ISBN 1-4390-7984-6) is available. It assumes no prior experience in computer programming, but it progresses rather quickly to the development of interesting and nontrivial applications. The fourth edition of *Practical Management Science* depends in no way on this companion VBA book, but we encourage instructors to incorporate some VBA into their management science courses. This is not only fun, but students quickly learn to appreciate its power. If you are interested in adopting *VBA for Modelers,* contact your local Cengage Learning representative.

## Acknowledgments

This book has gone through several stages of reviews, and it is a much better product because of them. The majority of the reviewers' suggestions were very good ones, and we have attempted to incorporate them. We would like to extend our appreciation to:

Sue Abdinnour, Wichita State University
Robert Aboolian, California State University–San Marcos
Mohammad Ahmadi, University of Tennessee at Chattanooga
Kelly Alvey, Old Dominion University
Jerry Bilbrey, Anderson University
Fattaneh Cauley, Pepperdine University
Gordon Corzine, University of Massachusetts–Boston
Parthasarati Dileepan, University of Tennessee at Chattanooga
Ehsan Elahi, University of Massachusetts–Boston
Kathryn Ernstberger, Indiana University Southeast
Levon R. Hayrapetyan, Houston Baptist University

Max Peter Hoefer, Pace University
Harvey Iglarsh, Georgetown University
D. K. Kim, Dalton State College
Mary Kurz, Clemson University
Larry J. LeBlanc, Vanderbilt University
Stephen Mahar, University of North Carolina–Wilmington
James Morris, University of Wisconsin–Madison
Khosrow Moshirvaziri, Caliornia State University–Long Beach
Ozgur Ozluk, San Francisco State University
Susan Palocsay, James Madison University
Prakash P. Shenoy, University of Kansas
Ekundayo Shittu, Tulane University
Steven Slezak, California Polytechnic State University–San Luis Obispo
Christine Spencer, University of Baltimore
Robert Stoll, Cleveland State University
Charles Watts, John Carroll University
Yuri Yatsenko, Houston Baptist University

We would also like to thank two special people. First, we want to thank our previous editor Curt Hinrichs. Although Curt has moved from this position and is no longer our editor, his vision in the early years was largely responsible for the success of the first and second editions of *Practical Management Science.* Second, we were lucky to move from one great editor to another in Charles McCormick Jr. Charles is a consummate professional, he is both patient and thorough, and his experience in the publishing business ensures that the tradition Curt started will be carried on.

In addition, we would like to thank Marketing Manager, Adam Marsh; Senior Developmental Editor, Laura Ansara; Content Project Manager, Holly Henjum; Art Director, Stacy Shirley; Editorial Assistants, Nora Heink and Courtney Bavaro; and Project Manager at MPS, Gunjan Chandola.

We would also enjoy hearing from you—we can be reached by e-mail. And please visit either of the following Web sites for more information and occasional updates:

▓ http://www.kelley.iu.edu/albrightbooks

▓ CengageBrain.com

**Wayne L. Winston** (winston@indiana.edu)
**S. Christian Albright** (albright@indiana.edu)
*Bloomington, Indiana*
*January 2011*

Lise Gagne/istockphoto

## ANALYSIS OF HIV/AIDS

Many of management science's most successful applications are traditional functional areas of business, including operations management, logistics, finance, and marketing. Indeed, many such applications are analyzed in this book. However, another area where management science has had a strong influence over the past two decades has been the analysis of the worldwide HIV/AIDS epidemic. Not only have theoretical models been developed, but even more important, they have also been *applied* to help understand the epidemic and reduce its spread. To highlight the importance of management science modeling in this area, an entire special issue (May–June 1998) of *Interfaces*, the journal that reports successful management science applications, was devoted to HIV/AIDS models. Some of the highlights are discussed here to give you an idea of what management science has to offer in this important area.

Kahn et al. (1998) provides an overview of the problem. They discuss how governments, public-health agencies, and health-care providers must determine how best to allocate scarce resources for HIV treatment and prevention among different programs and populations. They discuss in some depth how management science models have influenced, and will continue to influence, AIDS policy decisions. Other articles in the issue discuss more specific problems. Caulkins et al. (1998) analyze whether the distribution of difficult-to-reuse syringes would reduce the spread of HIV among injection drug users. Based on their model, they conclude that the extra expense of these types of syringes would not be worth the marginal benefit they might provide.

Paltiel and Freedberg (1998) investigate the costs and benefits of developing and administering treatments for cytomegalovirus (CMV), an infection to which HIV carriers are increasingly exposed. (Retinitis, CMV's most common manifestation, is associated with blindness and sometimes death.) Their model suggests that the costs compare unfavorably with alternative uses of scarce resources. Owens et al. (1998) analyze the effect of women's relapse to high-risk sexual and needle-sharing behavior on the costs and benefits of a voluntary program to screen women of childbearing age for HIV. They find, for example, that the effect of relapse to high-risk behaviors on screening program costs and benefits can be substantial, suggesting that behavioral interventions that produce sustained reductions in risk behavior, even if expensive, could be cost-saving.

The important point is that these articles (and others not mentioned here) base their results on rigorous management science models of the HIV/AIDS phenomenon. In addition, they are backed up with real data. They are not simply opinions of the authors. ■

## 2.1 INTRODUCTION

This book is all about spreadsheet modeling. By the time you are finished, you will have seen some reasonably complex—and realistic—models. Many of you will also be transformed into Excel "power" users. However, we don't want to start too quickly or assume too much background on your part. For practice in getting up to speed with basic Excel features, we have included an Excel tutorial on this textbook's essential resource Web site. (See the Excel Tutorial.xlsx file.) You can work through this tutorial at your own speed and cover the topics you need help with. Even if you have used Excel extensively, give this tutorial a look. You might be surprised how some of the tips can improve your productivity.

In addition, this chapter provides an introduction to Excel modeling and illustrates some interesting and relatively simple models. The chapter also covers the modeling process and includes some of the less well known, but particularly helpful, Excel tools that are available. These tools include data tables, Goal Seek, lookup tables, and auditing commands. Keep in mind, however, that our objective is not the same as that of the many "how-to" Excel books on the market. We are not teaching Excel just for its many interesting features. Rather, we plan to *use* these features to provide insights into real business problems. In short, Excel is a problem-solving tool, not an end in itself, in this book.

## 2.2 BASIC SPREADSHEET MODELING: CONCEPTS AND BEST PRACTICES

Most mathematical models, including spreadsheet models, involve *inputs*, *decision variables*, and *outputs*. The **inputs** have given fixed values, at least for the purposes of the model. The **decision variables** are those a decision maker controls. The **outputs** are the ultimate values of interest; they are determined by the inputs and the decision variables. For example, suppose a manager must place an order for a certain seasonal product. This product will go out of date fairly soon, so this is the only order that will be made for the product. The inputs are the fixed cost of the order; the unit variable cost of each item ordered; the price charged for each item sold; the salvage value for each item, if any, left in inventory after the product has gone out of date; and the demand for the product. The decision variable is the number of items to order. Finally, the key output is the profit (or loss) from the product. This output can also be broken down into the outputs that contribute to

Some inputs, such as demand in this example, contain a considerable degree of uncertainty. In some cases, as in Example 2.4 later in this chapter, this uncertainty is modeled explicitly.

it: the total ordering cost, the revenue from sales, and the salvage value from leftover items. These outputs must be calculated to obtain profit.

Spreadsheet modeling is the process of entering the inputs and decision variables into a spreadsheet and then relating them appropriately, by means of formulas, to obtain the outputs. After you have done this, you can then proceed in several directions. You might want to perform a sensitivity analysis to see how one or more outputs change as selected inputs or decision variables change. You might want to find the values of the decision variable(s) that minimize or maximize a particular output, possibly subject to certain constraints. You might also want to create charts that show graphically how certain parameters of the model are related.

These operations are illustrated with several examples in this chapter. Getting all the spreadsheet logic correct and producing useful results is a big part of the battle; however, we go farther by stressing good spreadsheet modeling *practices*. You probaby won't be developing spreadsheet models for your sole use; instead, you will be sharing them with colleagues or even a boss (or an instructor). The point is that other people will be reading and trying to make sense out of your spreadsheet models. Therefore, you should construct your spreadsheet models with *readability* in mind. Features that can improve readability include the following:

- A clear, logical layout to the overall model
- Separation of different parts of a model, possibly across multiple worksheets
- Clear headings for different sections of the model and for all inputs, decision variables, and outputs
- Use of range names
- Use of boldface, italics, larger font size, coloring, indentation, and other formatting features
- Use of cell comments
- Use of text boxes for assumptions and explanations

Obviously, the formulas and logic in any spreadsheet model must be correct; however, correctness will not take you very far if no one can understand what you have done. Much of the power of spreadsheets derives from their flexibility. A blank spreadsheet is like a big blank canvas waiting for you to insert useful data and formulas. Almost anything is allowed. However, you can abuse this power if you don't have an overall plan for what should go where. Plan ahead before diving in, and if your plan doesn't look good after you start filling in the spreadsheet, revise your plan.

The following example illustrates the process of building a spreadsheet model according to these guidelines. We build this model in stages. In the first stage, we build a model that is correct, but not very readable. At each subsequent stage, we modify the model to make it more readable. You do not need to go through each of these stages explicitly when you build your own models. You can often strive for the final stage right away, at least after you get accustomed to the modeling process. The various stages are shown here simply for contrast.

## EXAMPLE 2.1 ORDERING NCAA T-SHIRTS

It is March, and the annual NCAA Basketball Tournament is down to the final four teams. Randy Kitchell is a T-shirt vendor who plans to order T-shirts with the names of the final four teams from a manufacturer and then sell them to the fans. The fixed cost of any order is $750, the variable cost per T-shirt to Randy is $8, and Randy's selling price is $18. However, this price will be charged only until a week after the tournament. After that time, Randy figures that interest in the T-shirts will be low, so he plans to sell all remaining

T-shirts, if any, at $6 each. His best guess is that demand for the T-shirts during the full-price period will be 1500. He is thinking about ordering 1450 T-shirts, but he wants to build a spreadsheet model that will let him experiment with the uncertain demand and his order quantity. How should he proceed?

**Objective**   To build a spreadsheet model in a series of stages, all stages being correct but each stage being more readable and flexible than the previous stages.

## Solution

The logic behind the model is fairly simple, but the model is built for generality. Specifically, the formulas used allow for the order quantity to be less than, equal to, or greater than demand. If demand is greater than the order quantity, Randy will sell all the T-shirts ordered for $18 each. However, if demand is less than the order quantity, Randy will sell as many T-shirts as are demanded at the $18 price and all leftovers at the $6 price. You can implement this logic in Excel with an IF function.

A first attempt at a spreadsheet model appears in Figure 2.1. (See the file TShirt Sales Finished.xlsx, where each stage appears on a separate worksheet.) You enter a possible demand in cell B3, a possible order quantity in cell B4, and then calculate the profit in cell B5 with the formula

=-750-8*B4+IF(B3>B4,18*B4,18*B3+6*(B4-B3))

This formula subtracts the fixed and variable costs and then adds the revenue according to the logic just described.

Figure 2.1

**Base Model**

| | A | B |
|---|---|---|
| 1 | NCAA t-shirt sales | |
| 2 | | |
| 3 | Demand | 1500 |
| 4 | Order | 1450 |
| 5 | Profit | 13750 |

**Excel Function: IF**
*Excel's IF function is probably already familiar to you, but it is too important not to discuss. It has the syntax =IF(condition,resultIfTrue,resultIfFalse). The condition is any expression that is either true or false. The two expressions resultIfTrue and resultIfFalse can be any expressions you would enter in a cell: numbers, text, or other Excel functions (including other IF functions). Note that if either expression is text, it must be enclosed in double quotes, such as*

=IF(Score>=90,"A","B")

*Finally, condition can be complex combinations of conditions, using the keywords AND or OR. Then the syntax is, for example,*

=IF(AND(Score1<60,Score2<60),"Fail","Pass")

Never hard code numbers into Excel formulas. Use cell references instead.

This model in Figure 2.1 is entirely correct, but it isn't very readable or flexible because it breaks a rule that you should strive never to break: It *hard codes* input values into the profit formula. A spreadsheet model should *never* include input numbers in formulas. Instead, the spreadsheet model should store input values in separate cells and then include *cell references* to these inputs in its formulas. A remedy appears in Figure 2.2. Here, the inputs have been entered in the range B3:B6, and the profit formula in cell B10 has been changed to

=-B3-B4*B9+IF(B8>B9,B5*B9,10*B8+B6*(B9-B8))

Figure 2.2

Model with Input
Cells

| | A | B |
|---|---|---|
| 1 | NCAA t-shirt sales | |
| 2 | | |
| 3 | Fixed order cost | $750 |
| 4 | Variable cost | $8 |
| 5 | Selling price | $18 |
| 6 | Discount price | $6 |
| 7 | | |
| 8 | Demand | 1500 |
| 9 | Order | 1450 |
| 10 | Profit | $13,750 |

This is exactly the same formula as before, but it is now more flexible. If an input changes, the profit recalculates automatically. Most important, the inputs are no longer buried in the formula.[1]

Still, the profit formula is not very readable as it stands. You can make it more readable by using range names. The mechanics of range names are covered in detail later in this chapter. For now, the results of using range names for cells B3 through B6, B8, and B9 are shown in Figure 2.3. This model looks exactly like the previous model, but the formula in cell B10 is now

=-Fixed_order_cost-Variable_cost*Order+IF(Demand>Order,
Selling_price*Order,Selling_price*Demand+Discount_Price*(Order-Demand))

This formula is admittedly more long-winded, but it is certainly easier to read.

Figure 2.3

Model with Range
Names in Profit
Formula

| | A | B | C | D | E | F |
|---|---|---|---|---|---|---|
| 1 | NCAA t-shirt sales | | | | | |
| 2 | | | | | | |
| 3 | Fixed order cost | $750 | | Range names used | | |
| 4 | Variable cost | $8 | | Demand | ='Model 3'!$B$8 | |
| 5 | Selling price | $18 | | Discount_price | ='Model 3'!$B$6 | |
| 6 | Discount price | $6 | | Fixed_order_cost | ='Model 3'!$B$3 | |
| 7 | | | | Order | ='Model 3'!$B$9 | |
| 8 | Demand | 1500 | | Selling_price | ='Model 3'!$B$5 | |
| 9 | Order | 1450 | | Variable_cost | ='Model 3'!$B$4 | |
| 10 | Profit | $13,750 | | | | |

Randy might like to have profit broken down into various costs and revenues (Figure 2.4), rather than one single profit cell. The formulas in cells B12, B13, B15, and B16 are straightforward, so they are not repeated here. You can then accumulate these to get profit in cell B17 with the formula

=-(B12+B13)+(B15+B16)

Figure 2.4

Model with
Intermediate
Outputs

| | A | B | C | D | E | F |
|---|---|---|---|---|---|---|
| 1 | NCAA t-shirt sales | | | | | |
| 2 | | | | | | |
| 3 | Fixed order cost | $750 | | Range names used | | |
| 4 | Variable cost | $8 | | Demand | ='Model 4'!$B$8 | |
| 5 | Selling price | $18 | | Discount_price | ='Model 4'!$B$6 | |
| 6 | Discount price | $6 | | Fixed_order_cost | ='Model 4'!$B$3 | |
| 7 | | | | Order | ='Model 4'!$B$9 | |
| 8 | Demand | 1500 | | Selling_price | ='Model 4'!$B$5 | |
| 9 | Order | 1450 | | Variable_cost | ='Model 4'!$B$4 | |
| 10 | | | | | | |
| 11 | Costs | | | | | |
| 12 | Fixed cost | $750 | | | | |
| 13 | Variable costs | $11,600 | | | | |
| 14 | Revenues | | | | | |
| 15 | Full-price shirts | $26,100 | | | | |
| 16 | Discount-price shirts | $0 | | | | |
| 17 | Profit | $13,750 | | | | |

[1]Some people refer to such numbers buried in formulas as *magic numbers* because they just seem to appear out of nowhere. Avoid magic numbers!

Figure 2.5

Model with
Category Labels and
Color Coding

| | A | B | C | D | E | F |
|---|---|---|---|---|---|---|
| 1 | NCAA t-shirt sales | | | | | |
| 2 | | | | | | |
| 3 | **Input variables** | | | **Range names used** | | |
| 4 | Fixed order cost | $750 | | Demand | ='Model 5'!$B$10 | |
| 5 | Variable cost | $8 | | Discount_price | ='Model 5'!$B$7 | |
| 6 | Selling price | $18 | | Fixed_order_cost | ='Model 5'!$B$4 | |
| 7 | Discount price | $6 | | Order | ='Model 5'!$B$13 | |
| 8 | | | | Selling_price | ='Model 5'!$B$6 | |
| 9 | **Uncertain variable** | | | Variable_cost | ='Model 5'!$B$5 | |
| 10 | Demand | 1500 | | | | |
| 11 | | | | | | |
| 12 | **Decision variable** | | | | | |
| 13 | Order | 1450 | | | | |
| 14 | | | | | | |
| 15 | **Output variables** | | | | | |
| 16 | Costs | | | | | |
| 17 | Fixed cost | $750 | | | | |
| 18 | Variable costs | $11,600 | | | | |
| 19 | Revenues | | | | | |
| 20 | Full-price shirts | $26,100 | | | | |
| 21 | Discount-price shirts | $0 | | | | |
| 22 | Profit | $13,750 | | | | |

Of course, range names could be used for these intermediate output cells, but this is probably more work than it's worth. You should always use some judgment when deciding how many range names to use.

If Randy's assistant is presented with this model, how does she know at a glance which cells contain inputs or decision variables or outputs? Labels and/or color coding can help to distinguish these types. A blue/red/gray color-coding style has been applied in Figure 2.5, along with descriptive labels in boldface. The blue cells at the top are input cells, the red cell in the middle is a decision variable, and the gray cell at the bottom is the key output.[2] There is nothing sacred about this particular convention. Feel free to adopt your own convention and style, but be sure to use it consistently.

The model in Figure 2.5 is still not the last word on this example. As shown in later examples, you can create data tables to see how sensitive profit is to the inputs, the demand, and the order quantity. You can also create charts to show any numerical results graphically. But this is enough for now. You can see that the model in Figure 2.5 is now much more readable and flexible than the original model in Figure 2.1.  ▪

Because good spreadsheet style is so important, the appendix to this chapter discusses a few tools for editing and documenting your spreadsheet models. Use these tools right away and as you progress through the book.

In the rest of this chapter, we discuss a number of interesting examples and introduce important modeling concepts (such as sensitivity analysis), important Excel features (such as data tables), and even some important business concepts (such as

## FUNDAMENTAL INSIGHT

### Spreadsheet Layout and Documentation

If you want your spreadsheets to be used (and you want your value in your company to rise), give a lot of thought to your spreadsheet layout and then document your work carefully. For layout, think about whether certain data are best oriented in rows or columns, whether your work is better placed in a single sheet or in multiple sheets, and so on. For documentation, use descriptive labels and headings, color coding, cell comments, and text boxes to make your spreadsheets more readable. It takes time and careful planning to design and then document your spreadsheet models, but the time is well spent. And if you come back in a few days to a spreadsheet model you developed and you can't make heads or tails of it, don't be afraid to redesign your work completely—from the ground up.

---

[2]This color convention shows up clearly in the Excel files that accompany the book. However, in this two-color book (shades of gray and blue), it is difficult to see the color-coding scheme. We recommend that you look not only at the figures in the book, but at the actual Excel files.

net present value). To get the most from these examples, follow along at your own PC, starting with a blank spreadsheet. It is one thing to read about spreadsheet modeling; it is quite another to actually *do* it!

## 2.3 COST PROJECTIONS

In this next example, a company wants to project its costs of producing products, given that material and labor costs are likely to increase through time. We build a simple model and then use Excel's charting capabilities to obtain a graphical image of projected costs.

---

**EXAMPLE** | **2.2 PROJECTING THE COSTS OF BOOKSHELVES AT WOODWORKS**

The Woodworks Company produces a variety of custom-designed wood furniture for its customers. One favorite item is a bookshelf, made from either cherry or oak. The company knows that wood prices and labor costs are likely to increase in the future. Table 2.1 shows the number of board-feet and labor hours required for a bookshelf, the current costs per board-foot and labor hour, and the anticipated annual increases in these costs. (The top row indicates that either type of bookshelf requires 30 board-feet of wood and 16 hours of labor.) Build a spreadsheet model that enables the company to experiment with the growth rates in wood and labor costs so that a manager can see, both numerically and graphically, how the costs of the bookshelves vary in the next few years.

**Table 2.1    Input Data for Manufacturing a Bookshelf**

| Resource | Cherry | Oak | Labor |
|---|---|---|---|
| Required per bookshelf | 30 | 30 | 16 |
| Current unit cost | $5.50 | $4.30 | $18.50 |
| Anticipated annual cost increase | 2.4% | 1.7% | 1.5% |

**Business Objectives[3]**    To build a model that allows Woodworks to see, numerically and graphically, how its costs of manufacturing bookshelves increase in the future and to allow the company to answer what-if questions with this model.

**Excel Objectives**    To learn good spreadsheet practices, to enable copying formulas with the careful use of relative and absolute addresses, and to create line charts from multiple series of data.

### Solution

Listing the key variables in a table before developing the actual spreadsheet model is useful, so we will continue to do this in many later examples (see Table 2.2.) This practice forces you to examine the roles of the variables—which are inputs, which are decision variables, and which are outputs. Although the variables and their roles are fairly clear for this example, later examples will require more thought.

---

[3]In later chapters, we simply list the "Objective" of each example as we did in Example 2.1. However, because this chapter has been written to enhance basic spreadsheet skills, we separate the business objectives from the Excel objectives.

Table 2.2    Key Variables for the Bookshelf Manufacturing Example

| Input variables | Wood and labor requirements per bookshelf, current unit costs of wood and labor, anticipated annual increases in unit costs |
| Output variables | Projected unit costs of wood and labor, projected total bookshelf costs |

The reasoning behind the model is straightforward. You first project the unit costs for wood and labor into the future. Then for any year you multiply the unit costs by the required numbers of board-feet and labor hours per bookshelf. Finally, you add the wood and labor costs to obtain the total cost of a bookshelf.

## DEVELOPING THE SPREADSHEET MODEL

The completed spreadsheet model appears in Figure 2.6 and in the file Bookshelf Costs.xlsx.[4] You can develop it with the following steps.

**Figure 2.6**

**Bookshelf Cost Model**

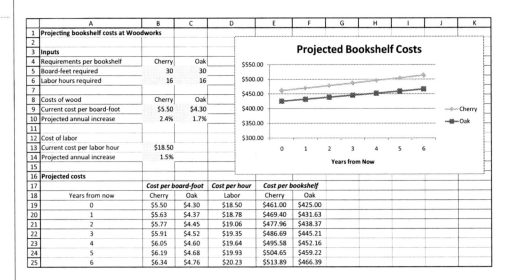

**Inputs.** You should usually enter the inputs for a model in the upper-left corner of a worksheet as you can see in the shaded ranges in Figure 2.6, using the data from Table 2.1. We have used our standard convention of coloring inputs—the numbers from the statement of the problem—blue. You can develop your own convention, but the input cells should be distinguished in some way. Note that the inputs are grouped logically and are explained with appropriate labels. You should always document your spreadsheet model with informational labels. Also, note that by entering inputs explicitly in input cells, you can *refer* to them later in Excel formulas.

**Design output table.** Plan ahead for how you want to structure your outputs. We created a table where there is a row for every year in the future (year 0 corresponds to the current year), there are three columns for projected unit costs (columns B–D), and there are two columns for projected total bookshelf costs (columns E–F). The headings reflect this design. Of course, this isn't the only possible design, but it works well. The important point is that you should have *some* logical design in mind before diving in.

[4]This textbook's essential resource Web site includes templates and completed files for all examples in the book, where all of the latter have "Finished" appended to their file names. However, especially in this chapter, we suggest that you start with a blank spreadsheet and follow the step-by-step instructions on your own.

**3 Projected unit costs of wood.** The dollar values in the range B19:F25 are all calculated from Excel formulas. Although the logic in this example is straightforward, it is still important to have a strategy in mind before you enter formulas. In particular, you should always try to design your spreadsheet so that you can enter a *single* formula and then copy it. This saves work and avoids errors. For the costs per board-foot in columns B and C, enter the formula

=B9

in cell B19 and copy it to cell C19. Then enter the general formula

=B19*(1+B$10)

in cell B20 and copy it to the range B20:C25. We assume you know the rules for absolute and relative addresses (dollar sign for absolute, no dollar sign for relative), but it takes some planning to use these so that copying is possible. Make sure you understand why we made row 10 absolute but column B relative.

**Excel Tip:** *Relative and Absolute Addresses in Formulas*

*Relative and absolute addresses are used in Excel formulas to facilitate copying. A dollar sign next to a column or row address indicates that the address is absolute and will not change when copying. The lack of a dollar sign indicates that the address is relative and will change when copying. After you select a cell in a formula, you can press the F4 key repeatedly to cycle through the relative/absolute possibilities, for example, =B4 (both column and row relative), =$B$4 (both column and row absolute), =B$4 (column relative, row absolute), and =$B4 (column absolute, row relative).*

**4 Projected unit labor costs.** To calculate projected hourly labor costs, enter the formula

=B13

in cell D19. Then enter the formula

=D19*(1+B$14)

in cell D20 and copy it down column D.

**5 Projected bookshelf costs.** Each bookshelf cost is the sum of its wood and labor costs. By a careful use of absolute and relative addresses, you can enter a single formula for these costs—for all years and for both types of wood. To do this, enter the formula

=B$5*B19+B$6*$D19

in cell E19 and copy it to the range E19:F25. The idea here is that the units of wood and labor per bookshelf are always in rows 5 and 6, and the projected unit labor cost is always in column D, but all other references are relative to allow copying.

**6 Chart.** A chart is a valuable addition to any table of data, especially in the business world, so charting in Excel is a skill worth mastering. Although not everyone agrees, the many changes Microsoft made regarding charts in Excel 2007 and 2010 help you create charts more efficiently and effectively. We illustrate some of the possibilities here, but we urge you to experiment with other possibilities on your own. Start by selecting the range E18:F25—yes, including the labels in row 18. Next, click on the Line dropdown list on the Insert ribbon and select the Line with Markers type. You instantly get the basic line chart you want, with one series for Cherry and another for Oak. Also, when the chart is selected (that is, it has a border around it), you see three Chart Tools ribbons: Design, Layout, and Format. The most important button on any of these ribbons is the Select Data button on the Design ribbon. It lets you choose the ranges of the data for charting in case

Figure 2.7

Select Data
Dialog Box

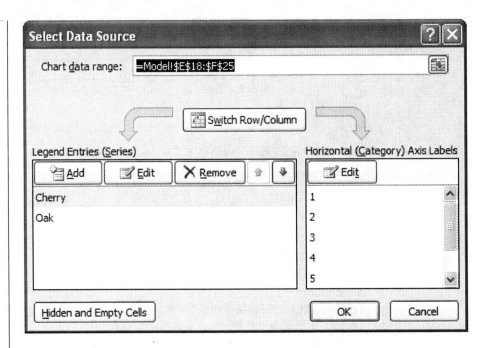

Figure 2.8

Dialog Box for
Changing
Horizontal
Axis Labels

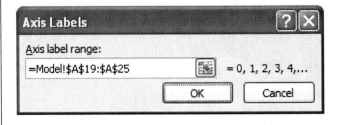

*The many chart
options are easily
accessible from the
three Chart Tools
ribbons in Excel 2007
and 2010. Don't be
afraid to experiment
with them to produce
professional-looking
charts.*

Excel's default choices (which are based on the selected range when you create the chart) are wrong. Click on Select Data now to obtain the dialog box in Figure 2.7. On the left, you control the series (one series or multiple series) being charted; on the right, you control the data used for the horizontal axis. By selecting E18:F25, you have the series on the left correct, including the names of these series (Cherry and Oak), but if you didn't, you could select one of the series and click on Edit to change it. The data on the horizontal axis is currently the default 1, 2, and so on. To make it the data in column A, click on the Edit button on the right and select the range A19:A25. (See Figure 2.8.) Your chart is now correctly labeled and charts the correct data. Beyond this, you can experiment with various formatting options to make the chart even better. For example, we rescaled the vertical axis to start at $300 rather than $0 (right-click on the numbers on the vertical axis and select Format Axis, or look at the many options on the Axes dropdown list on the Layout ribbon), and we added a chart title at the top and a title for the horizontal axis at the bottom (see buttons on the Labels group on the Layout ribbon). You can spend a lot of time fine-tuning charts—maybe even *too* much time—but professional-looking charts are definitely appreciated.

## Using the Model for What-If Questions

The model in Figure 2.6 can now be used to answer many what-if questions. In fact, many models are built for the purpose of permitting experimentation with various scenarios. The important point is that the model has been built in such a way that a manager can enter any desired values in the input cells, and all of the outputs, including the chart, will update automatically. As a simple example, if the annual percentage increases for wood costs are twice as high as Woodworks anticipated, you can enter these higher values in row 10 and immediately see the effect, as shown in Figure 2.9. By comparing bookshelf costs in this scenario to those in the original scenario, the projected cost in year 6 for cherry bookshelves, for example, increases by about 5.5%, from $513.89 to $542.26.

Figure 2.9    Effect of Higher Increases in Wood Costs

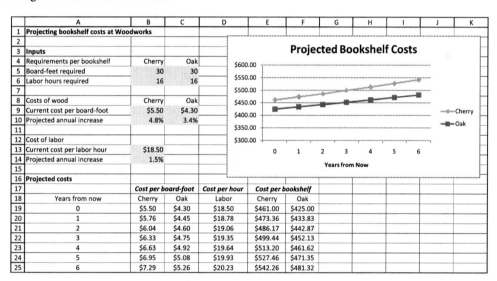

| | A | B | C | D | E | F | G | H |
|---|---|---|---|---|---|---|---|---|
| 1 | Projecting bookshelf costs at Woodworks | | | | | | | |
| 2 | | | | | | | | |
| 3 | Inputs | | | | | | | |
| 4 | Requirements per bookshelf | Cherry | Oak | | | | | |
| 5 | Board-feet required | 30 | 30 | | | | | |
| 6 | Labor hours required | 16 | 16 | | | | | |
| 7 | | | | | | | | |
| 8 | Costs of wood | Cherry | Oak | | | | | |
| 9 | Current cost per board-foot | $5.50 | $4.30 | | | | | |
| 10 | Projected annual increase | 4.8% | 3.4% | | | | | |
| 11 | | | | | | | | |
| 12 | Cost of labor | | | | | | | |
| 13 | Current cost per labor hour | $18.50 | | | | | | |
| 14 | Projected annual increase | 1.5% | | | | | | |
| 15 | | | | | | | | |
| 16 | Projected costs | | | | | | | |
| 17 | | Cost per board-foot | | Cost per hour | Cost per bookshelf | | | |
| 18 | Years from now | Cherry | Oak | Labor | Cherry | Oak | | |
| 19 | 0 | $5.50 | $4.30 | $18.50 | $461.00 | $425.00 | | |
| 20 | 1 | $5.76 | $4.45 | $18.78 | $473.36 | $433.83 | | |
| 21 | 2 | $6.04 | $4.60 | $19.06 | $486.17 | $442.87 | | |
| 22 | 3 | $6.33 | $4.75 | $19.35 | $499.44 | $452.13 | | |
| 23 | 4 | $6.63 | $4.92 | $19.64 | $513.20 | $461.62 | | |
| 24 | 5 | $6.95 | $5.08 | $19.93 | $527.46 | $471.35 | | |
| 25 | 6 | $7.29 | $5.26 | $20.23 | $542.26 | $481.32 | | |

*A carefully constructed model—with no input numbers buried in formulas—allows a manager to answer many what-if questions with a few keystrokes.*

You should appreciate by now why burying input numbers inside Excel formulas is such a bad practice. For example, if you had buried the annual increases of wood costs from row 10 in the formulas in columns B and C, imagine how difficult it would be to answer the what-if question in the previous paragraph. You would first have to find and then change all the numbers in the formulas, which is a lot of work. Even worse, it is likely to lead to errors. ■

## 2.4  BREAKEVEN ANALYSIS

Many business problems require you to find the appropriate level of some activity. This might be the level that maximizes profit (or minimizes cost), or it might be the level that allows a company to break even—no profit, no loss. We discuss a typical breakeven analysis in the following example.

EXAMPLE    2.3 BREAKEVEN ANALYSIS AT QUALITY SWEATERS

The Quality Sweaters Company sells hand-knitted sweaters. The company is planning to print a catalog of its products and undertake a direct mail campaign. The cost of printing the catalog is $20,000 plus $0.10 per catalog. The cost of mailing each catalog (including postage, order forms, and buying names from a mail-order database) is $0.15. In addition, the company plans to include direct reply envelopes in its mailings and incurs $0.20 in extra costs for each direct mail envelope used by a respondent. The average size of a customer order is $40, and the company's variable cost per order (due primarily to labor and material costs) averages about 80% of the order's value—that is, $32. The company plans to mail 100,000 catalogs. It wants to develop a spreadsheet model to answer the following questions:

1. How does a change in the response rate affect profit?
2. For what response rate does the company break even?
3. If the company estimates a response rate of 3%, should it proceed with the mailing?
4. How does the presence of uncertainty affect the usefulness of the model?

**Business Objectives**    To create a model to determine the company's profit and to see how sensitive the profit is to the response rate from the mailing.

**Excel Objectives**    To learn how to work with range names, to learn how to answer what-if questions with one-way data tables, to introduce Excel's Goal Seek tool, and to learn how to document and audit Excel models with cell comments and the auditing toolbar.

## Solution

The key variables appear in Table 2.3. Note that we have designated all variables as input variables, decision variables, or output variables. Furthermore, there is typically a key output variable, in this case, profit, that is of most concern. (In the next few chapters, we refer to it as the *objective* variable.) Therefore, we distinguish this key output variable from the other output variables that we calculate along the way.

**Table 2.3    Key Variables in Quality Sweaters Problem**

| | |
|---|---|
| **Input variables** | Various unit costs, average order size, response rate |
| **Decision variable** | Number mailed |
| **Key output variable** | Profit |
| **Other output variables** | Number of responses, revenue, and cost totals |

The logic for converting inputs and decision variable into outputs is straightforward. After you do this, you can investigate how the response rate affects the profit with a sensitivity analysis.

The completed spreadsheet model appears in Figure 2.10. (See the file Breakeven Analysis.xlsx.) First, note the clear layout of the model. The input cells are colored blue, they are separated from the outputs, headings are boldfaced, several headings are indented, numbers are formatted appropriately, and a list to the right spells out all range names we have used. (See the next Excel Tip on how to create this list.) Also, following the convention we use throughout the book, the decision variable (number mailed) is colored red, and the bottom-line output (profit) is colored gray.

*Adopt some layout and formatting conventions, even if they differ from ours, to make your spreadsheets readable and easy to follow.*

Figure 2.10  Quality Sweaters Model

| | A | B | C | D | E | F | G | H | I |
|---|---|---|---|---|---|---|---|---|---|
| 1 | Quality Sweaters direct mail model | | | | | | Range names used | | |
| 2 | | | | | | | Average_order | =Model!$B$11 | |
| 3 | Catalog inputs | | | Model of responses | | | Fixed_cost_of_printing | =Model!$B$4 | |
| 4 | Fixed cost of printing | $20,000 | | Response rate | 8% | | Number_mailed | =Model!$B$8 | |
| 5 | Variable cost of printing mailing | $0.25 | | Number of responses | 8000 | | Number_of_responses | =Model!$E$5 | |
| 6 | | | | | | | Profit | =Model!$E$13 | |
| 7 | Decision variable | | | Model of revenue, costs, and profit | | | Response_rate | =Model!$E$4 | |
| 8 | Number mailed | 100000 | | Total Revenue | $320,000 | | Total_cost | =Model!$E$12 | |
| 9 | | | | Fixed cost of printing | $20,000 | | Total_Revenue | =Model!$E$8 | |
| 10 | Order inputs | | | Total variable cost of printing mailing | $25,000 | | Variable_cost_of_printing_mailing | =Model!$B$5 | |
| 11 | Average order | $40 | | Total variable cost of orders | $257,600 | | Variable_cost_per_order | =Model!$B$12 | |
| 12 | Variable cost per order | $32.20 | | Total cost | $302,600 | | | | |
| 13 | | | | Profit | $17,400 | | | | |

*We refer to this as the Create from Selection shortcut. If you like it, you can get the dialog box in Figure 2.11 even more quickly: press Ctrl+Shift+F3.*

**Excel Tip: *Creating Range Names***

*To create a range name for a range of cells (which could be a single cell), highlight the cell(s), click in the Name Box just to the left of the Formula Bar, and type a range name. Alternatively, if a column (or row) of labels appears next to the cells to be range-named, you can use these labels as the range names. To do this, highlight the labels and the cells to be named (for example, A4:B5 in Figure 2.10), select Create from Selection on the Formulas ribbon, and make sure the appropriate box in the resulting dialog box (see Figure 2.11) is checked. The labels in our example are to the left of the cells to be named, so the Left column box should be checked. This is a very quick way to create range names, and we did it for all range names in the example. In fact, by keeping your finger on the Ctrl key, you can select multiple ranges.[5] After all your ranges are selected, you can sometimes create all your range names in one step. Note that if a label contains any "illegal" range-name characters, such as a space, the illegal characters are converted to underscores.*

**Figure 2.11**

**Range Name Create Dialog Box**

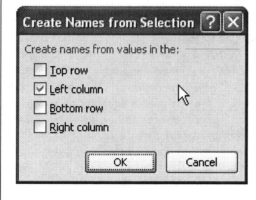

*If you like this tip, you can perform it even faster: press the F3 key to bring up the Paste Name dialog box. (This works only if there is at least one range name in the workbook.)*

**Excel Tip: *Pasting Range Names***

*Including a list of the range names in your spreadsheet is useful for documentation purposes. To do this, select a cell (such as cell G4 in Figure 2.10), select the Use in Formula dropdown list from the Formulas ribbon, and then click on the Paste List option. You get a list of all range names and their cell addresses. However, if you change any of these range names (delete one, for example), the paste list does not update automatically; you have to create it again.*

[5]Many users apparently believe range names are more work than they are worth. This shortcut for creating range names helps to remedy this problem.

To create this model, you can proceed through the following steps.

**1** **Headings and range names.** We have named a lot of cells, more than you might want to name, but you will see their value when you create formulas. In general, we strongly support range names, but it is possible to go overboard. You can waste time naming ranges that do not *really* need to be named. Of course, you can use the Create from Selection shortcut described previously to speed up the process.[6]

**2** **Values of input variables and the decision variable.** Enter these values and format them appropriately. As usual, we have used our blue/red/gray color-coding scheme. Note that the number mailed has been designated as a *decision* variable, not as an input variable (and it is colored red, not blue). This is because the company gets to choose the value of this variable. Finally, note that some of the values have been combined in the statement of the problem. For example, the $32.20 in cell B12 is really 80% of the $40 average order size, plus the $0.20 per return envelope. To document this process, comments appear in a few cells, as shown in Figure 2.12.

Figure 2.12    Cell Comments in Model

| | A | B | C | D | E | F | G | H | I |
|---|---|---|---|---|---|---|---|---|---|
| 1 | Great Threads direct mail model | | | | | | Range names used | | |
| 2 | | | | | Trial value, will do | | | | =Model!$B$11 |
| 3 | Catalog inputs | | | Model of responses | sensitivity analysis on | printing | | | =Model!$B$4 |
| 4 | Fixed cost of printing | $20,000 | Includes $0.10 for printing and $0.15 for mailing each catalog | | 8% | | Number_mailed | | =Model!$B$8 |
| 5 | Variable cost of printing mailing | $0.25 | | ponses | 8000 | | Number_of_responses | | =Model!$E$5 |
| 6 | | | | | | | Profit | | =Model!$E$13 |
| 7 | Decision variable | | | Model of revenue, costs, and profit | | | Response_rate | | =Model!$E$4 |
| 8 | Number mailed | 100000 | | Total Revenue | $320,000 | | Total_cost | | =Model!$E$12 |
| 9 | | | | Fixed cost of printing | $20,000 | | Total_Revenue | | =Model!$E$8 |
| 10 | Order inputs | | Includes 80% of the average $40 order size, plus $0.20 per return envelope | t of printing mailing | $25,000 | | Variable_cost_of_printing_mailing | | =Model!$B$5 |
| 11 | Average order | $40 | | t of orders | $257,600 | | Variable_cost_per_order | | =Model!$B$12 |
| 12 | Variable cost per order | $32.20 | | | $302,600 | | | | |
| 13 | | | | Profit | $17,400 | | | | |

**Excel Tip:** *Inserting Cell Comments*
*Inserting comments in cells is a great way to document your spreadsheet models without introducing excessive clutter. To enter a comment in a cell, right-click on the cell, select the Insert Comment item, and type your comment. This creates a little red mark in the cell, indicating a comment, and you can see the comment by resting the cursor over the cell. When a cell contains a comment, you can edit or delete the comment by right-clicking on the cell and selecting the appropriate item. If you want all the cell comments to be visible (for example, in a printout as in Figure 2.12), click on the File tab (or Office button in Excel 2007), then on Options (Excel Options in Excel 2007), then on the Advanced link, and select the Comment & Indicator option from the Display group. Note that the Indicator Only option is the default.*

## CHANGES IN EXCEL 2010

After Microsoft got all of us used to the Office button in the upper left corner of all Office 2007 applications, it switched to a File tab in Office 2010. The menu structure under this File tab is slightly different from the structure under the Office button, but the functionality is basically the same. In particular, this is where you go to change most of the Excel options.

---

[6] We have heard of one company that does not allow any formulas in its corporate spreadsheets to include cell references; they must all reference range names. This is probably too extreme, but that company's formulas are certainly easy to read.

**③ Model the responses.** You have not yet specified the response rate to the mailing, so enter *any* reasonable value, such as 8%, in the Response_rate cell. You will perform sensitivity on this value later on. Then enter the formula

=Number_mailed*Response_rate

in cell E5. (Are you starting to see the advantage of range names?)

**④ Model the revenue, costs, and profits.** Enter the formula

=Number_of_responses*Average_order

in cell E8, enter the formulas

=Fixed_cost_of_printing

=Variable_cost_of_printing_mailing*Number_mailed

and

=Number_of_responses*Variable_cost_per_order

in cells E9, E10, and E11, enter the formula

=SUM(E9:E11)

in cell E12, and enter the formula

=Total_revenue-Total_cost

in cell E13. These formulas should all be self-explanatory, especially because of the range names used.

**Excel Tip: *Entering Formulas with Range Names***
*To enter a formula that contains range names, you do not have to type the full range names. You actually have two convenient options. One, you can point to the cells, and range names will appear in your formulas. Or two, you can start typing the range name in the formula, and after a few letters, Excel will show you a list you can choose from.*

### Forming a One-Way Data Table

*Data tables are also called what-if tables. They let you see what happens to selected outputs as selected inputs change.*

Now that a basic model has been created, the questions posed by the company can be answered. For question 1, you can form a one-way data table to show how profit varies with the response rate as shown in Figure 2.13. Data tables are used often in this book, so make sure you understand how to create them. We will walk you through the procedure once or twice, but from then on, you are on your own. First, enter a sequence of trial values of the response rate in column A, and enter a link to profit in cell B17 with the formula =Profit. This cell is shaded for emphasis, but this isn't necessary. (In general, other outputs could be part of the table, and they would be placed in columns C, D, and so on. There would be a link to each output in row 17.) Finally, highlight the entire table range, A17:B27, and select Data Table from the What-If Analysis dropdown list on the Data ribbon to bring up the

**Figure 2.13**
**Data Table for Profit**

| | A | B | C | D | E | F |
|---|---|---|---|---|---|---|
| 15 | Question 1 - sensitivity of profit to response rate | | | | | |
| 16 | Response rate | Profit | | Profit versus Response Rate | | |
| 17 | | $17,400 | | | | |
| 18 | 1% | -$37,200 | | | | |
| 19 | 2% | -$29,400 | | | | |
| 20 | 3% | -$21,600 | | | | |
| 21 | 4% | -$13,800 | | | | |
| 22 | 5% | -$6,000 | | | | |
| 23 | 6% | $1,800 | | | | |
| 24 | 7% | $9,600 | | | | |
| 25 | 8% | $17,400 | | | | |
| 26 | 9% | $25,200 | | | | |
| 27 | 10% | $33,000 | | | | |

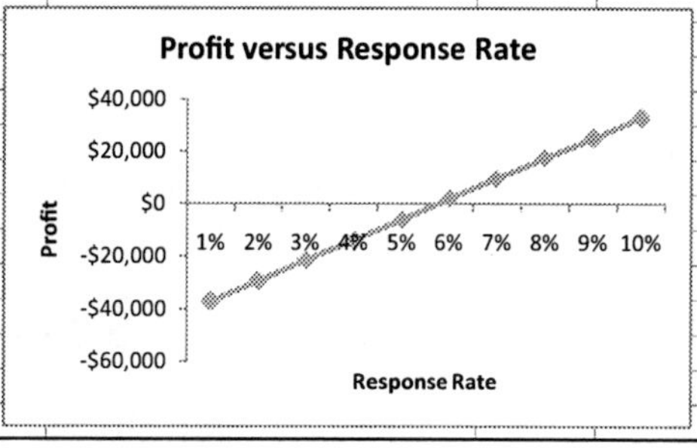

Figure 2.14

Data Table Dialog
Box

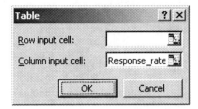

dialog box in Figure 2.14. Fill it in as shown to indicate that the only input, Response_rate, is listed along a column. (You can enter either a range name or a cell address in this dialog box. The easiest way is to point to the cell.)

When you click on OK, Excel substitutes each response rate value in the table into the Response_rate cell, recalculates profit, and reports it in the table. For a final touch, you can create a chart of the values in the data table. (To do this, highlight the A18:B27 range and select the type of chart you want from the Insert ribbon. Then you can fix it up by adding titles, removing the legend, and making other modifications to suit your taste.)

**Excel Tool: *One-Way Data Table***
*A one-way data table allows you to see how one or more output variables vary as a single input variable varies over a selected range of values. These input values can be arranged vertically in a column or horizontally in a row. We will explain only the vertical arrangement because it is the most common. To create the table, enter the input values in a column range, such as A18:A27 of Figure 2.13, and enter links to one or more output cells in columns to the right and one row above the inputs, as in cell B17 of Figure 2.13. Then highlight the entire table, beginning with the upper-left blank cell (A17 in the figure), select Data Table from the What-If Analysis dropdown list on the Data ribbon, and fill in the resulting dialog box as in Figure 2.14. Leave the Row Input cell blank and use the cell where the original value of the input variable lives as the Column Input cell. When you click on OK, each value in the left column of the table is substituted into the column input cell, the spreadsheet recalculates, and the resulting value of the output is placed in the table. Also, if you click anywhere in the body of the table (B18:B27 in the figure), you will see that Excel has entered the TABLE function to remind you that a data table lives here. Note that the column input cell must be on the same worksheet as the table itself; otherwise, Excel issues an error.*

As the chart indicates, profit increases in a linear manner as the response rate varies. More specifically, each percentage point increase in the response rate increases profit by $7800. Here is the reasoning. Each percentage point increase in response rate results in $100{,}000(0.01) = 1000$ more orders. Each order yields a revenue of $40, on average, but incurs a variable cost of $32.20. The net gain in profit is $7.80 per order, or $7800 for 1000 orders.

## USING GOAL SEEK

From the data table, you can see that profit changes from negative to positive when the response rate is somewhere between 5% and 6%. Question 2 asks for the exact breakeven point. You could find this by trial and error, but it is easier to use Excel's Goal Seek tool. Essentially, Goal Seek is used to solve a *single* equation in a *single* unknown. Here, the equation is Profit=0, and the unknown is the response rate. In Excel terminology, the unknown is called the **changing cell** because you can change it to make the equation true.

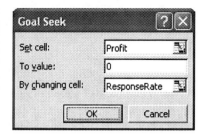

**Figure 2.15**

Goal Seek Dialog
Box

To implement Goal Seek, select Goal Seek from the What-If Analysis dropdown list on the Data ribbon and fill in the resulting dialog box as shown in Figure 2.15. (Range names or cell addresses can be used in the top and bottom boxes, but a *number* must be entered in the middle box.) After you click on OK, the Response_rate and Profit cells have values 5.77% and $0. In words, if the response rate is 5.77%, Great Threads breaks even. If the response rate is greater than 5.77%, the company makes money; if the rate is less than 5.77%, the company loses money. Of course, this assumes that the company mails 100,000 catalogs. If it sends more or fewer catalogs, the breakeven response rate will change.

**Excel Tool:** *Goal Seek*

*The purpose of the Goal Seek tool is to solve one equation in one unknown. Specifically, Goal Seek allows you to vary a single* input *cell to force a single* output *cell to a selected value. To use it, select Goal Seek from the What-If Analysis dropdown list on the Data ribbon and fill in the resulting dialog box in Figure 2.15. Enter a reference to the output cell in the Set cell box, enter the numeric value you want the output cell to equal in the To value box, and enter a reference to the input cell in the By changing cell box. Note that Goal Seek sometimes stops when the Set cell is close, but not* exactly *equal to, the desired value. To improve Goal Seek's accuracy, click on the File tab (the Office button in Excel 2007), then Options (Excel Options in Excel 2007), and then the Formulas link. Then check the Enable iterative calculation box and reduce Maximum Change to any desired level of precision. We chose a precision level of 0.000001. For this level of precision, Goal Seek searches until profit is within 0.000001 of the desired value, $0.*

### Limitations of the Model

Question 3 asks whether the company should proceed with the mailing if the response rate is only 3%. From the data table (see Figure 2.13), the apparent answer is no, because profit is negative. However, like many companies, we are taking a short-term view with this reasoning. The model does not include the fact that many customers who respond to direct mail will *reorder* in the future. The company nets $7.80 per order. If each of the respondents ordered two more times, say, the company would earn 3000($7.80)(2) = $46,800 more than appears in the model, and profit would then be positive. The moral is that managers must look at the long-term impact of their decisions. However, if you want to incorporate the long term explicitly into the model, you must build a more complex model.

Finally, question 4 asks about the impact of uncertainty in the model. Obviously, not all model inputs are known with certainty. For example, the size of an order is not always $40—it might range, say, from $10 to $100. When there is a high degree of uncertainty about model inputs, it makes little sense to talk about *the* profit level or *the* breakeven response rate. It makes more sense to talk about the *probability* that profit will have a certain value or the *probability* that the company will break even. You will see how this can be done in the following example and in many more such examples in Chapters 10 through 12.

*Later chapters,
especially Chapters 10
through 12, deal
explicitly with
uncertainty.*

### Using the Formula Auditing Tool

The model in this example is fairly small and simple. Even so, you can use a handy Excel feature to see how all the parts fit together. This is the Formula Auditing tool, which is available on the Formulas ribbon. See Figure 2.16.

Figure 2.16

Formula Auditing
Toolbar

*The Formula Auditing
tool is indispensable
for untangling the logic
in a spreadsheet,
especially if someone
else developed it.*

The Trace Precedents and Trace Dependents buttons are probably the most useful buttons in this group. To see which formulas have direct links to the Number_of_responses cell, select this cell and click on the Trace Dependents button. Arrows are drawn to each cell that directly depends on the number of responses, as shown in Figure 2.17. Alternatively, to see which cells are used to create the formula in the Total_revenue cell, select this cell and click on the Trace Precedents button. Now you see that the Average_order and Number_of_responses cells are used directly to calculate revenue, as shown in Figure 2.18. Using these two buttons, you can trace your logic (or someone else's logic) as far backward or forward as you like. When you are finished, just click on the Remove Arrows button.

Figure 2.17

Dependents of
Number_of_
responses Cell

| | A | B | C | D | E |
|---|---|---|---|---|---|
| 1 | Great Threads direct mail model | | | | |
| 2 | | | | | |
| 3 | Catalog inputs | | | Model of responses | |
| 4 | Fixed cost of printing | $20,000 | | Response rate | 8% |
| 5 | Variable cost of printing mailing | $0.25 | | Number of responses | 8000 |
| 6 | | | | | |
| 7 | Decision variable | | | Model of revenue, costs, and profit | |
| 8 | Number mailed | 100000 | | Total Revenue | $320,000 |
| 9 | | | | Fixed cost of printing | $20,000 |
| 10 | Order inputs | | | Total variable cost of printing mailing | $25,000 |
| 11 | Average order | $40 | | Total variable cost of orders | $257,600 |
| 12 | Variable cost per order | $32.20 | | Total cost | $302,600 |
| 13 | | | | Profit | $17,400 |

Figure 2.18

Precedents of
Total_revenue Cell

| | A | B | C | D | E |
|---|---|---|---|---|---|
| 1 | Great Threads direct mail model | | | | |
| 2 | | | | | |
| 3 | Catalog inputs | | | Model of responses | |
| 4 | Fixed cost of printing | $20,000 | | Response rate | 8% |
| 5 | Variable cost of printing mailing | $0.25 | | Number of responses | 8000 |
| 6 | | | | | |
| 7 | Decision variable | | | Model of revenue, costs, and profit | |
| 8 | Number mailed | 100000 | | Total Revenue | $320,000 |
| 9 | | | | Fixed cost of printing | $20,000 |
| 10 | Order inputs | | | Total variable cost of printing mailing | $25,000 |
| 11 | Average order | $40 | | Total variable cost of orders | $257,600 |
| 12 | Variable cost per order | $32.20 | | Total cost | $302,600 |
| 13 | | | | Profit | $17,400 |

**Excel Tool:** *Formula Auditing Toolbar*
*The formula auditing toolbar allows you to see dependents of a selected cell (which cells have formulas that reference this cell) or precedents of a given cell (which cells are referenced in this cell's formula). In fact, you can even see dependents or precedents that reside on a different worksheet. In this case, the auditing arrows appear as dashed lines and point to a small spreadsheet icon. By double-clicking on the dashed line, you can see a list of dependents or precedents on other worksheets. These tools are especially*

*useful for understanding how someone else's spreadsheet works. Unlike in pre-2007 versions of Excel, the Formula Auditing tools in Excel 2007 and 2010 are clearly visible on the Formulas ribbon.* ▪

## MODELING ISSUES

*You can place charts on the same worksheet as the underlying data or on separate chart sheets. The choice is a matter of personal preference.*

Is the spreadsheet layout in Figure 2.12 the best possible layout? This question is not too crucial because this model is so small. However, we have put all the inputs together (usually a good practice), and we have put all the outputs together in a logical order. You might want to put the answers to questions 1 and 2 on separate worksheets, but with such a small model, it is arguably better to keep everything on a single worksheet. We generally avoid separate worksheets unless things start getting bigger and more complex.

One other issue is the placement of the chart. From the Chart Tools Design ribbon, you can click on the Move Chart button to select whether you want to place the chart on the worksheet (floating above the cells) or on a separate chart sheet that has no rows or columns. This choice depends on your personal preference—neither choice is necessarily better than the other—but for this small model, we favor keeping everything on a single worksheet.

Finally, we could have chosen the number mailed, rather than the response rate, as the basis for a sensitivity analysis. A sensitivity analysis is typically based on an uncertain input variable, such as the response rate, or a decision variable that the decision maker controls. Fortunately, there is no limit to the number of data tables you can create for a particular model. ▪

## PROBLEMS

*Solutions for problems whose numbers appear within a colored box can be found in the Student Solutions Files. Refer to this book's preface for purchase information.*

### Skill-Building Problems

1. The sensitivity analysis in the Quality Sweaters example was on the response rate. Suppose now that the response rate is *known* to be 8%, and the company wants to perform a sensitivity analysis on the number mailed. After all, this is a variable under direct control of the company. Create a one-way data table and a corresponding line chart of profit versus the number mailed, where the number mailed varies from 80,000 to 150,000 in increments of 10,000. Does it appear, from the results you see here, that there is an optimal number to mail, from all possible values, that maximizes profit? Write a concise memo to management about your results.

2. Continuing the previous problem, use Goal Seek for *each* value of number mailed (once for 80,000, once for 90,000, and so on). For each, find the response rate that allows the company to break even. Then chart these values, where the number mailed is on the horizontal axis, and the breakeven response rate is on the vertical axis. Explain the behavior in this chart in a brief memo to management.

3. In the Quality Sweaters model, the range E9:E11 does not have a range name. Open your completed Excel file and name this range **Costs**. Then look at the formula in cell E12. It does *not* automatically use the new range name. Modify the formula so that it does. Then click on cell G4 and paste the new list of range names over the previous list.

### Skill-Extending Problem

4. As the Quality Sweaters problem is now modeled, if all inputs remain fixed except for the number mailed, profit will increase indefinitely as the number mailed increases. This hardly seems realistic—the company could become infinitely rich. Discuss realistic ways to modify the model so that this unrealistic behavior is eliminated.

In the following example, we again attempt to find the appropriate level of some activity: how much of a product to order when customer demand for the product is uncertain. Two important features of this example are the presence of quantity discounts and the explicit use of probabilities to model uncertain demand. Except for these features, the problem is very similar to the one discussed in Example 2.1.

| EXAMPLE | 2.4 ORDERING WITH QUANTITY DISCOUNTS AT SAM'S BOOKSTORE |
|---------|---------------------------------------------------------|

Sam's Bookstore, with many locations across the United States, places orders for all of the latest books and then distributes them to its individual bookstores. Sam's needs a model to help it order the appropriate number of any title. For example, Sam's plans to order a popular new hardback novel, which it will sell for $30. It can purchase any number of this book from the publisher, but due to quantity discounts, the unit cost for all books it orders depends on the number ordered. Specifically, if the number ordered is less than 1000, the unit cost is $24. After each 1000, the unit cost drops: to $23 for at least 1000 copies, to $22.25 for at least 2000, to $21.75 for at least 3000, and to $21.30 (the lowest possible unit cost) for at least 4000. For example, if Sam's orders 2500 books, its total cost is $22.25(2500) = $55,625. Sam's is very uncertain about the demand for this book—it estimates that demand could be anywhere from 500 to 4500. Also, as with most hardback novels, this one will eventually come out in paperback. Therefore, if Sam's has any hardbacks left when the paperback comes out, it will put them on sale for $10, at which price, it believes all leftovers will be sold. How many copies of this hardback novel should Sam's order from the publisher?

**Business Objectives**   To create a model to determine the company's profit, given fixed values of demand and the order quantity, and then to model the demand uncertainty explicitly and to choose the expected profit-maximizing order quantity.

**Excel Objectives**   To learn how to build in complex logic with IF formulas, to get online help about Excel functions with the $f_x$ button, to learn how to use lookup functions, to see how two-way data tables allow you to answer more extensive what-if questions, and to learn about Excel's SUMPRODUCT function.

### Solution

The key variables for this model appear in Table 2.4. The primary modeling tasks are (1) to show how any combination of demand and order quantity determines the number of units sold, both at the regular price and at the leftover sale price, and (2) to calculate the total ordering cost for any order quantity. After you accomplish these tasks, you can model the uncertainty of demand explicitly and then find the optimal order quantity.

Table 2.4   Key Variables for Sam's Bookstore Problem

| | |
|---|---|
| **Input variables** | Unit prices, table of unit costs specifying quantity discount structure |
| **Uncertain variable** | Demand |
| **Decision variable** | Order quantity |
| **Key output variable** | Profit |
| **Other output variables** | Units sold at each price, revenue, and cost totals |

The first step is to develop a spreadsheet model to calculate Sam's profit for any order quantity and any possible demand. Then you can perform a sensitivity analysis to see how profit depends on these two quantities. Finally, you can decide how Sam's might choose the optimal order quantity.

## DEVELOPING THE SPREADSHEET MODEL

The profit model appears in Figure 2.19. (See the file Quantity Discounts.xlsx.) Note that the order quantity and demand in the Order_quantity and Demand cells are trial values. (Comments in these cells are a reminder of this.) You can put any values in these cells, just to test the logic of the model. The Order_quantity cell is colored red because the company can choose its value. In contrast, the Demand cell is colored green here and in later chapters to indicate that this input value is uncertain and is being treated explicitly as such. Also, note that a table is used to indicate the quantity discounts cost structure. You can use the following steps to build the model.

**Figure 2.19  Sam's Profit Model**

| | A | B | C | D | E | F | G | H | I | J | K |
|---|---|---|---|---|---|---|---|---|---|---|---|
| 1 | Ordering decision with quantity discounts | | | | | | | Range names used: | | | |
| 2 | | | | | | | | Cost | | | =Model!$B$18 |
| 3 | Inputs | | | Quantity discount structure | | | | CostLookup | | | =Model!$D$5:$E$9 |
| 4 | Unit cost - see table to right | | | At least | Unit cost | | | Demand | | | =Model!$B$12 |
| 5 | Regular price | $30 | | 0 | $24.00 | | | Leftover_price | | | =Model!$B$6 |
| 6 | Leftover price | $10 | | 1000 | $23.00 | | | Order_quantity | | | =Model!$B$9 |
| 7 | | | | 2000 | $22.25 | | | Probabilities | | | =Model!$B$35:$J$35 |
| 8 | Decision variable | | | 3000 | $21.75 | | | Profit | | | =Model!$B$19 |
| 9 | Order quantity | 2500 | | 4000 | $21.30 | | | Regular_price | | | =Model!$B$5 |
| 10 | | | | | | | | Revenue | | | =Model!$B$17 |
| 11 | Uncertain quantity | | | | | | | Units_sold_at_leftover_price | | | =Model!$B$16 |
| 12 | Demand | 2000 | | | | | | Units_sold_at_regular_price | | | =Model!$B$15 |
| 13 | | | | | | | | | | | |
| 14 | Profit model | | | | | | | | | | |
| 15 | Units sold at regular price | 2000 | | | | | | | | | |
| 16 | Units sold at leftover price | 500 | | | | | | | | | |
| 17 | Revenue | $65,000 | | | | | | | | | |
| 18 | Cost | $55,625 | | | | | | | | | |
| 19 | Profit | $9,375 | | | | | | | | | |

**①  Inputs and range names.**  Enter all inputs and name the ranges as indicated. Note that the Create from Selection shortcut was used to name all ranges except for CostLookup and Probabilities. For these latter two, you can highlight the ranges and enter the names in the Name Box—the "manual" method. (Why the difference? To use the Create from Selection shortcut, you must have appropriate labels in adjacent cells. Sometimes this is simply not convenient.)

**②  Revenues.**  The company can sell only what it has, and it sells any leftovers at the discounted sale price. Therefore, enter the formulas

=MIN(Order_quantity,Demand)

=IF(Order_quantity>Demand, Order_quantity-Demand,0)

and

=Units_sold_at_regular_price*Regular_price
+Units_sold_at_leftover_price*Leftover_price

in cells B15, B16, and B17. The logic in the first two of these cells is necessary to account correctly for the cases when the order quantity is greater than demand and when it is less than or equal to demand. Note that you could use the following equivalent alternative to the IF function in cell B16:

=MAX(Order_quantity-Demand,0)

*If you want to learn more about how an Excel function operates, click on the $f_x$ button next to the Formula bar. This is called the Insert Function button, although some people call it the Function Wizard. If there is already a function, such as an IF function, in a cell and you then click on the $f_x$ button, you will get help on this function. If you select an empty cell and then click on the $f_x$ button, you can choose a function to get help on. (The same help is available from the Function Library group on the Formulas ribbon.)*

**③ Total ordering cost.** Depending on the order quantity, you can find the appropriate unit cost from the unit cost table and multiply it by the order quantity to obtain the total ordering cost. This can be accomplished with a complex nested IF formula, but a much better way is to use the VLOOKUP function. Specifically, enter the formula

=VLOOKUP(Order_quantity,CostLookup,2)*Order_quantity

in cell B18. The VLOOKUP part of this formula says to compare the order quantity to the first (leftmost) column of the table in the CostLookup range and return the corresponding value in the second column (because the last argument is 2).

*The VLOOKUP function acts like a tax table, where you look up the tax corresponding to your adjusted gross income from a table of incomes and taxes. To use it, first create a vertical lookup table, with values to use for comparison listed in the left column of the table and corresponding output values in as many columns to the right as you like. (See the CostLookup range in Figure 2.19 for an example.) Then the VLOOKUP function takes three or four arguments: (1) the value you want to compare to the values in the left column; (2) the lookup table range; (3) the index of the column you want the returned value to come from, where the index of the left column is 1, the index of the next column is 2, and so on; and optionally (4) TRUE (for an approximate match, the default) or FALSE (for an exact match). If you omit the last argument, the values in the left column of the table must be entered in ascending order. (See online help for more details.) If the last argument is TRUE or is omitted, Excel scans down the leftmost column of the table and finds the last entry less than or equal to the first argument. (In this sense, it finds an approximate match.) There is also an HLOOKUP function that works exactly the same way, except that the lookup table is arranged in rows, not columns.*

**④ Profit.** Calculate the profit with the formula

=Revenue-Cost

## Two-Way Data Table

*A two-way data table allows you to see how a single output varies as two inputs vary simultaneously.*

The next step is to create a two-way data table for profit as a function of the order quantity and demand (see Figure 2.20). To create this table, first enter a link to the profit with the formula =Profit in cell A22, and enter possible order quantities and possible demands in column A and row 22, respectively. (We used the same values for both order quantity and demand, from 500 to 4500 in increments of 500. This is not necessary—the demand could change in increments of 100 or even 1—but it is reasonable. Perhaps Sam's is required by the publisher to order in multiples of 500.) Then select Data Table from the What-If Analysis dropdown list on the Data ribbon, and enter the Demand cell as the Row Input cell and the Order_quantity cell as the Column Input cell (see Figure 2.21).

Figure 2.20    Profit as a Function of Order Quantity and Demand

| | A | B | C | D | E | F | G | H | I | J |
|---|---|---|---|---|---|---|---|---|---|---|
| 21 | Data table of profit as a function of order quantity (along side) and demand (along top) | | | | | | | | | |
| 22 | $9,375 | 500 | 1000 | 1500 | 2000 | 2500 | 3000 | 3500 | 4000 | 4500 |
| 23 | 500 | $3,000 | $3,000 | $3,000 | $3,000 | $3,000 | $3,000 | $3,000 | $3,000 | $3,000 |
| 24 | 1000 | -$3,000 | $7,000 | $7,000 | $7,000 | $7,000 | $7,000 | $7,000 | $7,000 | $7,000 |
| 25 | 1500 | -$9,500 | $500 | $10,500 | $10,500 | $10,500 | $10,500 | $10,500 | $10,500 | $10,500 |
| 26 | 2000 | -$14,500 | -$4,500 | $5,500 | $15,500 | $15,500 | $15,500 | $15,500 | $15,500 | $15,500 |
| 27 | 2500 | -$20,625 | -$10,625 | -$625 | $9,375 | $19,375 | $19,375 | $19,375 | $19,375 | $19,375 |
| 28 | 3000 | -$25,250 | -$15,250 | -$5,250 | $4,750 | $14,750 | $24,750 | $24,750 | $24,750 | $24,750 |
| 29 | 3500 | -$31,125 | -$21,125 | -$11,125 | -$1,125 | $8,875 | $18,875 | $28,875 | $28,875 | $28,875 |
| 30 | 4000 | -$35,200 | -$25,200 | -$15,200 | -$5,200 | $4,800 | $14,800 | $24,800 | $34,800 | $34,800 |
| 31 | 4500 | -$40,850 | -$30,850 | -$20,850 | -$10,850 | -$850 | $9,150 | $19,150 | $29,150 | $39,150 |

Figure 2.21

Dialog Box for
Two-Way Data Table

**Excel Tool: *Two-Way Data Table***
*A two-way data table allows you to see how a single* output *cell varies as you vary two* input *cells. (Unlike a one-way data table, only a* single *output cell can be chosen.) To create this type of table, enter a reference to the output cell in the top-left corner of the table, enter possible values of the two inputs below and to the right of this corner cell, and highlight the entire table. Then select Data Table from the What-If Analysis dropdown on the Data ribbon, and enter references to the cells where the original two input variables live. The Row Input cell corresponds to the values along the top row of the table, and the Column Input cell corresponds to the values along the left-most column of the table. When you click on OK, Excel substitutes each pair of input values into these two input cells, recalculates the spreadsheet, and enters the corresponding output value in the table. By clicking on any cell in the body of the table, you can see that Excel also enters the function TABLE as a reminder that the cell is part of a data table.*

The resulting data table shows that profit depends heavily on both order quantity and demand and (by scanning across rows) how higher demands lead to larger profits. But which order quantity Sam's should select is still unclear. Remember that Sam's has complete control over the order quantity (it can choose the *row* of the data table), but it has no direct control over demand (it cannot choose the column).

The ordering decision depends not only on which demands are *possible,* but on which demands are *likely* to occur. The usual way to express this information is with a set of probabilities that sum to 1. Suppose Sam's estimates these as the values in row 35 of Figure 2.22. These estimates are probably based on other similar books it has sold in the past. The most likely demands are 2000 and 2500, with other values on both sides less likely. You can use these probabilities to find an *expected* profit for each order quantity. This expected profit is a weighted average of the profits in any row in the data table, using the probabilities as the weights. The easiest way to do this is to enter the formula

=SUMPRODUCT(B23:J23,Probabilities)

*This is actually a preview of decision making under uncertainty. To calculate an expected profit, you multiply each profit by its probability and add the products. This topic is covered in depth in Chapter 9.*

Figure 2.22   Comparison of Expected Profits

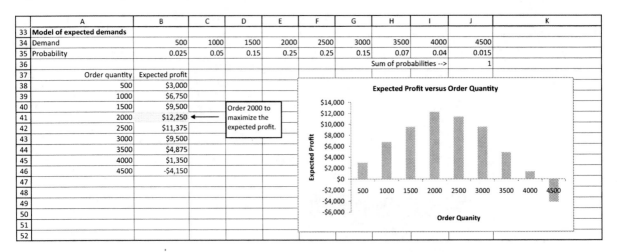

| | A | B | C | D | E | F | G | H | I | J | K |
|---|---|---|---|---|---|---|---|---|---|---|---|
| 33 | Model of expected demands | | | | | | | | | | |
| 34 | Demand | 500 | 1000 | 1500 | 2000 | 2500 | 3000 | 3500 | 4000 | 4500 | |
| 35 | Probability | 0.025 | 0.05 | 0.15 | 0.25 | 0.25 | 0.15 | 0.07 | 0.04 | 0.015 | |
| 36 | | | | | | | Sum of probabilities --> | | | 1 | |
| 37 | Order quantity | Expected profit | | | | | | | | | |
| 38 | 500 | $3,000 | | | | | | | | | |
| 39 | 1000 | $6,750 | | | | | | | | | |
| 40 | 1500 | $9,500 | | | | | | | | | |
| 41 | 2000 | $12,250 | | | | | | | | | |
| 42 | 2500 | $11,375 | | | | | | | | | |
| 43 | 3000 | $9,500 | | | | | | | | | |
| 44 | 3500 | $4,875 | | | | | | | | | |
| 45 | 4000 | $1,350 | | | | | | | | | |
| 46 | 4500 | -$4,150 | | | | | | | | | |
| 47 | | | | | | | | | | | |
| 48 | | | | | | | | | | | |
| 49 | | | | | | | | | | | |
| 50 | | | | | | | | | | | |
| 51 | | | | | | | | | | | |
| 52 | | | | | | | | | | | |

in cell B38 and copy it down to cell B46. You can also create a bar chart of these expected profits, as shown in Figure 2.22. (Excel refers to these as *column charts*. The height of each bar is the expected profit for that particular order quantity.)

### Excel Function: SUMPRODUCT

*The SUMPRODUCT function takes two range arguments, which must be exactly the same size and shape, and it sums the products of the corresponding values in these two ranges. For example, the formula =SUMPRODUCT(A10:B11,E12:F13) is a shortcut for a formula involving the sum of 4 products: =A10\*E12+A11\*E13+B10\*F12+B11\*F13. This is an extremely useful function, especially when the ranges involved are large, and it is used repeatedly throughout this book. (Actually, the SUMPRODUCT function can have more than two range arguments, all of the same size and shape, but the most common use of SUMPRODUCT is when only two ranges are involved.)*

The largest of the expected profits, $12,250, corresponds to an order quantity of 2000, so we would recommend that Sam's order 2000 copies of the book. This does not guarantee that Sam's will make a profit of $12,250—the actual profit depends on the eventual demand—but it represents a reasonable way to proceed in the face of uncertain demand. You will learn much more about making decisions under uncertainty and the expected value criterion in Chapter 9. ▪

## PROBLEMS

### Skill-Building Problems

5. In some ordering problems, like the one for Sam's Bookstore, whenever demand exceeds existing inventory, the excess demand is not lost but is filled by expedited orders—at a premium cost to the company. Change Sam's model to reflect this behavior. Assume that the unit cost of expediting is $40, well above the highest regular unit cost.

6. The spreadsheet model for Sam's Bookstore contains a two-way data table for profit versus order quantity and demand. Experiment with Excel's chart types to create a chart that shows this information graphically in an intuitive format. (Choose the format you would choose to give a presentation to your boss.)

**7.** In the Sam's Bookstore problem, the quantity discount structure is such that *all* the units ordered have the same unit cost. For example, if the order quantity is 2500, then each unit costs $22.25. Sometimes the quantity discount structure is such that the unit cost for the first so many items is one value, the unit cost for the next so many units is a slightly lower value, and so on. Modify the model so that Sam's pays $24 for units 1 to 1500, $23 for units 1501 to 2500, and $22 for units 2501 and above. For example, the total cost for an order quantity of 2750 is 1500(24) + 1000(23) + 250(22). (*Hint*: Use IF functions, not VLOOKUP.)

## Skill-Extending Problems

**8.** The current spreadsheet model essentially finds the expected profit in several steps. It first finds the profit in cell B19 for a *fixed* value of demand. Then it uses a data table to find the profit for each of several demands, and finally it uses SUMPRODUCT to find the expected profit. Modify the model so that expected profit is found directly, without a data table. To do this, change row 11 so that instead of a single demand, there is a list of possible demands, those currently in row 34. Then insert a new row below row 11 that lists the probabilities of these demands. Next, in the rows below the Profit Model label, calculate the units sold, revenue, cost, and profit for *each* demand. For example, the quantities in column C will be for the second possible demand. Finally, use SUMPRODUCT to calculate *expected* profit below the Profit row.

**9.** Continuing Problem 5, create a two-way data table for expected profit with order quantity along the side and unit expediting cost along the top. Allow the order quantity to vary from 500 to 4500 in increments of 500, and allow the unit expediting cost to vary from $36 to $45 in increments of $1. Each column of this table will allow you to choose an optimal order quantity for a given unit expediting cost. How does this best order quantity change as the unit expediting cost increases? Write up your results in a concise memo to management. (*Hint*: You will have to modify the existing spreadsheet model so that there is a cell for expected profit that changes automatically when you change either the order quantity or the unit expediting cost. See Problem 8 for guidelines.)

# 2.6 ESTIMATING THE RELATIONSHIP BETWEEN PRICE AND DEMAND

The following example illustrates a very important modeling concept: estimating relationships between variables by **curve fitting.** You will study this topic in much more depth in the discussion of regression in Chapter 14, but the ideas can be illustrated at a relatively low level by taking advantage of some of Excel's useful features.

---

EXAMPLE | **2.5 ESTIMATING SENSITIVITY OF DEMAND TO PRICE AT THE LINKS COMPANY**

The Links Company sells its golf clubs at golf outlet stores throughout the United States. The company knows that demand for its clubs varies considerably with price. In fact, the price has varied over the past 12 months, and the demand at each price level has been observed. The data are in the data sheet of the file Golf Club Demand.xlsx (see Figure 2.23.) For example, during the past month, when the price was $390, 6800 sets of clubs were sold. (The demands in column C are in hundreds of units. The cell comment in cell C3 reminds you of this.) The company wants to estimate the relationship between demand and price and then use this estimated relationship to answer the following questions:

1. Assuming the unit cost of producing a set of clubs is $250 and the price must be a multiple of $10, what price should Links charge to maximize its profit?

2. How does the optimal price depend on the unit cost of producing a set of clubs?

3. Is the model an accurate representation of reality?

Figure 2.23

**Demand and Price Data for Golf Clubs**

|   | A | B | C |
|---|---|---|---|
| 1 | Demand for golf clubs | | |
| 2 | | | |
| 3 | Month | Price | Demand |
| 4 | 1 | 450 | 45 |
| 5 | 2 | 300 | 103 |
| 6 | 3 | 440 | 49 |
| 7 | 4 | 360 | 86 |
| 8 | 5 | 290 | 125 |
| 9 | 6 | 450 | 52 |
| 10 | 7 | 340 | 87 |
| 11 | 8 | 370 | 68 |
| 12 | 9 | 500 | 45 |
| 13 | 10 | 490 | 44 |
| 14 | 11 | 430 | 58 |
| 15 | 12 | 390 | 68 |

**Business Objectives**   To estimate the relationship between demand and price, and to use this relationship to find the optimal price to charge.

**Excel Objectives**   To illustrate Excel's Trendline tool, and to illustrate conditional formatting.

## Solution

This example is divided into two parts: estimating the relationship between price and demand, and creating the profit model.

### Estimating the Relationship Between Price and Demand

A scatterplot of demand versus price appears in Figure 2.24. (This can be created in the usual way with Excel's Scatter chart.) Obviously, demand decreases as price increases, but the goal is to quantify this relationship. Therefore, after creating this chart, right-click on any point on the chart to bring up the dialog box in Figure 2.25. This allows you to super-impose several different curves (including a straight line) on the scatterplot. We consider

**Figure 2.24**

**Scatterplot of Demand Versus Price**

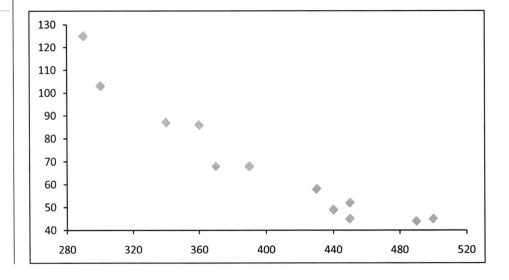

three possibilities, the **linear, power,** and **exponential** curves, defined by the following general equations (where $y$ and $x$, a general output and a general input, correspond to demand and price for this example):

- Linear: $y = a + bx$
- Power: $y = ax^b$
- Exponential: $y = ae^{bx}$

Before proceeding, we describe some general properties of these three functions because of their widespread applicability. The linear function is the easiest. Its graph is a straight line. When $x$ changes by 1 unit, $y$ changes by $b$ units. The constant $a$ is called the intercept, and $b$ is called the slope.

The power function is a curve except in the special case where the exponent $b$ is 1. (Then it is a straight line.) Assuming that $a$ is positive, the shape of this curve depends primarily on the exponent $b$. If $b > 1$, $y$ increases at an increasing rate as $x$ increases. If $0 < b < 1$, $y$ increases, but at a decreasing rate, as $x$ increases. Finally, if $b < 0$, $y$ decreases as $x$ increases. An important property of the power curve is that when $x$ changes by 1%, $y$ changes by a constant percentage, and this percentage is approximately equal to $b$%. For example, if $y = 100x^{-2.35}$, then every 1% increase in $x$ leads to an approximate 2.35% decrease in $y$.

The exponential function also represents a curve whose shape depends on the constant $b$ in the exponent. Again, assume that $a$ is positive. Then if $b > 0$, $y$ increases as $x$ increases; if $b < 0$, $y$ decreases as $x$ increases. An important property of the exponential function is that if $x$ changes by 1 unit, $y$ changes by a constant percentage, and this percentage is approximately equal to $100 \times b$%. For example, if $y = 100e^{-0.014x}$, then whenever $x$ increases by 1 unit, $y$ decreases by approximately 1.4%. Here $e$ is the special number 2.7182 . . . , and $e$ to any power can be calculated in Excel with the EXP function. For example, you can calculate $e^{-0.014}$ with the formula =EXP(-0.014).

**Figure 2.25**

**Trendline Options Dialog Box**

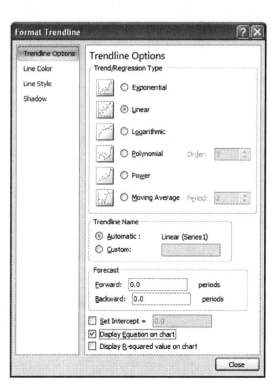

Returning to the example, if you superimpose any of these curves on the scatterplot of demand versus price, Excel chooses the best-fitting curve of that type. Better yet, if you check the Display Equation on Chart option, you see the equation of this best-fitting curve. Doing this for each type of curve gives the results in Figures 2.26, 2.27, and 2.28. (The equations might not appear exactly as in the figures. However, they can be resized and reformatted to appear as shown.)

Figure 2.26

**Best-Fitting Straight Line**

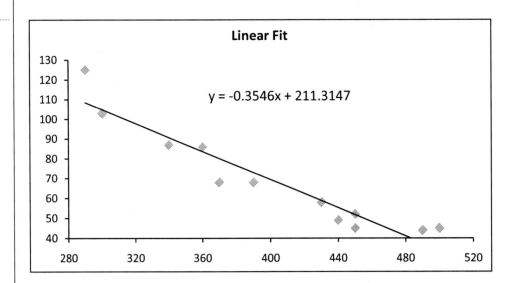

Figure 2.27

**Best-Fitting Power Curve**

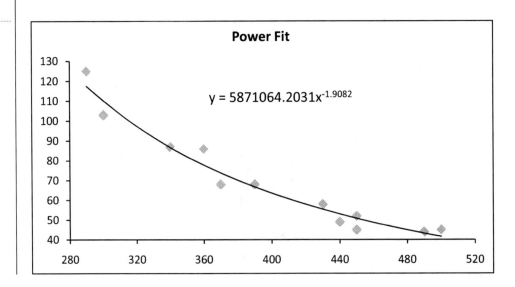

Figure 2.28    Best-Fitting Exponential Curve

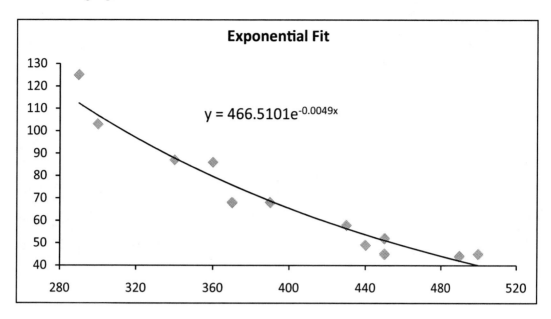

Each of these curves provides the best-fitting member of its "family" to the demand/price data, but which of these three is best overall? You can answer this question by finding the **mean absolute percentage error** (MAPE) for each of the three curves. To do so, for any price in the data set and any of the three curves, first predict demand by substituting the given price into the equation for the curve. The predicted demand is typically not the same as the observed demand, so you can calculate the absolute percentage error (APE) with the general formula:

$$\text{APE} = \frac{|\text{Observed demand} - \text{Predicted demand}|}{\text{Observed demand}} \qquad \textbf{(2.1)}$$

Then for any curve, MAPE is the average of these APE values. The curve with the smallest MAPE is the best fit overall.

The calculations appear in Figure 2.29. After (manually) entering the parameters of the equations from the scatterplots into column B, you can proceed as follows.

❶ **Predicted demands.** Substitute observed prices into the linear, power, and exponential functions to obtain the predicted demands in columns E, F, and G. Specifically, enter the formulas

=$B$19+$B$20*B4
=$B$22*B4^$B$23

and

=$B$25*EXP($B$26*B4)

in cells E19, F19, and G19, and copy them down their respective columns.

**Figure 2.29**　Finding the Best-Fitting Curve Overall

| | A | B | C | D | E | F | G | H | I | J |
|---|---|---|---|---|---|---|---|---|---|---|
| 17 | **Parameters of best-fitting curves** | | | | | **Prediction** | | | **Absolute percentage error** | |
| 18 | Linear | | | | Linear | Power | Exponential | Linear | Power | Exponential |
| 19 | Intercept | 211.31 | | | 51.74 | 50.80 | 51.20 | 14.98% | 12.89% | 13.78% |
| 20 | Slope | -0.3546 | | | 104.93 | 110.12 | 106.94 | 1.87% | 6.91% | 3.83% |
| 21 | Power | | | | 55.29 | 53.02 | 53.78 | 12.83% | 8.21% | 9.75% |
| 22 | Constant | 5871064 | | | 83.65 | 77.76 | 79.65 | 2.73% | 9.58% | 7.38% |
| 23 | Exponent | -1.9082 | | | 108.48 | 117.48 | 112.32 | 13.22% | 6.01% | 10.14% |
| 24 | Exponential | | | | 51.74 | 50.80 | 51.20 | 0.50% | 2.31% | 1.53% |
| 25 | Constant | 466.51 | | | 90.75 | 86.73 | 87.87 | 4.31% | 0.32% | 1.00% |
| 26 | Exponent | -0.00491 | | | 80.11 | 73.80 | 75.84 | 17.81% | 8.53% | 11.52% |
| 27 | | | | | 34.01 | 41.55 | 40.06 | 24.42% | 7.67% | 10.99% |
| 28 | | | | | 37.56 | 43.18 | 42.07 | 14.65% | 1.86% | 4.38% |
| 29 | | | | | 58.83 | 55.40 | 56.49 | 1.43% | 4.48% | 2.61% |
| 30 | | | | | 73.02 | 66.75 | 68.74 | 7.38% | 1.84% | 1.09% |
| 31 | | | | | | | | | | |
| 32 | | | | | | | **MAPE** | 9.68% | 5.88% | 6.50% |

② **Average percentage errors.** Apply Equation (2.1) to calculate APEs in columns H, I, and J. Specifically, enter the general formula

=ABS($C4-E19)/$C4

in cell H19 and copy it to the range H19:J30. (Do you see why column C is made absolute? Remember that this is where the observed demands are stored.)

③ **MAPE.** Average the APEs in each column with the AVERAGE function to obtain the MAPEs in row 32.

Evidently, the power curve provides the best fit, with a MAPE of 5.88%. In other words, its predictions are off, on average, by 5.88%. This power curve predicts that each 1% increase in price leads to an approximate 1.9% decrease in demand. (Economists call this relationship *elastic*—demand is quite sensitive to price.)

### DEVELOPING THE PROFIT MODEL

Now we move to the profit model, using the best-fitting power curve to predict demand from price. The key variables appear in Table 2.5. Note there is now one input variable, unit variable cost, and one decision variable, unit price. (The red background for the decision variable distinguishes it as such.) The profit model is straightforward to develop using the following steps (see Figure 2.30).

**Table 2.5**　Key Variables for Golf Club Problem

| | |
|---|---|
| **Input variable** | Unit cost to produce |
| **Decision variable** | Unit price |
| **Key output variable** | Profit |
| **Other output variables** | Predicted demand, total revenue, total cost |

Figure 2.30

Profit Model

| | A | B | C | D | E |
|---|---|---|---|---|---|
| 1 | Profit model, using best fitting power curve for estimating demand | | | | |
| 2 | | | | | |
| 3 | Parameters of best-fitting power curve (from Estimation sheet) | | | | |
| 4 | Constant | 5871064 | | | |
| 5 | Exponent | -1.9082 | | | |
| 6 | | | | | |
| 7 | Monetary inputs | | | | |
| 8 | Unit cost to produce | $250 | | | |
| 9 | | | | | |
| 10 | Decision variable | | | | |
| 11 | Unit price (trial value) | $400 | | | |
| 12 | | | | | |
| 13 | Profit model | | | | |
| 14 | Predicted demand | 63.601 | | | |
| 15 | Total revenue | $25,441 | | | |
| 16 | Total cost | $15,900 | | | |
| 17 | Profit | $9,540 | | | |

**1 Predicted demand.** Calculate the *predicted* demand in cell B14 with the formula

=B4*B11^B5

This uses the power function that was estimated earlier.

**2 Revenue, cost, profit.** Enter the following formulas in cells B15, B16, and B17:

=B11*B14

=B8*B14

and

=B15-B16

The assumption here is that the company produces exactly enough sets of clubs to meet customer demand.

**Maximizing Profit**   To see which price maximizes profit, you can build the data table shown in Figure 2.31. Here, the column input cell is B11 and the linking formula in cell B25 is =B17. The corresponding scatter chart shows that profit first increases and then decreases. You can find the maximum profit and corresponding price in at least three ways. First, you can attempt to read them from the chart. Second, you can scan down the data table for the maximum profit, which is shown in the figure. The following Excel Tip describes a third method that uses some of Excel's more powerful features.

**Excel Tip: *Conditional Formatting***
*Cell B53 in Figure 2.31 is colored because it corresponds to the maximum profit in the column, but Excel's Conditional Formatting tool can do this for you—automatically.[7] To color the maximum profit, select the range of profits, B26:B75, click on the Conditional Formatting dropdown arrow, then Top/Bottom Rules, and then Top 10 Items to bring up the dialog box in Figure 2.32. By asking for the top 1 item, the maximum value in the range is colored. You can experiment with the many other Conditional Formatting options. This is a great tool.*

[7]The value in cell B52 also appears to be the maximum, but to two decimals, it is slightly lower.

Figure 2.31

Profit as a
Function of Price

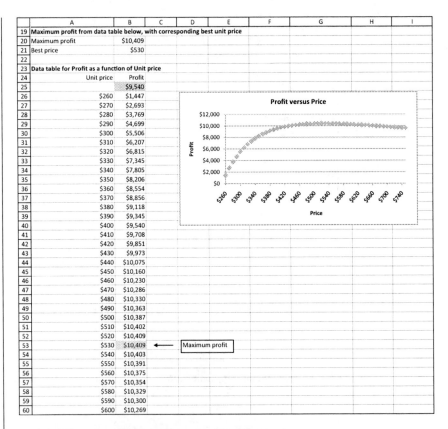

Figure 2.32

Conditional
Formatting
Dialog Box

What about the corresponding best price, shown in cell B21 of Figure 2.31? You could enter this manually, but wouldn't it be nice if you could get Excel to find the maximum profit in the data table, determine the price in the cell to its left, and report it in cell B21, all automatically? This is indeed possible. Just enter the formula

=INDEX(A26:A75,MATCH(B20,B26:B75,0),1)

in cell B21, and the best price appears. This formula uses two Excel functions, MATCH and INDEX. MATCH compares the first argument (the maximum profit in cell B20) to the range specified in the second argument (the range of profits), and returns the index of the cell where a match appears. (The third argument, 0, specifies that you want an *exact* match.) In this case, the MATCH function returns 28 because the maximum profit is in the 28th cell of the profits range. Then the INDEX function is called effectively as =INDEX(A26:A75,28,1). The first argument is the range of prices, the second is a row index, and the third is a column index. Very simply, this function says to return the value in the 28th row and first column of the prices range.

To learn more about these functions, you can click on the $f_x$ button and examine the functions in the Lookup & Reference category. After experimenting, you can see that the

INDEX and MATCH combination solves the problem. You don't have to memorize these functions, although this combination really does come in handy. Rather, you can often solve a problem by investigating some of Excel's less well-known features. You don't even need a manual—everything is in online help.

## Sensitivity to Variable Cost

We now return to question 2 in the example: How does the best price change as the unit variable cost changes? You can answer this question with a two-way data table. Remember that this is a data table with two inputs—one along the left side and the other across the top row—and a single output. The two inputs for this problem are unit variable cost and unit price, and the single output is profit. The corresponding data table is in the range A83:F168, the top part of which appears in Figure 2.33. To develop this table, enter desired inputs in column A and row 83, enter the linking formula =B17 in cell A83 (it always goes in the top-left corner of a two-way data table), highlight the entire table, select Data Table from the What-If Analysis dropdown list, and enter B8 as the Row Input cell and B11 as the Column Input cell.

**Figure 2.33** Profit as a Function of Unit Cost and Unit Price

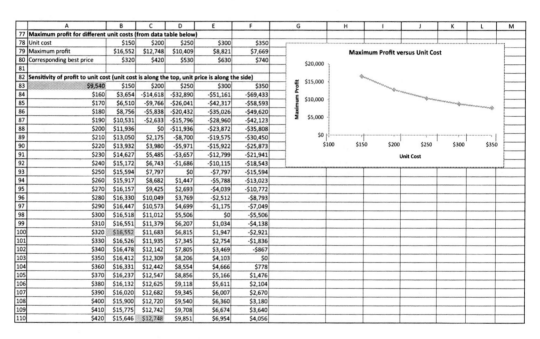

| | A | B | C | D | E | F | G | H | I | J | K | L | M |
|---|---|---|---|---|---|---|---|---|---|---|---|---|---|
| 77 | Maximum profit for different unit costs (from data table below) | | | | | | | | | | | | |
| 78 | Unit cost | $150 | $200 | $250 | $300 | $350 | | | | | | | |
| 79 | Maximum profit | $16,552 | $12,748 | $10,409 | $8,821 | $7,669 | | | | | | | |
| 80 | Corresponding best price | $320 | $420 | $530 | $630 | $740 | | | | | | | |
| 81 | | | | | | | | | | | | | |
| 82 | Sensitivity of profit to unit cost (unit cost is along the top, unit price is along the side) | | | | | | | | | | | | |
| 83 | $9,540 | $150 | $200 | $250 | $300 | $350 | | | | | | | |
| 84 | $160 | $3,654 | -$14,618 | -$32,890 | -$51,161 | -$69,433 | | | | | | | |
| 85 | $170 | $6,510 | -$9,766 | -$26,041 | -$42,317 | -$58,593 | | | | | | | |
| 86 | $180 | $8,756 | -$5,838 | -$20,432 | -$35,026 | -$49,620 | | | | | | | |
| 87 | $190 | $10,531 | -$2,633 | -$15,796 | -$28,960 | -$42,123 | | | | | | | |
| 88 | $200 | $11,936 | $0 | -$11,936 | -$23,872 | -$35,808 | | | | | | | |
| 89 | $210 | $13,050 | $2,175 | -$8,700 | -$19,575 | -$30,450 | | | | | | | |
| 90 | $220 | $13,932 | $3,980 | -$5,971 | -$15,922 | -$25,873 | | | | | | | |
| 91 | $230 | $14,627 | $5,485 | -$3,657 | -$12,799 | -$21,941 | | | | | | | |
| 92 | $240 | $15,172 | $6,743 | -$1,686 | -$10,115 | -$18,543 | | | | | | | |
| 93 | $250 | $15,594 | $7,797 | $0 | -$7,797 | -$15,594 | | | | | | | |
| 94 | $260 | $15,917 | $8,682 | $1,447 | -$5,788 | -$13,023 | | | | | | | |
| 95 | $270 | $16,157 | $9,425 | $2,693 | -$4,039 | -$10,772 | | | | | | | |
| 96 | $280 | $16,330 | $10,049 | $3,769 | -$2,512 | -$8,793 | | | | | | | |
| 97 | $290 | $16,447 | $10,573 | $4,699 | -$1,175 | -$7,049 | | | | | | | |
| 98 | $300 | $16,518 | $11,012 | $5,506 | $0 | -$5,506 | | | | | | | |
| 99 | $310 | $16,551 | $11,379 | $6,207 | $1,034 | -$4,138 | | | | | | | |
| 100 | $320 | $16,552 | $11,683 | $6,815 | $1,947 | -$2,921 | | | | | | | |
| 101 | $330 | $16,526 | $11,935 | $7,345 | $2,754 | -$1,836 | | | | | | | |
| 102 | $340 | $16,478 | $12,142 | $7,805 | $3,469 | -$867 | | | | | | | |
| 103 | $350 | $16,412 | $12,309 | $8,206 | $4,103 | $0 | | | | | | | |
| 104 | $360 | $16,331 | $12,442 | $8,554 | $4,666 | $778 | | | | | | | |
| 105 | $370 | $16,237 | $12,547 | $8,856 | $5,166 | $1,476 | | | | | | | |
| 106 | $380 | $16,132 | $12,625 | $9,118 | $5,611 | $2,104 | | | | | | | |
| 107 | $390 | $16,020 | $12,682 | $9,345 | $6,007 | $2,670 | | | | | | | |
| 108 | $400 | $15,900 | $12,720 | $9,540 | $6,360 | $3,180 | | | | | | | |
| 109 | $410 | $15,775 | $12,742 | $9,708 | $6,674 | $3,640 | | | | | | | |
| 110 | $420 | $15,646 | $12,748 | $9,851 | $6,954 | $4,056 | | | | | | | |

As before, you can scan the columns of the data table for the maximum profits and enter them (manually) in rows 79 and 80. (Alternatively, you can use the Excel features described in the previous Excel Tip to accomplish these tasks. Take a look at the finished version of the file for details. This file also explains how conditional formatting is used to color the maximum profit in *each* column of the table.) Then you can create a chart of maximum profit (or best price) versus unit cost. The chart in Figure 2.33 shows that the maximum profit decreases, but at a decreasing rate as the unit cost increases.

## Limitations of the Model

Question 3 asks you to step back from all these details and evaluate whether the model is realistic. First, there is no real reason to restrict golf club prices to multiples of $10. This was only required so that a data table could be used to find the profit-maximizing price. Ideally, you should search over *all* possible prices to find the profit-maximizing price. Fortunately, Excel's built-in Solver tool enables you to accomplish this task fairly easily. The problem of finding a profit-maximizing price is an example of an **optimization model.** In optimization models, you try to maximize or minimize a specified output cell by changing the values of the decision variable cells. Chapters 3–8 and 16 contain a detailed discussion of optimization models.

A second possible limitation of the model is the implicit assumption that price is the *only* factor that influences demand. In reality, other factors, such as advertising, the state of the economy, competitors' prices, strength of competition, and promotional expenses, also influence demand. In Chapter 14, you will learn how to use multiple regression to analyze the dependence of one variable on two or more other variables. This technique allows you to incorporate other factors into the model for profit.

A final limitation of the model is that demand might not *equal* sales. For example, if actual demand for golf clubs during a year is 70,000 but the company's annual capacity is only 50,000, the company will observe sales of only 50,000. This will cause it to underestimate *actual* demand, and the curve-fitting method will produce biased predictions. (Can you guess the probable effect on pricing decisions?)

## Other Modeling Issues

The layout of the Golf Club Demand.xlsx file is fairly straightforward. However, note that instead of a single worksheet, there are two worksheets, partly for logical purposes and partly to reduce clutter. There is one worksheet for estimation of the demand function and the various scatterplots, and there is another for the profit model.

One last issue is the placement of the data tables for the sensitivity analysis. You might be inclined to put these on a separate Sensitivity worksheet. However, Excel does not allow you to build a data table on one worksheet that uses a row or column input cell from *another* worksheet. Therefore, you are forced to put the data tables on the same worksheet as the profit model. ▪

## PROBLEMS

### Skill-Building Problems

10. Suppose you have an extra six months of data on demands and prices, in addition to the data in the example. These extra data points are (350,84), (385,72), (410,67), (400,62), (330,92), and (480,53). (The price is shown first and then the demand at that price.) After adding these points to the original data, use Excel's Trendline tool to find the best-fitting linear, power, and exponential trend lines. Finally, calculate the MAPE for each of these, based on all 18 months of data. Does the power curve still have the smallest MAPE?

11. Consider the power curve $y = 10000x^{-2.35}$. Calculate $y$ when $x = 5$; when $x = 10$; and when $x = 20$. For each of these values of $x$, find the percentage change in $y$ when $x$ increases by 1%. That is, find the percent-

age change in $y$ when $x$ increases from 5 to 5.05; when it increases from 10 to 10.1; and when it increases from 20 to 20.2. Is this percentage change constant? What number is it very close to? Write a brief memo on what you have learned about power curves from these calculations.

12. Consider the exponential curve $y = 1000e^{-0.014x}$. Calculate $y$ when $x = 5$; when $x = 10$; and when $x = 20$. For each of these values of $x$, find the percentage change in $y$ when $x$ increases by one unit. That is, find the percentage change in $y$ when $x$ increases from 5 to 6; when it increases from 10 to 11; and when it increases from 20 to 21. Is this percentage change constant? When expressed as a decimal, what number is it very close to? Write a brief memo on

what you have learned about exponential curves from these calculations.

## Skill-Extending Problem

13. In the profit model in this section, we used the power curve to relate demand and price because it has the lowest MAPE. However, the exponential curve was not far behind. Rework the profit model using the exponential curve to relate demand to price. Write a brief memo indicating whether you get basically the same results as with the power curve or you get substantially different results.

## 2.7 DECISIONS INVOLVING THE TIME VALUE OF MONEY

In many business situations, cash flows are received at different points in time, and a company must determine a course of action that maximizes the "value" of cash flows. Here are some examples:

- Should a company buy a more expensive machine that lasts for 10 years or a less expensive machine that lasts for 5 years?
- What level of plant capacity is best for the next 20 years?
- A company must market one of several midsize cars. Which car should it market?

To make decisions when cash flows are received at different points in time, the key concept is that the later a dollar is received, the less valuable the dollar is. For example, suppose you can invest money at a 5% annual interest rate. Then $1.00 received now is essentially equivalent to $1.05 a year from now. The reason is that if you have $1.00 now, you can invest it and gain $0.05 in interest in one year. If $r = 0.05$ is the interest rate (expressed as a decimal), we can write this as

$$\$1.00 \text{ now} = \$1.05 \text{ a year from now} = \$1.00(1 + r) \qquad (2.2)$$

Dividing both sides of Equation (2.2) by $1 + r$, we can rewrite it as

$$\$1.00 \times 1/(1 + r) \text{ now} = \$1.00 \text{ a year from now} \qquad (2.3)$$

The value $1/(1 + r)$ in Equation (2.3) is called the **discount factor,** and it is always less than 1. The quantity on the left, which evaluates to $0.952 for $r = 0.05$, is called the **present value** of $1.00 received a year from now. The idea is that if you had $0.952 now, you could invest it at 5% and have it grow to $1.00 in a year.

In general, if money can be invested at annual rate $r$ compounded each year, then $1 received $t$ years from now has the same value as $1/(1 + r)^t$ dollars received today—that is, the $1 is discounted by the discount factor raised to the $t$ power. If you multiply a cash flow received $t$ years from now by $1/(1 + r)^t$ to obtain its present value, then the total of these present values over all years is called the **net present value (NPV)** of the cash flows. Basic financial theory states that projects with positive NPVs increase the value of the company, whereas projects with negative NPVs decrease the value of the company.

The rate $r$ (usually called the **discount rate**) used by major corporations generally comes from some version of the **capital asset pricing model.** The value of $r$ used to evaluate any particular project depends on a number of things and can vary from project to project. Because this is the focus of finance courses, we will not pursue it here. But given a suitable value of $r$, the following example illustrates how spreadsheet models and the time value of money can be used to make complex business decisions.

---

The **discount factor** is 1 divided by (1 plus the **discount rate**). To discount a cash flow that occurs $t$ years from now, multiply it by the discount factor raised to the $t$ power. The **NPV** is the sum of all discounted cash flows.

---

### The Time Value of Money

Money earned in the future is less valuable than money earned today, for the simple reason that money earned today can be invested to earn interest. Similarly, costs incurred in the future are less "costly" than costs incurred today, which is why you don't simply sum up revenues and costs in a multiperiod model. You instead *discount* future revenues and costs for a fair comparison with revenues and costs incurred today. The resulting sum of discounted cash flows is the net present value (NPV), and it forms the cornerstone of much of financial theory and applications.

---

## EXAMPLE 2.6 CALCULATING NPV AT ACRON

Acron is a large drug company. At the current time, the beginning of year 0, Acron is trying to decide whether one of its new drugs, Niagra, is worth pursuing. Niagra is in the final stages of development and will be ready to enter the market one year from now. The final cost of development, to be incurred at the beginning of year 1, is $9.3 million. Acron estimates that the demand for Niagra will gradually grow and then decline over its useful lifetime of 20 years. Specifically, the company expects its gross margin (revenue minus cost) to be $1.2 million in year 1, then to increase at an annual rate of 10% through year 8, and finally to decrease at an annual rate of 5% through year 20. Acron wants to develop a spreadsheet model of its 20-year cash flows, assuming its cash flows, other than the initial development cost, are incurred at the *ends* of the respective years.[8] Using an annual discount rate of 12% for the purpose of calculating NPV, the drug company wants to answer the following questions:

1. Is the drug worth pursuing, or should Acron abandon it now and not incur the $9.3 million development cost?

2. How do changes in the model inputs change the answer to question 1?

3. How realistic is the model?

**Business Objectives**   To develop a model that calculates the NPV of Acron's cash flows, to use this model to determine whether the drug should be developed further and then marketed, and to see how sensitive the answer to this question is to model parameters.

**Excel Objectives**   To illustrate efficient selection and copying of large ranges and to learn Excel's NPV function.

### Solution

The key variables in Acron's problem appear in Table 2.6. The first two rows contain the inputs stated in the problem. We have made a judgment call as to which of these are known with some certainty and which are uncertain. Although we won't do so in this chapter, a thorough study of Acron's problem would treat this uncertainty explicitly, probably with simulation. For now, you can accept the values given in the statement of the problem and leave the simulation for a later chapter.

---

[8]To simplify the model, taxes are ignored.

Table 2.6    Key Variables for Acron's Problem

| Input variables | Development cost, first year gross margin, rate of increase during early years, years of growth, rate of decrease in later years, discount rate |
|---|---|
| Key output variable | NPV |
| Other calculated variables | Yearly gross margins |

The model of Acron's cash flows appears in Figure 2.34. As with many financial spreadsheet models that extend over a multiyear period, you enter "typical" formulas in the first year or two and then copy this logic down to all years. (In a previous edition, we made the years go across, not down. In that case, splitting the screen is useful so that you can see the first and last years of data. Splitting the screen is explained in the following Excel Tip. The main reason we modified the model to have the years go down, not across, is that it now fits easily on a screen, without needing to split the screen.)

**Figure 2.34**

**Acron's Model of 20-Year NPV**

| | A | B | C | D | E | F | G |
|---|---|---|---|---|---|---|---|
| 1 | Calculating NPV at Acron | | | Range names used: | | | |
| 2 | | | | Development_cost | | =Model!$B$4 | |
| 3 | Inputs | | | Discount_rate | | =Model!$B$9 | |
| 4 | Development cost | 9.3 | | Gross_margin_year_1 | | =Model!$B$5 | |
| 5 | Gross margin year 1 | 1.2 | | Gross_margin | | =Model!$B$13:$B$32 | |
| 6 | Rate of increase | 10% | | Increase_through_year | | =Model!$B$7 | |
| 7 | Increase through year | 8 | | Rate_of_decrease | | =Model!$B$8 | |
| 8 | Rate of decrease | 5% | | Rate_of_increase | | =Model!$B$6 | |
| 9 | Discount rate | 12% | | | | | |
| 10 | | | | | | | |
| 11 | Cash flows | | | | | | |
| 12 | End of year | Gross margin | | | | | |
| 13 | 1 | 1.2000 | | | | | |
| 14 | 2 | 1.3200 | | | | | |
| 15 | 3 | 1.4520 | | | | | |
| 16 | 4 | 1.5972 | | | | | |
| 17 | 5 | 1.7569 | | | | | |
| 18 | 6 | 1.9326 | | | | | |
| 19 | 7 | 2.1259 | | | | | |
| 20 | 8 | 2.3385 | | | | | |
| 21 | 9 | 2.2215 | | | | | |
| 22 | 10 | 2.1105 | | | | | |
| 23 | 11 | 2.0049 | | | | | |
| 24 | 12 | 1.9047 | | | | | |
| 25 | 13 | 1.8095 | | | | | |
| 26 | 14 | 1.7190 | | | | | |
| 27 | 15 | 1.6330 | | | | | |
| 28 | 16 | 1.5514 | | | | | |
| 29 | 17 | 1.4738 | | | | | |
| 30 | 18 | 1.4001 | | | | | |
| 31 | 19 | 1.3301 | | | | | |
| 32 | 20 | 1.2636 | | | | | |
| 33 | | | | | | | |
| 34 | NPV | 3.3003 | | | | | |

**Excel Tip: *Splitting the Screen***
*To split the screen horizontally, drag the separator just to the right of the bottom scrollbar to the left. To split the screen vertically, drag the separator just above the right scrollbar downward. Drag either separator back to its original position to remove the split.*

### DEVELOPING THE SPREADSHEET MODEL

To create the model, complete the following steps. (See the file Calculating NPV.xlsx.)

**① Inputs and range names.** Enter the given input data in the blue cells, and name the ranges as shown. As usual, note that the range names for cells B4 through B9 can be created all at once with the Create from Selection shortcut, as can the range name for the gross margins in column B. In the latter case, highlight the whole range B12:B32 and then use the Create from Selection shortcut.

**2** **Cash flows.** Start by entering the formula

=Gross_margin_year_1

in cell B13 for the year 1 gross margin. Then enter the general formula

=IF(A14<=Increase_through_year,B13*(1+Rate_of_increase),
B13*(1-Rate_of_decrease))

in cell B14 and copy it down to cell B32 to calculate the other yearly gross margins. Note how this IF function checks the year index in column A to see whether sales are still increasing or have started to decrease. Of course, by using the (range-named) input cells in this formula, you can change any of these inputs in cells B6 through B8, and the calculated cells will automatically update. This is a *much* better practice than embedding the numbers in the formula itself.

**Excel Tip:** *Efficient Selection*
*An easy way to select a large range, assuming that the first and last cells of the range are visible, is to select the first cell and then, with your finger on the Shift key, select the last cell. (Don't forget that you can split the screen horizontally and/or vertically to make these first and last cells visible when the range is large.) This selects the entire range and is easier than scrolling.[9]*

*Use the Ctrl+Enter shortcut to enter a formula in a range all at once. It is equivalent to copying.*

**Excel Tip:** *Efficient Copying with Ctrl+Enter*
*An easy way to enter the same formula in a range all at once is to select the range (as in the preceding Excel Tip), type the formula, and press Ctrl+Enter (both keys at once). After you get used to this shortcut, you will probably use it all the time.*

**3** **Net present value.** The NPV is based on the sequence of cash flows in column B. From the general discussion of NPV, to discount everything back to the beginning of year 1, the value in cell B13 should be multiplied by $1/(1 + r)^1$, the value in cell B14 should be multiplied by $1/(1 + r)^2$, and so on, and these quantities should be summed to obtain the NPV. (Here, $r = 0.12$ is the discount rate.) Fortunately, however, Excel has a built-in NPV function to accomplish this calculation. To use it, enter the formula

=-Development_cost+NPV(Discount_rate,Gross_margin)

in cell B34. The NPV function takes two arguments: the discount rate and a range of cash flows. Furthermore, it assumes that the first cell in this range is the cash flow at the *end* of year 1, the second cell is the cash flow at the end of year 2, and so on. This explains why the development cost is subtracted *outside* of the NPV function—it is incurred at the *beginning* of year 1. In general, any cash flow incurred at the beginning of year 1 must be placed outside the NPV function.

To get some understanding of NPV, note that the *sum* of the cash flows in column B is slightly more than $34.14 million, but the NPV (aside from the development cost) is only about $12.60 million. This is because values further into the future are discounted so heavily. At the extreme, the $1.2636 million cash flow in year 20 is equivalent to only $1.2636[1/(1 + 0.12)^{20}] = \$0.131$ million now.

*The stream of cash flows in the NPV function must occur at the ends of year 1, year 2, and so on. If the timing is irregular, you can discount "manually" or you can use Excel's XNPV function.*

**Excel Function:** *NPV*
*The NPV function takes two arguments, the discount rate (entered as a decimal, such as 0.12 for 12%) and a stream of cash flows. These cash flows are assumed to occur in consecutive years, starting at the end of year 1. If there is an initial cash flow at the beginning of year 1, such as an initial investment, it should be entered outside the NPV function. (There is also an XNPV function that has three arguments: a discount rate, a series of cash flows, and a series of dates when the cash flows occur. Because these dates do not have to be equally spaced*

---

[9]You can find other tips like this for increasing your efficiency in the Excel Tutorial.xlsx file on this textbook's essential resource Web site.

through time, this function is considerably more flexible than the NPV function. We will not use the XNPV function in this book, but you can learn more about it in Excel's online help.)

## Deciding Whether to Continue with the Drug

NPV calculations are typically used to see whether a certain project should be undertaken. If the NPV is positive, the project is worth pursuing. If the NPV is negative, the company should look for other places to invest its money. Figure 2.34 shows that the NPV for this drug is positive, over $3 million.[10] Therefore, if Acron is comfortable with its predictions of future cash flows, it should continue with the development and marketing of the drug. However, Acron might first want to see how sensitive the NPV is to changes in the sales predictions. After all, these predictions are intelligent guesses at best.

One possible sensitivity analysis appears in Figure 2.35. Here you can build a one-way data table to see how the NPV changes when the number of years of increase (the input in cell B7) changes. Again, the important question is whether the NPV stays positive. It certainly does when the input variable is greater than its current value of 8. However, if sales start decreasing soon enough—that is, if the value in B7 is 3 or less—the NPV turns negative. This should probably not concern Acron, because its best guess for the years of increase is considerably greater than 3.

| | D | E | F |
|---|---|---|---|
| 11 | Sensitivity to years of increase (cell B7) | | |
| 12 | | 3.3003 | |
| 13 | 3 | -0.7190 | |
| 14 | 4 | 0.1374 | |
| 15 | 5 | 0.9687 | |
| 16 | 6 | 1.7739 | |
| 17 | 7 | 2.5516 | |
| 18 | 8 | 3.3003 | |
| 19 | 9 | 4.0181 | |
| 20 | 10 | 4.7027 | |

Another possibility is to see how long *and* how good the good years are. To do this, you can create the two-way data table shown in Figure 2.36, where cell B6 is the row input cell and cell B7 is the column input cell. Now you can see that if sales increase through year 6, all reasonable yearly increases result in a positive NPV. However, if sales increase only through year 5, then a low enough yearly increase can produce a negative NPV. Acron might want to step back and estimate how likely these bad scenarios are before proceeding with the drug.

| | D | E | F | G | H | I | J |
|---|---|---|---|---|---|---|---|
| 22 | Sensitivity to rate of increase in early years (cell B6) and years of increase (cell B7) | | | | | | |
| 23 | 3.3003 | 5% | 6% | 7% | 8% | 9% | 10% |
| 24 | 3 | -1.3405 | -1.2184 | -1.0951 | -0.9708 | -0.8454 | -0.7190 |
| 25 | 4 | -0.8203 | -0.6352 | -0.4469 | -0.2554 | -0.0606 | 0.1374 |
| 26 | 5 | -0.3383 | -0.0897 | 0.1652 | 0.4265 | 0.6943 | 0.9687 |
| 27 | 6 | 0.1074 | 0.4195 | 0.7419 | 1.0750 | 1.4189 | 1.7739 |
| 28 | 7 | 0.5182 | 0.8934 | 1.2838 | 1.6899 | 2.1123 | 2.5516 |
| 29 | 8 | 0.8958 | 1.3330 | 1.7912 | 2.2711 | 2.7738 | 3.3003 |
| 30 | 9 | 1.2413 | 1.7392 | 2.2643 | 2.8182 | 3.4023 | 4.0181 |
| 31 | 10 | 1.5559 | 2.1125 | 2.7033 | 3.3306 | 3.9963 | 4.7027 |

[10]You might wonder why we didn't discount back to the beginning of the current year, year 0, instead of year 1. This is a fairly arbitrary decision on our part. To discount back to year 0, you would simply divide the current NPV by 1.12. The important point, however, is that this would have no bearing on Acron's decision: A positive NPV would stay positive, and a negative NPV would stay negative.

## Limitations of the Model

Probably the major flaw in this model is that it ignores uncertainty, and future cash flows are highly uncertain, due mainly to uncertain demand for the drug. Incorporating uncertainty into this type of model will be covered when we discuss simulation in Chapters 10 and 11. Aside from this uncertainty, there are almost always ways to make *any* model more realistic—at the cost of increased complexity. For example, you could model the impact of competition on Niagra's profitability. Alternatively, you could allow Acron to treat its prices as decision variables. However, this might influence the likelihood of competition entering the market, which would certainly complicate the model. The point is that this model is only a start. When millions of dollars are at stake, a more thorough analysis is certainly warranted. ▪

# PROBLEMS

## Skill-Building Problems

**14.** Modify Acron's model so that development lasts for an extra year. Specifically, assume that development costs of $7.2 million and $2.1 million are incurred at the beginnings of years 1 and 2, and then the sales in the current model occur one year later, that is, from year 2 until year 21. Again, calculate the NPV discounted back to the beginning of year 1, and perform the same sensitivity analyses. Comment on the effects of this change in timing.

**15.** Modify Acron's model so that sales increase, then stay steady, and finally decrease. Specifically, assume that the gross margin is $1.2 million in year 1, then increases by 10% annually through year 6, then stays constant through year 10, and finally decreases by 5% annually through year 20. Perform a sensitivity analysis with a two-way data table to see how NPV varies with the length of the increase period (currently 6 years) and the length of the constant period (currently 4 years). Comment on whether Acron should pursue the drug, given your results.

**16.** Create a one-way data table in the Acron model to see how the NPV varies with discount rate, which is allowed to vary from 8% to 18% in increments of 0.5%. Explain intuitively why the results go in the direction they go—that is, the NPV decreases as the discount rate increases. Should Acron pursue the drug for all of these discount rates?

## Skill-Extending Problems

**17.** The NPV function automatically discounts each of the cash flows and sums the discounted values. Verify that it does this correctly for Acron's model by calculating the NPV the long way. That is, discount each cash flow and then sum these discounted values. Use Excel formulas to do this, but don't use the NPV function. (*Hint:* Remember that the discounted value of $1 received $t$ years from now is $1/(1 + r)^t$ dollars today.)

**18.** In a situation such as Acron's, where a one-time cost is followed by a sequence of cash flows, the **internal rate of return** (IRR) is the discount rate that makes the NPV equal to 0. The idea is that if the discount rate is greater than the IRR, the company will not pursue the project, but if the discount rate is less than the IRR, the project is financially attractive.

    **a.** Use Excel's Goal Seek tool to find the IRR for the Acron model.

    **b.** Excel also has an IRR function. Look it up in online help to see how it works, and then use it on Acron's model. Of course, you should get the same IRR as in part **a.**

    **c.** Verify that the NPV is negative when the discount rate is slightly greater than the IRR, and that it is positive when the discount rate is slightly less than the IRR.

**19.** The XNPV function can calculate NPV for any (possibly irregular) series of cash flows. Look this function up in Excel's online help. Then use it to develop a spreadsheet model that finds the NPV of the following series: a payment of $25,000 today (assumed to be June 15, 2010), and cash inflows of $10,000 on March 1, 2011; $15,000 on September 15, 2011; $8000 on January 20, 2012; $20,000 on April 1, 2012; and $10,000 on May 15, 2012. Discount these back to "today" using a discount rate of 12%.

# 2.8 CONCLUSION

The examples in this chapter provide a glimpse of things to come in later chapters. You have seen the spreadsheet modeling approach to realistic business problems, learned how to design spreadsheet models for readability, and explored some of Excel's powerful tools, particularly data tables. In addition, at least three important themes have emerged from these examples: relating inputs and decision variables to outputs by means of appropriate formulas, optimization (for example, finding a "best" order quantity), and the role of uncertainty (uncertain response rate or demand). Although you have not yet learned the tools to explore these themes fully, you will have plenty of opportunities to do so in the rest of this book.

## Summary of Key Management Science Terms

| Term | Explanation | Page |
|------|-------------|------|
| Model inputs | The numeric values that are given in any problem statement | 2 |
| Decision variables | The variables a decision maker has control over to obtain better solutions | 2 |
| Model outputs | The numeric values that result from combinations of inputs and decision variables through the use of logical formulas | 2 |
| Net present value (NPV) | The current worth of a stream of cash flows that occur in the future | 35 |
| Discount rate | Interest rate used for discounting future cash flows to get the net present value | 35 |

## Summary of Key Excel Terms

| Term | Explanation | Excel | Page |
|------|-------------|-------|------|
| IF function | Useful for implementing logic | =IF(*condition,resultIfTrue, resultIfFalse*) | 4 |
| Relative, absolute cell addresses | Useful for copying formulas; absolute row or column stays fixed, relative row or column "moves" | A1 (relative), $A1 or A$1 (mixed), $A$1 (absolute); press F4 to cycle through possibilities | 9 |
| Range names | Useful for making formulas more meaningful | Type name in Name box, or use Create from Selection shortcut (Ctrl+Shift+F3) | 13 |
| Pasting range names | Provides a list of all range names in the current workbook | Use Paste List from Use in Formula dropdown list (F3) | 13 |
| Cell comments | Useful for documenting contents of the cell | Right-click on cell, select Insert Comment menu item | 14 |
| One-way data table | Shows how one or more outputs vary as a single input varies | Use Data Table from What-If Analysis dropdown list | 16 |
| Goal Seek | Solves one equation in one unknown | Use Goal Seek from What-If Analysis dropdown list | 17 |
| Formula Auditing toolbar | Useful for checking which cells are related to other cells through formulas | Use Formula Auditing buttons on Formulas ribbon | 18 |
| $f_x$ button | Useful for getting help on Excel functions | On Formula Bar | 22 |

*(continued)*

| Term | Explanation | Excel | Page |
|------|-------------|-------|------|
| VLOOKUP function | Useful for finding a particular value based on a comparison | =VLOOKUP(*valueToCompare, lookupTable, columnToReturn*) | 22 |
| Two-way data table | Shows how a single output varies as two inputs vary | Use Data Table from What-If Analysis dropdown list | 23 |
| SUMPRODUCT function | Calculates the sum of products of values in two (or more) similar-sized ranges | =SUMPRODUCT(*range1,range2*) | 24 |
| Trendline tool | Superimposes the best-fitting line or curve of a particular type on a scatter chart or time series graph | With chart selected, right-click on any point and select Add Trendline | 27 |
| Conditional formatting | Formats cells depending on whether specified conditions hold | Use Conditional Formatting on Home ribbon | 31 |
| Splitting screen | Useful for separating the screen horizontally and/or vertically | Use screen splitters at top and right of scrollbars | 37 |
| Efficient selection | Useful for selecting a large rectangular range | While pressing the Shift key, click on upper-left and bottom-right cells of range | 38 |
| Efficient copying | Shortcut for copying a formula to a range | Select the range, enter the formula, and press Ctrl+Enter | 38 |
| NPV function | Calculates NPV of a stream of cash flows at the ends of consecutive years, starting in year 1 | =NPV(*discountRate,cashFlows*) | 38 |

## PROBLEMS

### Skill-Building Problems

**20.** Julie James is opening a lemonade stand. She believes the fixed cost per week of running the stand is $50.00. Her best guess is that she can sell 300 cups per week at $0.50 per cup. The variable cost of producing a cup of lemonade is $0.20.

  **a.** Given her other assumptions, what level of sales volume will enable Julie to break even?

  **b.** Given her other assumptions, discuss how a change in sales volume affects profit.

  **c.** Given her other assumptions, discuss how a change in sales volume and variable cost jointly affect profit.

  **d.** Use Excel's Formula Auditing tools to show which cells in your spreadsheet affect profit directly.

**21.** You are thinking of opening a Broadway play, *I Love You, You're Mediocre, Now Get Better!* It will cost $5 million to develop the show. There are 8 shows per week, and you project the show will run for 100 weeks. It costs $1000 to open the theater each night. Tickets sell for $50.00, and you earn an average of $1.50 profit per ticket holder from concessions. The theater holds 800, and you expect 80% of the seats to be full.

  **a.** Given your other assumptions, how many weeks will the play have to run for you to earn a 100% return on the play's development cost?

  **b.** Given your other assumptions, how does an increase in the percentage of seats full affect profit?

  **c.** Given your other assumptions, determine how a joint change in the average ticket price and number of weeks the play runs influence profit.

  **d.** Use Excel's Formula Auditing tools to show which cells in the spreadsheet are directly affected by the percentage of seats full.

**22.** You are thinking of opening a small copy shop. It costs $5000 to rent a copier for a year, and it costs $0.03 per copy to operate the copier. Other fixed costs of running the store will amount to $400 per month. You plan to charge an average of $0.10 per copy, and the store will be open 365 days per year. Each copier can make up to 100,000 copies per year.

  **a.** For one to five copiers rented and daily demands of 500, 1000, 1500, and 2000 copies per day, find annual profit. That is, find annual profit for *each* of these combinations of copiers rented and daily demand.

  **b.** If you rent three copiers, what daily demand for copies will allow you to break even?

**c.** Graph profit as a function of the number of copiers for a daily demand of 500 copies; for a daily demand of 2000 copies. Interpret your graphs.

**23.** Georgia McBeal is trying to save for her retirement. She believes she can earn 10% on average each year on her retirement fund. Assume that at the beginning of each of the next 40 years, Georgia will allocate $x$ dollars to her retirement fund. If at the beginning of a year Georgia has $y$ dollars in her fund, by the end of the year, it will grow to $1.1y$ dollars. How much should Georgia allocate to her retirement fund each year to ensure that she will have $1 million at the end of 40 years? What key factors are being ignored in this analysis of the amount saved for retirement?

**24.** A European call option on a stock earns the owner an amount equal to the price at expiration minus the exercise price, if the price of the stock on which the call is written exceeds the exercise price. Otherwise, the call pays nothing. A European put option earns the owner an amount equal to the exercise price minus the price at expiration, if the price at expiration is less than the exercise price. Otherwise, the put pays nothing. The file P02_24.xlsx contains a template that finds (based on the well-known Black–Scholes formula) the price of a European call and put based on the following inputs: today's stock price, the duration of the option (in years), the option's exercise price, the risk-free rate of interest (per year), and the annual volatility in stock price. For example, a 40% volatility means approximately that the standard deviation of annual percentage changes in the stock price is 40%.
  **a.** Consider a six-month European call option with exercise price $40. Assume a current stock price of $35, a risk-free rate of 5%, and an annual volatility of 40%. Determine the price of the call option.
  **b.** Use a data table to show how a change in volatility changes the value of the option. Give an intuitive explanation for your results.
  **c.** Use a data table to show how a change in today's stock price changes the option's value. Give an intuitive explanation for your results.
  **d.** Use a data table to show how a change in the option's duration changes the option's value. Give an intuitive explanation for your results.

**25.** Repeat parts **a–d** of the previous problem for a six-month European put option with exercise price $40. Again, assume a current stock price of $35, a risk-free rate of 5%, and an annual volatility of 40%.

**26.** The file P02_26.xlsx lists sales (in millions of dollars) of Dell Computer during the period 1987–1997 (where year 1 corresponds to 1987).
  **a.** Fit a power and an exponential trend curve to these data. Which fits the data better?
  **b.** Use your part **a** answer to predict 1999 sales for Dell.

**c.** Use your part **a** answer to describe how the sales of Dell have grown from year to year.
  **d.** Search the Web for more recent Dell sales data. Then repeat the preceding parts using all of the data.

**27.** Dataware is trying to determine whether to give a $10 rebate, cut the price $6, or have no price change on a software product. Currently, 40,000 units of the product are sold each week for $45 apiece. The variable cost of the product is $5. The most likely case appears to be that a $10 rebate will increase sales 30%, and half of all people will claim the rebate. For the price cut, the most likely case is that sales will increase 20%.
  **a.** Given all other assumptions, what increase in sales from the rebate would make the rebate and price cut equally desirable?
  **b.** Dataware does not really know the increase in sales that will result from a rebate or price cut. However, the company is sure that the rebate will increase sales by between 15% and 40% and that the price cut will increase sales by between 10% and 30%. Perform a sensitivity analysis that could be used to help determine Dataware's best decision.

**28.** The file P02_28.xlsx gives the annual sales for Microsoft (in millions of dollars) for the years 1984–1993, where 1984 = year 1.
  **a.** Fit an exponential curve to these data.
  **b.** Assuming you are back in 1993, by what percentage do you estimate that Microsoft has grown each year, based on this historical data?
  **c.** Why can't a high rate of exponential growth continue for a long time?
  **d.** Rather than an exponential curve, what curve might better represent the growth of a new technology?
  **e.** Search the Web for more recent Microsoft sales data. Then repeat the preceding parts using all the data.

**29.** Assume that the number of units sold of a product is given by $100 - 0.5P + 26\sqrt{A}$, where $P$ is the price (in dollars) charged for the product and $A$ is the amount spent on advertising (in thousands of dollars). Each unit of the product costs $5 to produce. Use a data table to find the combination of price and advertising that maximizes profit.

**30.** A company manufacturers a product in the U.S. and sells it in England. The unit cost of manufacturing is $50. The current exchange rate (dollars per pound) is 1.51. The demand function, which indicates how many units the company can sell in England as a function of price (in pounds) is of the power type, with constant 27556759 and exponent $-2.4$.
  **a.** Develop a model for the company's profit (in dollars) as a function of the price it charges (in pounds). Then use a data table to find the profit-maximizing price to the nearest pound.

**b.** If the exchange rate varies from its current value, does the profit-maximizing price increase or decrease? Does the maximum profit increase or decrease?

**31.** The yield of a chemical reaction is defined as the ratio (expressed as a percentage) of usable output to the amount of raw material input. Suppose the yield of a chemical reaction depends on the length of time the process is run and the temperature at which the process is run. The yield can be expressed as follows:

$$\text{Yield} = 90.79 - 1.095x_1 - 1.045x_2 - 2.781x_1^2 - 2.524x_2^2 - 0.775x_1x_2$$

Here $x_1 = $ (Temperature $- 125)/10$ and $x_2 = $ (Time $- 300)/30$, where temperature is measured in degrees Fahrenheit, and time is measured in seconds. Use a data table to find the temperature and time settings that maximize the yield of this process.

**32.** A bond is currently selling for $1040. It pays the amounts listed in the file P02_32.xlsx at the ends of the next six years. The yield of the bond is the interest rate that would make the NPV of the bond's payments equal to the bond's price. Use Excel's Goal Seek tool to find the yield of the bond.

**33.** Assume the demand for a company's drug Wozac during the current year is 50,000, and assume demand will grow at 5% a year. If the company builds a plant that can produce $x$ units of Wozac per year, it will cost $16x$. Each unit of Wozac is sold for $3. Each unit of Wozac produced incurs a variable production cost of $0.20. It costs $0.40 per year to operate a unit of capacity. Determine how large a Wozac plant the company should build to maximize its expected profit over the next 10 years.

**34.** Consider a project with the following cash flows: year 1, $-$400; year 2, $200; year 3, $600; year 4, $-$900; year 5, $1000; year 6, $250; year 7, $230. Assume a discount rate of 15% per year.
   **a.** Find the project's NPV if cash flows occur at the ends of the respective years.
   **b.** Find the project's NPV if cash flows occur at the beginnings of the respective years.
   **c.** Find the project's NPV if cash flows occur at the middles of the respective years.

**35.** A software company is considering translating its program into French. Each unit of the program sells for $50 and incurs a variable cost of $10 to produce. Currently, the size of the market for the product is 300,000 units per year, and the English version of the software has a 30% share of the market. The company estimates that the market size will grow by 10% a year for the next five years, and at 5% per year after that. It will cost the company $6 million to create a French version of the program. The translation will increase its market share to 40%. Given a 10-year planning horizon, for what discount rates is it profitable to create the French version of the software?

**36.** The payback of a project is the number of years it takes before the project's total cash flow is positive. Payback ignores the time value of money. It is interesting, however, to see how differing assumptions on project growth impact payback. Suppose, for example, that a project requires a $300 million investment at year 0 (right now). The project yields cash flows for 10 years, and the year 1 cash flow will be between $30 million and $100 million. The annual cash flow growth will be between 5% and 25% per year. (Assume that this growth is the *same* each year.) Use a data table to see how the project payback depends on the year 1 cash flow and the cash flow growth rate.

## Skill-Extending Problems

**37.** You are entering the widget business. It costs $500,000, payable in year 1, to develop a prototype. This cost can be depreciated on a straight-line basis during years 1–5. Each widget sells for $40 and incurs a variable cost of $20. During year 1, the market size is 100,000, and the market is growing at 10% per year. You believe you will attain a 30% market share. Profits are taxed at 40%, but there are no taxes on *negative* profits.
   **a.** Given your other assumptions, what market share is needed to ensure a total free cash flow (FCF) of $0 over years 1 to 5? (*Note:* FCF during a year equals after-tax profits plus depreciation minus fixed costs, if any.)
   **b.** Explain how an increase in market share changes profit.
   **c.** Explain how an increase in market size growth changes profit.
   **d.** Use Excel's auditing tool to show how the market growth assumption influences your spreadsheet.

**38.** Suppose you are borrowing $25,000 and making monthly payments with 1% interest. Show that the monthly payments should equal $556.11. The key relationships are that for any month $t$

(Ending month $t$ balance)
= (Ending month $t - 1$ balance)
   $- $ ((Monthly payment) $-$ (Month $t$ interest))

(Month $t$ interest) = (Beginning month $t$ balance) $\times$ (Monthly interest rate)

Of course, the ending month 60 balance must equal 0.

**39.** You are thinking of starting Peaco, which will produce Peakbabies, a product that competes with Ty's Beanie Babies. In year 0 (right now), you will incur costs of $4 million to build a plant. In year 1, you expect to sell 80,000 Peakbabies for a unit price of $25. The price of $25 will remain unchanged through years 1 to 5. Unit sales are expected to grow by the same percentage ($g$) each year. During years 1 to 5, Peaco incurs two types of costs: variable costs and SG&A (selling, general, and administrative) costs. Each year, variable costs equal half of revenue. During year 1, SG&A costs equal 40% of revenue. This percentage is assumed to drop 2% per year, so during year 2, SG&A costs will equal 38% of revenue, and so on. Peaco's goal is to have profits for years 0 to 5 sum to 0 (ignoring the time value of money). This will ensure that the $4 million investment in year 0 is paid back by the end of year 5. What annual percentage growth rate $g$ does Peaco require to pay back the plant cost by the end of year 5?

40. Suppose the demand (in thousands) for a toaster is given by $100p^{-2}$, where $p$ is the price in dollars charged for the toaster.
    a. If the variable cost of producing a toaster is $10, what price maximizes profit?
    b. The elasticity of demand is defined as the percentage change in demand created by a 1% change in price. Using a data table, show that the demand for toasters has constant elasticity, that is, the elasticity doesn't depend on the price. Would this be true if the demand for toasters were linear in price?

41. The file P02_41.xlsx contains the cumulative number of bits (in trillions) of DRAM (a type of computer memory) produced and the price per bit (in thousandths of a cent).
    a. Fit a power curve that can be used to show how price per bit drops with increased production. This relationship is known as the learning curve.
    b. Suppose the cumulative number of bits doubles. Create a prediction for the price per bit. Does the change in the price per bit depend on the current price?

42. A large U.S. drug company, Pharmco, has 100 million yen coming due in one year. Currently the yen is worth $0.01. Because the value of the yen in U.S. dollars in one year is unknown, the value of this 100 million yen in U.S. dollars is highly uncertain. To hedge its risk, Pharmco is thinking of buying one-year put options on the yen with an exercise price of $0.008. For example, if the yen falls in value a year from now to $0.007, the owner of the put receives $0.001. The price of such a put is $0.00007. Show how the dollar value of Pharmco's receipts and hedging expenses depends on the number of puts purchased and the final $/yen exchange rate. Assume final exchange rates between 0.006 $/yen and 0.015 $/yen are possible.

43. The file P02_43.xlsx contains a template for a car loan. Specifically, once values are entered in the blue cells, you need to enter formulas in the gray cells to calculate the amount financed, the monthly payment (assuming that monthly payments stay the same throughout the term of the loan), the total interest paid, and an amortization schedule. For the latter, fill in the *entire* gray area with formulas, but use IF functions so that blanks appear past the term of the loan.

44. The IRR is the discount rate $r$ that makes a project have an NPV of $0. You can find IRR in Excel with the built-in IRR function, using the syntax =IRR(range of cash flows). However, it can be tricky. In fact, if the IRR is not near 10%, this function might not find an answer, and you would get an error message. Then you must try the syntax =IRR(range of cash flows, guess), where "guess" is your best guess for the IRR. It is best to try a range of guesses (say, $-90\%$ to 100%). Find the IRR of the project described in Problem 34.

45. A project does not necessarily have a unique IRR. (Refer to the previous problem for more information on IRR.) Show that a project with the following cash flows has two IRRs: year 1, $-\$20$; year 2, $82; year 3, $-\$60$; year 4, $2. (*Note:* It can be shown that if the cash flow of a project changes sign only once, the project is guaranteed to have a unique IRR.)

46. The file P02_46.xlsx contains data on prices of products for several of a chain store's locations, a discount schedule offered to customers depending on how much they spend, and commission rates of the salespeople at the various stores. Your job is to develop an invoice form. Specifically, you should enter formulas in the gray cells so that whenever data are entered in the blue cells, the formulas in the gray cells calculate automatically. As an extra, use data validation in cell B23 so that the user can choose a city from a list of cities where the chain has its stores.

# APPENDIX TIPS FOR EDITING AND DOCUMENTING SPREADSHEETS

Editing and documenting your spreadsheet models is crucial, and the following tips make these tasks much easier.

## Format Appropriately

Appropriate formatting can make a spreadsheet model much easier to read. To boldface, for example, select one or more cells and click on the **B** button on the Home ribbon (or press Ctrl+B). Similarly, to italicize, indent, increase or decrease the number of decimal places, right-justify, or perform other common formatting tasks, use the buttons on the Home ribbon or shortcut keys.

## Use Range Names

Naming ranges takes time but makes formulas much easier to read and understand. To enter a range name, highlight any cell or range of cells and enter a name for the range in the Name box (just to the left of the Formula Bar). If you want to edit or delete range names, select Name Manager on the Formulas ribbon. Here are some other options you have from the Defined Names group on the Formulas ribbon.

- After you have named some ranges, you can get a list of them in your spreadsheet by placing the cursor at the top of the range where you want the list to be placed, selecting the Use in Formula dropdown list on the Formulas ribbon, and clicking on the Paste List option. Alternatively, you can press the F3 button.

- Suppose you have labels such as Fixed Cost, Variable Cost, Revenue, and Profit in the range A3:A6, with their values next to them in column B. If you want to name the cells in column B with the labels in column A, highlight the range A3:B6, select Create from Selection on the Formulas ribbon (or press Ctrl+Shift+F3), and make sure the Left Column box is checked. This creates the range names you want. A similar trick works if you have descriptive labels *above* columns of data you want to name.

- If you have a formula, such as =SUM(A10:A20), and then you name the range A10:A20 Costs, say, the formula does *not* change automatically to =SUM(Costs). However, you can make it adapt to your new range name by selecting Apply Names from the Define Name dropdown list on the Formulas ribbon.

- Sometimes you might want to use the *same* range name, such as Total_cost, on multiple worksheets of a workbook. For example, you might want Total_cost to refer to cell B26 in Sheet1 and to cell C59 in Sheet2. The trick is to use a *sheet*-level name rather than a *workbook*-level name for one or both versions of Total_cost. This is easy to do from the Name Manager. When you define a new name, just select a worksheet as the Scope of the name.

## Use Text Boxes

Text boxes are very useful for documenting your work. To enter an explanation or any other text into a text box, click on the Text Box button on the Insert ribbon, drag a box, and start typing. This technique is *much* better than typing explanations into cells because text boxes have word wrap. Therefore, text in text boxes is much easier to edit than text in cells.

## Use Cell Comments

Cell comments provide another good way to document your work. To enter a comment in a cell, select the cell and right-click. This brings up a dialog box (which is also useful for other tasks such as formatting). Click on the Insert Comment item to enter a comment. If a comment is already in the cell, this menu will contain Edit Comment and Delete Comment items. The cells with comments should have small red triangles in their corners. When you hover the cursor over the cell, the comment appears.

## Other Tips

Finally, we urge you once again to open the Excel Tutorial.xlsx file on the Essential Resource Web site and work through it. The file includes a number of techniques that will make you a better and more efficient Excel user.

# Introduction to Optimization Modeling

© Keith Dannemiller/Corbis

## OPTIMIZING MANUFACTURING OPERATIONS AT GE PLASTICS

The General Electric Company (GE) is a global organization that must deliver products to its customers anywhere in the world in the right quantity, at the right time, and at a reasonable cost. One arm of GE is GE Plastics (GEP), a $5 billion business that supplies plastics and raw materials to such industries as automotive, appliance, computer, and medical equipment. (GEP has now been reorganized into GE Advanced Materials [GEAM].) As described in Tyagi et al. (2004), GEP practiced a "pole-centric" manufacturing approach, making each product in the geographic area (Americas, Europe, or Pacific) where it was to be delivered. However, it became apparent in the early 2000s that this approach was leading to higher distribution costs and mismatches in capacity as more of GEP's demand was originating in the Pacific region. Therefore, the authors of the article were asked to develop a global optimization model to aid GEP's manufacturing planning. Actually, GEP consists of seven major divisions, distinguished primarily by the capability of their products to withstand heat. The fastest growing of these divisions, the high performance polymer (HPP) division, was chosen as the pilot for the new global approach.

All GEP divisions operate as two-echelon manufacturing systems. The first echelon consists of resin plants, which convert raw material stocks into resins and ship them to the second echelon, the finishing plants. These latter plants combine the resins with additives to produce various grades of the end products. Each physical plant consists of several "plant lines" that operate independently, and each of these plant lines is capable of producing multiple products. All end products are then shipped to GE Polymerland warehouses throughout the world. GE Polymerland is a wholly owned subsidiary that acts as the commercial front for GEP. It handles all customer sales and deliveries from its network of distribution centers and warehouses in more than 20 countries. Because of its experience with customers, GE Polymerland is able to aid the GEP divisions in their planning processes by supplying forecasts of demands and prices for the various products in the various global markets. These forecasts are key inputs to the optimization model.

The optimization model itself attempts to maximize the total contribution margin over a planning horizon, where the contribution margin equals revenues minus the sum of manufacturing, material, and distribution costs. There are demand constraints, manufacturing capacity constraints, and network flow constraints. The decision variables include (1) the amount of resin produced at each resin plant line that will be used at each finishing plant line, and (2) the amount of each end product produced at each finishing plant line that will be shipped to each geographic region. The completed model has approximately 3100 decision variables and 1100 constraints and is completely linear. It was developed and solved in Excel (using LINGO, a commercial optimization solver, not Excel's Solver add-in), and execution time is very fast—about 10 seconds.

The demand constraints are handled in an interesting way. The authors of the study constrain manufacturing to produce no more than the forecasted demands, but they do not force manufacturing to meet these demands. Ideally, manufacturing would meet demands exactly. However, because of its rapid growth, capacity at HPP in 2002 appeared (at the time of the study) to be insufficient to meet the demand in 2005 and later years. The authors faced this challenge in two ways. First, in cases where demand exceeds capacity, they let their model of maximizing total contribution margin determine which demands to satisfy. The least profitable demands are simply not met. Second, the authors added a new resin plant to their model that would come on line in the year 2005 and provide much needed capacity. They ran the model several times for the year 2005 (and later years), experimenting with the location of the new plant. Although some of the details are withheld in the article for confidentiality reasons, the authors indicate that senior management approved the investment of a Europe-based plant that would cost more than $200 million in plant and equipment. This plant was planned to begin operations in 2005 and ramp up to full production capacity by 2007.

The decision support system developed in the study has been a success at the HPP division since its introduction in 2002. Although the article provides no specific dollar gains from the use of the model, it is noteworthy that the other GEP divisions are adopting similar models for their production planning. ∎

## 3.1 INTRODUCTION

In this chapter, we introduce spreadsheet optimization, one of the most powerful and flexible methods of quantitative analysis. The specific type of optimization we will discuss here is **linear programming** (LP). LP is used in all types of organizations, often on a daily basis, to solve a wide variety of problems. These include problems in labor scheduling, inventory management, selection of advertising media, bond trading, management of cash flows, operation of an electrical utility's hydroelectric system, routing of delivery vehicles, blending in oil refineries, hospital staffing, and many others. The goal of this chapter is to introduce the basic elements of LP: the types of problems it can solve, how LP problems can be modeled in Excel, and how Excel's powerful Solver add-in can be used to find optimal solutions. Then in the next few chapters we will examine a variety of LP applications, and we will also look at applications of integer and nonlinear programming, two important extensions of LP.

## 3.2 INTRODUCTION TO OPTIMIZATION

Before we discuss the details of LP modeling, it is useful to discuss optimization in general. All optimization problems have several common elements. They all have *decision variables*, the variables whose values the decision maker is allowed to choose. Either directly or indirectly, the values of these variables determine such outputs as total cost, revenue, and profit. Essentially, they are the variables a company or organization must know to function properly; they determine everything else. All optimization problems have an *objective function* (**objective**, for short) to be optimized—maximized or minimized.[1] Finally, most optimization problems have **constraints** that must be satisfied. These are usually physical, logical, or economic restrictions, depending on the nature of the problem. In searching for the values of the decision variables that optimize the objective, only those values that satisfy all of the constraints are allowed.

Excel uses its own terminology for optimization, and we will use it as well. Excel refers to the decision variables as the **changing cells**. These cells must contain numbers that are allowed to change freely; they are *not* allowed to contain formulas. Excel refers to the objective as the **objective cell**. There can be only one objective cell, which could contain profit, total cost, total distance traveled, or others, and it must be related through formulas to the changing cells. When the changing cells change, the objective cell should change accordingly.

> The **changing cells** contain the values of the decision variables.
>
> The **objective cell** contains the objective to be minimized or maximized.
>
> The **constraints** impose restrictions on the values in the changing cells.

Finally, there must be appropriate cells and cell formulas that operationalize the constraints. For example, one constraint might indicate that the amount of labor used can be no more than the amount of labor available. In this case there must be cells for each of these two quantities, and typically at least one of them (probably the amount of labor used) will be related through formulas to the changing cells. Constraints can come in a variety of forms. One very common form is **nonnegativity**. This type of constraint states that changing cells must have nonnegative (zero or positive) values. Nonnegativity constraints are usually included for physical reasons. For example, it is impossible to produce a negative number of automobiles.

> **Nonnegativity** constraints imply that changing cells must contain nonnegative values.

*Typically, most of your effort goes into the model development step.*

There are basically two steps in solving an optimization problem. The first step is the *model development* step. Here you decide what the decision variables are, what the objective is, which constraints are required, and how everything fits together. If you are developing an algebraic model, you must derive the correct algebraic expressions. If you are developing a spreadsheet model, the main focus of this book, you must relate all variables with appropriate cell formulas. In particular, you must ensure that your model contains formulas that relate the changing cells to the objective cell and formulas that operationalize the constraints. This model development step is where most of your effort goes.

---

[1]Actually, some optimization models are *multicriteria* models that try to optimize several objectives simultaneously. However, we will not discuss multicriteria models in this book.

The second step in any optimization model is to *optimize*. This means that you must systematically choose the values of the decision variables that make the objective as large (for maximization) or small (for minimization) as possible and cause all of the constraints to be satisfied. Some terminology is useful here. Any set of values of the decision variables that satisfies all of the constraints is called a **feasible solution**. The set of all feasible solutions is called the **feasible region**. In contrast, an **infeasible solution** is a solution that violates at least one constraint. Infeasible solutions are disallowed. The desired feasible solution is the one that provides the best value—minimum for a minimization problem, maximum for a maximization problem—for the objective. This solution is called the **optimal solution**.

---

A **feasible solution** is a solution that satisfies all of the constraints.

The **feasible region** is the set of all feasible solutions.

An **infeasible solution** violates at least one of the constraints.

The **optimal solution** is the feasible solution that optimizes the objective.

---

*An algorithm is basically a plan of attack. It is a prescription for carrying out the steps required to achieve some goal, such as finding an optimal solution. An algorithm is typically translated into a computer program that does the work.*

Although most of your effort typically goes into the model development step, much of the published research in optimization has been about the optimization step. Algorithms have been devised for searching through the feasible region to find the optimal solution. One such algorithm is called the **simplex method**. It is used for *linear* models. There are other more complex algorithms used for other types of models (those with integer decision variables and/or nonlinearities).

We will not discuss the details of these algorithms. They have been programmed into the Excel's **Solver** add-in. All you need to do is develop the model and then tell Solver what the objective cell is, what the changing cells are, what the constraints are, and what type of model (linear, integer, or nonlinear) you have. Solver then goes to work, finding the best feasible solution with the appropriate algorithm. You should appreciate that if you used a trial-and-error procedure, even a clever and fast one, it could take hours, weeks, or even years to complete. However, by using the appropriate algorithm, Solver typically finds the optimal solution in a matter of seconds.

Before concluding this discussion, we mention that there is really a *third* step in the optimization process: **sensitivity analysis**. You typically choose the most likely values of input variables, such as unit costs, forecasted demands, and resource availabilities, and then find the optimal solution for these particular input values. This provides a single "answer." However, in any realistic situation, it is wishful thinking to believe that all of the input values you use are exactly correct. Therefore, it is useful—indeed, mandatory in most applied studies—to follow up the optimization step with what-if questions. What if the unit costs increased by 5%? What if forecasted demands were 10% lower? What if resource availabilities could be increased by 20%? What effects would such changes have on the optimal solution? This type of sensitivity analysis can be done in an informal manner or it can be highly structured. Fortunately, as with the optimization step itself, good software allows you to obtain answers to various what-if questions quickly and easily.

## 3.3 A TWO-VARIABLE PRODUCT MIX MODEL

We begin with a very simple two-variable example of a *product mix* problem. This is a type of problem frequently encountered in business where a company must decide its product mix—how much of each of its potential products to produce—to maximize its net profit. You will see how to model this problem algebraically and then how to model it in Excel. You will also see how to find its optimal solution with Solver. Next, because it contains only two decision variables, you will see how it can be solved graphically. Although this graphical solution is not practical for most realistic problems, it provides useful insights into general LP models. The final step is then to ask a number of what-if questions about the completed model.

EXAMPLE **3.1 ASSEMBLING AND TESTING COMPUTERS**

The PC Tech company assembles and then tests two models of computers, Basic and XP. For the coming month, the company wants to decide how many of each model to assembly and then test. No computers are in inventory from the previous month, and because these models are going to be changed after this month, the company doesn't want to hold any inventory after this month. It believes the most it can sell this month are 600 Basics and 1200 XPs. Each Basic sells for $300 and each XP sells for $450. The cost of component parts for a Basic is $150; for an XP it is $225. Labor is required for assembly and testing. There are at most 10,000 assembly hours and 3000 testing hours available. Each labor hour for assembling costs $11 and each labor hour for testing costs $15. Each Basic requires five hours for assembling and one hour for testing, and each XP requires six hours for assembling and two hours for testing. PC Tech wants to know how many of each model it should produce (assemble and test) to maximize its net profit, but it cannot use more labor hours than are available, and it does not want to produce more than it can sell.

**Objective** To use LP to find the best mix of computer models that stays within the company's labor availability and maximum sales constraints.

## Solution

*Tables such as this one serve as a bridge between the problem statement and the ultimate spreadsheet (or algebraic) model.*

In all optimization models, you are given a variety of numbers—the inputs—and you are asked to make some decisions that optimize an objective, while satisfying all constraints. We summarize this information in a table such as Table 3.1. We believe it is a good idea to create such a table before diving into the modeling details. In particular, you always need to identify the appropriate decision variables, the appropriate objective, and the constraints, and you should always think about the relationships between them. Without a clear idea of these elements, it is almost impossible to develop a correct algebraic or spreadsheet model.

**Table 3.1   Variables and Constraints for Two-Variable Product Mix Model**

| | |
|---|---|
| **Input variables** | Hourly labor costs, labor availabilities, labor required for each computer, costs of component parts, unit selling prices, and maximum sales |
| **Decision variables (changing cells)** | Number of each computer model to produce (assemble and test) |
| **Objective cell** | Total net profit |
| **Other calculated variables** | Labor of each type used |
| **Constraints** | Labor used ≤ Labor available, Number produced ≤ Maximum sales |

The decision variables in this product mix model are fairly obvious. The company must decide two numbers: how many Basics to produce and how many XPs to produce. Once these are known, they can be used, along with the problem inputs, to calculate the number of computers sold, the labor used, and the revenue and cost. However, as you will see with other models in this chapter and the next few chapters, determining the decision variables is not always this obvious.

## An Algebraic Model

In the traditional *algebraic* solution method, you first identify the decision variables.[2] In this small problem they are the numbers of computers to produce. We label these $x_1$ and $x_2$, although any other labels would do. The next step is to write expressions for the total net profit and the constraints in terms of the $x$s. Finally, because only nonnegative amounts can be produced, explicit constraints are added to ensure that the $x$s are nonnegative. The resulting **algebraic model** is

$$\text{Maximize } 80x_1 + 129x_2$$

subject to:

$$5x_1 + 6x_2 \leq 10000$$

$$x_1 + 2x_2 \leq 3000$$

$$x_1 \leq 600$$

$$x_2 \leq 1200$$

$$x_1, x_2 \geq 0$$

To understand this model, consider the objective first. Each Basic produced sells for $300, and the total cost of producing it, including component parts and labor, is $150 + 5(11) + 1(15) = \$220$, so the profit margin is $80. Similarly, the profit margin for an XP is $129. Each profit margin is multiplied by the number of computers produced and these products are then summed over the two computer models to obtain the total net profit.

The first two constraints are similar. For example, each Basic requires five hours for assembling and each XP requires six hours for assembling, so the first constraint says that the total hours required for assembling is no more than the number available, 10,000. The third and fourth constraints are the maximum sales constraints for Basics and XPs. Finally, negative amounts cannot be produced, so nonnegativity constraints on $x_1$ and $x_2$ are included.

For many years all LP problems were modeled this way in textbooks. In fact, many commercial LP computer packages are still written to accept LP problems in essentially this format. Since around 1990, however, a more intuitive method of expressing LP problems has emerged. This method takes advantage of the power and flexibility of spreadsheets. Actually, LP problems could always be *modeled* in spreadsheets, but now with the addition of Solver, spreadsheets have the ability to *solve*—that is, optimize—LP problems as well. We use Excel's Solver for all examples in this book.[3]

*Many commercial optimization packages require, as input, an algebraic model of a problem. If you ever use one of these packages, you will be required to think algebraically.*

*This graphical approach works only for problems with two decision variables.*

## A Graphical Solution

When there are only two decision variables in an LP model, as there are in this product mix model, you can solve the problem graphically. Although this **graphical solution** approach is not practical in most realistic optimization models—where there are many more than two decision variables—the graphical procedure illustrated here still yields important insights for general LP models.

---

[2]This is not a book about algebraic models; the main focus is on *spreadsheet* modeling. However, we present algebraic models of the examples in this chapter for comparison with the corresponding spreadsheet models.

[3]The Solver add-in built into Microsoft Excel was developed by a third-party software company, Frontline Systems. This company develops much more powerful versions of Solver for commercial sales, but its standard version built into Office suffices for us. More information about Solver software offered by Frontline is given in a brief appendix to this chapter.

In general, if the two decision variables are labeled $x_1$ and $x_2$, then the steps of the method are to express the constraints and the objective in terms of $x_1$ and $x_2$, graph the constraints to find the feasible region [the set of all pairs $(x_1, x_2)$ satisfying the constraints, where $x_1$ is on the horizontal axis and $x_2$ is on the vertical axis], and then move the objective through the feasible region until it is optimized.

To do this for the product mix problem, note that the constraint on assembling labor hours can be expressed as $5x_1 + 6x_2 \leq 10000$. To graph this, consider the associated equality (replacing $\leq$ with $=$) and find where the associated line crosses the axes. Specifically, when $x_1 = 0$, then $x_2 = 10000/6 = 1666.7$, and when $x_2 = 0$, then $x_1 = 10000/5 = 2000$. This provides the line labeled "assembling hour constraint" in Figure 3.1. It has slope $-5/6 = -0.83$. The set of all points that satisfy the assembling hour constraint includes the points on this line plus the points *below* it, as indicated by the arrow drawn from the line. (The feasible points are below the line because the point $(0, 0)$ is obviously below the line, and $(0, 0)$ clearly satisfies the assembly hour constraint.) Similarly, the testing hour and maximum sales constraints can be graphed as shown in the figure. The points that satisfy all three of these constraints and are nonnegative comprise the feasible region, which is below the dark lines in the figure.

**Figure 3.1**

**Graphical Solution to Two-Variable Product Mix Problem**

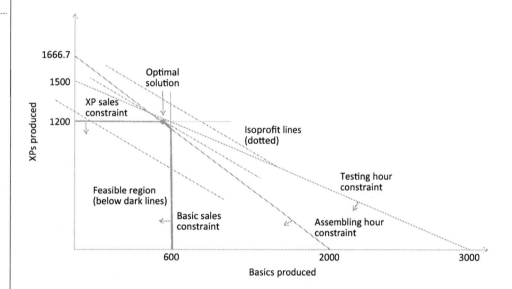

To see which feasible point maximizes the objective, it is useful to draw a sequence of lines where, for each, the objective is a constant. A typical line is of the form $80x_1 + 129x_2 = c$, where $c$ is a constant. Any such line has slope $-80/129 = -0.620$, regardless of the value of $c$. This line is steeper than the testing hour constraint line (slope $-0.5$), but not as steep as the assembling hour constraint line (slope $-0.83$). The idea now is to move a line with this slope up and to the right, making $c$ larger, until it just barely touches the feasible region. The last feasible point that it touches is the optimal point.

Several lines with slope $-0.620$ are shown in Figure 3.1. The middle dotted line is the one with the largest net profit that still touches the feasible region. The associated optimal point is clearly the point where the assembling hour and XP maximum sales lines intersect. You will eventually find (from Solver) that this point is $(560, 1200)$, but even if you didn't have the Solver add-in, you could find the coordinates of this point by solving two equations (the ones for assembling hours and XP maximum sales) in two unknowns.

Again, the graphical procedure illustrated here can be used only for the simplest of LP models, those with two decision variables. However, the type of behavior pictured in Figure 3.1 generalizes to *all* LP problems. In general, all feasible regions are (the multidimensional versions of) polygons. That is, they are bounded by straight lines (actually *hyperplanes*) that intersect at several *corner points*. There are five corner points in Figure 3.1, three of which are on the axes. (One of them is (0,0).) When the dotted objective line is moved as far as possible toward better values, the last feasible point it touches is one of the corner points. The actual corner point it last touches is determined by the slopes of the objective and constraint lines. Because there are only a finite number of corner points, it suffices to search among this finite set, not the infinite number of points in the entire feasible region.[4] This insight is largely responsible for the efficiency of the simplex method for solving LP problems.

---

---

### A Spreadsheet Model

We now turn our focus to *spreadsheet* modeling. There are many ways to develop an LP **spreadsheet model**. Everyone has his or her own preferences for arranging the data in the various cells. We do not provide exact prescriptions, but we do present enough examples to help you develop good habits. The common elements in all LP spreadsheet models are the inputs, changing cells, objective cell, and constraints.

- **Inputs.** All numerical inputs—that is, all numeric data given in the statement of the problem—should appear somewhere in the spreadsheet. Our convention is to color all of the input cells blue. We also try to put most of the inputs in the upper left section of the spreadsheet. However, we sometimes violate this latter convention when certain inputs fit more naturally somewhere else.

- **Changing cells.** Instead of using variable names, such as *xs*, spreadsheet models use a set of designated cells for the decision variables. The values in these changing cells can be changed to optimize the objective. The values in these cells must be allowed to vary freely, so there should *not* be any formulas in the changing cells. To designate them clearly, our convention is to color them red.

- **Objective cell.** One cell, called the objective cell, contains the value of the objective. Solver systematically varies the values in the changing cells to optimize the value in the objective cell. This cell must be linked, either directly or indirectly, to the changing cells by formulas. Our convention is to color the objective cell gray.[5]

---

[4]This is not entirely true. If the objective line is exactly parallel to one of the constraint lines, there can be *multiple optimal solutions*—a whole line segment of optimal solutions. Even in this case, however, at least one of the optimal solutions is a corner point.

[5]Our blue/red/gray color scheme shows up very effectively on a color monitor. For users of previous editions who are used to colored *borders*, we find that it is easier in Excel 2007 and Excel 2010 to color the cells rather than put borders around them.

※ **Constraints.** Excel does not show the constraints directly on the spreadsheet. Instead, they are specified in a Solver dialog box, to be discussed shortly. For example, a set of related constraints might be specified by

B16:C16<=B18:C18

This implies two separate constraints. The value in B16 must be less than or equal to the value in B18, and the value in C16 must be less than or equal to the value in C18. We will always assign range names to the ranges that appear in the constraints. Then a typical constraint might be specified as

Number_to_produce<=Maximum_sales

This is much easier to read and understand. (If you find that range names take too long to create, you certainly do not have to use them. Solver models work fine with cell addresses only.)

※ **Nonnegativity.** Normally, the decision variables—that is, the values in the changing cells—must be nonnegative. These constraints do not need to be written explicitly; you simply check an option in the Solver dialog box to indicate that the changing cells should be nonnegative. Note, however, that if you want to constrain any *other* cells to be nonnegative, you must specify these constraints explicitly.

### Overview of the Solution Process

As mentioned previously, the complete solution of a problem involves three stages. In the model development stage you enter all of the inputs, trial values for the changing cells, and formulas relating these in a spreadsheet. This stage is the most crucial because it is here that all of the ingredients of the model are included and related appropriately. In particular, the spreadsheet *must* include a formula that relates the objective to the changing cells, either directly or indirectly, so that if the values in the changing cells vary, the objective value varies accordingly. Similarly, the spreadsheet must include formulas for the various constraints (usually their left sides) that are related directly or indirectly to the changing cells.

After the model is developed, you can proceed to the second stage—invoking Solver. At this point, you formally designate the objective cell, the changing cells, the constraints, and selected options, and you tell Solver to find the *optimal* solution. If the first stage has been done correctly, the second stage is usually very straightforward.

The third stage is sensitivity analysis. Here you see how the optimal solution changes (if at all) as selected inputs are varied. This often provides important insights about the behavior of the model.

We now illustrate this procedure for the product mix problem in Example 3.1.

### WHERE DO THE NUMBERS COME FROM?

Textbooks typically state a problem, including a number of input values, and proceed directly to a solution—without saying where these input values might come from. However, finding the correct input values can sometimes be the most difficult step in a real-world situation. (Recall that finding the necessary data is step 2 of the overall modeling process, as discussed in Chapter 1.) There are a variety of inputs in PC Tech's problem, some easy to find and others more difficult. Here are some ideas on how they might be obtained.

- The unit costs in rows 3, 4, and 10 should be easy to obtain. (See Figure 3.2.) These are the going rates for labor and the component parts. Note, however, that the labor costs are probably regular-time rates. If the company wants to consider overtime hours, then the overtime rate (and labor hours availability during overtime) would be necessary, and the model would need to be modified.

Figure 3.2    Two-Variable Product Mix Model with an Infeasible Solution

| | A | B | C | D | E | F | G |
|---|---|---|---|---|---|---|---|
| 1 | Assembling and testing computers | | | | Range names used: | | |
| 2 | | | | | Hours_available | =Model!$D$21:$D$22 | |
| 3 | Cost per labor hour assembling | $11 | | | Hours_used | =Model!$B$21:$B$22 | |
| 4 | Cost per labor hour testing | $15 | | | Maximum_sales | =Model!$B$18:$C$18 | |
| 5 | | | | | Number_to_produce | =Model!$B$16:$C$16 | |
| 6 | Inputs for assembling and testing a computer | | | | Total_profit | =Model!$D$25 | |
| 7 | | Basic | XP | | | | |
| 8 | Labor hours for assembly | 5 | 6 | | | | |
| 9 | Labor hours for testing | 1 | 2 | | | | |
| 10 | Cost of component parts | $150 | $225 | | | | |
| 11 | Selling price | $300 | $450 | | | | |
| 12 | Unit margin | $80 | $129 | | | | |
| 13 | | | | | | | |
| 14 | Assembling, testing plan (# of computers) | | | | | | |
| 15 | | Basic | XP | | | | |
| 16 | Number to produce | 600 | 1200 | | | | |
| 17 | | <= | <= | | | | |
| 18 | Maximum sales | 600 | 1200 | | | | |
| 19 | | | | | | | |
| 20 | Constraints (hours per month) | Hours used | | Hours available | | | |
| 21 | Labor availability for assembling | 10200 | <= | 10000 | | | |
| 22 | Labor availability for testing | 3000 | <= | 3000 | | | |
| 23 | | | | | | | |
| 24 | Net profit ($ this month) | Basic | XP | Total | | | |
| 25 | | $48,000 | $154,800 | $202,800 | | | |

- The resource usages in rows 8 and 9, often called *technological coefficients*, should be available from the production department. These people know how much labor it takes to assemble and test these computer models.

- The unit selling prices in row 11 have actually been *chosen* by PC Tech's management, probably in response to market pressures and the company's own costs.

- The maximum sales values in row 18 are probably forecasts from the marketing and sales department. These people have some sense of how much they can sell, based on current outstanding orders, historical data, and the prices they plan to charge.

- The labor hour availabilities in rows 21 and 22 are probably based on the current workforce size and possibly on new workers who could be hired in the short run. Again, if these are regular-time hours and overtime is possible, the model would have to be modified to include overtime.

DEVELOPING THE SPREADSHEET MODEL

The spreadsheet model appears in Figure 3.2. (See the file Product Mix 1.xlsx.) To develop this model, use the following steps.

① **Inputs.** Enter all of the inputs from the statement of the problem in the shaded cells as shown.

② **Range names.** Create the range names shown in columns E and F. Our convention is to enter enough range names, but not to go overboard. Specifically, we enter enough range names so that the setup in the Solver dialog box, to be explained shortly, is entirely in terms of range names. Of course, you can add more range names if you like (or you can omit them altogether). The following tip indicates a quick way to create range names.

Excel Tip: *Shortcut for Creating Range Names*
*Select a range such as A16:C16 that includes nice labels in column A and the range you want to name in columns B and C. Then, from the Formulas ribbon, select Create from Selection and accept the default. You automatically get the labels in cells A16 as the range name for the range B16:C16. This shortcut illustrates the usefulness of adding concise but informative labels next to ranges you want to name.*

③ **Unit margins.** Enter the formula

=B11−B8*$B$3−B9*$B$4−B10

in cell B12 and copy it to cell C12 to calculate the unit profit margins for the two models. ( Enter relative/absolute addresses that allow you to copy whenever possible.)

④ **Changing cells.** Enter any two values for the changing cells in the Number_to_produce range. Any trial values can be used initially; Solver eventually finds the optimal values. Note that the two values shown in Figure 3.2 cannot be optimal because they use more assembling hours than are available. However, you do not need to worry about satisfying constraints at this point; Solver takes care of this later on.

*At this stage, it is pointless to try to outguess the optimal solution. Any values in the changing cells will suffice.*

⑤ **Labor hours used.** To operationalize the labor availability constraints, you must calculate the amounts used by the production plan. To do this, enter the formula

=SUMPRODUCT(B8:C8,Number_to_produce)

in cell B21 for assembling and copy it to cell B22 for testing. This formula is a shortcut for the following fully written out formula:

=B8*B16+C8*C16

*The "linear" in linear programming is all about sums of products. Therefore, the SUMPRODUCT function is natural and should be used whenever possible.*

The SUMPRODUCT function is very useful in spreadsheet models, especially LP models, and you will see it often. Here, it multiplies the number of hours per computer by the number of computers for each model and then sums these products over the two models. When there are only two products in the sum, as in this example, the SUMPRODUCT formula is not really any simpler than the written-out formula. However, imagine that there are 50 models. Then the SUMPRODUCT formula is *much* simpler to enter (and read). For this reason, use it whenever possible. Note that each range in this function, B8:C8 and Number_to_produce, is a one-row, two-column range. It is important in the SUMPRODUCT function that the two ranges be exactly the same size and shape.

⑥ **Net profits.** Enter the formula

=B12*B16

in cell B25, copy it to cell C25, and sum these to get the total net profit in cell D25. This latter cell is the objective to maximize. Note that if you didn't care about the net profits for the two *individual* models, you could calculate the total net profit with the formula

=SUMPRODUCT(B12:C12,Number_to_produce)

As you see, the SUMPRODUCT function appears once again. It and the SUM function are the most used functions in LP models.

## Experimenting with Possible Solutions

The next step is to specify the changing cells, the objective cell, and the constraints in a Solver dialog box and then instruct Solver to find the optimal solution. However, before you do this, it is instructive to try a few guesses in the changing cells. There are two reasons for doing so. First, by entering different sets of values in the changing cells, you can confirm that the formulas in the other cells are working correctly. Second, this experimentation can help you to develop a better understanding of the model.

For example, the profit margin for XPs is much larger than for Basics, so you might suspect that the company will produce only XPs. The most it can produce is 1200 (maximum sales), and this uses fewer labor hours than are available. This solution appears in Figure 3.3. However, you can probably guess that it is far from optimal. There are still many labor hours available, so the company could use them to produce some Basics and make more profit.

You can continue to try different values in the changing cells, attempting to get as large a total net profit as possible while staying within the constraints. Even for this small model with only two changing cells, the optimal solution is not totally obvious. You can only imagine how much more difficult it is when there are hundreds or even thousands of changing cells and many constraints. This is why software such as Excel's Solver is required. Solver uses a quick and efficient algorithm to search through all feasible solutions (or more specifically, all corner points) and eventually find the optimal solution. Fortunately, it is quite easy to use, as we now explain.

Figure 3.3    Two-Variable Product Mix Model with a Suboptimal Solution

| | A | B | C | D | E | F | G |
|---|---|---|---|---|---|---|---|
| 1 | Assembling and testing computers | | | | Range names used: | | |
| 2 | | | | | Hours_available | =Model!$D$21:$D$22 | |
| 3 | Cost per labor hour assembling | $11 | | | Hours_used | =Model!$B$21:$B$22 | |
| 4 | Cost per labor hour testing | $15 | | | Maximum_sales | =Model!$B$18:$C$18 | |
| 5 | | | | | Number_to_produce | =Model!$B$16:$C$16 | |
| 6 | Inputs for assembling and testing a computer | | | | Total_profit | =Model!$D$25 | |
| 7 | | Basic | XP | | | | |
| 8 | Labor hours for assembly | 5 | 6 | | | | |
| 9 | Labor hours for testing | 1 | 2 | | | | |
| 10 | Cost of component parts | $150 | $225 | | | | |
| 11 | Selling price | $300 | $450 | | | | |
| 12 | Unit margin | $80 | $129 | | | | |
| 13 | | | | | | | |
| 14 | Assembling, testing plan (# of computers) | | | | | | |
| 15 | | Basic | XP | | | | |
| 16 | Number to produce | 0 | 1200 | | | | |
| 17 | | <= | <= | | | | |
| 18 | Maximum sales | 600 | 1200 | | | | |
| 19 | | | | | | | |
| 20 | Constraints (hours per month) | Hours used | | Hours available | | | |
| 21 | Labor availability for assembling | 7200 | <= | 10000 | | | |
| 22 | Labor availability for testing | 2400 | <= | 3000 | | | |
| 23 | | | | | | | |
| 24 | Net profit ($ this month) | Basic | XP | Total | | | |
| 25 | | $0 | $154,800 | $154,800 | | | |

To invoke Excel's Solver, select Solver from the Data ribbon. (If there is no such item on your PC, you need to *load* Solver. To do so, click on the Office button, then Excel Options, then Add-Ins, and then Go at the bottom of the dialog box. This shows you the list of available add-ins. If there is a Solver Add-in item in the list, check it to load Solver. If there is no such item, you need to rerun the Microsoft Office installer and elect to install Solver. It should be included in a typical install, but some people elect not to install it the first time around.) The dialog box in Figure 3.4 appears.[6] It has three important sections that you must fill in: the objective cell, the changing cells, and the constraints. For the product mix problem, you can fill these in by typing cell references or you can point, click, and drag the appropriate ranges in the usual way. Better yet, if there are any named ranges, these range names appear instead of cell addresses when you drag the ranges. In fact, for reasons of readability, our convention is to use only range names, not cell addresses, in this dialog box.

**Figure 3.4**

**Solver Dialog Box (in Excel 2010)**

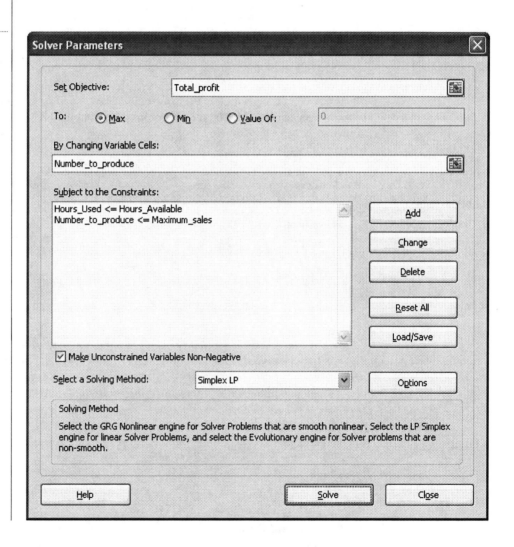

[6]This is the new Solver dialog box for Excel 2010. It is more convenient than similar dialog boxes in previous versions because the typical settings now all appear in a *single* dialog box. In previous versions you have to click on Options to complete the typical settings.

*Our usual procedure is to use the mouse to select the relevant ranges for the Solver dialog box. Fortunately, if these ranges have already been named, then the range names will automatically replace the cell addresses.*

**1** **Objective.** Select the Total_profit cell as the objective cell, and click on the Max option. (Actually, the default option is Max.)

**2** **Changing cells.** Select the Number_to_produce range as the changing cells.

**3** **Constraints.** Click on the Add button to bring up the dialog box in Figure 3.5. Here you specify a typical constraint by entering a cell reference or range name on the left, the type of constraint from the dropdown list in the middle, and a cell reference, range name, or numeric value on the right. Use this dialog box to enter the constraint

Number_to_produce <= Maximum_sales

(*Note:* You can type these range names into the dialog box, or you can drag them in the usual way. If you drag them, the cell addresses shown in the figure eventually change into range names if range names exist.) Then click on the Add button and enter the constraint

Hours_used <= Hours_available

Then click on OK to get back to the Solver dialog box. The first constraint says to produce no more than can be sold. The second constraint says to use no more labor hours than are available.

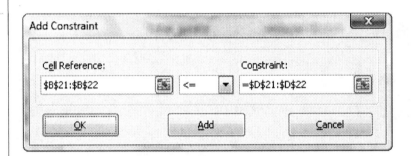

*The <= signs in cells B17:C17 and C21:C22 (see Figure 3.2 or Figure 3.3) are not a necessary part of the Excel model. They are entered simply as labels in the spreadsheet and do not substitute for entering the constraints in the Add Constraint dialog box. However, they help to document the model, so we include them in all of the examples. In fact, you should try to plan your spreadsheet models so that the two sides of a constraint are in nearby cells, with "gutter" cells in between where you can attach labels like <=, >=, or =. This convention tends to make the resulting spreadsheet models much more readable.*

*Constraints typically come in groups. Beginners often enter these one at a time, such as B16<=B18 and C16<=C18, in the Solver dialog box. This can lead to a long list of constraints, and it is time-consuming. It is better to enter them as a group, as in B16:C16<=B18:C18. This is not only quicker, but it also takes advantage of range names you have created. For example, this group ends up as Number_to_produce ≤ Maximum_Sales.*

**4 Nonnegativity.** Because negative production quantities make no sense, you must tell Solver *explicitly* to make the changing cells nonnegative. To do this, check the Make Unconstrained Variables Non-Negative option shown in Figure 3.4. This automatically ensures that all changing cells are nonnegative. (In previous versions of Solver, you have to click on the Options button and then check the Assume Non-Negative option in the resulting dialog box.)

**5 Linear model.** There is one last step before clicking on the Solve button. As stated previously, Solver uses one of several numerical algorithms to solve various types of models. The models discussed in this chapter are all *linear* models. (We will discuss the properties that distinguish linear models shortly.) Linear models can be solved most efficiently with the simplex method. To instruct Solver to use this method, make sure Simplex LP is selected in the Select a Solving Method dropdown list in Figure 3.4. (In previous versions of Solver, you have to click on the Options button and then check the Assume Linear Model option in the resulting dialog box. In fact, from now on, if you are using a pre-2010 version of Excel and we instruct you to use the simplex method, you should check the Assume Linear Model option. In contrast, if we instruct you to use a nonlinear algorithm, you should uncheck the Assume Linear Model option.)

**6 Optimize.** Click on the Solve button in the dialog box in Figure 3.4. At this point, Solver does its work. It searches through a number of possible solutions until it finds the optimal solution. (You can watch the progress on the lower left of the screen, although for small models the process is virtually instantaneous.) When it finishes, it displays the message shown in Figure 3.6. You can then instruct it to return the values in the changing cells to their original (probably nonoptimal) values or retain the optimal values found by Solver. In most cases you should choose the latter. For now, click on the OK button to keep the Solver solution. You should see the solution shown in Figure 3.7.

**Figure 3.6**
**Solver Results Message**

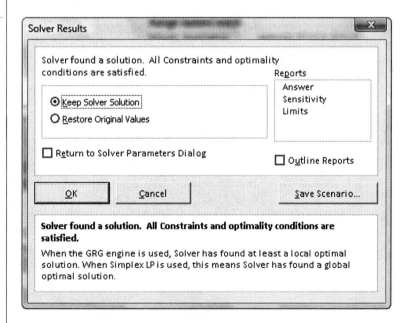

**Solver Tip:** *Messages from Solver*
*Actually, the message in Figure 3.6 is the one you hope for. However, in some cases Solver is not able to find an optimal solution, in which case one of several other messages appears. We discuss some of these later in the chapter.*

Figure 3.7

Two-Variable Product Mix Model with the Optimal Solution

| | A | B | C | D | E | F | G |
|---|---|---|---|---|---|---|---|
| 1 | **Assembling and testing computers** | | | | **Range names used:** | | |
| 2 | | | | | Hours_available | =Model!$D$21:$D$22 | |
| 3 | Cost per labor hour assembling | $11 | | | Hours_used | =Model!$B$21:$B$22 | |
| 4 | Cost per labor hour testing | $15 | | | Maximum_sales | =Model!$B$18:$C$18 | |
| 5 | | | | | Number_to_produce | =Model!$B$16:$C$16 | |
| 6 | Inputs for assembling and testing a computer | | | | Total_profit | =Model!$D$25 | |
| 7 | | Basic | XP | | | | |
| 8 | Labor hours for assembly | 5 | 6 | | | | |
| 9 | Labor hours for testing | 1 | 2 | | | | |
| 10 | Cost of component parts | $150 | $225 | | | | |
| 11 | Selling price | $300 | $450 | | | | |
| 12 | Unit margin | $80 | $129 | | | | |
| 13 | | | | | | | |
| 14 | Assembling, testing plan (# of computers) | | | | | | |
| 15 | | Basic | XP | | | | |
| 16 | Number to produce | 560 | 1200 | | | | |
| 17 | | <= | <= | | | | |
| 18 | Maximum sales | 600 | 1200 | | | | |
| 19 | | | | | | | |
| 20 | Constraints (hours per month) | Hours used | | Hours available | | | |
| 21 | Labor availability for assembling | 10000 | <= | 10000 | | | |
| 22 | Labor availability for testing | 2960 | <= | 3000 | | | |
| 23 | | | | | | | |
| 24 | Net profit ($ this month) | Basic | XP | Total | | | |
| 25 | | $44,800 | $154,800 | $199,600 | | | |

## Discussion of the Solution

This solution says that PC Tech should produce 560 Basics and 1200 XPs. This plan uses all available labor hours for assembling, has a few leftover labor hours for testing, produces as many XPs as can be sold, and produces a few less Basics than could be sold. No plan can provide a net profit larger than this one—that is, without violating at least one of the constraints.

The solution in Figure 3.7 is typical of solutions to optimization models in the following sense. Of all the inequality constraints, some are satisfied exactly and others are not. In this solution the XP maximum sales and assembling labor constraints are met exactly. We say that they are **binding**. However, the Basic maximum sales and testing labor constraints are **nonbinding**. For these nonbinding constraints, the differences between the two sides of the inequalities are called **slack**.[7] You can think of the binding constraints as bottlenecks. They are the constraints that prevent the objective from being improved. If it were not for the binding constraints on maximum sales and labor, PC Tech could obtain an even larger net profit.

> An inequality constraint is **binding** if the solution makes it an equality. Otherwise, it is **nonbinding**, and the positive difference between the two sides of the constraint is called the **slack**.

---

[7]Some analysts use the term *slack* only for ≤ constraints and the term *surplus* for ≥ constraints. We refer to both of these as *slack*—the absolute difference between the two sides of the constraint.

In a typical optimal solution, you should usually pay particular attention to two aspects of the solution. First, you should check which of the changing cells are *positive* (as opposed to 0). Generically, these are the "activities" that are done at a positive level. In a product mix model, they are the products included in the optimal mix. Second, you should check which of the constraints are binding. Again, these represent the bottlenecks that keep the objective from improving. ▪

---

### Binding and Nonbinding Constraints

Most optimization models contain constraints expressed as inequalities. In an optimal solution, each such constraint is either binding (holds as an equality) or nonbinding. It is extremely important to identify the binding constraints because they are the constraints that prevent the objective from improving.

A typical constraint is on the availability of a resource. If such a constraint is binding, the objective could typically improve by having more of that resource. But if such a resource constraint is nonbinding, more of that resource would not improve the objective at all.

---

## 3.4 SENSITIVITY ANALYSIS

*Indeed, many analysts view the "finished" model as a starting point for all sorts of what-if questions. We agree.*

Having found the optimal solution, it might appear that the analysis is complete. But in real LP applications the solution to a *single* model is hardly ever the end of the analysis. It is almost always useful to perform a sensitivity analysis to see how (or if) the optimal solution changes as one or more inputs vary. We illustrate systematic ways of doing so in this section. Actually, we discuss two approaches. The first uses an optional sensitivity report that Solver offers. The second uses an add-in called SolverTable that one of the authors (Albright) developed.

### 3.4.1 Solver's Sensitivity Report

When you run Solver, the dialog box in Figure 3.6 offers you the option to obtain a sensitivity report.[8] This report is based on a well-established theory of sensitivity analysis in optimization models, especially LP models. This theory was developed around algebraic models that are arranged in a "standardized" format. Essentially, all such algebraic models look alike, so the same type of sensitivity report applies to all of them. Specifically, they have an objective function of the form $c_1 x_1 + \cdots + c_n x_n$, where $n$ is the number of decision variables, the $c$s are constants, and the $x$s are the decision variables, and each constraint can be expressed as $a_1 x_1 + \cdots + a_n x_n \leq b$, $a_1 x_1 + \cdots + a_n x_n \geq b$, or $a_1 x_1 + \cdots + a_n x_n = b$, where the $a$s and $b$s are constants. **Solver's sensitivity report** performs two types of sensitivity analysis: (1) on the coefficients of the objective, the $c$s, and (2) on the right sides of the constraints, the $b$s.

---

[8]It also offers Answer and Limits reports. We don't find these particularly useful, so we will not discuss them here.

We illustrate the typical analysis by looking at the sensitivity report for PC Tech's product mix model in Example 3.1. For convenience, the algebraic model is repeated here.

$$\text{Maximize } 80x_1 + 129x_2$$

subject to:

$$5x_1 + 6x_2 \leq 10000$$

$$x_1 + 2x_2 \leq 3000$$

$$x_1 \leq 600$$

$$x_2 \leq 1200$$

$$x_1, x_2 \geq 0$$

On this Solver run, a sensitivity report is requested in Solver's final dialog box. (See Figure 3.6.) The sensitivity report appears on a new worksheet, as shown in Figure 3.8.[9] It contains two sections. The top section is for sensitivity to changes in the two coefficients, 80 and 129, of the decision variables in the objective. Each row in this section indicates how the optimal solution changes if one of these coefficients changes. The bottom section is for the sensitivity to changes in the right sides, 10000 and 3000, of the labor constraints. Each row of this section indicates how the optimal solution changes if one of these availabilities changes. (The maximum sales constraints represent a special kind of constraint—*upper bounds* on the changing cells. Upper bound constraints are handled in a special way in the Solver sensitivity report, as described shortly.)

**Figure 3.8**

**Solver Sensitivity Results**

| A | B | C | D | E | F | G | H |
|---|---|---|---|---|---|---|---|
| 6 | Variable Cells | | | | | | |
| 7 | | | Final | Reduced | Objective | Allowable | Allowable |
| 8 | Cell | Name | Value | Cost | Coefficient | Increase | Decrease |
| 9 | $B$16 | Number to produce Basic | 560 | 0 | 80 | 27.5 | 80 |
| 10 | $C$16 | Number to produce XP | 1200 | 33 | 129 | 1E+30 | 33 |
| 11 | | | | | | | |
| 12 | Constraints | | | | | | |
| 13 | | | Final | Shadow | Constraint | Allowable | Allowable |
| 14 | Cell | Name | Value | Price | R.H. Side | Increase | Decrease |
| 15 | $B$21 | Labor availability for assembling Used | 10000 | 16 | 10000 | 200 | 2800 |
| 16 | $B$22 | Labor availability for testing Used | 2960 | 0 | 3000 | 1E+30 | 40 |

Now let's look at the specific numbers and their interpretation. In the first row of the top section, the *allowable increase* and *allowable decrease* indicate how much the coefficient of profit margin for Basics in the objective, currently 80, could change before the optimal product mix would change. If the coefficient of Basics stays within this allowable range, from 0 (decrease of 80) to 107.5 (increase of 27.5), the optimal product mix—the set of values in the changing cells—does not change at all. However, outside of these limits, the optimal mix between Basics and XPs *might* change.

[9]If your table looks different from ours, make sure you chose the Simplex LP method (or checked Assume Linear Model in pre-2010 versions of Solver). Otherwise, Solver uses a nonlinear algorithm and produces a different type of sensitivity report.

To see what this implies, change the selling price in cell B11 from 300 to 299, so that the profit margin for Basics decreases to $79. This change is well within the allowable decrease of 80. If you rerun Solver, you will obtain the *same* values in the changing cells, although the objective value will decrease. Next, change the value in cell B11 to 330. This time, the profit margin for Basics increases by 30 from its original value of $300. This change is outside the allowable increase, so the solution might change. If you rerun Solver, you will indeed see a change—the company now produces 600 Basics and fewer than 1200 XPs.

The *reduced costs* in the second column indicate, in general, how much the objective coefficient of a decision variable that is currently 0 or at its upper bound must change before that variable changes (becomes positive or decreases from its upper bound). The interesting variable in this case is the number of XPs, currently at its upper bound of 1200. The reduced cost for this variable is 33, meaning that the number of XPs will stay at 1200 unless the profit margin for XPs decreases by at least $33. Try it. Starting with the original inputs, change the selling price for XPs to $420, a change of less than $33. If you rerun Solver, you will find that the optimal plan still calls for 1200 XPs. Then change the selling price to $410, a change of more than $33 from the original value. After rerunning Solver, you will find that *fewer* than 1200 XPs are in the optimal mix.

---

The **reduced cost** for any decision variable with value 0 in the optimal solution indicates how much better that coefficient must be before that variable enters at a positive level. The reduced cost for any decision variable at its upper bound in the optimal solution indicates how much worse its coefficient must be before it will decrease from its upper bound. The reduced cost for any variable between 0 and its upper bound in the optimal solution is irrelevant.

---

Now turn to the bottom section of the report in Figure 3.8. Each row in this section corresponds to a constraint, although upper bound constraints on changing cells are omitted in this section. To have this part of the report make economic sense, the model should be developed as has been done here, where the right side of each constraint is a numeric constant (not a formula). Then the report indicates how much these right-side constants can change before the optimal solution changes. To understand this more fully, the concept of a shadow price is required. A **shadow price** indicates the change in the objective when a right-side constant changes.

---

The term **shadow price** is an economic term. It indicates the change in the optimal value of the objective when the right side of some constraint changes by one unit.

---

A shadow price is reported for each constraint. For example, the shadow price for the assembling labor constraint is 16. This means that if the right side of this constraint increases by one hour, from 10000 to 10001, the optimal value of the objective will increase by $16. It works in the other direction as well. If the right side of this constraint *decreases* by one hour, from 10000 to 9999, the optimal value of the objective will decrease by $16. However, as the right side continues to increase or decrease, this $16 change in the objective might not continue. This is where the reported allowable increase and allowable decrease are relevant. As long as the right side increases or decreases within its allowable limits, the same shadow price of 16 still applies. Beyond these limits, however, a different shadow price might apply.

You can prove this for yourself. First, increase the right side of the assembling labor constraint by 200 (exactly the allowable increase), from 10000 to 10200, and rerun Solver. (Don't forget to reset other inputs to their original values.) You will see that the objective indeed increases by 16(200)=$3200, from $199,600 to $202,800. Now increase this right side by one more hour, from 10200 to 10201 and rerun Solver. You will observe that the objective doesn't increase at all. This means that the shadow price beyond 10200 is *less than* 16; in fact, it is zero. This is typical. When a right side increases beyond its allowable increase, the new shadow price is typically less than the original shadow price (although it doesn't always fall to zero, as in this example).

The idea is that a constraint "costs" the company by keeping the objective from being better than it would be. A shadow price indicates how much the company would be willing to pay (in units of the objective) to "relax" a constraint. In this example, the company would be willing to pay $16 for each extra assembling hour. This is because such a change would increase the net profit by $16. But beyond a certain point—200 hours in this example—further relaxation of the constraint does no good, and the company is not willing to pay for any further increases.

The constraint on testing hours is slightly different. It has a shadow price of zero. In fact, the shadow price for a nonbinding constraint is always zero, which makes sense. If the right side of this constraint is changed from 3000 to 3001, nothing at all happens to the optimal product mix or the objective value; there is just one more unneeded testing hour. However, the allowable decrease of 40 indicates that something *does* change when the right side reaches 2960. At this point, the constraint becomes binding—the testing hours used equal the testing hours available—and beyond this, the optimal product mix starts to change. By the way, the allowable increase for this constraint, shown as 1+E30, means that it is essentially infinite. The right side of this constraint can be increased above 3000 indefinitely and absolutely nothing will change in the optimal solution.

## 3.4.2 SolverTable Add-In

The reason Solver's sensitivity report makes sense for the product mix model is that the spreadsheet model is virtually a direct translation of a standard algebraic model. Unfortunately, given the flexibility of spreadsheets, this is not always the case. We have seen many perfectly good spreadsheet models—and have developed many ourselves—that are structured quite differently from their standard algebraic-model counterparts. In these cases, we have found Solver's sensitivity report to be more confusing than useful. Therefore, Albright developed an Excel add-in called SolverTable. **SolverTable** allows you to ask sensitivity questions about any of the input variables, not just coefficients of the objective and right sides of constraints, and it provides straightforward answers.

The SolverTable add-in is on this book's essential resource Web site.[10] To install it, simply copy the SolverTable files to a folder on your hard drive. These files include the add-in itself (the .xlam file) and the online help files. To load SolverTable, you can proceed in one of two ways:

1. Open the **SolverTable.xlam** file just as you open any other Excel file.

2. Go to the add-ins list in Excel (click on the Office button, then Excel Options, then Add-Ins, then Go) and check the SolverTable item. If it isn't in the list, Browse for the **SolverTable.xlam** file.

The advantage of the second option is that if SolverTable is checked in the add-ins list, it will automatically open every time you open Excel, at least until you uncheck its item in the list.

The SolverTable add-in was developed to mimic Excel's built-in data table tool. Recall that data tables allow you to vary one or two inputs in a spreadsheet model and see instantaneously how selected outputs change. SolverTable is similar except that it runs Solver for every new input (or pair of inputs), and the newest version also provides automatic charts of the results. There are two ways it can be used.

1. **One-way table.** A one-way table means that there is a *single* input cell and *any number* of output cells. That is, there can be a single output cell or multiple output cells.

2. **Two-way table.** A two-way table means that there are *two* input cells and one or more output cells. (You might recall that an Excel two-way data table allows only *one* output. SolverTable allows more than one. It creates a separate table for each output as a function of the two inputs.)

We illustrate some of the possibilities for the product mix example. Specifically, we check how sensitive the optimal production plan and net profit are to (1) changes in the selling price of XPs, (2) the number of labor hours of both types available, and (3) the maximum sales of the two models.

We assume that the model has been formulated and optimized, as shown in Figure 3.7, and that the SolverTable add-in has been loaded. To run SolverTable, click on the Run SolverTable button on the SolverTable ribbon. You will be asked whether there is a Solver model on the active sheet. (Note that the *active* sheet at this point should be the sheet containing the model. If it isn't, click on Cancel and then activate this sheet.) You are then given the choice between a one-way or a two-way table. For the first sensitivity question, choose the one-way option. You will see the dialog box in Figure 3.9. For the sensitivity analysis on the XP selling price, fill it in as shown. Note that ranges can be entered as cell addresses or range names. Also, multiple ranges in the Outputs box should be separated by commas.

---

[10]It is also available from the Free Downloads link on the authors' Web site at www.kelley.iu.edu/albrightbooks. Actually, there are several versions of SolverTable available, each for a particular version of Solver. The one described in the text is for Solver in Excel 2007 or 2010. This Web site contains more information about these versions, as well as possible updates to SolverTable.

Figure 3.9

SolverTable One-
Way Dialog Box

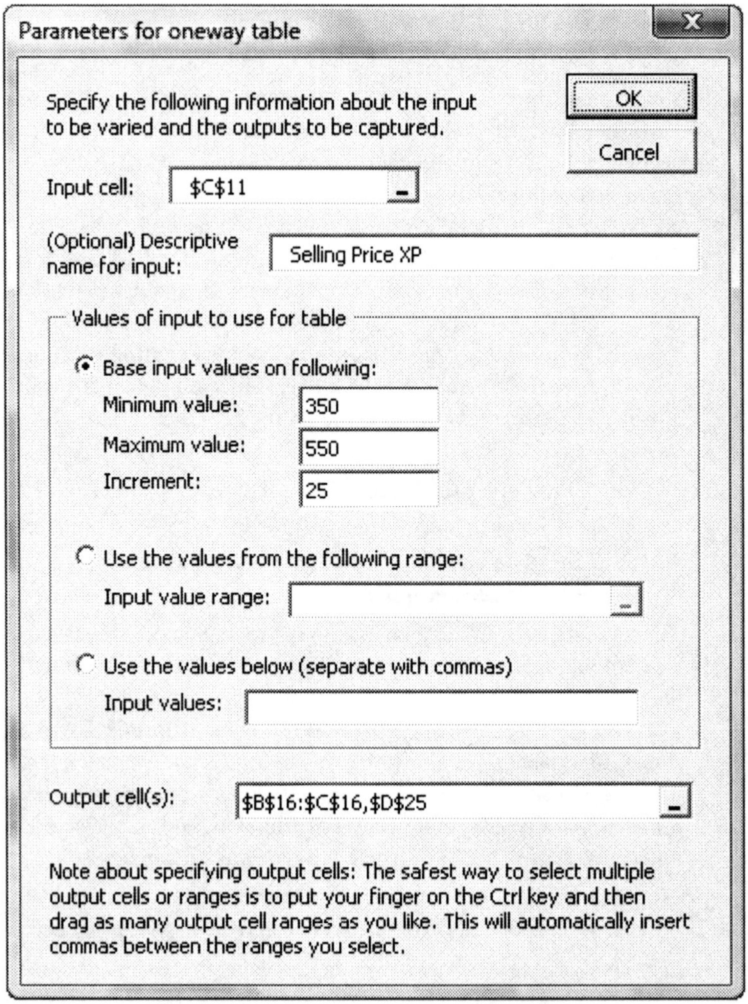

**Parameters for oneway table** ✕

Specify the following information about the input
to be varied and the outputs to be captured.

OK

Cancel

Input cell: $C$11 ▪

(Optional) Descriptive
name for input: Selling Price XP

Values of input to use for table

⦿ Base input values on following:

Minimum value: 350

Maximum value: 550

Increment: 25

○ Use the values from the following range:

Input value range: ▪

○ Use the values below (separate with commas)

Input values:

Output cell(s): $B$16:$C$16,$D$25 ▪

Note about specifying output cells: The safest way to select multiple
output cells or ranges is to put your finger on the Ctrl key and then
drag as many output cell ranges as you like. This will automatically insert
commas between the ranges you select.

Figure 3.10

SolverTable Results
for Varying XP Price

| | A | B | C | D | E | F | G |
|---|---|---|---|---|---|---|---|
| 1 | **Oneway analysis for Solver model in Model worksheet** | | | | | | |
| 2 | | | | | | | |
| 3 | Selling Price XP (cell $C$11) values along side, output cell(s) along top | | | | | | |
| 4 | | Number_to_produce_1 | Number_to_produce_2 | Total_profit | | | |
| 5 | $350 | 600 | 1166.667 | $81,833 | | | |
| 6 | $375 | 600 | 1166.667 | $111,000 | | | |
| 7 | $400 | 600 | 1166.667 | $140,167 | | | |
| 8 | $425 | 560 | 1200 | $169,600 | | | |
| 9 | $450 | 560 | 1200 | $199,600 | | | |
| 10 | $475 | 560 | 1200 | $229,600 | | | |
| 11 | $500 | 560 | 1200 | $259,600 | | | |
| 12 | $525 | 560 | 1200 | $289,600 | | | |
| 13 | $550 | 560 | 1200 | $319,600 | | | |

*Excel Tip:* *Selecting Multiple Ranges*

*If you need to select multiple output ranges, the trick is to keep your finger on the Ctrl key as you drag the ranges. This automatically enters the separating comma(s) for you. Actually, the same trick works for selecting multiple changing cell ranges in Solver's dialog box.*

When you click on OK, Solver solves a separate optimization problem for each of the nine rows of the table and then reports the requested outputs (number produced and net profit) in the table, as shown in Figure 3.10. It can take a while, depending on the speed of your computer and the complexity of the model, but everything is automatic. However, if you want to update this table—by using different XP selling prices in column A, for example—you must repeat the procedure. Note that if the requested outputs are included in named ranges, the range names are used in the SolverTable headings. For example, the label Number_to_produce_1 indicates that this output is the first cell in the Number_to_produce range. The label Total_profit indicates that this output is the *only* cell in the Total_profit range. (If a requested output is not part of a named range, its cell address is used as the label in the SolverTable results.)

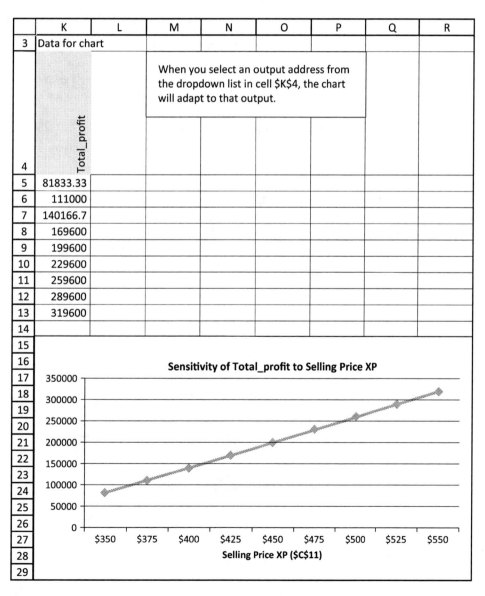

**Figure 3.11**

Associated SolverTable Chart for Net Profit

The outputs in this table show that when the selling price of XPs is relatively low, the company should make as many Basics as it can sell and a few less XPs, but when the selling price is relatively high, the company should do the opposite. Also, the net profit increases steadily through this range. You can calculate these changes (which are not part of the SolverTable output) in column E. The increase in net profit per every extra $25 in XP selling price is close to, but not always exactly equal to, $30,000.

SolverTable also produces the chart in Figure 3.11. There is a dropdown list in cell K4 where you can choose any of the SolverTable outputs. (We selected the net profit, cell D25.) The chart then shows the data for that column from the table in Figure 3.10. Here there is a steady increase (slope about $30,000) in net profit as the XP selling price increases.

The second sensitivity question asks you to vary two inputs, the two labor availabilities, simultaneously. This requires a two-way SolverTable, so fill in the SolverTable dialog box as shown in Figure 3.12. Here two inputs and two input ranges are specified, and multiple output cells are again allowed. An output table is generated for *each* of the output cells, as shown in Figure 3.13. For example, the top table shows how the optimal number of Basics varies as the two labor availabilities vary. Comparing the columns of this top table, it is apparent that the optimal number of Basics becomes increasingly sensitive to the available assembling hours as the number of available testing hours increases. The SolverTable output also includes two charts (not shown here) that let you graph any row or any column of any of these tables.

The third sensitivity question, involving maximum sales of the two models, reveals the flexibility of SolverTable. Instead of letting these two inputs vary independently in a two-way SolverTable, it is possible to let both of them vary according to a *single* percentage change. For example, if this percentage change is 10%, both maximum sales increase by

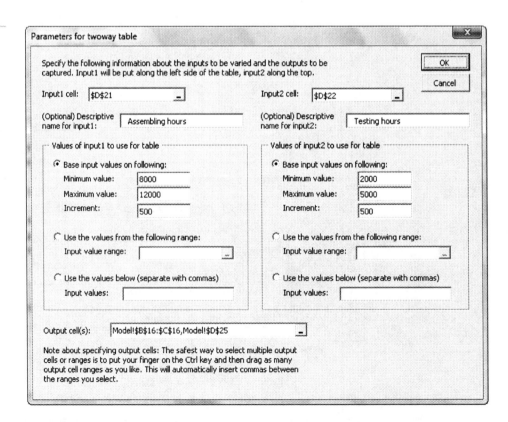

**Figure 3.12**

SolverTable Two-Way Dialog Box

Figure 3.13

Two-Way SolverTable Results

| | A | B | C | D | E | F | G | H | I |
|---|---|---|---|---|---|---|---|---|---|
| 3 | Assembling hours (cell $D$21) values along side, Testing hours (cell $D$22) values along top, output cell in corner | | | | | | | | |
| 4 | Number_to_produce_1 | 2000 | 2500 | 3000 | 3500 | 4000 | 4500 | 5000 | |
| 5 | 8000 | 600 | 250 | 160 | 160 | 160 | 160 | 160 | |
| 6 | 8500 | 600 | 500 | 260 | 260 | 260 | 260 | 260 | |
| 7 | 9000 | 600 | 600 | 360 | 360 | 360 | 360 | 360 | |
| 8 | 9500 | 600 | 600 | 460 | 460 | 460 | 460 | 460 | |
| 9 | 10000 | 600 | 600 | 560 | 560 | 560 | 560 | 560 | |
| 10 | 10500 | 600 | 600 | 600 | 600 | 600 | 600 | 600 | |
| 11 | 11000 | 600 | 600 | 600 | 600 | 600 | 600 | 600 | |
| 12 | 11500 | 600 | 600 | 600 | 600 | 600 | 600 | 600 | |
| 13 | 12000 | 600 | 600 | 600 | 600 | 600 | 600 | 600 | |
| 14 | | | | | | | | | |
| 15 | Number_to_produce_2 | 2000 | 2500 | 3000 | 3500 | 4000 | 4500 | 5000 | |
| 16 | 8000 | 700 | 1125 | 1200 | 1200 | 1200 | 1200 | 1200 | |
| 17 | 8500 | 700 | 1000 | 1200 | 1200 | 1200 | 1200 | 1200 | |
| 18 | 9000 | 700 | 950 | 1200 | 1200 | 1200 | 1200 | 1200 | |
| 19 | 9500 | 700 | 950 | 1200 | 1200 | 1200 | 1200 | 1200 | |
| 20 | 10000 | 700 | 950 | 1200 | 1200 | 1200 | 1200 | 1200 | |
| 21 | 10500 | 700 | 950 | 1200 | 1200 | 1200 | 1200 | 1200 | |
| 22 | 11000 | 700 | 950 | 1200 | 1200 | 1200 | 1200 | 1200 | |
| 23 | 11500 | 700 | 950 | 1200 | 1200 | 1200 | 1200 | 1200 | |
| 24 | 12000 | 700 | 950 | 1200 | 1200 | 1200 | 1200 | 1200 | |
| 25 | | | | | | | | | |
| 26 | Total_profit | 2000 | 2500 | 3000 | 3500 | 4000 | 4500 | 5000 | |
| 27 | 8000 | $138,300 | $165,125 | $167,600 | $167,600 | $167,600 | $167,600 | $167,600 | |
| 28 | 8500 | $138,300 | $169,000 | $175,600 | $175,600 | $175,600 | $175,600 | $175,600 | |
| 29 | 9000 | $138,300 | $170,550 | $183,600 | $183,600 | $183,600 | $183,600 | $183,600 | |
| 30 | 9500 | $138,300 | $170,550 | $191,600 | $191,600 | $191,600 | $191,600 | $191,600 | |
| 31 | 10000 | $138,300 | $170,550 | $199,600 | $199,600 | $199,600 | $199,600 | $199,600 | |
| 32 | 10500 | $138,300 | $170,550 | $202,800 | $202,800 | $202,800 | $202,800 | $202,800 | |
| 33 | 11000 | $138,300 | $170,550 | $202,800 | $202,800 | $202,800 | $202,800 | $202,800 | |
| 34 | 11500 | $138,300 | $170,550 | $202,800 | $202,800 | $202,800 | $202,800 | $202,800 | |
| 35 | 12000 | $138,300 | $170,550 | $202,800 | $202,800 | $202,800 | $202,800 | $202,800 | |

10%. The trick is to modify the model so that one percentage-change cell drives changes in both maximum sales. The modified model appears in Figure 3.14. Starting with the original model, enter the original values, 600 and 1200, in new cells, E18 and F18. (Do *not* copy the range B18:C18 to E18:F18. This would make the right side of the constraint

Figure 3.14

Modified Model for Simultaneous Changes

| | A | B | C | D | E | F | G | H |
|---|---|---|---|---|---|---|---|---|
| 1 | **Assembling and testing computers** | | | | | | | |
| 2 | | | | | | | | |
| 3 | Cost per labor hour assembling | $11 | | | | | | |
| 4 | Cost per labor hour testing | $15 | | | | | | |
| 5 | | | | | | | | |
| 6 | Inputs for assembling and testing a computer | | | | | | | |
| 7 | | Basic | XP | | | | | |
| 8 | Labor hours for assembly | 5 | 6 | | | | | |
| 9 | Labor hours for testing | 1 | 2 | | | | | |
| 10 | Cost of component parts | $150 | $225 | | | | | |
| 11 | Selling price | $300 | $450 | | | | | |
| 12 | Unit margin | $80 | $129 | | | | | |
| 13 | | | | | | | | |
| 14 | Assembling, testing plan (# of computers) | | | | | | | |
| 15 | | Basic | XP | | | | | |
| 16 | Number to produce | 560 | 1200 | | | | | |
| 17 | | <= | <= | | Original values | | % change in both | |
| 18 | Maximum sales | 600 | 1200 | | 600 | 1200 | 0% | |
| 19 | | | | | | | | |
| 20 | Constraints (hours per month) | Hours used | | Hours available | | | | |
| 21 | Labor availability for assembling | 10000 | <= | 10000 | | | | |
| 22 | Labor availability for testing | 2960 | <= | 3000 | | | | |
| 23 | | | | | | | | |
| 24 | Net profit ($ this month) | Basic | XP | Total | | | | |
| 25 | | $44,800 | $154,800 | $199,600 | | | | |

E18:F18, which is not the desired behavior.) Then enter any percentage change in cell G18. Finally, enter the *formula*

=E18*(1+$G$18)

in cell B18 and copy it to cell C18. Now a one-way SolverTable can be used with the percentage change in cell G18 to drive two different inputs simultaneously. Specifically, the SolverTable dialog box should be set up as in Figure 3.15, with the corresponding results in Figure 3.16.

You should always scan these sensitivity results to see if they make sense. For example, if the company can sell 20% or 30% more of both models, it makes no more profit than if it can sell only 10% more. The reason is labor availability. By this point, there isn't enough labor to produce the increased demand.

It is always possible to run a sensitivity analysis by changing inputs manually in the spreadsheet model and rerunning Solver. The advantages of SolverTable, however, are that it enables you to perform a *systematic* sensitivity analysis for any selected inputs and outputs, and it keeps track of the results in a table and associated chart(s). You will see other applications of this useful add-in later in this chapter and in the next few chapters.

### 3.4.3 Comparison of Solver's Sensitivity Report and SolverTable

Sensitivity analysis in optimization models is extremely important, so it is important that you understand the pros and cons of the two tools in this section. Here are some points to keep in mind.

## Figure 3.15

SolverTable One-Way Dialog Box

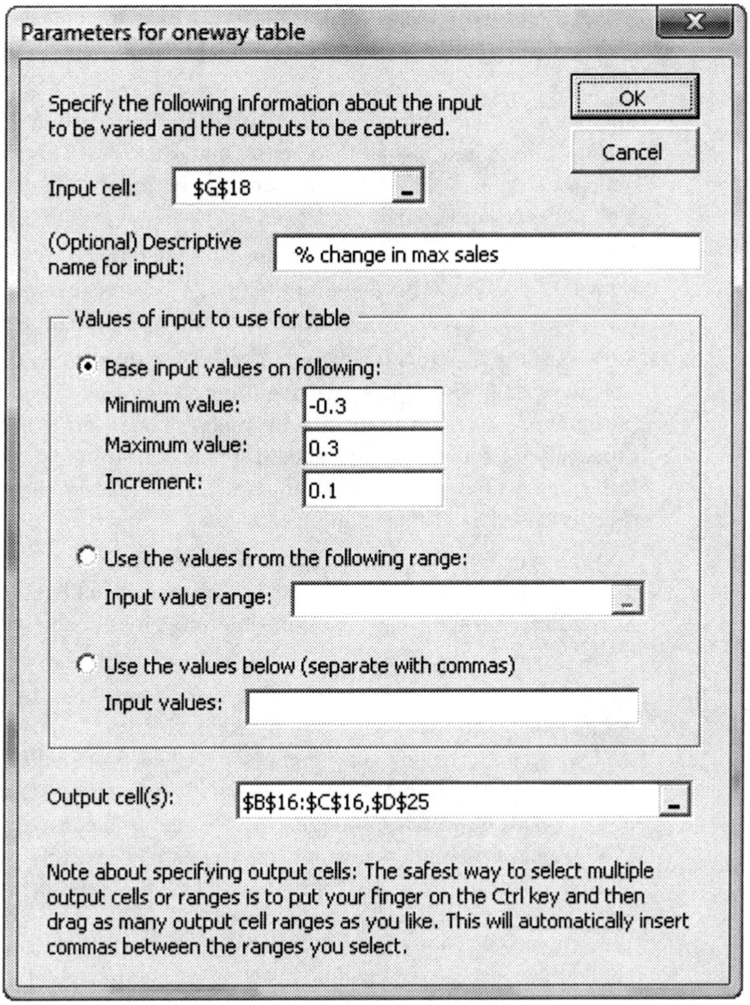

**Parameters for oneway table** ☒

Specify the following information about the input to be varied and the outputs to be captured.

Input cell: `$G$18` ▫

(Optional) Descriptive name for input: `% change in max sales`

**Values of input to use for table**

◉ Base input values on following:

| | |
|---|---|
| Minimum value: | `-0.3` |
| Maximum value: | `0.3` |
| Increment: | `0.1` |

○ Use the values from the following range:

Input value range: `                    ` ▫

○ Use the values below (separate with commas)

Input values: `                    `

Output cell(s): `$B$16:$C$16,$D$25` ▫

OK  Cancel

Note about specifying output cells: The safest way to select multiple output cells or ranges is to put your finger on the Ctrl key and then drag as many output cell ranges as you like. This will automatically insert commas between the ranges you select.

## Figure 3.16

Sensitivity to Percentage Change in Maximum Sales

| | A | B | C | D | E | F | G |
|---|---|---|---|---|---|---|---|
| 3 | % change in max sales (cell $G$18) values along side, output cell(s) along top | | | | | | |
| 4 | | Number_to_produce_1 | Number_to_produce_2 | Total_profit | $B$12 | | |
| 5 | -30% | 420 | 840 | $141,960 | $80 | | |
| 6 | -20% | 480 | 960 | $162,240 | $80 | | |
| 7 | -10% | 540 | 1080 | $182,520 | $80 | | |
| 8 | 0% | 560 | 1200 | $199,600 | $80 | | |
| 9 | 10% | 500 | 1250 | $201,250 | $80 | | |
| 10 | 20% | 500 | 1250 | $201,250 | $80 | | |
| 11 | 30% | 500 | 1250 | $201,250 | $80 | | |

- Solver's sensitivity report focuses only on the coefficients of the objective and the right sides of the constraints. SolverTable allows you to vary *any* of the inputs.

- Solver's sensitivity report provides very useful information through its reduced costs, shadow prices, and allowable increases and decreases. This same information can be obtained with SolverTable, but it requires a bit more work and some experimentation with the appropriate input ranges.

- Solver's sensitivity report is based on changing only one objective coefficient or one right side at a time. This one-at-a-time restriction prevents you from answering certain questions directly. SolverTable is much more flexible in this respect.

- Solver's sensitivity report is based on a well-established mathematical theory of sensitivity analysis in linear programming. If you lack this mathematical background—as many users do—the outputs can be difficult to understand, especially for somewhat nonstandard spreadsheet formulations. In contrast, SolverTable's outputs are straightforward. You can vary one or two inputs and see directly how the optimal solution changes.

- Solver's sensitivity report is not even available for integer-constrained models, and its interpretation for nonlinear models is more difficult than for linear models. SolverTable's outputs have the same interpretation for any type of optimization model.

- Solver's sensitivity report comes with Excel. SolverTable is a separate add-in that is not included with Excel—but it is included with this book and is freely available from the Free Downloads link at the authors' Web site, www.kelley.iu.edu/albrightbooks. Because the SolverTable software essentially automates Solver, which has a number of its own idiosyncrasies, some users have had problems with SolverTable on their PCs. We have tried to document these on our Web site, and we are hoping that the revised Solver in Excel 2010 helps to alleviate these problems.

In summary, each of these tools can be used to answer certain questions. We tend to favor SolverTable because of its flexibility, but in the optimization examples in this chapter and the next few chapters we will illustrate both tools to show how each can provide useful information.

## 3.5 PROPERTIES OF LINEAR MODELS

Linear programming is an important subset of a larger class of models called **mathematical programming models**.[11] All such models select the levels of various activities that can be performed, subject to a set of constraints, to maximize or minimize an objective such as total profit or total cost. In PC Tech's product mix example, the activities are the numbers of PCs to produce, and the purpose of the model is to find the levels of these activities that maximize the total net profit subject to specified constraints.

In terms of this general setup—selecting the optimal levels of activities—there are three important properties that LP models possess that distinguish them from general mathematical programming models: *proportionality*, *additivity*, and *divisibility*. We discuss these properties briefly in this section.

---

[11]The word *programming* in linear programming or mathematical programming has nothing to do with computer programming. It originated with the British term *programme*, which is essentially a plan or a schedule of operations.

### 3.5.1 Proportionality

**Proportionality** means that if the level of any activity is multiplied by a constant factor, the contribution of this activity to the objective, or to any of the constraints in which the activity is involved, is multiplied by the same factor. For example, suppose that the production of Basics is cut from its optimal value of 560 to 280—that is, it is multiplied by 0.5. Then the amounts of labor hours from assembling and from testing Basics are both cut in half, and the net profit contributed by Basics is also cut in half.

Proportionality is a perfectly valid assumption in the product mix model, but it is often violated in certain types of models. For example, in various *blending* models used by petroleum companies, chemical outputs vary in a nonlinear manner as chemical inputs are varied. If a chemical input is doubled, say, the resulting chemical output is not necessarily doubled. This type of behavior violates the proportionality property, and it takes us into the realm of *nonlinear* optimization, which we discuss in Chapters 7 and 8.

### 3.5.2 Additivity

The **additivity** property implies that the sum of the contributions from the various activities to a particular constraint equals the total contribution to that constraint. For example, if the two PC models use, respectively, 560 and 2400 testing hours (as in Figure 3.7), then the total number used in the plan is the *sum* of these amounts, 2960 hours. Similarly, the additivity property applies to the objective. That is, the value of the objective is the *sum* of the contributions from the various activities. In the product mix model, the net profits from the two PC models add up to the total net profit. The additivity property implies that the contribution of any decision variable to the objective or to any constraint is *independent* of the levels of the other decision variables.

### 3.5.3 Divisibility

The **divisibility** property simply means that both integer and noninteger levels of the activities are allowed. In the product mix model, we got integer values in the optimal solution, 560 and 1200, just by luck. For slightly different inputs, they could easily have been fractional values. In general, if you want the levels of some activities to be integer values, there are two possible approaches: (1) You can solve the LP model without integer constraints, and if the solution turns out to have fractional values, you can attempt to round them to integer values; or (2) you can explicitly constrain certain changing cells to contain integer values. The latter approach, however, takes you into the realm of *integer programming*, which we study in Chapter 6. At this point, we simply state that integer problems are *much* more difficult to solve than problems without integer constraints.

### 3.5.4 Discussion of Linear Properties

The previous discussion of these three properties, especially proportionality and additivity, is fairly abstract. How can you recognize whether a model satisfies proportionality and additivity? This is easy if the model is described algebraically. In this case the objective must be of the form

$$a_1 x_1 + a_2 x_2 + \cdots + a_n x_n$$

where $n$ is the number of decision variables, the $a$s are constants, and the $x$s are decision variables. This expression is called a *linear combination* of the $x$s. Also, each constraint must be equivalent to a form where the left side is a linear combination of the $x$s and the right side is a constant. For example, the following is a typical linear constraint:

$$3x_1 + 7x_2 - 2x_3 \leq 50$$

It is not quite so easy to recognize proportionality and additivity—or the lack of them—in a spreadsheet model, because the logic of the model is typically embedded in a series of cell formulas. However, the ideas are the same. First, the objective cell must ultimately (possibly through a series of formulas in intervening cells) be a sum of products of constants and changing cells, where a "constant" means that it does not depend on changing cells. Second, each side of each constraint must ultimately be either a constant or a sum of products of constants and changing cells. This explains why linear models contain so many SUM and SUMPRODUCT functions.

It is usually easier to recognize when a model is *not* linear. Two particular situations that lead to nonlinear models are when (1) there are products or quotients of expressions involving changing cells or (2) there are nonlinear functions, such as squares, square roots, or logarithms, that involve changing cells. These are typically easy to spot, and they guarantee that the model is nonlinear.

*Real-life problems are almost never exactly linear. However, linear approximations often yield very useful results.*

Whenever you model a real problem, you usually make some simplifying assumptions. This is certainly the case with LP models. The world is frequently *not* linear, which means that an entirely realistic model typically violates some or all of the three properties in this section. However, numerous successful applications of LP have demonstrated the usefulness of linear models, even if they are only *approximations* of reality. If you suspect that the violations are serious enough to invalidate a linear model, you should use an integer or nonlinear model, as we illustrate in Chapters 6–8.

In terms of Excel's Solver, if the model is linear—that is, if it satisfies the proportionality, additivity, and divisibility properties—you should check the Simplex option (or the Assume Linear Model option in pre-2010 versions of Excel). Then Solver uses the simplex method, a very efficient method for a linear model, to solve the problem. Actually, you can check the Simplex option even if the divisibility property is violated—that is, for linear models with integer-constrained variables—but Solver then embeds the simplex method in a more complex algorithm (branch and bound) in its solution procedure.

### 3.5.5 Linear Models and Scaling[12]

In some cases you might be sure that a model is linear, but when you check the Simplex option (or the Assume Linear Model option) and then solve, you get a Solver message to the effect that the conditions for linearity are not satisfied. This can indicate a logical error in your formulation, so that the proportionality and additivity conditions are indeed not satisfied. However, it can also indicate that Solver erroneously *thinks* the linearity conditions are not satisfied, which is typically due to roundoff error in its calculations—not any error on your part. If the latter occurs and you are convinced that the model is correct, you can try *not* using the simplex method to see whether that works. If it does not, you should consult your instructor. It is possible that the non-simplex algorithm employed by Solver simply cannot find the solution to your problem.

In any case, it always helps to have a *well-scaled* model. In a well-scaled model, all of the numbers are roughly the same magnitude. If the model contains some very large numbers—100,000 or more, say—and some very small numbers—0.001 or less, say—it is *poorly scaled* for the methods used by Solver, and roundoff error is far more likely to be an issue, not only in Solver's test for linearity conditions but in all of its algorithms.

---

[12]This section might seem overly technical. However, when you develop a model that you are sure is linear and Solver then tells you it doesn't satisfy the linear conditions, you will appreciate this section.

*You can decrease the chance of getting an incorrect "Conditions for Assume Linear Model are not satisfied" message by changing Solver's Precision setting.*

If you believe your model is poorly scaled, there are three possible remedies. The first is to check the Use Automatic Scaling option in Solver. (It is found by clicking on the Options button in the main Solver dialog box.) This might help and it might not; we have had mixed success. (Frontline Systems, the company that develops Solver, has told us that the only drawback to checking this box is that the solution procedure can be slower.) The second option is to redefine the units in which the various quantities are defined. Finally, you can change the Precision setting in Solver's Options dialog box to a larger number, such 0.00001 or 0.0001. (The default has five zeros.)

**Excel Tip:** *Rescaling a Model*
*Suppose you have a whole range of input values expressed, say, in dollars, and you would like to reexpress them in thousands of dollars, that is, you would like to divide each value by 1000. There is a simple copy/paste way to do this. Enter the value 1000 in some unused cell and copy it. Then highlight the range you want to rescale, and from the Paste drop-down menu, select Paste Special and then the Divide option. No formulas are required; your original values are automatically rescaled (and you can then delete the 1000 cell). You can use this same method to add, subtract, or multiply by a constant.*

## 3.6 INFEASIBILITY AND UNBOUNDEDNESS

In this section we discuss two of the things that can go wrong when you invoke Solver. Both of these might indicate that there is a mistake in the model. Therefore, because mistakes are common in LP models, you should be aware of the error messages you might encounter.

### 3.6.1 Infeasibility

The first problem is **infeasibility**. Recall that a solution is *feasible* if it satisfies all of the constraints. Among all of the feasible solutions, you are looking for the one that optimizes the objective. However, it is possible that there are no feasible solutions to the model. There are generally two reasons for this: (1) there is a mistake in the model (an input was entered incorrectly, such as a ≤ symbol instead of a ≥) or (2) the problem has been so constrained that there are no solutions left. In the former case, a careful check of the model should find the error. In the latter case, you might need to change, or even eliminate, some of the constraints.

*A perfectly reasonable model can have no feasible solutions because of too many constraints.*

To show how an infeasible problem could occur, suppose in PC Tech's product mix problem you change the maximum sales constraints to *minimum* sales constraints (and leave everything else unchanged). That is, you change these constraints from ≤ to ≥. If Solver is then used, the message in Figure 3.17 appears, indicating that Solver cannot find a feasible solution. The reason is clear: There is no way, given the constraints on labor hours, that the company can produce these minimum sales values. The company's only choice is to set at least one of the minimum sales values lower. In general, there is no foolproof way to remedy the problem when a "no feasible solution" message appears. Careful checking and rethinking are required.

### 3.6.2 Unboundedness

A second type of problem is **unboundedness**. In this case, the model has been formulated in such a way that the objective is unbounded—that is, it can be made as large (or as small, for minimization problems) as you like. If this occurs, you have probably entered a wrong input or forgotten some constraints. To see how this could occur in the product mix problem,

**Figure 3.17**

**No Feasible Solution Message**

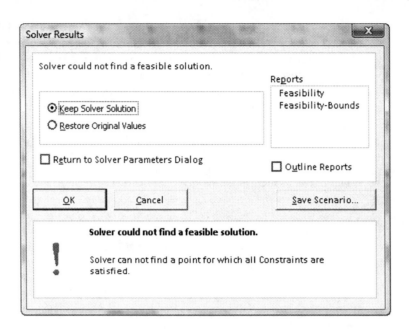

**Figure 3.18**

**Unbounded Solution Message**

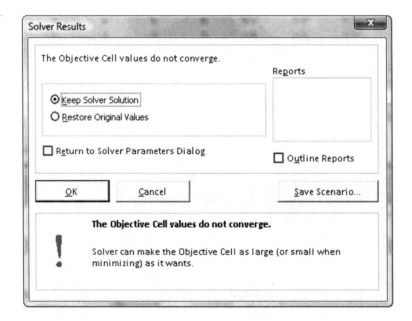

suppose that you change *all* constraints to be ≤ instead of ≥. Now there is no upper bound on how much labor is available or how many PCs the company can sell. If you make this change in the model and then use Solver, the message in Figure 3.18 appears, stating that the objective cell does not converge. In other words, the total net profit can grow without bound.

### 3.6.3 Comparison of Infeasibility and Unboundedness

*Except in very rare situations, if Solver informs you that your model is unbounded, you have made an error.*

Infeasibility and unboundedness are quite different in a practical sense. It is quite possible for a reasonable model to have no feasible solutions. For example, the marketing department might impose several constraints, the production department might add some more, the engineering department might add even more, and so on. Together, they might constrain the problem so much that there are no feasible solutions left. The only way out is to change or eliminate some of the constraints. An unboundedness problem is quite different. There is no way a realistic model can have an unbounded solution. If you get the message shown in Figure 3.18, then you must have made a mistake: You entered an input incorrectly, you omitted one or more constraints, or there is a logical error in your model.

## PROBLEMS

*Solutions for problems whose numbers appear within a colored box can be found in the Student Solutions Files. Refer to this book's preface for purchase information.*

### Skill-Building Problems

**1.** Other sensitivity analyses besides those discussed could be performed on the product mix model. Use SolverTable to perform each of the following. In each case keep track of the values in the changing cells and the objective cell, and discuss your findings.
   a. Let the selling price for Basics vary from $220 to $350 in increments of $10.
   b. Let the labor cost per hour for assembling vary from $5 to $20 in increments of $1.
   c. Let the labor hours for testing a Basic vary from 0.5 to 3.0 in increments of 0.5.
   d. Let the labor hours for assembling and testing an XP vary independently, the first from 4.5 to 8.0 and the second from 1.5 to 3.0, both in increments of 0.5.

**2.** In PC Tech's product mix problem, assume there is another PC model, the VXP, that the company can produce in addition to Basics and XPs. Each VXP requires eight hours for assembling, three hours for testing, $275 for component parts, and sells for $560. At most 50 VXPs can be sold.
   a. Modify the spreadsheet model to include this new product, and use Solver to find the optimal product mix.
   b. You should find that the optimal solution is *not* integer-valued. If you round the values in the changing cells to the nearest integers, is the resulting solution still feasible? If not, how might you obtain a feasible solution that is at least close to optimal?

**3.** Continuing the previous problem, perform a sensitivity analysis on the selling price of VXPs. Let this price vary from $500 to $650 in increments of $10, and keep track of the values in the changing cells and the objective cell. Discuss your findings.

**4.** Again continuing Problem 2, suppose that you want to force the optimal solution to be integers. Do this in Solver by adding a new constraint. Select the changing cells for the left side of the constraint, and in the middle dropdown list, select the "int" option. How does the optimal integer solution compare to the optimal noninteger solution in Problem 2? Are the changing cell values rounded versions of those in

Problem 2? Is the objective value more or less than in Problem 2?

**5.** If all of the inputs in PC Tech's product mix problem are nonnegative (as they should be for any realistic version of the problem), are there any input values such that the resulting model has no feasible solutions? (Refer to the graphical solution.)

**6.** There are five corner points in the feasible region for the product mix problem. We identified the coordinates of one of them: (560, 1200). Identify the coordinates of the others.
   a. Only one of these other corner points has positive values for both changing cells. Discuss the changes in the selling prices of either or both models that would be necessary to make this corner point optimal.
   b. Two of the other corner points have one changing cell value positive and the other zero. Discuss the changes in the selling prices of either or both models that would be necessary to make either of these corner points optimal.

### Skill-Extending Problems

**7.** Using the graphical solution of the product mix model as a guide, suppose there are only 2800 testing hours available. How do the answers to the previous problem change? (Is the previous solution still optimal? Is it still feasible?)

**8.** Again continuing Problem 2, perform a sensitivity analysis where the selling prices of Basics and XPs simultaneously change by the same percentage, but the selling price of VXPs remains at its original value. Let the percentage change vary from −25% to 50% in increments of 5%, and keep track of the values in the changing cells and the total profit. Discuss your findings.

**9.** Consider the graphical solution to the product mix problem. Now imagine that another constraint—*any* constraint—is added. Which of the following three things are possible: (1) the feasible region shrinks; (2) the feasible region stays the same; (3) the feasible region expands? Which of the following three things are possible: (1) the optimal value in objective cell decreases; (2) the optimal value in objective cell stays the same; (3) the optimal value in objective cell increases? Explain your answers. Do they hold just for this particular model, or do they hold in general?

## 3.7 A LARGER PRODUCT MIX MODEL

The problem we examine in this section is a direct extension of the product mix model in the previous section. There are two modifications. First, the company makes eight computer models, not just two. Second, testing can be done on either of two lines, and these two lines have different characteristics.

---

**EXAMPLE** | **3.2 PRODUCING COMPUTERS AT PC TECH**

As in the previous example, PC Tech must decide how many of each of its computer models to assemble and test, but there are now eight available models, not just two. Each computer must be assembled and then tested, but there are now two lines for testing. The first line tends to test faster, but its labor costs are slightly higher, and each line has a certain number of hours available for testing. Any computer can be tested on either line. The inputs for the model are same as before: (1) the hourly labor costs for assembling and testing, (2) the required labor hours for assembling and testing any computer model, (3) the cost of component parts for each model, (4) the selling prices for each model, (5) the maximum sales for each model, and (6) labor availabilities. These input values are listed in the file Product Mix 2.xlsx. As before, the company wants to determine the product mix that maximizes its total net profit.

**Objective** To use LP to find the mix of computer models that maximizes total net profit and stays within the labor hour availability and maximum sales constraints.

### WHERE DO THE NUMBERS COME FROM?

The same comments as in Example 3.1 apply here.

### Solution

Table 3.2 lists the variables and constraints for this model. You must choose the number of computers of each model to produce on each line, the sum of which cannot be larger than the maximum that can be sold. This choice determines the labor hours of each type used and all revenues and costs. No more labor hours can be used than are available.

---

Table 3.2  Variables and Constraints for Larger Product Mix Model

| | |
|---|---|
| **Input variables** | Hourly labor costs, labor availabilities, labor required for each computer, costs of component parts, unit selling prices, and maximum sales |
| **Decision variables (changing cells)** | Numbers of computer of each model to test on each line |
| **Objective cell** | Total net profit |
| **Other calculated variables** | Number of each computer model produced, hours of labor used for assembling and for each line of testing |
| **Constraints** | Computers produced ≤ Maximum sales |
| | Labor hours used ≤ Labor hours available |

---

It is probably not immediately obvious what the changing cells should be for this model (at least not before you look at Table 3.2). You might think that the company simply needs to decide how many computers of each model to produce. However, because of the two testing lines, this is not enough information. The company must also decide how many of each model to test *on each line*. For example, suppose they decide to test 100 model 4s on line 1 and 300 model 4s on line 2. This means they will need to assemble (and ultimately sell) 400 model 4s. In other words, given the detailed plan of how many to test on each line, everything else is determined. But without the detailed plan, there is not enough information to complete the model. This is the type of reasoning you must go through to determine the appropriate changing cells for any LP model.

### An Algebraic Model

We will not spell out the algebraic model for this expanded version of the product mix model because it is so similar to the two-variable product mix model. However, we will say that it is larger, and hence probably more intimidating. Now we need decision variables of the form $x_{ij}$, the number of model $j$ computers to test on line $i$, and the total net profit and each labor availability constraint will include a long SUMPRODUCT formula involving these variables. Instead of focusing on these algebraic expressions, we turn directly to the spreadsheet model.

### DEVELOPING THE SPREADSHEET MODEL

The spreadsheet in Figure 3.19 illustrates the solution procedure for PC Tech's product mix problem. (See the file Product Mix 2.xlsx.) The first stage is to develop the spreadsheet model step by step.

**1 Inputs.** Enter the various inputs in the blue ranges. Again, remember that our convention is to color all input cells blue. Enter only *numbers*, not formulas, in input cells. They should always be numbers directly from the problem statement. (In this case, we supplied them in the spreadsheet template.)

**2 Range names.** Name the ranges indicated. According to our convention, there are enough named ranges so that the Solver dialog box contains only range names, no cell addresses. Of course, you can name additional ranges if you like. (Note that you can again use the range-naming shortcut explained in the Excel tip for the previous example. That is, you can take advantage of labels in adjacent cells, except for the Profit cell.)

**3 Unit margins.** Note that two rows of these are required, one for each testing line, because the costs of testing on the two lines are not equal. To calculate them, enter the formula

=B$13-$B$3*B$9-$B$4*B10-B$12

in cell B14 and copy it to the range B14:I15.

**4 Changing cells.** As discussed above, the changing cells are the red cells in rows 19 and 20. You do *not* have to enter the values shown in Figure 3.19. You can use any trial values initially; Solver will eventually find the *optimal* values. Note that the four values shown in Figure 3.19 cannot be optimal because they do not satisfy all of the constraints. Specifically, this plan uses more labor hours for assembling than are available. However, you do not need to worry about satisfying constraints at this point; Solver will take care of this later.

**5 Labor used.** Enter the formula

=SUMPRODUCT(B9:E9,Total_computers_produced)

in cell B26 to calculate the number of assembling hours used. Similarly, enter the formulas

=SUMPRODUCT(B10:I10,Number_tested_on_line_1)

Figure 3.19   Larger Product Mix Model with Infeasible Solution

| | A | B | C | D | E | F | G | H | I | J |
|---|---|---|---|---|---|---|---|---|---|---|
| 1 | **Assembling and testing computers** | | | | | | | | | |
| 2 | | | | | | | | | | |
| 3 | Cost per labor hour assembling | $11 | | | | | | | | |
| 4 | Cost per labor hour testing, line 1 | $19 | | | | | | | | |
| 5 | Cost per labor hour testing, line 2 | $17 | | | | | | | | |
| 6 | | | | | | | | | | |
| 7 | Inputs for assembling and testing a computer | | | | | | | | | |
| 8 | | Model 1 | Model 2 | Model 3 | Model 4 | Model 5 | Model 6 | Model 7 | Model 8 | |
| 9 | Labor hours for assembly | 4 | 5 | 5 | 5 | 5.5 | 5.5 | 5.5 | 6 | |
| 10 | Labor hours for testing, line 1 | 1.5 | 2 | 2 | 2 | 2.5 | 2.5 | 2.5 | 3 | |
| 11 | Labor hours for testing, line 2 | 2 | 2.5 | 2.5 | 2.5 | 3 | 3 | 3.5 | 3.5 | |
| 12 | Cost of component parts | $150 | $225 | $225 | $225 | $250 | $250 | $250 | $300 | |
| 13 | Selling price | $350 | $450 | $460 | $470 | $500 | $525 | $530 | $600 | |
| 14 | Unit margin, tested on line 1 | $128 | $132 | $142 | $152 | $142 | $167 | $172 | $177 | |
| 15 | Unit margin, tested on line 2 | $122 | $128 | $138 | $148 | $139 | $164 | $160 | $175 | |
| 16 | | | | | | | | | | |
| 17 | Assembling, testing plan (# of computers) | | | | | | | | | |
| 18 | | Model 1 | Model 2 | Model 3 | Model 4 | Model 5 | Model 6 | Model 7 | Model 8 | |
| 19 | Number tested on line 1 | 0 | 0 | 0 | 0 | 0 | 500 | 1000 | 800 | |
| 20 | Number tested on line 2 | 0 | 0 | 0 | 1250 | 0 | 0 | 0 | 0 | |
| 21 | Total computers produced | 0 | 0 | 0 | 1250 | 0 | 500 | 1000 | 800 | |
| 22 | | <= | <= | <= | <= | <= | <= | <= | <= | |
| 23 | Maximum sales | 1500 | 1250 | 1250 | 1250 | 1000 | 1000 | 1000 | 800 | |
| 24 | | | | | | | | | | |
| 25 | Constraints (hours per month) | Hours used | | Hours available | | | | | | |
| 26 | Labor availability for assembling | 19300 | <= | 20000 | | | | | | |
| 27 | Labor availability for testing, line 1 | 6150 | <= | 5000 | | | | | | |
| 28 | Labor availability for testing, line 2 | 3125 | <= | 6000 | | | | | | |
| 29 | | | | | | | | | | |
| 30 | Net profit ($ per month) | Model 1 | Model 2 | Model 3 | Model 4 | Model 5 | Model 6 | Model 7 | Model 8 | Totals |
| 31 | Tested on line 1 | $0 | $0 | $0 | $0 | $0 | $83,500 | $172,000 | $141,600 | $397,100 |
| 32 | Tested on line 2 | $0 | $0 | $0 | $184,375 | $0 | $0 | $0 | $0 | $184,375 |
| 33 | | | | | | | | | | $581,475 |
| 34 | | | | | | | | | | |
| 35 | **Range names used:** | | | | | | | | | |
| 36 | Hours_available | =Model!$D$26:$D$28 | | | | | | | | |
| 37 | Hours_used | =Model!$B$26:$B$28 | | | | | | | | |
| 38 | Maximum_sales | =Model!$B$23:$I$23 | | | | | | | | |
| 39 | Number_tested_on_line_1 | =Model!$B$19:$I$19 | | | | | | | | |
| 40 | Number_tested_on_line_2 | =Model!$B$20:$I$20 | | | | | | | | |
| 41 | Total_computers_produce d | =Model!$B$21:$I$21 | | | | | | | | |
| 42 | Total_profit | =Model!$J$33 | | | | | | | | |

and

=SUMPRODUCT(B11:I11,Number_tested_on_line_2)

in cells B27 and B28 for the labor hours used on each testing line.

**Excel Tip:** *Copying formulas with range names*
*When you enter a range name in an Excel formula and then copy the formula, the range name reference acts like an absolute reference. Therefore, it wouldn't work to copy the formula in cell B27 to cell B28. However, this would work if range names hadn't been used. This is one potential disadvantage of range names that you should be aware of.*

⑥ **Revenues, costs, and profits.** The area from row 30 down shows the summary of monetary values. Actually, only the total profit in cell J33 is needed, but it is also useful to calculate the net profit from each computer model on each testing line. To obtain these, enter the formula

=B14*B19

in cell B31 and copy it to the range B31:I32. Then sum these to obtain the totals in column J. The total in cell J33 is the objective to maximize.

### Experimenting with Other Solutions

Before going any further, you might want to experiment with other values in the changing cells. However, it is a real challenge to guess the optimal solution. It is tempting to fill up the changing cells corresponding to the largest unit margins. However, this totally ignores their use of the scarce labor hours. If you can guess the optimal solution to this model, you are better than we are!

### USING SOLVER

The Solver dialog box should be filled out as shown in Figure 3.20. (Again, note that there are enough named ranges so that only range names appear in this dialog box.) Except that this model has two rows of changing cells, the Solver setup is identical to the one in Example 3.1.

**Figure 3.20**

**Solver Dialog Box**

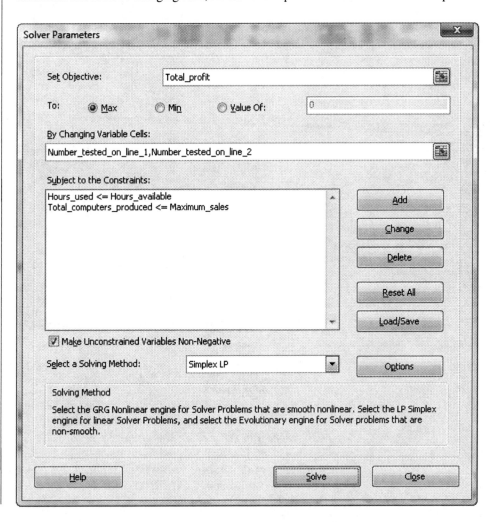

You typically gain
insights into a solution
by checking which
constraints are binding
and which contain
slack.

## Discussion of the Solution

When you click on Solve, you obtain the optimal solution shown in Figure 3.21. The optimal plan is to produce computer models 1, 4, 6, and 7 only, some on testing line 1 and others on testing line 2. This plan uses all of the available labor hours for assembling and testing on line 1, but about 1800 of the testing line 2 hours are not used. Also, maximum sales are achieved only for computer models 1, 6, and 7. This is typical of an LP solution. Some of the constraints are met exactly—they are binding—whereas others contain a certain amount of slack. The binding constraints prevent PC Tech from earning an even higher profit.

Figure 3.21    Optimal Solution to Larger Product Mix Model

| | A | B | C | D | E | F | G | H | I | J |
|---|---|---|---|---|---|---|---|---|---|---|
| 1 | Assembling and testing computers | | | | | | | | | |
| 2 | | | | | | | | | | |
| 3 | Cost per labor hour assembling | $11 | | | | | | | | |
| 4 | Cost per labor hour testing, line 1 | $19 | | | | | | | | |
| 5 | Cost per labor hour testing, line 2 | $17 | | | | | | | | |
| 6 | | | | | | | | | | |
| 7 | Inputs for assembling and testing a computer | | | | | | | | | |
| 8 | | Model 1 | Model 2 | Model 3 | Model 4 | Model 5 | Model 6 | Model 7 | Model 8 | |
| 9 | Labor hours for assembly | 4 | 5 | 5 | 5 | 5.5 | 5.5 | 5.5 | 6 | |
| 10 | Labor hours for testing, line 1 | 1.5 | 2 | 2 | 2 | 2.5 | 2.5 | 2.5 | 3 | |
| 11 | Labor hours for testing, line 2 | 2 | 2.5 | 2.5 | 2.5 | 3 | 3 | 3.5 | 3.5 | |
| 12 | Cost of component parts | $150 | $225 | $225 | $225 | $250 | $250 | $250 | $300 | |
| 13 | Selling price | $350 | $450 | $460 | $470 | $500 | $525 | $530 | $600 | |
| 14 | Unit margin, tested on line 1 | $128 | $132 | $142 | $152 | $142 | $167 | $172 | $177 | |
| 15 | Unit margin, tested on line 2 | $122 | $128 | $138 | $148 | $139 | $164 | $160 | $175 | |
| 16 | | | | | | | | | | |
| 17 | Assembling, testing plan (# of computers) | | | | | | | | | |
| 18 | | Model 1 | Model 2 | Model 3 | Model 4 | Model 5 | Model 6 | Model 7 | Model 8 | |
| 19 | Number tested on line 1 | 1500 | 0 | 0 | 125 | 0 | 0 | 1000 | 0 | |
| 20 | Number tested on line 2 | 0 | 0 | 0 | 475 | 0 | 1000 | 0 | 0 | |
| 21 | Total computers produced | 1500 | 0 | 0 | 600 | 0 | 1000 | 1000 | 0 | |
| 22 | | <= | <= | <= | <= | <= | <= | <= | <= | |
| 23 | Maximum sales | 1500 | 1250 | 1250 | 1250 | 1000 | 1000 | 1000 | 800 | |
| 24 | | | | | | | | | | |
| 25 | Constraints (hours per month) | Hours used | | Hours available | | | | | | |
| 26 | Labor availability for assembling | 20000 | <= | 20000 | | | | | | |
| 27 | Labor availability for testing, line 1 | 5000 | <= | 5000 | | | | | | |
| 28 | Labor availability for testing, line 2 | 4187.5 | <= | 6000 | | | | | | |
| 29 | | | | | | | | | | |
| 30 | Net profit ($ per month) | Model 1 | Model 2 | Model 3 | Model 4 | Model 5 | Model 6 | Model 7 | Model 8 | Totals |
| 31 | Tested on line 1 | $191,250 | $0 | $0 | $19,000 | $0 | $0 | $172,000 | $0 | $382,250 |
| 32 | Tested on line 2 | $0 | $0 | $0 | $70,063 | $0 | $163,500 | $0 | $0 | $233,563 |
| 33 | | | | | | | | | | $615,813 |

**Excel Tip:** *Roundoff Error*
*Because of the way numbers are stored and calculated on a computer, the optimal values in the changing cells and elsewhere can contain small roundoff errors. For example, the value that really appears in cell E20 on one of our Excel 2007 PCs is 475.000002015897, not exactly 475. For all practical purposes, this number can be treated as 475, and we have formatted it as such in the spreadsheet. (We have been told that roundoff in Solver results should be less of a problem in Excel 2010.)*

## Sensitivity Analysis

If you want to experiment with different inputs to this problem, you can simply change the inputs and then rerun Solver. The second time you use Solver, you do not have to specify the objective and changing cells or the constraints. Excel remembers all of these settings and saves them when you save the file.

You can also use SolverTable to perform a more systematic sensitivity analysis on one or more input variables. One possibility appears in Figure 3.22, where the number of available assembling labor hours is allowed to vary from 18,000 to 25,000 in increments of 1000, and the numbers of computers produced and profit are designated as outputs.

**Figure 3.22   Sensitivity to Assembling Labor Hours**

| | A | B | C | D | E | F | G | H | I | J |
|---|---|---|---|---|---|---|---|---|---|---|
| 3 | Assembling labor (cell $D$26) values along side, output cell(s) along top | | | | | | | | | |
| 4 | | Total_computers_produced_1 | Total_computers_produced_2 | Total_computers_produced_3 | Total_computers_produced_4 | Total_computers_produced_5 | Total_computers_produced_6 | Total_computers_produced_7 | Total_computers_produced_8 | Total_profit |
| 5 | 18000 | 1500 | 0 | 0 | 200 | 0 | 1000 | 1000 | 0 | $556,813 |
| 6 | 19000 | 1500 | 0 | 0 | 400 | 0 | 1000 | 1000 | 0 | $586,313 |
| 7 | 20000 | 1500 | 0 | 0 | 600 | 0 | 1000 | 1000 | 0 | $615,813 |
| 8 | 21000 | 1500 | 0 | 0 | 800 | 0 | 1000 | 1000 | 0 | $645,313 |
| 9 | 22000 | 1500 | 0 | 0 | 1000 | 0 | 1000 | 1000 | 0 | $674,813 |
| 10 | 23000 | 1500 | 0 | 0 | 1200 | 0 | 1000 | 1000 | 0 | $704,313 |
| 11 | 24000 | 1500 | 0 | 700 | 1250 | 0 | 1000 | 500 | 0 | $724,750 |
| 12 | 25000 | 1500 | 0 | 1250 | 1250 | 0 | 1000 | 60 | 0 | $727,170 |
| 13 | | | | | | | | | | |

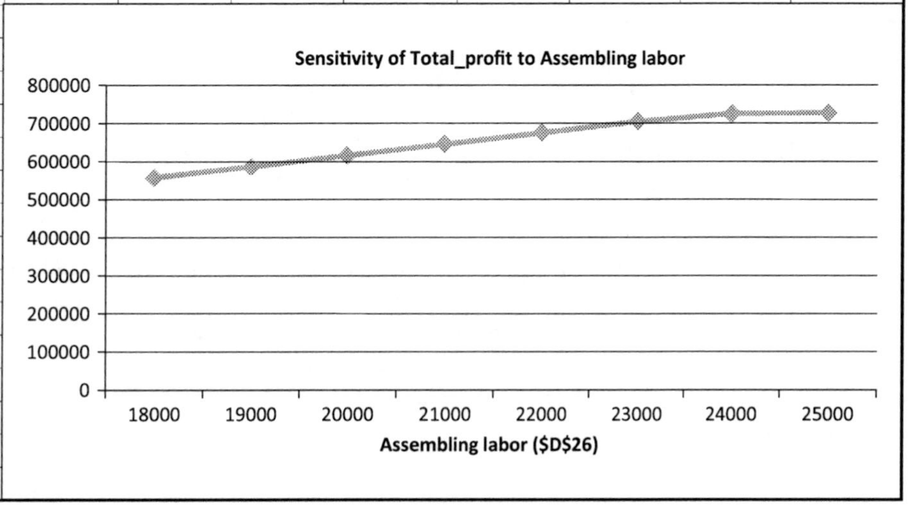

Sensitivity of Total_profit to Assembling labor

There are several ways to interpret the output from this sensitivity analysis. First, you can look at columns B through I to see how the product mix changes as more assembling labor hours become available. For assembling labor hours from 18,000 to 23,000, the only thing that changes is that more model 4s are produced. Beyond 23,000, however, the company starts to produce model 3s and produces fewer model 7s. Second, you can see how extra labor hours add to the total profit. Note exactly what this increased profit means. For example, when labor hours increase from 20,000 to 21,000, the model requires that the company must *pay* $11 apiece for these extra hours (if it uses them). But the *net* effect is that profit increases by $29,500, or $29.50 per extra hour. In other words, the labor cost increases by $11,000 [=$11(1000)], but this is more than offset by the increase in revenue that comes from having the extra labor hours.

As column J illustrates, it is worthwhile for the company to obtain extra assembling labor hours, even though it has to to pay for them, because its profit increases. However, the increase in profit per extra labor hour—the *shadow price* of assembling labor hours—is not constant. In the top part of the table, it is $29.50 (per extra hour), but it then decreases to $20.44 and then $2.42. The accompanying SolverTable chart of column J illustrates this decreasing shadow price through its decreasing slope.

SolverTable Technical Tip: *Charts and Roundoff*
*As SolverTable makes all of its Solver runs, it reports and then charts the values found by Solver. These can include small roundoff errors and slightly misleading charts. For example, the chart in Figure 3.23 shows one possibility, where we varied the cost of testing on line 2 and charted the assembling hours used. Throughout the range, this output value was 20,000, but because of slight roundoff (19999.9999999292 and 20000.0000003259) in two of the cells, the chart doesn't appear to be flat. If you see this behavior, you can change it manually.*

Figure 3.23

A Misleading
SolverTable Chart

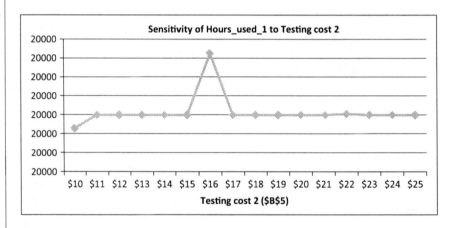

Finally, you can gain additional insight from Solver's sensitivity report, shown in Figure 3.24. However, you have to be very careful in interpreting this report. Unlike Example 3.1, there are no upper bound (maximum sales) constraints on the *changing cells*. The maximum sales constraints are on the total computers produced (row 21 of the model), not the changing cells. Therefore, the only nonzero reduced costs in the top part of the table are for changing cells currently at zero (not those at their upper bounds as in the previous example). Each nonzero reduced cost indicates how much the profit margin for this activity would have to change before this activity would be profitable.

Also, there is a row in the bottom part of the table for each constraint, *including* the maximum sales constraints. The interesting values are again the shadow prices. The first two indicate the amount the company would pay for an extra assembling or line 1 testing labor hour. (Does the 29.5 value look familiar? Compare it to the SolverTable results above.) The shadow prices for all *binding* maximum sales constraints indicate how much more profit the company could make if it could increase its demand by one computer of that model.

**Figure 3.24** Solver's Sensitivity Report

| | B | C | D | E | F | G | H |
|---|---|---|---|---|---|---|---|
| 6 | Variable Cells | | | | | | |
| 7 | | | Final | Reduced | Objective | Allowable | Allowable |
| 8 | Cell | Name | Value | Cost | Coefficient | Increase | Decrease |
| 9 | $B$19 | Number tested on line 1 Model 1 | 1500 | 0 | 127.5 | 1E+30 | 2.125 |
| 10 | $C$19 | Number tested on line 1 Model 2 | 0 | -20 | 132 | 20 | 1E+30 |
| 11 | $D$19 | Number tested on line 1 Model 3 | 0 | -10 | 142 | 10 | 1E+30 |
| 12 | $E$19 | Number tested on line 1 Model 4 | 125 | 0 | 152 | 2.833 | 1.7 |
| 13 | $F$19 | Number tested on line 1 Model 5 | 0 | -25.875 | 142 | 25.875 | 1E+30 |
| 14 | $G$19 | Number tested on line 1 Model 6 | 0 | -2.125 | 167 | 2.125 | 1E+30 |
| 15 | $H$19 | Number tested on line 1 Model 7 | 1000 | 0 | 172 | 1E+30 | 4.125 |
| 16 | $I$19 | Number tested on line 1 Model 8 | 0 | -6.75 | 177 | 6.75 | 1E+30 |
| 17 | $B$20 | Number tested on line 2 Model 1 | 0 | -2.125 | 122 | 2.125 | 1E+30 |
| 18 | $C$20 | Number tested on line 2 Model 2 | 0 | -20 | 127.5 | 20 | 1E+30 |
| 19 | $D$20 | Number tested on line 2 Model 3 | 0 | -10 | 137.5 | 10 | 1E+30 |
| 20 | $E$20 | Number tested on line 2 Model 4 | 475 | 0 | 147.5 | 1.136 | 2.083 |
| 21 | $F$20 | Number tested on line 2 Model 5 | 0 | -23.75 | 138.5 | 23.75 | 1E+30 |
| 22 | $G$20 | Number tested on line 2 Model 6 | 1000 | 0 | 163.5 | 1E+30 | 1.25 |
| 23 | $H$20 | Number tested on line 2 Model 7 | 0 | -6.375 | 160 | 6.375 | 1E+30 |
| 24 | $I$20 | Number tested on line 2 Model 8 | 0 | -2.5 | 174.5 | 2.5 | 1E+30 |
| 25 | | | | | | | |
| 26 | Constraints | | | | | | |
| 27 | | | Final | Shadow | Constraint | Allowable | Allowable |
| 28 | Cell | Name | Value | Price | R.H. Side | Increase | Decrease |
| 29 | $B$26 | Labor availability for assembling Hours used | 20000 | 29.5 | 20000 | 3250 | 2375 |
| 30 | $B$27 | Labor availability for testing, line 1 Hours used | 5000 | 2.25 | 5000 | 950 | 250 |
| 31 | $B$28 | Labor availability for testing, line 2 Hours used | 4187.5 | 0 | 6000 | 1E+30 | 1812.5 |
| 32 | $B$21 | Total computers produced Model 1 | 1500 | 6.125 | 1500 | 166.667 | 812.5 |
| 33 | $C$21 | Total computers produced Model 2 | 0 | 0 | 1250 | 1E+30 | 1250 |
| 34 | $D$21 | Total computers produced Model 3 | 0 | 0 | 1250 | 1E+30 | 1250 |
| 35 | $E$21 | Total computers produced Model 4 | 600 | 0 | 1250 | 1E+30 | 650 |
| 36 | $F$21 | Total computers produced Model 5 | 0 | 0 | 1000 | 1E+30 | 1000 |
| 37 | $G$21 | Total computers produced Model 6 | 1000 | 1.25 | 1000 | 431.818 | 590.909 |
| 38 | $H$21 | Total computers produced Model 7 | 1000 | 4.125 | 1000 | 100 | 590.909 |
| 39 | $I$21 | Total computers produced Model 8 | 0 | 0 | 800 | 1E+30 | 800 |

The information in this sensitivity report is all relevant and definitely provides some insights if studied carefully. However, this really requires you to know the exact rules Solver uses to create this report. That is, it requires a fairly in-depth knowledge of the theory behind LP sensitivity analysis, more than we have provided here. Fortunately, we believe the same basic information—and more—can be obtained in a more intuitive way by creating several carefully chosen SolverTable reports. ▨

## PROBLEMS

### Skill-Building Problems

*Note*: All references to the product mix model in the following problems are to the *larger* product mix model in this section.

**10.** Modify PC Tech's product mix model so that there is no maximum sales constraint. (This is easy to do in the Solver dialog box. Just highlight the constraint and click on the Delete button.) Does this make the problem unbounded? Does it change the optimal solution at all? Explain its effect.

**11.** In the product mix model it makes sense to change the maximum sales constraint to a "minimum sales" constraint, simply by changing the direction of the inequality. Then the input values in row 23 can be considered customer demands that must be met. Make this change and rerun Solver. What do you find? What do you find if you run Solver again, this time making the values in row 23 one-quarter of their current values?

**12.** Use SolverTable to run a sensitivity analysis on the cost per assembling labor hour, letting it vary from $5 to $20 in increments of $1. Keep track of the computers produced in row 21, the hours used in the range B26:B28, and the total profit. Discuss your findings. Are they intuitively what you expected?

**13.** Create a two-way SolverTable for the product mix model, where total profit is the only output and the two inputs are the testing line 1 hours and testing line 2 hours available. Let the former vary from 4000 to 6000 in increments of 500, and let the latter vary from 3000 to 5000 in increments of 500. Discuss the changes in profit you see as you look across the various rows of the table. Discuss the changes in profit you see as you look down the various columns of the table.

**14.** Model 8 has fairly high profit margins, but it isn't included at all in the optimal mix. Use SolverTable, along with some experimentation on the correct range, to find the (approximate) selling price required for model 8 before it enters the optimal product mix.

### Skill-Extending Problems

**15.** Suppose that you want to increase *all three* of the resource availabilities in the product mix model simultaneously by the same percentage. You want this percentage to vary from -25% to 50% in increments of 5%. Modify the spreadsheet model slightly so that this sensitivity analysis can be performed with a *one-way* SolverTable, using the percentage change as the single input. Keep track of the computers produced in row 21, the hours used in the range B26:B28, and the total profit. Discuss the results.

**16.** Some analysts complain that spreadsheet models are difficult to resize. You can be the judge of this. Suppose the current product mix problem is changed so that there is an extra resource, packaging labor hours, and two additional PC models, 9 and 10. What additional input data are required? What modifications are necessary in the spreadsheet model (including range name changes)? Make up values for any extra required input data and incorporate these into a modified spreadsheet model. Then optimize with Solver. Do you conclude that it is easy to resize a spreadsheet model? (By the way, it turns out that algebraic models are typically *much* easier to resize.)

**17.** In Solver's sensitivity report for the product mix model, the allowable decrease for available assembling hours is 2375. This means that something happens when assembling hours fall to $20{,}000 - 2375 = 17{,}625$. See what this means by first running Solver with 17,626 available hours and then again with 17,624 available hours. Explain how the two solutions compare to the original solution and to each other.

---

## 3.8 A MULTIPERIOD PRODUCTION MODEL

The product mix examples illustrate a very important type of LP model. However, LP models come in many forms. For variety, we now present a quite different type of model that can also be solved with LP. (In the next few chapters we provide other examples, linear and otherwise.) The distinguishing feature of the following model is that it relates decisions made during several time periods. This type of problem occurs when a company must make a decision now that will have ramifications in the future. The company does not want to focus completely on the short run and forget about the long run.

EXAMPLE | 3.3 PRODUCING FOOTBALLS AT PIGSKIN

The Pigskin Company produces footballs. Pigskin must decide how many footballs to produce each month. The company has decided to use a six-month planning horizon. The forecasted monthly demands for the next six months are 10,000, 15,000, 30,000, 35,000, 25,000, and 10,000. Pigskin wants to meet these demands on time, knowing that it currently has 5000 footballs in inventory and that it can use a given month's production to help meet the demand for that month. (For simplicity, we assume that production occurs during the month, and demand occurs at the end of the month.) During each month there is enough production capacity to produce up to 30,000 footballs, and there is enough storage capacity to store up to 10,000 footballs at the end of the month, after demand has occurred. The forecasted production costs per football for the next six months are $12.50, $12.55, $12.70, $12.80, $12.85, and $12.95, respectively. The holding cost per football held in inventory at the end of any month is figured at 5% of the production cost for that month. (This cost includes the cost of storage and also the cost of money tied up in inventory.) The selling price for footballs is not considered relevant to the production decision because Pigskin will satisfy all customer demand exactly when it occurs—at whatever the selling price is. Therefore, Pigskin wants to determine the production schedule that minimizes the total production and holding costs.

**Objective** To use LP to find the production schedule that meets demand on time and minimizes total production and inventory holding costs.

### WHERE DO THE NUMBERS COME FROM?

The input values for this problem are not all easy to find. Here are some thoughts on where they might be obtained. (See Figure 3.25.)

- The initial inventory in cell B4 should be available from the company's database system or from a physical count.

- The unit production costs in row 8 would probably be estimated in two steps. First, the company might ask its cost accountants to estimate the current unit production cost. Then it could examine historical trends in costs to estimate inflation factors for future months.

- The holding cost percentage in cell B5 is typically difficult to determine. Depending on the type of inventory being held, this cost can include storage and handling, rent, property taxes, insurance, spoilage, and obsolescence. It can also include capital costs—the cost of money that could be used for other investments.

- The demands in row 18 are probably forecasts made by the marketing and sales department. They might be "seat-of-the-pants" forecasts, or they might be the result of a formal quantitative forecasting procedure as discussed in Chapter 14. Of course, if there are already some orders on the books for future months, these are included in the demand figures.

- The production and storage capacities in rows 14 and 22 are probably supplied by the production department. They are based on the size of the workforce, the available machinery, availability of raw materials, and physical space.

## Solution

The variables and constraints for this model are listed in Table 3.3. There are two keys to relating these variables. First, the months cannot be treated independently. This is because the ending inventory in one month is the beginning inventory for the next month. Second, to ensure that demand is satisfied on time, the amount on hand after production in each month must be at least as large as the demand for that month. This constraint must be included explicitly in the model.

---

**Table 3.3    Variables and Constraints for Production/Inventory Planning Model**

| | |
|---|---|
| **Input variables** | Initial inventory, unit holding cost percentage, unit production costs, forecasted demands, production and storage capacities |
| **Decision variables (changing cells)** | Monthly production quantities |
| **Objective cell** | Total cost |
| **Other calculated variables** | Units on hand after production, ending inventories, monthly production and inventory holding costs |
| **Constraints** | Units on hand after production $\geq$ Demand (each month) |
| | Units produced $\leq$ Production capacity (each month) |
| | Ending inventory $\leq$ Storage capacity (each month) |

---

When you model this type of problem, you must be very specific about the *timing* of events. In fact, depending on the assumptions you make, there can be a variety of potential models. For example, when does the demand for footballs in a given month occur: at the beginning of the month, at the end of the month, or continually throughout the month? The same question can be asked about production in a given month. The answers to these two questions indicate how much of the production in a given month can be used to help satisfy the demand in that month. Also, are the maximum storage constraint and the holding cost based on the *ending* inventory in a month, the *average* amount of inventory in a month, or the *maximum* inventory in a month? Each of these possibilities is reasonable and could be implemented.

*By modifying the timing assumptions in this type of model, alternative—and equally realistic—models with very different solutions can be obtained.*

To simplify the model, we assume that (1) all production occurs at the beginning of the month, (2) all demand occurs *after* production, so that all units produced in a month can be used to satisfy that month's demand, and (3) the storage constraint and the holding cost are based on *ending* inventory in a given month. (You are asked to modify these assumptions in the problems.)

### An Algebraic Model

In the traditional algebraic model, the decision variables are the *production quantities* for the six months, labeled $P_1$ through $P_6$. It is also convenient to let $I_1$ through $I_6$ be the corresponding *end-of-month inventories* (after demand has occurred).[13] For example, $I_3$ is the number of footballs left over at the end of month 3. Therefore, the obvious constraints are on production and inventory storage capacities: $P_j \leq 30000$ and $I_j \leq 10000$ for $1 \leq j \leq 6$.

In addition to these constraints, *balance* constraints that relate the $P$s and $I$s are necessary. In any month the inventory from the previous month plus the current production equals the current demand plus leftover inventory. If $D_j$ is the forecasted demand for month $j$, the balance equation for month $j$ is

$$I_{j-1} + P_j = D_j + I_j$$

---

[13]This example illustrates a subtle difference between algebraic and spreadsheet models. It is often convenient in algebraic models to define "decision variables," in this case the $I$s, that are really determined by other decision variables, in this case the $P$s. In spreadsheet models, however, we typically define the changing cells as the smallest set of variables that must be chosen—in this case the production quantities. Then values that are determined by these changing cells, such as the ending inventory levels, can be calculated with spreadsheet formulas.

The balance equation for month 1 uses the known beginning inventory, 5000, for the previous inventory (the $I_{j-1}$ term). By putting all variables ($Ps$ and $Is$) on the left and all known values on the right (a standard LP convention), these balance constraints can be written as

$$P_1 - I_1 = 10000 - 5000$$

$$I_1 + P_2 - I_2 = 15000$$

$$I_2 + P_3 - I_3 = 30000$$

$$I_3 + P_4 - I_4 = 35000$$

$$I_4 + P_5 - I_5 = 25000$$

$$I_5 + P_6 - I_6 = 10000 \qquad\qquad (3.1)$$

As usual, there are nonnegativity constraints: all $Ps$ and $Is$ must be nonnegative.

What about meeting demand on time? This requires that in each month the inventory from the preceding month plus the current production must be at least as large as the current demand. But take a look, for example, at the balance equation for month 3. By rearranging it slightly, it becomes

$$I_3 = I_2 + P_3 - 30000$$

Now, the nonnegativity constraint on $I_3$ implies that the right side of this equation, $I_2 + P_3 - 30000$, is also nonnegative. But this implies that demand in month 3 is covered—the beginning inventory in month 3 plus month 3 production is at least 30000. Therefore, the nonnegativity constraints on the $Is$ *automatically* guarantee that all demands will be met on time, and no other constraints are needed. Alternatively, the constraint can be written directly as $I_2 + P_3 \geq 30000$. In words, the amount on hand after production in month 3 must be at least as large as the demand in month 3. The spreadsheet model takes advantage of this interpretation.

Finally, the objective to minimize is the sum of production and holding costs. It is the sum of unit production costs multiplied by $Ps$, plus unit holding costs multiplied by $Is$.

### DEVELOPING THE SPREADSHEET MODEL

The spreadsheet model of Pigskin's production problem is shown in Figure 3.25. (See the file Production Scheduling.xlsx.) The main feature that distinguishes this model from the product mix model is that some of the constraints, namely, the balance Equations (3.1), are built into the spreadsheet itself by means of formulas. This means that the only changing cells are the production quantities. The ending inventories shown in row 20 are *determined* by the production quantities and Equations (3.1). As you can see, the decision variables in an algebraic model (the $Ps$ and $Is$) are not *necessarily* the same as the changing cells in an equivalent spreadsheet model. (The only changing cells in the spreadsheet model correspond to the $Ps$.)

To develop the spreadsheet model in Figure 3.25, proceed as follows.

**1** **Inputs.** Enter the inputs in the blue cells. Again, these are all entered as *numbers* directly from the problem statement. (Unlike some spreadsheet modelers who prefer to put all inputs in the upper left corner of the spreadsheet, we enter the inputs wherever they fit most naturally. Of course, this takes some planning before diving in.)

**2** **Name ranges.** Name the ranges indicated. Note that all but one of these (Total_cost) can be named easily with the range-naming shortcut, using the labels in column A.

**Figure 3.25    Production Planning Model with a Suboptimal Solution**

| | A | B | C | D | E | F | G | H |
|---|---|---|---|---|---|---|---|---|
| 1 | Multiperiod production model | | | | | | | |
| 2 | | | | | | | | |
| 3 | Input data | | | | | | | |
| 4 | Initial inventory (100s) | 5000 | | | | | | |
| 5 | Holding cost as % of prod cost | 5% | | | | | | |
| 6 | | | | | | | | |
| 7 | Month | 1 | 2 | 3 | 4 | 5 | 6 | |
| 8 | Production cost/unit | $12.50 | $12.55 | $12.70 | $12.80 | $12.85 | $12.95 | |
| 9 | | | | | | | | |
| 10 | Production plan (all quantities are in 100s of footballs) | | | | | | | |
| 11 | Month | 1 | 2 | 3 | 4 | 5 | 6 | |
| 12 | Units produced | 15000 | 15000 | 30000 | 30000 | 25000 | 10000 | |
| 13 | | <= | <= | <= | <= | <= | <= | |
| 14 | Production capacity | 30000 | 30000 | 30000 | 30000 | 30000 | 30000 | |
| 15 | | | | | | | | |
| 16 | On hand after production | 20000 | 25000 | 40000 | 40000 | 30000 | 15000 | |
| 17 | | >= | >= | >= | >= | >= | >= | |
| 18 | Demand | 10000 | 15000 | 30000 | 35000 | 25000 | 10000 | |
| 19 | | | | | | | | |
| 20 | Ending inventory | 10000 | 10000 | 10000 | 5000 | 5000 | 5000 | |
| 21 | | <= | <= | <= | <= | <= | <= | |
| 22 | Storage capacity | 10000 | 10000 | 10000 | 10000 | 10000 | 10000 | |
| 23 | | | | | | | | |
| 24 | Summary of costs (all costs are in hundreds of dollars) | | | | | | | |
| 25 | Month | 1 | 2 | 3 | 4 | 5 | 6 | Totals |
| 26 | Production costs | $187,500.00 | $188,250.00 | $381,000.00 | $384,000.00 | $321,250.00 | $129,500.00 | $1,591,500.00 |
| 27 | Holding costs | $6,250.00 | $6,275.00 | $6,350.00 | $3,200.00 | $3,212.50 | $3,237.50 | $28,525.00 |
| 28 | Totals | $193,750.00 | $194,525.00 | $387,350.00 | $387,200.00 | $324,462.50 | $132,737.50 | $1,620,025.00 |
| 29 | | | | | | | | |
| 30 | Range names used | | | | | | | |
| 31 | Demand | =Model!$B$18:$G$18 | | | | | | |
| 32 | Ending_inventory | =Model!$B$20:$G$20 | | | | | | |
| 33 | On_hand_after_production | =Model!$B$16:$G$16 | | | | | | |
| 34 | Production_capacity | =Model!$B$14:$G$14 | | | | | | |
| 35 | Storage_capacity | =Model!$B$22:$G$22 | | | | | | |
| 36 | Total_Cost | =Model!$H$28 | | | | | | |
| 37 | Units_produced | =Model!$B$12:$G$12 | | | | | | |

③ **Production quantities.** Enter *any* values in the range Units_produced as production quantities. As always, you can enter values that you believe are good, maybe even optimal. This is not crucial, however, because Solver eventually finds the *optimal* production quantities.

*In multiperiod problems, there is often one formula for the first period and a slightly different (copyable) formula for all other periods.*

④ **On-hand inventory.** Enter the formula

=B4+B12

in cell B16. This calculates the first month's on-hand inventory after production (but before demand). Then enter the typical formula

=B20+C12

for on-hand inventory after production in month 2 in cell C16 and copy it across row 16.

⑤ **Ending inventories.** Enter the formula

=B16-B18

for ending inventory in cell B20 and copy it across row 20. This formula calculates ending inventory in the current month as on-hand inventory before demand minus the demand in that month.

**⑥** **Production and holding costs.** Enter the formula

=B8*B12

in cell B26 and copy it across to cell G26 to calculate the monthly production costs. Then enter the formula

=$B$5*B8*B20

in cell B27 and copy it across to cell G27 to calculate the monthly holding costs. Note that these are based on monthly ending inventories. Finally, calculate the cost totals in column H with the SUM function.

## USING SOLVER

To use Solver, fill out the main dialog box as shown in Figure 3.26. The logic behind the constraints is straightforward. The constraints are that (1) the production quantities cannot exceed the production capacities, (2) the on-hand inventories after production must be at least as large as demands, and (3) ending inventories cannot exceed storage capacities. Check the Non-Negative option, and then click on Solve.

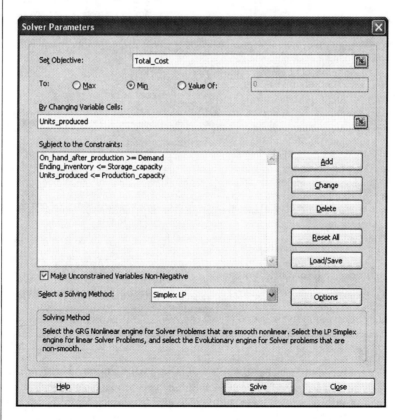

### Discussion of the Solution

The optimal solution from Solver appears in Figure 3.27. The solution can be interpreted best by comparing production quantities to demands. In month 1, Pigskin should produce just enough to meet month 1 demand (taking into account the initial inventory of 5000). In month 2, it should produce 5000 more footballs than month 2 demand, and then in month 3 it should produce just enough to meet month 3 demand, while still carrying the extra 5000 footballs in inventory from month 2 production. In month 4, Pigskin should finally use these 5000 footballs, along with the maximum production amount, 30,000, to meet month 4 demand. Then in months 5 and 6 it should produce exactly enough to meet these months' demands. The total cost is $1,535,563, most of which is production cost.

Figure 3.27    Optimal Solution for Production Planning Model

| | A | B | C | D | E | F | G | H |
|---|---|---|---|---|---|---|---|---|
| 1 | **Multiperiod production model** | | | | | | | |
| 2 | | | | | | | | |
| 3 | **Input data** | | | | | | | |
| 4 | Initial inventory (100s) | 5000 | | | | | | |
| 5 | Holding cost as % of prod cost | 5% | | | | | | |
| 6 | | | | | | | | |
| 7 | Month | 1 | 2 | 3 | 4 | 5 | 6 | |
| 8 | Production cost/unit | $12.50 | $12.55 | $12.70 | $12.80 | $12.85 | $12.95 | |
| 9 | | | | | | | | |
| 10 | **Production plan (all quantities are in 100s of footballs)** | | | | | | | |
| 11 | Month | 1 | 2 | 3 | 4 | 5 | 6 | |
| 12 | Units produced | 5000 | 20000 | 30000 | 30000 | 25000 | 10000 | |
| 13 | | <= | <= | <= | <= | <= | <= | |
| 14 | Production capacity | 30000 | 30000 | 30000 | 30000 | 30000 | 30000 | |
| 15 | | | | | | | | |
| 16 | On hand after production | 10000 | 20000 | 35000 | 35000 | 25000 | 10000 | |
| 17 | | >= | >= | >= | >= | >= | >= | |
| 18 | Demand | 10000 | 15000 | 30000 | 35000 | 25000 | 10000 | |
| 19 | | | | | | | | |
| 20 | Ending inventory | 0 | 5000 | 5000 | 0 | 0 | 0 | |
| 21 | | <= | <= | <= | <= | <= | <= | |
| 22 | Storage capacity | 10000 | 10000 | 10000 | 10000 | 10000 | 10000 | |
| 23 | | | | | | | | |
| 24 | **Summary of costs (all costs are in hundreds of dollars)** | | | | | | | |
| 25 | Month | 1 | 2 | 3 | 4 | 5 | 6 | Totals |
| 26 | Production costs | $62,500.00 | $251,000.00 | $381,000.00 | $384,000.00 | $321,250.00 | $129,500.00 | $1,529,250.00 |
| 27 | Holding costs | $0.00 | $3,137.50 | $3,175.00 | $0.00 | $0.00 | $0.00 | $6,312.50 |
| 28 | Totals | $62,500.00 | $254,137.50 | $384,175.00 | $384,000.00 | $321,250.00 | $129,500.00 | $1,535,562.50 |
| 29 | | | | | | | | |
| 30 | **Range names used** | | | | | | | |
| 31 | Demand | =Model!$B$18:$G$18 | | | | | | |
| 32 | Ending_inventory | =Model!$B$20:$G$20 | | | | | | |
| 33 | On_hand_after_production | =Model!$B$16:$G$16 | | | | | | |
| 34 | Production_capacity | =Model!$B$14:$G$14 | | | | | | |
| 35 | Storage_capacity | =Model!$B$22:$G$22 | | | | | | |
| 36 | Total_Cost | =Model!$H$28 | | | | | | |
| 37 | Units_produced | =Model!$B$12:$G$12 | | | | | | |

*You can often improve your intuition by trying to reason why Solver's solution is indeed optimal.*

Could you have guessed this optimal solution? Upon reflection, it makes perfect sense. Because the monthly holding costs are large relative to the differences in monthly production costs, there is little incentive to produce footballs before they are needed to take advantage of a "cheap" production month. Therefore, the Pigskin Company produces footballs in the month when they are needed—when possible. The only exception to this rule is the 20,000 footballs produced during month 2 when only 15,000 are needed. The extra 5000 footballs produced in month 2 are needed, however, to meet the month 4 demand of 35,000, because month 3 production capacity is used entirely to meet the month 3 demand.

Thus month 3 capacity is not available to meet the month 4 demand, and 5000 units of month 2 capacity are used to meet the month 4 demand.

FUNDAMENTAL INSIGHT

**Multiperiod Optimization Problems and Myopic Solutions**

Many optimization problems are of a multiperiod nature, where a sequence of decisions must be made over time. When making the *first* of these decisions, the one for this week or this month, say, it is usually best to include future decisions in the model, as has been done here. If you ignore future periods and make the initial decision based only on the first period, the resulting decision is called *myopic* (short-sighted). Myopic decisions are occasionally optimal, but not very often. The idea is that if you act now in a way that looks best in the short run, it might lead you down a strategically unattractive path for the long run.

## Sensitivity Analysis

*If you want SolverTable to keep track of a quantity that is not in your model, you need to create it with an appropriate formula in a new cell.*

SolverTable can now be used to perform a number of interesting sensitivity analyses. We illustrate two possibilities. First, note that the most inventory ever carried at the end of a month is 5000, although the storage capacity each month is 10,000. Perhaps this is because the holding cost percentage, 5%, is fairly large. Would more ending inventory be carried if this holding cost percentage were lower? Or would even less be carried if it were higher? You can check this with the SolverTable output shown in Figure 3.28. Now the single input cell is cell B5, and the *single* output is the maximum ending inventory ever held, which you can calculate in cell B31 with the formula

=MAX(Ending_inventory)

As the SolverTable results indicate, the storage capacity limit is reached only when the holding cost percentage falls to 1%. (This output doesn't indicate which month or how

Figure 3.28
**Sensitivity of Maximum Inventory to Holding Cost**

| | A | B | C | D | E | F | G |
|---|---|---|---|---|---|---|---|
| 3 | Holding cost % (cell $B$5) values along side, output cell(s) along top | | | | | | |
| 4 | | Max_inventory | | | | | |
| 5 | 1% | 10000 | | | | | |
| 6 | 2% | 5000 | | | | | |
| 7 | 3% | 5000 | | | | | |
| 8 | 4% | 5000 | | | | | |
| 9 | 5% | 5000 | | | | | |
| 10 | 6% | 5000 | | | | | |
| 11 | 7% | 5000 | | | | | |
| 12 | 8% | 5000 | | | | | |
| 13 | 9% | 5000 | | | | | |
| 14 | 10% | 5000 | | | | | |

many months the ending inventory is at the upper limit.) On the other hand, even when the holding cost percentage reaches 10%, the company still continues to hold a maximum ending inventory of 5000.

A second possible sensitivity analysis is suggested by the way the optimal production schedule would probably be implemented. The optimal solution to Pigskin's model specifies the production level for each of the next six months. In reality, however, the company would probably implement the model's recommendation only for the *first* month. Then at the beginning of the second month, it would gather new forecasts for the *next* six months, months 2 through 7, solve a new six-month model, and again implement the model's recommendation for the first of these months, month 2. If the company continues in this manner, we say that it is following a six-month **rolling planning horizon**.

The question, then, is whether the assumed demands (really, forecasts) toward the end of the planning horizon have much effect on the optimal production quantity in month 1. You would hope not, because these forecasts could be quite inaccurate. The two-way Solver table in Figure 3.29 shows how the optimal month 1 production quantity varies with the forecasted demands in months 5 and 6. As you can see, if the forecasted demands for months 5 and 6 remain fairly small, the optimal month 1 production quantity remains at 5000. This is good news. It means that the optimal production quantity in month 1 is fairly insensitive to the possibly inaccurate forecasts for months 5 and 6.

**Figure 3.29    Sensitivity of Month 1 Production to Demand in Months 5 and 6**

| | A | B | C | D | E | F | G | H | I | J |
|---|---|---|---|---|---|---|---|---|---|---|
| 3 | Month 5 demand (cell $F$18) values along side, Month 6 demand (cell $G$18) values along top, output cell in corner | | | | | | | | | |
| 4 | Units_produced_1 | 10000 | 20000 | 30000 | | | | | | |
| 5 | 10000 | 5000 | 5000 | 5000 | | | | | | |
| 6 | 20000 | 5000 | 5000 | 5000 | | | | | | |
| 7 | 30000 | 5000 | 5000 | 5000 | | | | | | |

Solver's sensitivity report for this model appears in Figure 3.30. The bottom part of this report is fairly straightforward to interpret. The first six rows are for sensitivity to changes in the storage capacity, whereas the last six are for sensitivity to changes in the demand. (There are no rows for the production capacity constraints, because these are simple upper-bound constraints on the decision variables. Recall that Solver's sensitivity report handles this type of constraint differently from "normal" constraints.) In contrast, the top part of the report is virtually impossible to unravel. This is because the objective coefficients of the decision variables are each based on *multiple* inputs. (Each is a combination of unit production costs and the holding cost percentage.) Therefore, if you want to know how the solution will change if you change a single unit production cost or the holding cost percentage, this report does not answer your question. This is one case where a sensitivity analysis with SolverTable is much more straightforward and intuitive. It allows you to change *any* of the model's inputs and directly see the effects on the solution.

## Modeling Issues

We assume that Pigskin uses a six-month planning horizon. Why six months? In multiperiod models such as this, the company has to make forecasts about the future, such as the

Figure 3.30    Solver Sensitivity Report for Production Planning Model

| | A | B | C | D | E | F | G | H |
|---|---|---|---|---|---|---|---|---|
| 6 | Variable Cells | | | | | | | |
| 7 | | | | Final | Reduced | Objective | Allowable | Allowable |
| 8 | | Cell | Name | Value | Cost | Coefficient | Increase | Decrease |
| 9 | | $B$12 | Units produced | 5000 | 0 | 16.318 | 1E+30 | 0.575 |
| 10 | | $C$12 | Units produced | 20000 | 0 | 15.743 | 0.575 | 0.478 |
| 11 | | $D$12 | Units produced | 30000 | -0.478 | 15.265 | 0.478 | 1E+30 |
| 12 | | $E$12 | Units produced | 30000 | -1.013 | 14.730 | 1.013 | 1E+30 |
| 13 | | $F$12 | Units produced | 25000 | 0 | 14.140 | 1.603 | 0.543 |
| 14 | | $G$12 | Units produced | 10000 | 0 | 13.598 | 0.543 | 13.598 |
| 15 | | | | | | | | |
| 16 | Constraints | | | | | | | |
| 17 | | | | Final | Shadow | Constraint | Allowable | Allowable |
| 18 | | Cell | Name | Value | Price | R.H. Side | Increase | Decrease |
| 19 | | $B$16 | On hand after production <= | 10000 | 0.575 | 10000 | 10000 | 5000 |
| 20 | | $C$16 | On hand after production <= | 20000 | 0 | 15000 | 5000 | 1E+30 |
| 21 | | $D$16 | On hand after production <= | 35000 | 0 | 30000 | 5000 | 1E+30 |
| 22 | | $E$16 | On hand after production <= | 35000 | 1.603 | 35000 | 5000 | 5000 |
| 23 | | $F$16 | On hand after production <= | 25000 | 0.543 | 25000 | 5000 | 20000 |
| 24 | | $G$16 | On hand after production <= | 10000 | 13.598 | 10000 | 10000 | 10000 |
| 25 | | $B$20 | Ending inventory >= | 0 | 0 | 10000 | 1E+30 | 10000 |
| 26 | | $C$20 | Ending inventory >= | 5000 | 0 | 10000 | 1E+30 | 5000 |
| 27 | | $D$20 | Ending inventory >= | 5000 | 0 | 10000 | 1E+30 | 5000 |
| 28 | | $E$20 | Ending inventory >= | 0 | 0 | 10000 | 1E+30 | 10000 |
| 29 | | $F$20 | Ending inventory >= | 0 | 0 | 10000 | 1E+30 | 10000 |
| 30 | | $G$20 | Ending inventory >= | 0 | 0 | 10000 | 1E+30 | 10000 |

level of customer demand. Therefore, the length of the planning horizon is usually the length of time for which the company can make reasonably accurate forecasts. Here, Pigskin evidently believes that it can forecast up to six months from now, so it uses a six-month planning horizon. ▪

# PROBLEMS

### Skill-Building Problems

**18.** Can you guess the results of a sensitivity analysis on the initial inventory in the Pigskin model? See if your guess is correct by using SolverTable and allowing the initial inventory to vary from 0 to 10,000 in increments of 1000. Keep track of the values in the changing cells and the objective cell.

**19.** Modify the Pigskin model so that there are eight months in the planning horizon. You can make up reasonable values for any extra required data. Don't forget to modify range names. Then modify the model

again so that there are only four months in the planning horizon. Do either of these modifications change the optimal production quantity in month 1?

**20.** As indicated by the algebraic formulation of the Pigskin model, there is no real need to calculate inventory on hand after production and constrain it to be greater than or equal to demand. An alternative is to calculate ending inventory directly and constrain it to be nonnegative. Modify the current spreadsheet model to do this. (Delete rows 16 and 17, and calculate ending inventory appropriately. Then add an *explicit* nonnegativity constraint on ending inventory.)

**21.** In one modification of the Pigskin problem, the maximum storage constraint and the holding cost are based on the *average* inventory (not ending inventory) for a given month, where the average inventory is defined as the sum of beginning inventory and ending inventory, divided by 2, and beginning inventory is *before* production or demand. Modify the Pigskin model with this new assumption, and use Solver to find the optimal solution. How does this change the optimal production schedule? How does it change the optimal total cost?

### Skill-Extending Problems

**22.** Modify the Pigskin spreadsheet model so that except for month 6, demand need not be met on time. The only requirement is that all demand be met eventually by the end of month 6. How does this change the optimal production schedule? How does it change the optimal total cost?

**23.** Modify the Pigskin spreadsheet model so that demand in any of the first five months must be met no later than a month late, whereas demand in month 6 must be met on time. For example, the demand in month 3 can be met partly in month 3 and partly in month 4. How does this change the optimal production schedule? How does it change the optimal total cost?

**24.** Modify the Pigskin spreadsheet model in the following way. Assume that the timing of demand and production are such that only 70% of the production in a given month can be used to satisfy the demand in that month. The other 30% occurs too late in that month and must be carried as inventory to help satisfy demand in later months. How does this change the optimal production schedule? How does it change the optimal total cost? Then use SolverTable to see how the optimal production schedule and optimal cost vary as the percentage of production usable for this month's demand (now 70%) is allowed to vary from 20% to 100% in increments of 10%.

---

## 3.9 A COMPARISON OF ALGEBRAIC AND SPREADSHEET MODELS

To this point you have seen three algebraic optimization models and three corresponding spreadsheet models. How do they differ? If you review the two product mix examples in this chapter, we believe you will agree that (1) the algebraic models are quite straightforward and (2) the spreadsheet models are almost direct translations into Excel of the algebraic models. In particular, each algebraic model has a set of *x*s that corresponds to the changing cell range in the spreadsheet model. In addition, each objective and each left side of each constraint in the spreadsheet model corresponds to a linear expression involving *x*s in the algebraic model.

However, the Pigskin production planning model is quite different. The spreadsheet model includes one set of changing cells, the production quantities, and everything else is related to these through spreadsheet formulas. In contrast, the algebraic model has *two* sets of variables, the *P*s for the production quantities and the *I*s for the ending inventories, and together these constitute the *decision variables*. These two sets of variables must then be related algebraically, and this is done through a series of *balance equations*.

This is a typical situation in algebraic models, where one set of variables (the production quantities) corresponds to the *real* decision variables, and other sets of variables, along with extra equations or inequalities, are introduced to capture the logic. We believe—and this belief is reinforced by many years of teaching experience—that this extra level of abstraction makes algebraic models much more difficult for typical users to develop and comprehend. It is the primary reason we have decided to focus almost exclusively on spreadsheet models in this book.

---

## 3.10 A DECISION SUPPORT SYSTEM

If your job is to develop an LP spreadsheet model to solve a problem such as Pigskin's production problem, then you will be considered the "expert" in LP. Many people who need to use such models, however, are *not* experts. They might understand the basic ideas behind LP and the types of problems it is intended to solve, but they will not know the details. In this case it is useful to provide these users with a **decision support system** (DSS) that can help them solve problems without having to worry about technical details.

We will not teach you in this book how to build a full-scale DSS, but we will show you what a typical DSS looks like and what it can do.[14] (We consider only DSSs built around spreadsheets. There are many other platforms for developing DSSs that we will not consider.) Basically, a spreadsheet-based DSS contains a spreadsheet model of a problem, such as the one in Figure 3.27. However, as a user, you will probably never even see this model. Instead, you will see a front end and a back end. The front end allows you to select input values for your particular problem. The user interface for this front end can include several features, such as buttons, dialog boxes, toolbars, and menus—the things you are used to seeing in Windows applications. The back end will then produce a report that explains the solution in nontechnical terms.

We illustrate a DSS for a slight variation of the Pigskin problem in the file Decision Support.xlsm. This file has three worksheets. When you open the file, you see the Explanation sheet shown in Figure 3.31. It contains two buttons, one for setting up the problem (getting the user's inputs) and one for solving the problem (running Solver). When you click on the Set Up Problem button, you are asked for the inputs: the initial inventory, the forecasted demands for each month, and others. An example appears in Figure 3.32. These input boxes should be self-explanatory, so that all you need to do is enter the values you

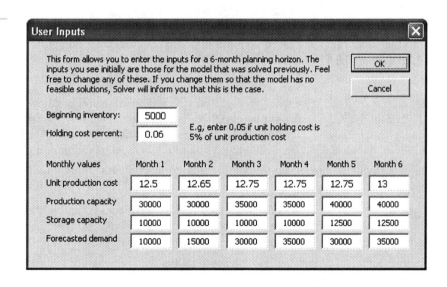

[14]For readers interested in learning more about this DSS, this textbook's essential resource Web site includes notes about its development in the file Developing the Decision Support Application.docx under Chapter 3 Example Files. If you are interested in learning more about spreadsheet DSSs in general, Albright has written the book *VBA for Modelers*, now in its third edition. It contains a primer on the Visual Basic for Applications language and presents many applications and instructions for creating DSSs with VBA.

want to try. (To speed up the process, the inputs from the previous run are shown by default.) After you have entered all of these inputs, you can take a look at the Model worksheet. This sheet contains a spreadsheet model similar to the one in Figure 3.27 but with the inputs you just entered.

Now go back to the Explanation sheet and click on the Find Optimal Solution button. This automatically sets up the Solver dialog box and runs Solver. There are two possibilities. First, it is possible that there is no feasible solution to the problem with the inputs you entered. In this case you see a message to this effect, as in Figure 3.33. In most cases, however, the problem has a feasible solution. In this case you see the Report sheet, which summarizes the optimal solution in nontechnical terms. Part of one sample output appears in Figure 3.34.

**Figure 3.33**

Indication of No
Feasible Solutions

**No solution** ✕

⚠ The Solver couldn't find a solution. Try a different set of inputs.

OK

**Figure 3.34**

Optimal Solution
Report

## Monthly schedule

**Month 1**

| Units | | Dollars | |
| --- | --- | --- | --- |
| Start with | 5000 | | |
| Produce | 5000 | Production cost | $62,500.00 |
| Demand is | 10000 | | |
| End with | 0 | Holding cost | $0.00 |

**Month 2**

| Units | | Dollars | |
| --- | --- | --- | --- |
| Start with | 0 | | |
| Produce | 15000 | Production cost | $189,750.00 |
| Demand is | 15000 | | |
| End with | 0 | Holding cost | $0.00 |

**Month 3**

| Units | | Dollars | |
| --- | --- | --- | --- |
| Start with | 0 | | |
| Produce | 30000 | Production cost | $382,500.00 |
| Demand is | 30000 | | |
| End with | 0 | Holding cost | $0.00 |

After studying this report, you can then click on the Solve Another Problem button, which takes you back to the Explanation sheet so that you can solve a new problem. All of this is done automatically with Excel macros. These macros use Microsoft's Visual Basic for Applications (VBA) programming language to automate various tasks. In most professional applications, nontechnical people need only to enter inputs and look at reports. Therefore, the Model sheet and VBA code will most likely be hidden and protected from end users.

## 3.11 CONCLUSION

This chapter has provided a good start to LP modeling—and to optimization modeling in general. You have learned how to develop three basic LP spreadsheet models, how to use Solver to find their optimal solutions, and how to perform sensitivity analyses with Solver's sensitivity reports or with the SolverTable add-in. You have also learned how to recognize whether a mathematical programming model satisfies the linear assumptions. In the next few chapters you will see a variety of other optimization models, but the three basic steps of model development, Solver optimization, and sensitivity analysis remain the same.

### Summary of Key Terms

| Term | Explanation | Excel | Page |
|---|---|---|---|
| Linear programming model | An optimization model with a linear objective and linear constraints | | 68 |
| Objective | The value, such as profit, to be optimized in an optimization model | | 69 |
| Constraints | Conditions that must be satisfied in an optimization model | | 69 |
| Changing cells | Cells that contain the values of the decision variables | Specify in Solver dialog box | 69 |
| Objective cell | Cell that contains the value of the objective | Specify in Solver dialog box | 69 |
| Nonnegativity constraints | Constraints that require the decision variables to be nonnegative, usually for physical reasons | | 69 |
| Feasible solution | A solution that satisfies all of the constraints | | 70 |
| Feasible region | The set of all feasible solutions | | 70 |
| Optimal solution | The feasible solution that has the best value of the objective | | 70 |
| Solver | Add-in that ships with Excel for performing optimization | Solver on Data ribbon | 70 |
| Simplex method | An efficient algorithm for finding the optimal solution in a linear programming model | | 70 |
| Sensitivity analysis | Seeing how the optimal solution changes as various input values change | | 70 |
| Algebraic model | A model that expresses the constraints and the objective algebraically | | 72 |
| Graphical solution | Shows the constraints and objective graphically so that the optimal solution can be identified; useful only when there are two decision variables | | 72 |
| Spreadsheet model | A model that uses spreadsheet formulas to express the logic of the model | | 74 |
| Binding constraint | A constraint that holds as an equality | | 82 |

*(continued)*

| Term | Explanation | Excel | Page |
|------|-------------|-------|------|
| Nonbinding constraint, slack | A constraint where there is a difference, the slack, between the two sides of the inequality | | 82 |
| Solver's sensitivity report | Report available from Solver that shows sensitivity to objective coefficients and right sides of constraints | Available in Solver dialog box after Solver runs | 83 |
| Reduced cost | Amount the objective coefficient of a variable currently equal to zero must change before it is optimal for that variable to be positive (or the amount the objective of a variable currently at its upper bound must change before that variable decreases from its upper bound) | | 85 |
| Shadow price | The change in the objective for a change in the right side of a constraint; indicates amount a company would pay for more of a scarce resource | | 85 |
| SolverTable | Add-in that performs sensitivity analysis to any inputs and reports results in tabular and graphical form | SolverTable ribbon | 87 |
| Selecting multiple ranges | Useful when changing cells, e.g., are in noncontiguous ranges | Pressing Ctrl key, drag ranges, one after the other | 89 |
| Mathematical programming model | Any optimization model, whether linear, integer, or nonlinear | | 94 |
| Proportionality, additivity, divisibility | Properties of optimization model that result in a linear programming model | | 94 |
| Infeasibility | Condition where a model has no feasible solutions | | 97 |
| Unboundedness | Condition where there is no limit to the objective; almost always a sign of an error in the model | | 97 |
| Rolling planning horizon | Multiperiod model where only the decision in the first period is implemented, and then a new multiperiod model is solved in succeeding periods | | 116 |
| Decision support system | User-friendly system where an end user can enter inputs to a model and see outputs, but need not be concerned with technical details | | 118 |

## PROBLEMS

### Skill-Building Problems

**25.** A chemical company manufactures three chemicals: A, B, and C. These chemicals are produced via two production processes: 1 and 2. Running process 1 for an hour costs $400 and yields 300 units of A, 100 units of B, and 100 units of C. Running process 2 for an hour costs $100 and yields 100 units of A and 100 units of B. To meet customer demands, at least 1000 units of A, 500 units of B, and 300 units of C must be produced daily.

**a.** Use Solver to determine a daily production plan that minimizes the cost of meeting the company's daily demands.

**b.** Confirm graphically that the daily production plan from part **a** minimizes the cost of meeting the company's daily demands.

**c.** Use SolverTable to see what happens to the decision variables and the total cost when the hourly processing cost for process 2 increases in increments of $0.50. How large must this cost increase be before the decision variables change?

What happens when it continues to increase beyond this point?

**26.** A furniture company manufactures desks and chairs. Each desk uses four units of wood, and each chair uses three units of wood. A desk contributes $400 to profit, and a chair contributes $250. Marketing restrictions require that the number of chairs produced be at least twice the number of desks produced. There are 2000 units of wood available.
  **a.** Use Solver to maximize the company's profit.
  **b.** Confirm graphically that the solution in part **a** maximizes the company's profit.
  **c.** Use SolverTable to see what happens to the decision variables and the total profit when the availability of wood varies from 1000 to 3000 in 100-unit increments. Based on your findings, how much would the company be willing to pay for each extra unit of wood over its current 2000 units? How much profit would the company lose if it lost any of its current 2000 units?

**27.** A farmer in Iowa owns 450 acres of land. He is going to plant each acre with wheat or corn. Each acre planted with wheat yields $2000 profit, requires three workers, and requires two tons of fertilizer. Each acre planted with corn yields $3000 profit, requires two workers, and requires four tons of fertilizer. There are currently 1000 workers and 1200 tons of fertilizer available.
  **a.** Use Solver to help the farmer maximize the profit from his land.
  **b.** Confirm graphically that the solution from part **a** maximizes the farmer's profit from his land.
  **c.** Use SolverTable to see what happens to the decision variables and the total profit when the availability of fertilizer varies from 200 tons to 2200 tons in 100-ton increments. When does the farmer discontinue producing wheat? When does he discontinue producing corn? How does the profit change for each 10-ton increment?

**28.** During the next four months, a customer requires, respectively, 500, 650, 1000, and 700 units of a commodity, and no backlogging is allowed (that is, the customer's requirements must be met on time). Production costs are $50, $80, $40, and $70 per unit during these months. The storage cost from one month to the next is $20 per unit (assessed on ending inventory). It is estimated that each unit on hand at the end of month 4 can be sold for $60. Assume there is no beginning inventory.
  **a.** Determine how to minimize the net cost incurred in meeting the demands for the next four months.
  **b.** Use SolverTable to see what happens to the decision variables and the total cost when the initial inventory varies from 0 to 1000 in 100-unit increments. How much lower would the total cost be if the company started with 100 units in inventory, rather than none?

Would this same cost decrease occur for every 100-unit increase in initial inventory?

**29.** A company faces the following demands during the next three weeks: week 1, 2000 units; week 2, 1000 units; week 3, 1500 units. The unit production costs during each week are as follows: week 1, $130; week 2, $140; week 3, $150. A holding cost of $20 per unit is assessed against each week's ending inventory. At the beginning of week 1, the company has 500 units on hand. In reality, not all goods produced during a month can be used to meet the current month's demand. To model this fact, assume that only half of the goods produced during a week can be used to meet the current week's demands.
  **a.** Determine how to minimize the cost of meeting the demand for the next three weeks.
  **b.** Revise the model so that the demands are of the form $D_t + k\Delta_t$, where $D_t$ is the original demand (from above) in month $t$, $k$ is a given factor, and $\Delta_t$ is an amount of change in month $t$ demand. (The Greek symbol *delta* is typically used to indicate change.) Develop the model in such a way that you can use SolverTable to analyze changes in the amounts produced and the total cost when $k$ varies from 0 to 10 in 1-unit increments, for any fixed values of the $\Delta_t$s. For example, try this when $\Delta_1 = 200$, $\Delta_2 = 500$, and $\Delta_3 = 300$. Describe the behavior you observe in the table. Can you find any reasonable $\Delta_t$s that induce *positive* production levels in week 3?

**30.** Maggie Stewart loves desserts, but due to weight and cholesterol concerns, she has decided that she must plan her desserts carefully. There are two possible desserts she is considering: snack bars and ice cream. After reading the nutrition labels on the snack bar and ice cream packages, she learns that each serving of a snack bar weighs 37 grams and contains 120 calories and 5 grams of fat. Each serving of ice cream weighs 65 grams and contains 160 calories and 10 grams of fat. Maggie will allow herself no more than 450 calories and 25 grams of fat in her daily desserts, but because she loves desserts so much, she requires at least 120 grams of dessert per day. Also, she assigns a "taste index" to each gram of each dessert, where 0 is the lowest and 100 is the highest. She assigns a taste index of 95 to ice cream and 85 to snack bars (because she prefers ice cream to snack bars).
  **a.** Use Solver to find the daily dessert plan that stays within her constraints and maximizes the total taste index of her dessert.
  **b.** Confirm graphically that the solution from part **a** maximizes Maggie's total taste index.
  **c.** Use a two-way Solver table to see how the optimal dessert plan varies when the calories per snack bar and per ice cream vary. Let the former vary from 80 to 200 in increments of 10, and let the latter vary from 120 to 300 in increments of 10.

**31.** For a telephone survey, a marketing research group needs to contact at least 600 wives, 480 husbands, 400 single adult males, and 440 single adult females. It costs $3 to make a daytime call and (because of higher labor costs) $5 to make an evening call. The file P03_31.xlsx lists the results that can be expected. For example, 30% of all daytime calls are answered by a wife, 15% of all evening calls are answered by a single male, and 40% of all daytime calls are not answered at all. Due to limited staff, at most 40% of all phone calls can be evening calls.
   a. Determine how to minimize the cost of completing the survey.
   b. Use SolverTable to investigate changes in the unit cost of either type of call. Specifically, investigate changes in the cost of a daytime call, with the cost of an evening call fixed, to see when (if ever) *only* daytime calls or *only* evening calls will be made. Then repeat the analysis by changing the cost of an evening call and keeping the cost of a daytime call fixed.

**32.** A furniture company manufactures tables and chairs. Each table and chair must be made entirely out of oak or entirely out of pine. A total of 15,000 board feet of oak and 21,000 board feet of pine are available. A table requires either 17 board feet of oak or 30 board feet of pine, and a chair requires either 5 board feet of oak or 13 board feet of pine. Each table can be sold for $800, and each chair for $300.
   a. Determine how the company can maximize its revenue.
   b. Use SolverTable to investigate the effects of simultaneous changes in the selling prices of the products. Specifically, see what happens to the total revenue when the selling prices of oak products change by a factor $1 + k_1$ and the selling prices of pine products change by a factor $1 + k_2$. Revise your model from the previous problem so that you can use SolverTable to investigate changes in total revenue as $k_1$ and $k_2$ both vary from $-0.3$ to $0.3$ in increments of $0.1$. Can you conclude that total revenue changes *linearly* within this range?

**33.** A manufacturing company makes two products. Each product can be made on either of two machines. The time (in hours) required to make each product on each machine is listed in the file P03_33.xlsx. Each month, 500 hours of time are available on each machine. Each month, customers are willing to buy up to the quantities of each product at the prices also given in the same file. The company's goal is to maximize the revenue obtained from selling units during the next two months.
   a. Determine how the company can meet this goal. Assume that it will not produce any units in a month that it cannot sell in that month.

   b. Use SolverTable to see what happens if customer demands for each product in each month simultaneously change by a factor $1 + k$. Revise the model so that you can use SolverTable to investigate the effect of this change on total revenue as $k$ varies from $-0.3$ to $0.3$ in increments of $0.1$. Does revenue change in a linear manner over this range? Can you explain intuitively why it changes in the way it does?

**34.** There are three factories on the Momiss River. Each emits two types of pollutants, labeled $P_1$ and $P_2$, into the river. If the waste from each factory is processed, the pollution in the river can be reduced. It costs $1500 to process a ton of factory 1 waste, and each ton processed reduces the amount of $P_1$ by 0.10 ton and the amount of $P_2$ by 0.45 ton. It costs $1000 to process a ton of factory 2 waste, and each ton processed reduces the amount of $P_1$ by 0.20 ton and the amount of $P_2$ by 0.25 ton. It costs $2000 to process a ton of factory 3 waste, and each ton processed reduces the amount of $P_1$ by 0.40 ton and the amount of $P_2$ by 0.30 ton. The state wants to reduce the amount of $P_1$ in the river by at least 30 tons and the amount of $P_2$ by at least 40 tons.
   a. Use Solver to determine how to minimize the cost of reducing pollution by the desired amounts. Are the LP assumptions (proportionality, additivity, divisibility) reasonable in this problem?
   b. Use SolverTable to investigate the effects of increases in the minimal reductions required by the state. Specifically, see what happens to the amounts of waste processed at the three factories and the total cost if both requirements (currently 30 and 40 tons, respectively) are increased by the *same* percentage. Revise your model so that you can use SolverTable to investigate these changes when the percentage increase varies from 10% to 100% in increments of 10%. Do the amounts processed at the three factories and the total cost change in a linear manner?

## Skill-Extending Problems

**35.** A company manufactures two types of trucks. Each truck must go through the painting shop and the assembly shop. If the painting shop were completely devoted to painting type 1 trucks, 800 per day could be painted, whereas if the painting shop were completely devoted to painting type 2 trucks, 700 per day could be painted. If the assembly shop were completely devoted to assembling truck 1 engines, 1500 per day could be assembled, whereas if the assembly shop were completely devoted to assembling truck 2 engines, 1200 per day could be assembled. It is possible, however, to paint *both* types of trucks in the painting shop. Similarly, it is possible to assemble both types in the assembly shop. Each type 1 truck contributes $1000 to profit; each type 2 truck contributes $1500. Use Solver to maximize the company's profit. (*Hint*: One approach, but not the only approach, is to try a graphical procedure first and then deduce the constraints from the graph.)

36. A company manufactures mechanical heart valves from the heart valves of pigs. Different heart operations require valves of different sizes. The company purchases pig valves from three different suppliers. The cost and size mix of the valves purchased from each supplier are given in the file P03_36.xlsx. Each month, the company places an order with each supplier. At least 500 large, 300 medium, and 300 small valves must be purchased each month. Because of the limited availability of pig valves, at most 500 valves per month can be purchased from each supplier.
    a. Use Solver to determine how the company can minimize the cost of acquiring the needed valves.
    b. Use SolverTable to investigate the effect on total cost of increasing its minimal purchase requirements each month. Specifically, see how the total cost changes as the minimal purchase requirements of large, medium, and small valves all increase from their original values by the *same* percentage. Revise your model so that SolverTable can be used to investigate these changes when the percentage increase varies from 2% to 20% in increments of 2%. Explain intuitively what happens when this percentage is at least 16%.

37. A company that builds sailboats wants to determine how many sailboats to build during each of the next four quarters. The demand during each of the next four quarters is as follows: first quarter, 160 sailboats; second quarter, 240 sailboats; third quarter, 300 sailboats; fourth quarter, 100 sailboats. The company must meet demands on time. At the beginning of the first quarter, the company has an inventory of 40 sailboats. At the beginning of each quarter, the company must decide how many sailboats to build during that quarter. For simplicity, assume that sailboats built during a quarter can be used to meet demand for that quarter. During each quarter, the company can build up to 160 sailboats with regular-time labor at a total cost of $1600 per sailboat. By having employees work overtime during a quarter, the company can build additional sailboats with overtime labor at a total cost of $1800 per sailboat. At the end of each quarter (after production has occurred and the current quarter's demand has been satisfied), a holding cost of $80 per sailboat is incurred.
    a. Determine a production schedule to minimize the sum of production and inventory holding costs during the next four quarters.

    b. Use SolverTable to see whether any changes in the $80 holding cost per sailboat could induce the company to carry more or less inventory. Revise your model so that SolverTable can be used to investigate the effects on ending inventory during the four-quarter period of systematic changes in the unit holding cost. (Assume that even though the unit holding cost changes, it is still constant over the four-quarter period.) Are there any (nonnegative) unit holding costs that would induce the company to hold *more* inventory than it holds when the holding cost is $80? Are there any unit holding costs that would induce the company to hold *less* inventory than it holds when the holding cost is $80?

38. During the next two months an automobile manufacturer must meet (on time) the following demands for trucks and cars: month 1, 400 trucks and 800 cars; month 2, 300 trucks and 300 cars. During each month at most 1000 vehicles can be produced. Each truck uses two tons of steel, and each car uses one ton of steel. During month 1, steel costs $700 per ton; during month 2, steel is projected to cost $800 per ton. At most 2500 tons of steel can be purchased each month. (Steel can be used only during the month in which it is purchased.) At the beginning of month 1, 100 trucks and 200 cars are in the inventory. At the end of each month, a holding cost of $200 per vehicle is assessed. Each car gets 20 miles per gallon (mpg), and each truck gets 10 mpg. During each month, the vehicles produced by the company must average at least 16 mpg.
    a. Determine how to meet the demand and mileage requirements at minimum total cost.
    b. Use SolverTable to see how sensitive the total cost is to the 16 mpg requirement. Specifically, let this requirement vary from 14 mpg to 18 mpg in increments of 0.25 mpg. Explain intuitively what happens when the requirement is greater than 17 mpg.

39. A textile company produces shirts and pants. Each shirt requires two square yards of cloth, and each pair of pants requires three square yards of cloth. During the next two months the following demands for shirts and pants must be met (on time): month 1, 1000 shirts and 1500 pairs of pants; month 2, 1200 shirts and 1400 pairs of pants. During each month the following resources are available: month 1, 9000 square yards of cloth; month 2, 6000 square yards of cloth. In addition, cloth that is available during month 1 and is not used can be used during month 2. During each month it costs $8 to produce an article of clothing with regular-time labor and $16 with overtime labor. During each month a total of at most 2500 articles of clothing can be produced with regular-time labor, and an unlimited number of articles of clothing can be

produced with overtime labor. At the end of each month, a holding cost of $3 per article of clothing is incurred (There is no holding cost for cloth.)

a. Determine how to meet demands for the next two months (on time) at minimum cost. Assume that 100 shirts and 200 pairs of pants are already in inventory at the beginning of month 1.

b. Use a two-way SolverTable to investigate the effect on total cost of two *simultaneous* changes. The first change is to allow the ratio of overtime to regular-time production cost (currently $16/$8 = 2) to vary from 1.2 to 1.8 in increments of 0.2, while keeping the regular time cost at $8. The second change is to allow the production capacity *each* month (currently 2500) to decrease by 10% to 50% in increments of 10%. The idea here is that less regular-time capacity is available, but overtime becomes relatively cheaper. Is the net effect on total cost positive or negative?

40. Each year, a shoe manufacturing company faces demands (which must be met on time) for pairs of shoes as shown in the file P03_40.xlsx. Employees work three consecutive quarters and then receive one quarter off. For example, a worker might work during quarters 3 and 4 of one year and quarter 1 of the next year. During a quarter in which an employee works, he or she can produce up to 500 pairs of shoes. Each worker is paid $5000 per quarter. At the end of each quarter, a holding cost of $10 per pair of shoes is incurred.

a. Determine how to minimize the cost per year (labor plus holding) of meeting the demands for shoes. To simplify the model, assume that at the end of each year, the ending inventory is 0. (You can assume that a given worker gets the *same* quarter off during each year.)

b. Suppose the company can pay a flat fee for a training program that increases the productivity of all of its workers. Use SolverTable to see how much the company would be willing to pay for a training program that increases worker productivity from 500 pairs of shoes per quarter to $P$ pairs of shoes per quarter, where $P$ varies from 525 to 700 in increments of 25.

41. A small appliance manufacturer must meet (on time) the following demands: quarter 1, 3000 units; quarter 2, 2000 units; quarter 3, 4000 units. Each quarter, up to 2700 units can be produced with regular-time labor, at a cost of $40 per unit. During each quarter, an unlimited number of units can be produced with overtime labor, at a cost of $60 per unit. Of all units produced, 20% are unsuitable and cannot be used to meet demand. Also, at the end of each quarter, 10% of all units on hand spoil and cannot be used to meet any future demands. After each quarter's demand is satisfied and spoilage is accounted for, a cost of $15 per unit in ending inventory is incurred.

a. Determine how to minimize the total cost of meeting the demands of the next three quarters. Assume that 1000 usable units are available at the beginning of quarter 1.

b. The company wants to know how much money it would be worth to decrease the percentage of unsuitable items and/or the percentage of items that spoil. Write a short report that provides relevant information. Base your report on three uses of SolverTable: (1) where the percentage of unsuitable items decreases and the percentage of items that spoil stays at 10%, (2) where the percentage of unsuitable items stays at 20% and the percentage of items that spoil decreases, and (3) where both percentages decrease. Does the sum of the separate effects on total cost from the first two tables equal the combined effect from the third table? Include an answer to this question in your report.

42. A pharmaceutical company manufactures two drugs at Los Angeles and Indianapolis. The cost of manufacturing a pound of each drug depends on the location, as indicated in the file P03_42.xlsx. The machine time (in hours) required to produce a pound of each drug at each city is also shown in this table. The company must produce at least 1000 pounds per week of drug 1 and at least 2000 pounds per week of drug 2. It has 500 hours per week of machine time at Indianapolis and 400 hours per week at Los Angeles.

a. Determine how the company can minimize the cost of producing the required drugs.

b. Use SolverTable to determine how much the company would be willing to pay to purchase a combination of $A$ extra hours of machine time at Indianapolis and $B$ extra hours of machine time at Los Angeles, where $A$ and $B$ can be any positive multiples of 10 up to 50.

43. A company manufactures two products on two machines. The number of hours of machine time and labor depends on the machine and product as shown in the file P03_43.xlsx. The cost of producing a unit of each product depends on which machine produces it. These unit costs also appear in the same file. There are 200 hours available on each of the two machines, and there are 400 labor hours available total. This month at least 200 units of product 1 and at least 240 units of product 2 must be produced. Also, at least half of the product 1 requirement must be produced on machine 1, and at least half of the product 2 requirement must be produced on machine 2.

a. Determine how the company can minimize the cost of meeting this month's requirements.

b. Use SolverTable to see how much the "at least half" requirements are costing the company. Do this by changing *both* of these requirements from "at least half" to "at least *x* percent," where *x* can be any multiple of 5% from 0% to 50%.

## Modeling Problems

**44.** Suppose you use Solver to find the optimal solution to a maximization model. Then you remember that you omitted an important constraint. After adding the constraint and running Solver again, is the optimal value of the objective guaranteed to decrease? Why or why not?

**45.** Consider an optimization model with a number of resource constraints. Each indicates that the amount of the resource used cannot exceed the amount available. Why is the shadow price of such a resource constraint always zero when the amount used in the optimal solution is *less than* the amount available?

**46.** If you add a constraint to an optimization model, and the previously optimal solution satisfies the new constraint, will this solution still be optimal with the new constraint added? Why or why not?

**47.** Why is it generally necessary to add nonnegativity constraints to an optimization model? Wouldn't Solver automatically choose nonnegative values for the changing cells?

**48.** Suppose you have a *linear* optimization model where you are trying to decide which products to produce to maximize profit. What does the additive assumption imply about the profit objective? What does the proportionality assumption imply about the profit objective? Be as specific as possible. Can you think of any *reasonable* profit functions that would *not* be linear in the amounts of the products produced?

**49.** In a typical product mix model, where a company must decide how much of each product to produce to maximize profit, discuss possible situations where

there might not be any feasible solutions. Could these be realistic? If you had such a situation in your company, how might you proceed?

**50.** In a typical product mix model, where a company must decide how much of each product to produce to maximize profit, there are sometimes customer demands for the products. We used upper-bound constraints for these: Don't produce more than you can sell. Would it be realistic to have lower-bound constraints instead: Produce at least as much as is demanded? Would it be realistic to have both (where the upper bounds are greater than the lower bounds)? Would it be realistic to have equality constraints: Produce exactly what is demanded?

**51.** In a typical production scheduling model like Pigskin's, if there are no production capacity constraints—the company can produce as much as it needs in any time period—but there are storage capacity constraints and demand must be met on time, is it possible that there will be no feasible solutions? Why or why not?

**52.** In a production scheduling problem like Pigskin's, suppose the company must produce *several* products to meet customer demands. Would it suffice to solve a separate model for each product, as we did for Pigskin, or would one big model for all products be necessary? If the latter, discuss what this big model might look like.

**53.** In any optimization model such as those in this chapter, we say that the model is unbounded (and Solver will indicate as such) if there is no limit to the value of the objective. For example, if the objective is profit, then for any dollar value, no matter how large, there is a feasible solution with profit at least this large. In the real world, why are there never any unbounded models? If you run Solver on a model and get an "unbounded" message, what should you do?

Microsoft Office (or Excel) ships with a built-in version of Solver. This version and all other versions of Solver have been developed by Frontline Systems, not Microsoft. When you install Office (or Excel), you have the option of installing or not installing Solver. In most cases, a typical install should install Solver. To check whether Solver is installed on your system, open Excel, select the Office Button (or the File tab in Excel 2010), select Excel Options, select Add-Ins, and click on Go. If there is a Solver item in the list, Solver has been installed. (To actually add it in, make sure this item is checked.) Otherwise, you need to run the Office Setup program with the Add/Remove feature to install Solver. Users of previous versions of Excel (2003 or earlier) should note that the actual Solver add-in file is a different one in Excel 2007 or Excel 2010. In previous versions, it was Solver.xla; now it is Solver.xlam. However, the basic functionality is the same.

If you have used versions of Solver in Excel 2007 or earlier, you will see some changes in Solver for Excel 2010. First, the user interface is slightly different, as you have already seen in the screen shots of its main dialog box. Second, it now includes the Evolutionary algorithm, which used to be available only in the Premium Solver product. (Because of this, we no longer need to supply an educational version of Premium Solver with the book.) We will continue to use the Evolutionary algorithm extensively in Chapter 8. Third, the Solver algorithms have been revised to work better. Specifically, we have very rarely seen the annoying message about a model not being linear when we know it is linear. This message can still occur in certain models, but it is less likely to occur than in previous versions of Solver.

The built-in version of Solver is able to solve most problems you are likely to encounter. However, it has two important limitations you should be aware of. First, it allows only 200 changing cells. This might sound like plenty, but many real-world problems go well beyond 200 changing cells. Second, Solver for Excel 2010 allows only 100 constraints. (There was no such limit in previous versions.) For example, if you specify a constraint such as B15:B17<=D15:D17, this counts as three constraints against the 100-constraint limit. However, simple upper or lower bound constraints, such as B15<=100 or B15>=50, where B15 is a changing cell, do *not* count against the 100-constraint limit. If you want to solve larger problems, you will need to purchase one of Frontline's commercial versions of Solver. For more information, check Frontline Systems' Web site at www.solver.com.

Shelby Shelving is a small company that manufactures two types of shelves for grocery stores. Model S is the standard model; model LX is a heavy-duty version. Shelves are manufactured in three major steps: stamping, forming, and assembly. In the stamping stage, a large machine is used to stamp (i.e., cut) standard sheets of metal into appropriate sizes. In the forming stage, another machine bends the metal into shape. Assembly involves joining the parts with a combination of soldering and riveting. Shelby's stamping and forming machines work on both models of shelves. Separate assembly departments are used for the final stage of production.

The file Shelby Shelving.xlsx contains relevant data for Shelby. (See Figure 3.35.) The hours required on each machine for each unit of product are shown in the range B5:C6 of the Accounting Data sheet. For example, the production of one model S shelf requires 0.25 hour on the forming machine. Both the stamping and forming machines can operate for 800 hours each month. The model S assembly department has a monthly capacity of 1900 units. The model LX assembly department has a monthly capacity of only 1400 units. Currently Shelby is producing and selling 400 units of model S and 1400 units of model LX per month.

**Figure 3.35   Data for Shelby Case**

| | A | B | C | D | E | F | G | H | I |
|---|---|---|---|---|---|---|---|---|---|
| 1 | Shelby Shelving Data for Current Production Schedule | | | | | | | | |
| 2 | | | | | | | | | |
| 3 | Machine requirements (hours per unit) | | | | | Given monthly overhead cost data | | | |
| 4 | | Model S | Model LX | Available | | | Fixed | Variable S | Variable LX |
| 5 | Stamping | 0.3 | 0.3 | 800 | | Stamping | $125,000 | $80 | $90 |
| 6 | Forming | 0.25 | 0.5 | 800 | | Forming | $95,000 | $120 | $170 |
| 7 | | | | | | Model S Assembly | $80,000 | $165 | $0 |
| 8 | | Model S | Model LX | | | Model LX Assembly | $85,000 | $0 | $185 |
| 9 | Current monthly production | 400 | 1400 | | | | | | |
| 10 | | | | | | Standard costs of the shelves -- *based on the current production levels* | | | |
| 11 | Hours spent in departments | | | | | | Model S | Model LX | |
| 12 | | Model S | Model LX | Total s | | Direct materials | $1,000 | $1,200 | |
| 13 | Stamping | 120 | 420 | 540 | | Direct labor: | | | |
| 14 | Forming | 100 | 700 | 800 | | Stamping | $35 | $35 | |
| 15 | | | | | | Forming | $60 | $90 | |
| 16 | Percentages of time spent in departments | | | | | Assembly | $80 | $85 | |
| 17 | | Model S | Model LX | | | Total direct labor | $175 | $210 | |
| 18 | Stamping | 22.2% | 77.8% | | | Overhead allocation | | | |
| 19 | Forming | 12.5% | 87.5% | | | Stamping | $149 | $159 | |
| 20 | | | | | | Forming | $150 | $229 | |
| 21 | Unit selling price | $1,800 | $2,100 | | | Assembly | $365 | $246 | |
| 22 | | | | | | Total overhead | $664 | $635 | |
| 23 | Assembly capacity | 1900 | 1400 | | | Total cost | $1,839 | $2,045 | |

Model S shelves are sold for $1800, and model LX shelves are sold for $2100. Shelby's operation is fairly small in the industry, and management at Shelby believes it cannot raise prices beyond these levels because of the competition. However, the marketing department believes that Shelby can sell as much as it can produce at these prices. The costs of production are summarized in the Accounting Data sheet.

As usual, values in blue cells are given, whereas other values are calculated from these.

Management at Shelby just met to discuss next month's operating plan. Although the shelves are selling well, the overall profitability of the company is a concern. The plant's engineer suggested that the current production of model S shelves be cut back. According to him, "Model S shelves are sold for

$1800 per unit, but our costs are $1839. Even though we're selling only 400 units a month, we're losing money on each one. We should decrease production of model S." The controller disagreed. He said that the problem was the model S assembly department trying to absorb a large overhead with a small production volume. "The model S units are making a contribution to overhead. Even though production doesn't cover all of the fixed costs, we'd be worse off with lower production."

Your job is to develop an LP model of Shelby's problem, then run Solver, and finally make a recommendation to Shelby management, with a short verbal argument supporting the engineer or the controller.

## Notes on Accounting Data Calculations

The fixed overhead is distributed using activity-based costing principles. For example, at current production levels, the forming machine spends 100 hours on model S shelves and 700 hours on model LX shelves. The forming machine is used 800 hours of the month, of which 12.5% of the time is spent on model S shelves and 87.5% is spent on model LX shelves. The $95,000 of fixed overhead in the forming department is distributed as $11,875 (= 95,000 × 0.125) to model S shelves and $83,125 (= 95,000 × 0.875) to model LX shelves. The fixed overhead per unit of output is allocated as $29.69 (= 11,875/400) for model S and $59.38 (= 83,125/1400) for model LX. In the calculation of the standard overhead cost, the fixed and variable costs are added together, so that the overhead cost for the forming department allocated to a model S shelf is $149.69 (= 29.69 + 120, shown in cell G20 rounded up to $150). Similarly, the overhead cost for the forming department allocated to a model LX shelf is $229.38 (= 59.38 + 170, shown in cell H20 rounded down to $229). ▪

After graduating from business school, George Clark went to work for a Big Six accounting firm in San Francisco. Because his hobby has always been wine making, when he had the opportunity a few years later he purchased five acres plus an option to buy 35 additional acres of land in Sonoma Valley in Northern California. He plans eventually to grow grapes on that land and make wine with them. George knows that this is a big undertaking and that it will require more capital than he has at the present. However, he figures that if he persists, he will be able to leave accounting and live full time from his winery earnings by the time he is 40.

Because wine making is capital-intensive and because growing commercial-quality grapes with a full yield of five tons per acre takes at least eight years, George is planning to start small. This is necessitated by both his lack of capital and his inexperience in wine making on a large scale, although he has long made wine at home. His plan is first to plant the grapes on his land to get the vines started. Then he needs to set up a small trailer where he can live on weekends while he installs the irrigation system and does the required work to the vines, such as pruning and fertilizing. To help maintain a positive cash flow during the first few years, he also plans to buy grapes from other nearby growers so he can make his own label wine. He proposes to market it through a small tasting room that he will build on his land and keep open on weekends during the spring–summer season.

To begin, George is going to use $10,000 in savings to finance the initial purchase of grapes from which he will make his first batch of wine. He is also thinking about going to the Bank of Sonoma and asking for a loan. He knows that if he goes to the bank, the loan officer will ask for a business plan; so he is trying to pull together some numbers for himself first. This way he will have a rough notion of the profitability and cash flows associated with his ideas before he develops a formal plan with a pro forma income statement and balance sheet. He has decided to make the preliminary planning horizon two years and would like to estimate the profit over that period. His most immediate task is to decide how much of the $10,000 should be allocated to purchasing grapes for the first year and how much to purchasing grapes for the second year. In addition, each year he must decide how much he should allocate to purchasing grapes to make his favorite Petite Sirah and how much to purchasing grapes to make the more popular Sauvignon Blanc that seems to have been capturing the attention of a wider market during the last few years in California.

In the first year, each bottle of Petite Sirah requires $0.80 worth of grapes and each bottle of Sauvignon Blanc uses $0.70 worth of grapes. For the second year, the costs of the grapes per bottle are $0.75 and $0.85, respectively.

George anticipates that his Petite Sirah will sell for $8.00 a bottle in the first year and for $8.25 in the second year, while his Sauvignon Blanc's price remains the same in both years at $7.00 a bottle.

Besides the decisions about the amounts of grapes purchased in the two years, George must make estimates of the sales levels for the two wines during the two years. The local wine-making association has told him that marketing is the key to success in any wine business; generally, demand is directly proportional to the amount of effort spent on marketing. Thus, since George cannot afford to do any market research about sales levels due to his lack of capital, he is pondering how much money he should spend to promote each wine each year. The wine-making association has given him a rule of thumb that relates estimated demand to the amount of money spent on advertising. For instance, they estimate that for each dollar spent in the first year promoting the Petite Sirah, a demand for five bottles will be created; and for each dollar spent in the second year, a demand for six bottles will result. Similarly, for each dollar spent on advertising for the Sauvignon Blanc in the first year, up to eight bottles can be sold; and for each dollar spent in the second year, up to ten bottles can be sold.

[15]This case was written by William D. Whisler, California State University, Hayward.

The initial funds for the advertising will come from the $10,000 savings. Assume that the cash earned from wine sales in the first year is available in the second year.

A personal concern George has is that he maintain a proper balance of wine products so that he will be well positioned to expand his marketing capabilities when he moves to the winery and makes it his full-time job. Thus, in his mind it is important to ensure that the number of bottles of Petite Sirah sold each year falls in the range between 40% and 70% of the overall number of bottles sold.

## Questions

1. George needs help to decide how many grapes to buy, how much money to spend on advertising, how many bottles of wine to sell, and how much profit he can expect to earn over the two-year period. Develop a spreadsheet LP model to help him.
2. Solve the linear programming model formulated in Question 1.

*The following questions should be attempted only after Questions 1 and 2 have been answered correctly.*

3. After showing the business plan to the Bank of Sonoma, George learns that the loan officer is concerned about the market prices used in estimating the profits—recently it has been forecasted that Chile and Australia will be flooding the market with high-quality, low-priced white wines over the next couple of years. In particular, the loan officer estimates that the price used for the Sauvignon Blanc in the second year is highly speculative and realistically might be only half the price George calculated. Thus, the bank is nervous about lending the money because of the big effect such a decrease in price might have on estimated profits. What do you think?
4. Another comment the loan officer of the Bank of Sonoma has after reviewing the business plan is: "I see that you do have an allowance in your calculations for the carryover of inventory of unsold wine from the first year to the second year, but you do not have any cost associated with this. All companies must charge something for holding inventory, so you should redo your plans to allow for this." If the holding charges are $0.10 per bottle per year, how much, if any, does George's plan change?

5. The president of the local grape growers' association mentions to George that there is likely to be a strike soon over the unionization of the grape workers. (Currently they are not represented by any union.) This means that the costs of the grapes might go up by anywhere from 50% to 100%. How might this affect George's plan?
6. Before taking his business plan to the bank, George had it reviewed by a colleague at the accounting firm where he works. Although his friend was excited about the plan and its prospects, he was dismayed to learn that George had not used present value in determining his profit. "George, you are an accountant and must know that money has a time value; and although you are only doing a two-year planning problem, it still is important to calculate the present value profit." George replies, "Yes, I know all about present value. For big investments over long time periods, it is important to consider. But in this case, for a small investment and only a two-year time period, it really doesn't matter." Who is correct, George or his colleague? Why? Use an 8% discount factor in answering this question. Does the answer change if a 6% or 10% discount rate is used? Use a spreadsheet to determine the coefficients of the objective function for the different discount rates.
7. Suppose that the Bank of Sonoma is so excited about the prospects of George's wine-growing business that they offer to lend him an extra $10,000 at their best small business rate—28% plus a 10% compensating balance.[16] Should he accept the bank's offer? Why or why not?
8. Suppose that the rule of thumb George was given by the local wine-making association is incorrect. Assume that the number of bottles of Petite Sirah sold in the first and second years is at most four for each dollar spent on advertising. And likewise for the Sauvignon Blanc, assume that it can be at most only five in years 1 and 2.
9. How much could profits be increased if George's personal concerns (that Petite Sirah sales should account for between 40% and 70% of overall sales) are ignored?

---

[16]The compensating balance requirement means that only $9,000 of the $10,000 loan is available to George; the remaining $1,000 remains with the bank.

# Linear Programming Models

ROB KIM/Landov

## PRODUCTION, INVENTORY, AND DISTRIBUTION AT KELLOGG

The Kellogg Company is the largest cereal producer in the world and is a leading producer of convenience foods. Its worldwide sales in 1999 were nearly $7 billion. Kellogg's first product in 1906 was Corn Flakes, and it developed a variety of ready-to-eat cereals over the years, including Raisin Bran, Rice Krispies, Corn Pops, and others. Although the company continues to develop and market new cereals, it has recently gone into convenience foods, such as Pop-Tarts and Nutri-Grain cereal bars, and has also entered the health-food market. Kellogg produces hundreds of products and sells thousands of stock-keeping units (SKUs). Managing production, inventory, and distribution of these—that is, the daily operations—in a cost-effective manner is a challenge.

By the late 1980s, Kellogg realized that the increasing scale and complexity of its operations required optimization methods to coordinate its daily operations in a centralized manner. As described in Brown et al. (2001), a team of management scientists developed an optimization software system called KPS (Kellogg Planning System). This system was originally intended for operational (daily and weekly) decisions, but it expanded into a system for making tactical (longer-range) decisions about issues such as plant budgets, capacity expansion, and consolidation. By the turn of the century, KPS had been in use for about a decade. Operational decisions made by

KPS reduced production, inventory, and distribution costs by approximately $4.5 million per year. Better yet, the tactical side of KPS recently suggested a consolidation of production capacity that saved the company approximately $35 million to $40 million annually.

Kellogg operates 5 plants in the United States and Canada, has 7 distribution centers (DCs) in such areas as Los Angeles and Chicago, and has about 15 co-packers, companies that contract to produce or pack some of Kellogg's products. Customer demands are seen at the DCs and the plants. In the cereal business alone, Kellogg has to coordinate the packaging, inventorying, and distributing of 600 SKUs at about 27 locations with a total of about 90 productions lines and 180 packaging lines. This requires a tremendous amount of day-to-day coordination to meet customer demand at a low cost. The KPS operational system that guides operational decisions is essentially a large linear programming model that takes as its inputs the forecasted customer demands for the various products and specifies what should be produced, held, and shipped on a daily basis. The resulting model is similar to the Pigskin model of football production discussed in the previous chapter, except that it is *much* larger.

Specifically, for each week of its 30-week planning horizon, the model specifies (1) how much of each product to make on each production line at each facility, (2) how much of each SKU to pack on each packaging line at each facility, (3) how much inventory of each SKU to hold at each facility, and (4) how much of each SKU to ship from each location to other locations. In addition, the model has to take constraints into account. For example, the production within a given plant in a week cannot exceed the processing line capacity in that plant. Linear programming models such as Kellogg's tend to be very large—thousands of decision variables and hundreds or thousands of constraints—but the algorithms Kellogg uses are capable of optimizing such models very quickly. Kellogg runs its KPS model each Sunday morning and uses its recommendations in the ensuing week.

Kellogg's KPS illustrates a common occurrence when companies turn to management science for help. As stated earlier, the system was originally developed for making daily operational decisions. Soon, however, the company developed a tactical version of KPS for long-range planning on the order of 12 to 24 months. The tactical model is similar to the operational model except that time periods are now months, not days or weeks, and other considerations must be handled, such as limited product shelf lives. The point is, however, that when companies such as Kellogg become comfortable with management science methods in one part of their operations, they often look for other areas to apply similar methods. As with Kellogg, such methods can save the company millions of dollars. ■

## 4.1 INTRODUCTION

In a recent survey of Fortune 500 firms, 85% of those responding said that they used linear programming. In this chapter, we discuss some of the LP models that are most often applied to real applications. In this chapter's examples, you will discover how to build optimization models to

- purchase television ads
- schedule postal workers
- create an aggregate labor and production plan at a shoe company
- create a blending plan to transform crude oils into end products

- plan production of interdependent products at a drug company
- choose an investment strategy at a financial investment company
- manage a pension fund
- determine which of several hospitals use their inputs "efficiently"

The two basic goals of this chapter are to illustrate the wide range of real applications that can take advantage of LP and to increase your facility in modeling LP problems in Excel. We present a few principles that will help you model a wide variety of problems. The best way to learn, however, is to see many examples and work through numerous problems. In short, mastering the art of LP spreadsheet modeling takes hard work and practice, which you will find plenty of in this chapter.

Before continuing, remember that all of the models in this chapter are *linear* models as described in the previous chapter. This means that the target cell is ultimately (possibly through a series of formulas in intervening cells) a sum of products of constants and changing cells, where a *constant* is defined by the fact that it does not depend on changing cells. Similarly, each side of each constraint is either a constant or a sum of products of constants and changing cells. Also, each changing cell (except in a few cases where it is specified otherwise) is allowed to contain a continuous range of values, not just integer values. These properties allow Solver to use its very efficient simplex method to find the optimal solution.[1]

## 4.2 ADVERTISING MODELS

Many companies spend enormous amounts of money to advertise their products. They want to ensure that they are spending their money wisely. Typically, they want to reach large numbers of various groups of potential customers and keep their advertising costs as low as possible. The following example illustrates a simple model—and a reasonable extension of this model—for a company that purchases television ads.

---

**EXAMPLE** | **4.1 PURCHASING TELEVISION ADS**

The General Flakes Company sells a brand of low-fat breakfast cereal that appeals to people of all age groups and both genders. The company advertises this cereal in a variety of 30-second television ads, and these ads can be placed in a variety of television shows. The ads in different shows vary by cost—some 30-second slots are much more expensive than others—and by the types of viewers they are likely to reach. The company has segmented the potential viewers into six mutually exclusive categories: males age 18 to 35, males age 36 to 55, males over 55, females age 18 to 35, females age 36 to 55, and females over 55. A rating service can supply data on the numbers of viewers in each of these categories who will watch a 30-second ad on any particular television show. Each such viewer is called an *exposure*. The company has determined the required number of exposures it wants to obtain for each group. It wants to know how many ads to place on each of several television shows to obtain these required exposures at minimum cost. The data on costs per ad, numbers of exposures per ad, and minimal required exposures are listed in Table 4.1, where numbers of exposures are expressed in millions, and costs are in thousands of dollars. What should the company do?

---

[1]In the special cases where integer constraints are imposed on some changing cells, the Simplex LP option can still be chosen. However, Solver uses a somewhat different optimization algorithm when there are integer-constrained changing cells. This is covered in more depth in Chapter 6.

Table 4.1    Data for Advertising Problem

| Viewer Group/ TV Show | "Desperate Housewives" | "Monday Night Football" | "The Simpsons" | "Sports Center" | "The Real World" (MTV) | Lifetime Evening Movie | CNN | "Law & Order SVU" | Minimal Required Exposures |
|---|---|---|---|---|---|---|---|---|---|
| Men 18–35 | 5 | 6 | 5 | 0.5 | 0.7 | 0.1 | 0.1 | 3 | 60 |
| Men 36–55 | 3 | 5 | 2 | 0.5 | 0.2 | 0.1 | 0.2 | 5 | 60 |
| Men over 55 | 1 | 3 | 0 | 0.3 | 0 | 0 | 0.3 | 4 | 28 |
| Women 18–35 | 6 | 1 | 4 | 0.1 | 0.9 | 0.6 | 0.1 | 3 | 60 |
| Women 36–55 | 4 | 1 | 2 | 0.1 | 0.1 | 1.3 | 0.2 | 5 | 60 |
| Women over 55 | 2 | 1 | 0 | 0 | 0 | 0.4 | 0.3 | 4 | 28 |
| Cost per Ad | 140 | 100 | 80 | 9 | 13 | 15 | 8 | 140 | |

*This list is a small subset of shows from which a company could choose, but it is a good representation of the types of shows favored by various age groups and genders.*

**Objective**    To develop an LP spreadsheet model that relates the numbers of ads on various television shows to the exposures to various viewer groups, and to use Solver to find the minimum-cost advertising strategy that meets minimum exposure constraints.

## WHERE DO THE NUMBERS COME FROM?

The data for this problem would probably be straightforward to obtain, as suggested here:

- The advertising costs per ad are the going rates for 30-second slots for the various types of shows.

- The exposures per ad on the various shows are typically supplied by the media planning departments of advertising agencies. (However, see the "Modeling Issues" section at the end of this example.)

- The required numbers of exposures are probably determined internally by the company. The company's marketing department knows which population groups are its best customers and probably has some sense of the numbers of exposures the company should obtain for a general level of advertising.

## Solution

This problem is straightforward to model. As indicated in Table 4.2, the company needs to decide how many ads to place on each television show. This determines the total advertising cost, which becomes the objective to minimize, and the total number of exposures to each viewer group. The only constraint, other than nonnegativity, is that there must be at least the required number of exposures for each group.

Table 4.2    Variables and Constraints for Advertising Model

| | |
|---|---|
| Input variables | Cost per ad, exposures per ad, minimal required exposures |
| Decision variables (changing cells) | Numbers of ads to place on various types of shows |
| Objective (target cell) | Total advertising cost |
| Other calculated variables | Total exposures to each viewer group |
| Constraints | Actual exposures ≥ Required exposures |

### Comparison to Product Mix Model

Before continuing, note that this model is essentially the opposite of the product mix models in the previous chapter. With a product mix model, the goal is to make the values of the decision variables (numbers of items to produce) as large as possible to make a large profit. The constraints on resource availability impose a limit on these values. In contrast, the goal now is to make the values of the decision variables as *small* as possible to minimize cost. This time, the constraints on required exposures impose lower limits on these values. These two prototype LP models—maximizing profit subject to "less than or equal to" constraints, and minimizing cost subject to "greater than or equal to" constraints—are certainly not the only types of LP models that exist, but they are very common.

## DEVELOPING THE SPREADSHEET MODEL

The completed model for the advertising problem appears in Figure 4.1.[2] (See the file Advertising 1.xlsx.) The model can be created with the following steps:

**Figure 4.1** Optimal Solution for the Advertising Model

| | A | B | C | D | E | F | G | H | I |
|---|---|---|---|---|---|---|---|---|---|
| 1 | Advertising model | | | | | | | | |
| 2 | | | Note: All monetary values are in $1000s, and all | | | | | | |
| 3 | Inputs | | exposures to ads are in millions of exposures. | | | | | | |
| 4 | Exposures to various groups per ad | | | | | | | | |
| 5 | | Desperate Housewives | MNF | The Simpsons | Sports Center | The Real World | Lifetime movie | CNN | Law & Order SVU |
| 6 | Men 18-35 | 5 | 6 | 5 | 0.5 | 0.7 | 0.1 | 0.1 | 3 |
| 7 | Men 36-55 | 3 | 5 | 2 | 0.5 | 0.2 | 0.1 | 0.2 | 5 |
| 8 | Men >55 | 1 | 3 | 0 | 0.3 | 0 | 0 | 0.3 | 4 |
| 9 | Women 18-35 | 6 | 1 | 4 | 0.1 | 0.9 | 0.6 | 0.1 | 3 |
| 10 | Women 36-55 | 4 | 1 | 2 | 0.1 | 0.1 | 1.3 | 0.2 | 5 |
| 11 | Women >55 | 2 | 1 | 0 | 0 | 0 | 0.4 | 0.3 | 4 |
| 12 | Total viewers | 21 | 17 | 13 | 1.5 | 1.9 | 2.5 | 1.2 | 24 |
| 13 | | | | | | | | | |
| 14 | Cost per ad | 140 | 100 | 80 | 9 | 13 | 15 | 8 | 140 |
| 15 | Cost per million exposures | 6.667 | 5.882 | 6.154 | 6.000 | 6.842 | 6.000 | 6.667 | 5.833 |
| 16 | | | | | | | | | |
| 17 | Advertising plan | | | | | | | | |
| 18 | | Desperate Housewives | MNF | The Simpsons | Sports Center | The Real World | Lifetime movie | CNN | Law & Order SVU |
| 19 | Number ads purchased | 0.000 | 0.000 | 8.719 | 20.625 | 0.000 | 6.875 | 0.000 | 6.313 |
| 20 | | | | | | | | | |
| 21 | Constraints on numbers of exposures | | | | | | Range names used: | | |
| 22 | | Actual exposures | | Required exposures | | | Actual_exposures | =Model!$B$23:$B$28 | |
| 23 | Men 18-35 | 73.531 | >= | 60 | | | Number_ads_purchased | =Model!$B$19:$I$19 | |
| 24 | Men 36-55 | 60.000 | >= | 60 | | | Required_exposures | =Model!$D$23:$D$28 | |
| 25 | Men >55 | 31.438 | >= | 28 | | | Total_cost | =Model!$B$31 | |
| 26 | Women 18-35 | 60.000 | >= | 60 | | | | | |
| 27 | Women 36-55 | 60.000 | >= | 60 | | | | | |
| 28 | Women >55 | 28.000 | >= | 28 | | | | | |
| 29 | | | | | | | | | |
| 30 | Objective to minimize | | | | | | | | |
| 31 | Total cost | $1,870.000 | | | | | | | |

**①** **Input values and range names.** Enter the inputs from Table 4.1 in the shaded ranges, and name the ranges as shown.

**Excel Tip:** *Range Name Shortcut*
*We've said it before, but we'll say it again. Whenever possible, use short and descriptive labels such as in cells A19 and B22. Then you can take advantage of these labels, along with the Create from Selection shortcut, to name multiple ranges quickly.*

**②** **Ads purchased.** Enter *any* values in the Number_ads_purchased range. These are the only changing cells for this model.

**③** **Exposures obtained.** The numbers of ads purchased determine the numbers of exposures to the various viewer groups. To calculate these exposures, enter the formula

=SUMPRODUCT(B6:I6,Number_ads_purchased)

in cell B23 and copy it down to cell B28.

---

[2] From here on, to save space we typically show only the *optimal* solution. However, remember that when you develop a spreadsheet optimization model, you can enter *any* values in the changing cells initially. Solver will eventually find the optimal solution.

**④ Total cost.** The quantities of ads purchased also determine the total cost of advertising. Calculate this cost in cell B31 with the formula

=SUMPRODUCT(B14:I14,Number_ads_purchased)

## USING SOLVER

The main Solver dialog box appears in Figure 4.2. After filling it out as shown and checking the Non-Negative option and selecting the Simplex LP method, click on the Solve button to obtain the solution shown in Figure 4.1.

Figure 4.2

Solver Dialog Box for the Advertising Model

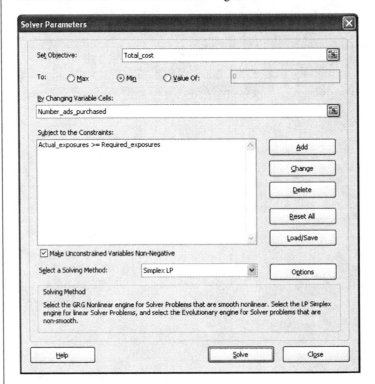

## Discussion of the Solution

The optimal solution is probably not the one you would have guessed. With a set of ads that cost very different amounts and reach very different mixes of viewers, it is difficult to guess the optimal strategy. For comparison, however, we calculated the total number of viewers from each type of ad in row 12 and divided the costs in row 14 by the numbers of viewers in row 12 to obtain the cost per million viewers in row 15. You might expect the ads with low cost per million viewers to be chosen most frequently. However, this is not necessarily the case. For example, "Monday Night Football" (MNF) has the second-lowest cost per million viewers, but the optimal solution doesn't include any ads for this show.

## Sensitivity Analysis

Solver's sensitivity report, shown in Figure 4.3, is enlightening for this solution. Here is a sample of the information it provides.

■ The company is not currently purchasing any ads on "Desperate Housewives." The reduced cost for this show implies that the cost per ad would have to decrease by at least 10 ($10,000) before it would be optimal to purchase any ads on this show.

■ The company is currently purchasing about 20 ads on "Sports Center." The allowable increase and decrease for this show indicate how much the cost per ad would have to

## Figure 4.3  Sensitivity Report for the Advertising Model

| | A | B | C | D | E | F | G | H |
|---|---|---|---|---|---|---|---|---|
| 6 | | Variable Cells | | | | | | |
| 7 | | | | Final | Reduced | Objective | Allowable | Allowable |
| 8 | | Cell | Name | Value | Cost | Coefficient | Increase | Decrease |
| 9 | | $B$19 | Number ads purchased Desperate Housewives | 0 | 10 | 140 | 1E+30 | 10 |
| 10 | | $C$19 | Number ads purchased MNF | 0 | 7.5 | 100 | 1E+30 | 7.5 |
| 11 | | $D$19 | Number ads purchased The Simpsons | 8.719 | 0 | 80 | 1.744 | 29.091 |
| 12 | | $E$19 | Number ads purchased Sports Center | 20.625 | 0 | 9 | 0.762 | 0.451 |
| 13 | | $F$19 | Number ads purchased The Real World | 0 | 0.5 | 13 | 1E+30 | 0.5 |
| 14 | | $G$19 | Number ads purchased Lifetime movie | 6.875 | 0 | 15 | 2.286 | 1.103 |
| 15 | | $H$19 | Number ads purchased CNN | 0 | 2.25 | 8 | 1E+30 | 2.25 |
| 16 | | $I$19 | Number ads purchased Law & Order SVU | 6.313 | 0 | 140 | 11.034 | 6.957 |
| 17 | | | | | | | | |
| 18 | | Constraints | | | | | | |
| 19 | | | | Final | Shadow | Constraint | Allowable | Allowable |
| 20 | | Cell | Name | Value | Price | R.H. Side | Increase | Decrease |
| 21 | | $B$23 | Men 18-35 Actual exposures | 73.531 | 0 | 60 | 13.531 | 1E+30 |
| 22 | | $B$24 | Men 36-55 Actual exposures | 60 | 15 | 60 | 44 | 5.116 |
| 23 | | $B$25 | Men >55 Actual exposures | 31.438 | 0 | 28 | 3.438 | 1E+30 |
| 24 | | $B$26 | Women 18-35 Actual exposures | 60 | 10 | 60 | 11 | 14.931 |
| 25 | | $B$27 | Women 36-55 Actual exposures | 60 | 5 | 60 | 44.889 | 4.889 |
| 26 | | $B$28 | Women >55 Actual exposures | 28 | 2.5 | 28 | 6.286 | 7.586 |

change before the optimal number of ads on the show would change. For example, if the price per ad increased above $9 + 0.762$ ($9762), the company might purchase fewer than 20 ads. How many fewer? You would have to rerun Solver to know.

- The constraint on exposures to men in the 36–55 age range has the largest shadow price, 15.000. If the company relaxed this constraint to require only 59 million exposures, it would save $15,000 in total advertising cost. On the other side, if the company required 61 million exposures to this group, rather than 60 million, its cost would increase by $15,000.

## A Dual-Objective Extension of the Model

*This is called a dual-objective optimization model. Typically, the two objectives are pulling in different directions, as they are here.*

This advertising model can be extended in a very natural way. General Flakes really has two competing objectives: (1) to obtain as many exposures as possible, and (2) to keep the total advertising cost as low as possible. In the original model, we decided to minimize total cost and constrain the exposures to be at least as large as a required level. An alternative is to maximize the total number of excess exposures and put a budget constraint on total cost. Here, *excess exposures* are those above the minimal required level.

To implement this alternative, only minor modifications to the original model are necessary, as shown in Figure 4.4. (See the file Advertising 2.xlsx.) You can do this with the following steps:

**1 Excess exposures.** For each viewer group, calculate the number of excess exposures by entering the formula

=B23-D23

in cell F23 and copying it down. Then sum these in cell B35 with the SUM function. This cell becomes the new target cell to maximize.

**2 Budget constraint.** Calculate the total cost exactly as before, but now constrain it to be less than or equal to a given budget in cell D32.

**3 Solver dialog box.** Modify the Solver dialog box as shown in Figure 4.5.

## Figure 4.4 Spreadsheet Model for Extension to the Advertising Problem

| | A | B | C | D | E | F | G | H | I |
|---|---|---|---|---|---|---|---|---|---|
| 1 | Two-objective advertising model | | | | | | | | |
| 2 | | | | Note: All monetary values are in $1000s, and all | | | | | |
| 3 | Inputs | | | exposures to ads are in millions of exposures. | | | | | |
| 4 | Exposures to various groups per ad | | | | | | | | |
| 5 | | Desperate Housewives | MNF | The Simpsons | Sports Center | The Real World | Lifetime movie | CNN | Law & Order SVU |
| 6 | Men 18-35 | 5 | 6 | 5 | 0.5 | 0.7 | 0.1 | 0.1 | 3 |
| 7 | Men 36-55 | 3 | 5 | 2 | 0.5 | 0.2 | 0.1 | 0.2 | 5 |
| 8 | Men >55 | 1 | 3 | 0 | 0.3 | 0 | 0 | 0.3 | 4 |
| 9 | Women 18-35 | 6 | 1 | 4 | 0.1 | 0.9 | 0.6 | 0.1 | 3 |
| 10 | Women 36-55 | 4 | 1 | 2 | 0.1 | 0.1 | 1.3 | 0.2 | 5 |
| 11 | Women >55 | 2 | 1 | 0 | 0 | 0 | 0.4 | 0.3 | 4 |
| 12 | Total viewers | 21 | 17 | 13 | 1.5 | 1.9 | 2.5 | 1.2 | 24 |
| 13 | | | | | | | | | |
| 14 | Cost per ad | 140 | 100 | 80 | 9 | 13 | 15 | 8 | 140 |
| 15 | Cost per million exposures | 6.667 | 5.882 | 6.154 | 6.000 | 6.842 | 6.000 | 6.667 | 5.833 |
| 16 | | | | | | | | | |
| 17 | Advertising plan | | | | | | | | |
| 18 | | Desperate Housewives | MNF | The Simpsons | Sports Center | The Real World | Lifetime movie | CNN | Law & Order SVU |
| 19 | Number ads purchased | 0.000 | 0.000 | 6.030 | 0.000 | 0.000 | 12.060 | 0.000 | 9.548 |
| 20 | | | | | | | | | |
| 21 | Constraints on numbers of exposures | | | | | | | Range names used: | |
| 22 | | Actual exposures | | Required exposures | | Excess exposures | | Actual_exposures | =Model!$B$23:$B$28 |
| 23 | Men 18-35 | 60.000 | >= | 60 | | 0.000 | | Budget | =Model!$D$32 |
| 24 | Men 36-55 | 61.005 | >= | 60 | | 1.005 | | Excess_exposures | =Model!$F$23:$F$28 |
| 25 | Men >55 | 38.191 | >= | 28 | | 10.191 | | Number_ads_purchased | =Model!$B$19:$I$19 |
| 26 | Women 18-35 | 60.000 | >= | 60 | | 0.000 | | Required_exposures | =Model!$D$23:$D$28 |
| 27 | Women 36-55 | 75.477 | >= | 60 | | 15.477 | | Total_cost | =Model!$B$32 |
| 28 | Women >55 | 43.015 | >= | 28 | | 15.015 | | Total_excess_exposures | =Model!$B$35 |
| 29 | | | | | | | | | |
| 30 | Budget constrain on total cost | | | | | | | | |
| 31 | | Total cost | | Budget | | | | | |
| 32 | | $2,000 | <= | $2,000 | | | | | |
| 33 | | | | | | | | | |
| 34 | Objective to maximize | | | | | | | | |
| 35 | Total excess exposures | 41.688 | | | | | | | |

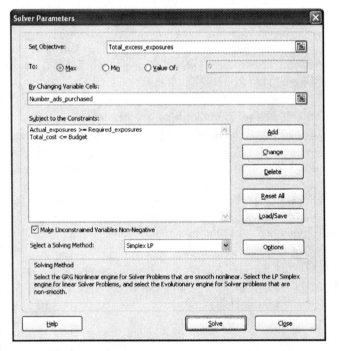

## Figure 4.5

Modified Solver Dialog Box for Extension to the Advertising Problem

At this point, you are probably wondering where the budget of $2 million in Figure 4.4 comes from. This requires some explanation of the solution strategy in this extension of the original model. The basic assumption is that the company has two objectives: to maximize total excess exposures *and* to minimize total cost. Unfortunately, it is impossible to do both because they are pulling in different directions. When you have a dual-objective problem such as this, you typically use one of the objectives as the target cell and constrain the other. Here, the company is asking how many excess exposures it can get for a given budget. There is no natural budget to use, and it makes perfect sense to ask questions such as these: How many exposures can the company get for $1.9 million? How many for $2.0 million? How many for $2.1 million?

*For dual-objective models, you optimize one objective and put a constraint on the other. Then you can use SolverTable to vary the right-hand side of this constraint. The result is a trade-off curve.*

Fortunately, SolverTable is the perfect tool to answer all of these questions in one step. You first develop the model as in Figure 4.4, using *any* budget such as $2.0 million in cell D32, and run Solver in the usual way. Then you run a one-way SolverTable, allowing the budget to vary over some desired range, and keep track of selected output variables. Typical results appear in Figure 4.6, which are based on the SolverTable settings in Figure 4.7. For low budget levels, the problem is infeasible—there is no way with this budget to obtain the required exposures. Above a certain budget level, the problem becomes feasible, and the optimal solutions are shown. As the budget increases, the company can clearly obtain larger numbers of excess exposures, but the optimal advertising strategy in columns B through I changes in a somewhat unpredictable way.

The results of this sensitivity analysis can be shown graphically in a **trade-off curve**, as in Figure 4.8. To create this, highlight the numbers in columns A and J of Figure 4.6 (from row 43 down) and insert a line chart. This chart illustrates the rather obvious fact that when the company is allowed to spend more on advertising, it can achieve more total excess exposures.

**Figure 4.6** Sensitivity of Optimal Solution to the Advertising Budget

| | A | B | C | D | E | F | G | H | I | J |
|---|---|---|---|---|---|---|---|---|---|---|
| 1 | Oneway analysis for Solver model in Model worksheet | | | | | | | | | |
| 2 | | | | | | | | | | |
| 3 | Budget (cell $D$32) values along side, output cell(s) along top | | | | | | | | | |
| 4 | | Number_ads_purchased_1 | Number_ads_purchased_2 | Number_ads_purchased_3 | Number_ads_purchased_4 | Number_ads_purchased_5 | Number_ads_purchased_6 | Number_ads_purchased_7 | Number_ads_purchased_8 | Total_excess_exposures |
| 5 | $1,800 | Not feasible | | | | | | | | |
| 6 | $1,850 | Not feasible | | | | | | | | |
| 7 | $1,900 | 0.000 | 0.000 | 8.208 | 0.000 | 0.000 | 1.887 | 0.000 | 8.679 | 23.717 |
| 8 | $1,950 | 0.000 | 0.000 | 6.934 | 0.000 | 0.000 | 8.491 | 0.000 | 9.057 | 32.726 |
| 9 | $2,000 | 0.000 | 0.000 | 6.030 | 0.000 | 0.000 | 12.060 | 0.000 | 9.548 | 41.688 |
| 10 | $2,050 | 0.000 | 0.000 | 5.653 | 0.000 | 0.000 | 11.307 | 0.000 | 10.201 | 50.583 |
| 11 | $2,100 | 0.000 | 0.000 | 5.276 | 0.000 | 0.000 | 10.553 | 0.000 | 10.854 | 59.477 |
| 12 | $2,150 | 0.000 | 0.000 | 4.899 | 0.000 | 0.000 | 9.799 | 0.000 | 11.508 | 68.372 |
| 13 | $2,200 | 0.000 | 0.000 | 4.523 | 0.000 | 0.000 | 9.045 | 0.000 | 12.161 | 77.266 |
| 14 | $2,250 | 0.000 | 0.000 | 4.146 | 0.000 | 0.000 | 8.291 | 0.000 | 12.814 | 86.161 |
| 15 | $2,300 | 0.000 | 0.000 | 3.769 | 0.000 | 0.000 | 7.538 | 0.000 | 13.467 | 95.055 |
| 16 | $2,350 | 0.000 | 0.000 | 3.392 | 0.000 | 0.000 | 6.784 | 0.000 | 14.121 | 103.950 |
| 17 | $2,400 | 0.000 | 0.000 | 3.015 | 0.000 | 0.000 | 6.030 | 0.000 | 14.774 | 112.844 |
| 18 | $2,450 | 0.000 | 0.000 | 2.638 | 0.000 | 0.000 | 5.276 | 0.000 | 15.427 | 121.739 |
| 19 | $2,500 | 0.000 | 0.000 | 2.261 | 0.000 | 0.000 | 4.523 | 0.000 | 16.080 | 130.633 |

Figure 4.7

SolverTable
Settings for
Sensitivity Analysis

**Parameters for oneway table**

Specify the following information about the input
to be varied and the outputs to be captured.

OK

Cancel

Input cell:     $D$32

(Optional) Descriptive
name for input:          Budget

Values of input to use for table

- Base input values on following:
  Minimum value:    1800
  Maximum value:    2500
  Increment:        50

- Use the values from the following range:
  Input value range:

- Use the values below (separate with commas)
  Input values:

Output cell(s):     $B$19:$I$19,$B$35

Note about specifying output cells: The safest way to select multiple
output cells or ranges is to put your finger on the Ctrl key and then
drag as many output cell ranges as you like. This will automatically insert
commas between the ranges you select.

Figure 4.8     Trade-Off Curve Between Total Excess Exposures and Total Cost

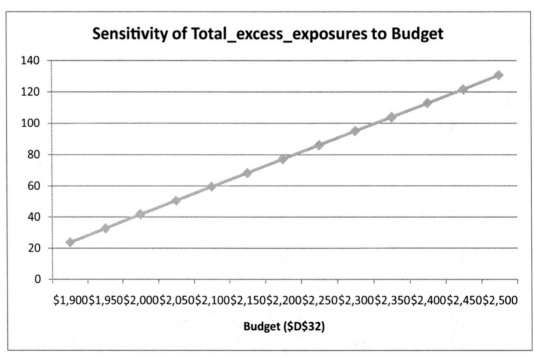

## Using Integer Constraints

The two advertising models to this point have allowed noninteger values in the changing cells. In reality, this is not allowed; the company cannot purchase, say, 6.313 ads on "Law & Order SVU." It must purchase integer numbers of ads. Given this, your first instinct is probably to round the optimal values in the changing cells to the nearest integers to obtain the optimal integer solution. Unfortunately, this can have unpredictable results. First, the rounded solution might not be feasible. Second, even if it is feasible, it might not be the *optimal* integer solution.

Although all of Chapter 6 is devoted to special types of *integer programming models*—those with integer constraints on at least some of the changing cells—we can preview the topic here. In fact, from a user's standpoint, there isn't much to it. To force the changing cells to have integer values, you simply add another constraint in the Solver dialog box, as shown in Figure 4.9. In the left text box, select the changing cell range. In the middle text box, select **int** (for integer). The right text box then automatically contains the word Integer. When you eventually click on Solve, you get the optimal integer solution shown in Figure 4.10.

*Use the int option in the Solver constraint dialog box to constrain changing cells to be integers.*

**Figure 4.9**

Specifying an
Integer Constraint

Consider the following about this integer solution:

- The total cost in the target cell is now worse (larger) than before. This illustrates the general rule that when *any* additional constraints are imposed, including integer constraints, the objective can only get worse or remain the same; it can never get better.

- The optimal integer solution is *not* the rounded noninteger solution. In fact, it isn't even close. (Compare the before and after "The Real World" and "Sports Center"

**Figure 4.10** Optimal Integer Solution to the Advertising Problem

| | A | B | C | D | E | F | G | H | I |
|---|---|---|---|---|---|---|---|---|---|
| 1 | Advertising model | | | | | | | | |
| 2 | | | | Note: All monetary values are in $1000s, and all | | | | | |
| 3 | Inputs | | | exposures to ads are in millions of exposures. | | | | | |
| 4 | Exposures to various groups per ad | | | | | | | | |
| 5 | | Desperate Housewives | MNF | The Simpsons | Sports Center | The Real World | Lifetime movie | CNN | Law & Order SVU |
| 6 | Men 18-35 | 5 | 6 | 5 | 0.5 | 0.7 | 0.1 | 0.1 | 3 |
| 7 | Men 36-55 | 3 | 5 | 2 | 0.5 | 0.2 | 0.1 | 0.2 | 5 |
| 8 | Men >55 | 1 | 3 | 0 | 0.3 | 0 | 0 | 0.3 | 4 |
| 9 | Women 18-35 | 6 | 1 | 4 | 0.1 | 0.9 | 0.6 | 0.1 | 3 |
| 10 | Women 36-55 | 4 | 1 | 2 | 0.1 | 0.1 | 1.3 | 0.2 | 5 |
| 11 | Women >55 | 2 | 1 | 0 | 0 | 0 | 0.4 | 0.3 | 4 |
| 12 | Total viewers | 21 | 17 | 13 | 1.5 | 1.9 | 2.5 | 1.2 | 24 |
| 13 | | | | | | | | | |
| 14 | Cost per ad | 140 | 100 | 80 | 9 | 13 | 15 | 8 | 140 |
| 15 | Cost per million exposures | 6.667 | 5.882 | 6.154 | 6.000 | 6.842 | 6.000 | 6.667 | 5.833 |
| 16 | | | | | | | | | |
| 17 | Advertising plan | | | | | | | | |
| 18 | | Desperate Housewives | MNF | The Simpsons | Sports Center | The Real World | Lifetime movie | CNN | Law & Order SVU |
| 19 | Number ads purchased | 0 | 0 | 8 | 16 | 2 | 6 | 0 | 7 |
| 20 | | | | | | | | | |
| 21 | Constraints on numbers of exposures | | | | | | | | |
| 22 | | Actual exposures | | Required exposures | | | | | |
| 23 | Men 18-35 | 71.000 | >= | 60 | | | | | |
| 24 | Men 36-55 | 60.000 | >= | 60 | | | | | |
| 25 | Men >55 | 32.800 | >= | 28 | | | | | |
| 26 | Women 18-35 | 60.000 | >= | 60 | | | | | |
| 27 | Women 36-55 | 60.600 | >= | 60 | | | | | |
| 28 | Women >55 | 30.400 | >= | 28 | | | | | |
| 29 | | | | | | | | | |
| 30 | Objective to minimize | | | | | | | | |
| 31 | Total cost | $1,880.000 | | | | | | | |

values, for example.) Rounding noninteger solutions sometimes works, and sometimes it doesn't. Using Solver with explicit integer constraints is always safer.

Specifying integer constraints in the Solver dialog box is easy. Be aware, however, that Solver must typically do a lot more work to solve problems with integer constraints.

- When there are integer constraints, Solver uses an algorithm—called *branch and bound*—that is significantly different from the simplex method. (Actually, the simplex method is still used to solve *subproblems,* but we won't discuss the details here.) Integer-constrained models are typically *much* harder to solve than models without any integer constraints. Although this small model still solves in a fraction of a second, larger integer models can take *minutes* or even *hours* of solution time.

- If the model is linear except for the integer constraints—that is, it satisfies the proportionality and additivity assumptions of linear models—you should still select the Simplex LP method. ▪

## MODELING ISSUES

The advertising model has one weakness, at least for realistic applications. Perhaps you have already spotted it: double-counting. Suppose a company runs three ads for the same product on a "Monday Night Football" telecast. Also, suppose that the rating service claims that an ad reaches, say, six million men age 18–35. How many *total* exposures do these three ads reach for this viewer group? Our model claims that it reaches 3(6) = 18 million. However, the *effective* number of exposures is probably lower than 18 million, for the simple reason that many of the *same* men are watching all three ads.

Unfortunately, many marketing models, including this one, are inherently nonlinear.

This presents two difficulties for the modeler. First, it is probably difficult to estimate the effective number of exposures to any viewer group when an ad is run multiple times on the same show. Second, even if a company can obtain such estimates, it faces a nonlinear model, as discussed in Chapter 7. This is because the proportionality assumption of LP no longer holds. Specifically, each extra ad on a given show reaches a decreasing number of *new* exposures. (We will revisit this model in Chapter 7.) ▪

## PROBLEMS

*Solutions for problems whose numbers appear within a colored box can be found in the Student Solutions Files. Refer to this book's preface for purchase information.*

### Skill-Building Problems

**1.** In addition to the constraints already in the (original) advertising model, suppose General Flakes also wants to obtain at least 180 million exposures to men and at least 160 million exposures to women. Does the current optimal solution satisfy these constraints? If not, modify the model as necessary, and rerun Solver to find the new optimal solution.

**2.** Suppose, as a matter of corporate policy, that General Flakes decides not to advertise on the Lifetime channel. Modify the original advertising model appropriately and find the new optimal solution. How much has it cost the company to make this policy decision?

**3.** Suppose, in addition to the shows already listed, General Flakes wants to open the possibility of purchasing ads on the "Good Morning America" show on ABC. Make up any reasonable input data you need to include this possibility in the (original) model, and find the optimal solution.

**4.** Suppose that General Flakes decides that it shouldn't place any more than 10 ads on any given show. Modify the (original) advertising model appropriately to incorporate this constraint, and then reoptimize (with integer constraints on the numbers of ads). Finally, run SolverTable to see how sensitive the optimal solution is to the maximum number of ads per show allowed. You can decide on a reasonable range for the sensitivity analysis.

**5.** In the dual-objective advertising model, we put a budget constraint on the total advertising cost and then maximized the total number of excess exposures. Do it the opposite way, reversing the roles of the two objectives. That is, model it so that you put a lower limit on the total number of excess exposures and minimize the total advertising cost. Then run a sensitivity analysis on this lower limit, and create a trade-off curve from the results of the sensitivity analysis.

**6.** Suppose there are *three* objectives, not just two: the total advertising cost, the total number of excess exposures to men, and the total number of excess exposures to women. Continuing the approach suggested in the previous problem, how might you proceed? Take it as far as you can, including a sensitivity analysis and a trade-off curve.

## 4.3 WORKER SCHEDULING MODELS

Many organizations must determine how to schedule employees to provide adequate service. The following example illustrates how LP can be used to schedule employees.

### EXAMPLE 4.2 POSTAL EMPLOYEE SCHEDULING

A post office requires different numbers of full-time employees on different days of the week. The number of full-time employees required each day is given in Table 4.3. Union rules state that each full-time employee must work five consecutive days and then receive two days off. For example, an employee who works Monday to Friday must be off on Saturday and Sunday. The post office wants to meet its daily requirements using only full-time employees. Its objective is to minimize the number of full-time employees on its payroll.

**Table 4.3** Employee Requirements for Post Office

| Day of Week | Minimum Number of Employees Required |
|---|---|
| Monday | 17 |
| Tuesday | 13 |
| Wednesday | 15 |
| Thursday | 19 |
| Friday | 14 |
| Saturday | 16 |
| Sunday | 11 |

**Objective** To develop an LP spreadsheet model that relates five-day shift schedules to daily numbers of employees available, and to use Solver on this model to find a schedule that uses the fewest number of employees and meets all daily workforce requirements.

#### WHERE DO THE NUMBERS COME FROM?

*In real employee-scheduling problems, much of the work involves forecasting and queueing analysis to obtain worker requirements. This must be done before an optimal schedule can be found.*

The only inputs needed for this problem are the minimum employee requirements in Table 4.3, but these are not easy to obtain. They would probably be obtained through a combination of two quantitative techniques: forecasting (Chapter 14) and queueing analysis (Chapter 13). The post office would first use historical data to forecast customer and mail arrival patterns throughout a typical week. It would then use queueing analysis to translate these arrival patterns into worker requirements on a daily basis. Actually, we have kept the problem relatively simple by considering only *daily* requirements. In a realistic setting, the organization might forecast worker requirements on an hourly or even a 15-minute basis.

## Solution

The variables and constraints for this problem appear in Table 4.4. The trickiest part is identifying the appropriate decision variables. Many students believe the decision variables should be the numbers of employees working on the various days of the week. Clearly, these values must eventually be determined. However, it is not enough to specify, say, that 18 employees are working on Monday. The problem is that this doesn't indicate when these 18 employees start their five-day shifts. Without this knowledge, it is impossible to implement the five-consecutive-day, two-day-off requirement. (If you don't believe this, try developing your own model with the wrong decision variables. You will eventually reach a dead end.)

### Table 4.4  Variables and Constraints for Postal Scheduling Problem

| | |
|---|---|
| **Input variables** | Minimum required number of workers each day |
| **Decision variables (changing cells)** | Number of employees working each of the five-day shifts (defined by their first day of work) |
| **Objective cell** | Total number of employees on the payroll |
| **Other calculated variables** | Number of employees working each day |
| **Constraints** | Employees working ≥ Employees required |

*The key to this model is choosing the correct changing cells.*

The trick is to define the decision variables as the numbers of employees working each of the seven possible five-day shifts. By knowing the values of these decision variables, the other output variables can be calculated. For example, the number working on Thursday is the sum of those who begin their five-day shifts on Sunday, Monday, Tuesday, Wednesday, and Thursday.

### FUNDAMENTAL INSIGHT

#### Choosing the Changing Cells

The changing cells, which are really just the decision variables, should always be chosen so that their values determine all required outputs in the model. In other words, their values should tell the company exactly how to run its business. Sometimes the choice of changing cells is obvious, but in many cases (as in this worker scheduling model), the proper choice of changing cells takes some deeper thinking about the problem. An improper choice of changing cells typically leads to a dead end, where their values do not supply enough information to calculate required outputs or implement certain constraints.

Note that this is a "wraparound" problem. We assume that the daily requirements in Table 4.3 and the worker schedules continue week after week. So, for example, if eight employees are assigned to the Thursday through Monday shift, these employees always wrap around from one week to the next on their five-day shift.

### DEVELOPING THE SPREADSHEET MODEL

The spreadsheet model for this problem is shown in Figure 4.11. (See the file Worker Scheduling.xlsx.) To form this spreadsheet, proceed as follows.

1 **Inputs and range names.** Enter the number of employees needed on each day of the week (from Table 4.3) in the blue cells, and create the range names shown.

2 **Employees beginning each day.** Enter *any* trial values for the number of employees beginning work on each day of the week in the Employees_starting range. These beginning

## Figure 4.11 Worker Scheduling Model with Optimal Solution

| | A | B | C | D | E | F | G | H | I | J | K |
|---|---|---|---|---|---|---|---|---|---|---|---|
| 1 | Worker scheduling model | | | | | | | | Range names used | | |
| 2 | | | | | | | | | Employees_available | =Model!$B$23:$H$23 | |
| 3 | Decision variables: number of employees starting their five-day shift on various days | | | | | | | | Employees_required | =Model!$B$25:$H$25 | |
| 4 | Mon | 6.33 | | | | | | | Employees_Starting | =Model!$B$4:$B$10 | |
| 5 | Tue | 5.00 | | | | | | | Total_employees | =Model!$B$28 | |
| 6 | Wed | 0.33 | | | | | | | | | |
| 7 | Thu | 7.33 | | | | | | | | | |
| 8 | Fri | 0.00 | | | | | | | | | |
| 9 | Sat | 3.33 | | | | | | | | | |
| 10 | Sun | 0.00 | | | | | | | | | |
| 11 | | | | | | | | | | | |
| 12 | Result of decisions: number of employees working on various days (along top) who started their shift on various days (along side) | | | | | | | | | | |
| 13 | | Mon | Tue | Wed | Thu | Fri | Sat | Sun | | | |
| 14 | Mon | 6.33 | 6.33 | 6.33 | 6.33 | 6.33 | | | | | |
| 15 | Tue | | 5.00 | 5.00 | 5.00 | 5.00 | 5.00 | | | | |
| 16 | Wed | | | 0.33 | 0.33 | 0.33 | 0.33 | 0.33 | | | |
| 17 | Thu | 7.33 | | | 7.33 | 7.33 | 7.33 | 7.33 | | | |
| 18 | Fri | 0.00 | 0.00 | | | 0.00 | 0.00 | 0.00 | | | |
| 19 | Sat | 3.33 | 3.33 | 3.33 | | | 3.33 | 3.33 | | | |
| 20 | Sun | 0.00 | 0.00 | 0.00 | 0.00 | | | 0.00 | | | |
| 21 | | | | | | | | | | | |
| 22 | Constraint on worker availabilities | | | | | | | | | | |
| 23 | Employees available | 17.00 | 14.67 | 15.00 | 19.00 | 19.00 | 16.00 | 11.00 | | | |
| 24 | | >= | >= | >= | >= | >= | >= | >= | | | |
| 25 | Employees required | 17 | 13 | 15 | 19 | 14 | 16 | 11 | | | |
| 26 | | | | | | | | | | | |
| 27 | Objective to maximize | | | | | | | | | | |
| 28 | Total employees | 22.33 | | | | | | | | | |

days determine the possible five-day shifts. For example, the employees in cell B4 work Monday through Friday.

**3** **Employees on hand each day.** The key to this solution is to realize that the numbers in the Employees_starting range—the changing cells—do not represent the number of workers who will show up each day. As an example, the number in cell B4 represent those who start on Monday and work Monday through Friday. Therefore, enter the formula

=$B$4

in cell B14 and copy it across to cell F14. Proceed similarly for rows 15–20, being careful to take wraparounds into account. For example, the workers starting on Thursday work Thursday through Sunday, plus Monday. Then calculate the total number who are available on each day by entering the formula

=SUM(B14:B20)

in cell B23 and copying it across to cell H23.

**Excel Tip:** *CTRL+Enter Shortcut*
*You often enter a typical formula in a cell and then copy it. One way to do this efficiently is to highlight the entire range, here B23:H23. Then enter the typical formula, here* **=SUM(B14:B20)***, and press* **Ctrl+Enter***. This has the same effect as copying, but it is slightly quicker.*

**4** **Total employees.** Calculate the total number of employees in cell B28 with the formula

=SUM(Employees_starting)

Note that there is no double-counting in this sum. For example, the employees in cells B4 and B5 are *not* the same people.

At this point, you might want to experiment with the numbers in the changing cell range to see whether you can guess an optimal solution (without looking at Figure 4.11). It is not that easy. Each worker who starts on a given day works the next four days as well, so when you find a solution that meets the minimal requirements for the various days, you usually have a few more workers available on some days than are needed.

### USING SOLVER

Invoke Solver and fill out its main dialog box as shown in Figure 4.12. (You don't need to include the integer constraints yet. We will discuss them shortly.) Make sure you check the Non-Negative option and use the Simplex LP method.

### Discussion of the Solution

The optimal solution shown in Figure 4.11 has one drawback: It requires the number of employees starting work on some days to be a fraction. Because part-time employees are not allowed, this solution is unrealistic. However, it is simple to add an integer constraint on the changing cells. This integer constraint appears in Figure 4.12. With this integer constraint, the optimal solution appears in Figure 4.13.

The changing cells in the optimal solution indicate the numbers of workers who start their five-day shifts on the various days. You can then look at the *columns* of the B14:H20 range to see which employees are working on any given day. This optimal solution is typical in scheduling problems. Due to a labor constraint—each employee must work five consecutive days and then have two days off—it is typically impossible to meet the minimum employee requirements exactly. To ensure that there are enough employees available on busy days, it is necessary to have more than enough on hand on light days.

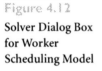

**Figure 4.12**

**Solver Dialog Box for Worker Scheduling Model**

Figure 4.13   Optimal Integer Solution to Worker Scheduling Model

| | A | B | C | D | E | F | G | H | I | J | K |
|---|---|---|---|---|---|---|---|---|---|---|---|
| 1 | Worker scheduling model | | | | | | | | Range names used | | |
| 2 | | | | | | | | | Employees_available | =Model!$B$23:$H$23 | |
| 3 | Decision variables: number of employees starting their five-day shift on various days | | | | | | | | Employees_required | =Model!$B$25:$H$25 | |
| 4 | Mon | 6 | | | | | | | Employees_Starting | =Model!$B$4:$B$10 | |
| 5 | Tue | 6 | | | | | | | Total_employees | =Model!$B$28 | |
| 6 | Wed | 0 | | | | | | | | | |
| 7 | Thu | 7 | | | | | | | | | |
| 8 | Fri | 0 | | | | | | | | | |
| 9 | Sat | 4 | | | | | | | | | |
| 10 | Sun | 0 | | | | | | | | | |
| 11 | | | | | | | | | | | |
| 12 | Result of decisions: number of employees working on various days (along top) who started their shift on various days (along side) | | | | | | | | | | |
| 13 | | Mon | Tue | Wed | Thu | Fri | Sat | Sun | | | |
| 14 | Mon | 6 | 6 | 6 | 6 | 6 | | | | | |
| 15 | Tue | | 6 | 6 | 6 | 6 | 6 | | | | |
| 16 | Wed | | | 0 | 0 | 0 | 0 | 0 | | | |
| 17 | Thu | 7 | | | 7 | 7 | 7 | 7 | | | |
| 18 | Fri | 0 | 0 | | | 0 | 0 | 0 | | | |
| 19 | Sat | 4 | 4 | 4 | | | 4 | 4 | | | |
| 20 | Sun | 0 | 0 | 0 | 0 | | | 0 | | | |
| 21 | | | | | | | | | | | |
| 22 | Constraint on worker availabilities | | | | | | | | | | |
| 23 | Employees available | 17 | 16 | 16 | 19 | 19 | 17 | 11 | | | |
| 24 | | >= | >= | >= | >= | >= | >= | >= | | | |
| 25 | Employees required | 17 | 13 | 15 | 19 | 14 | 16 | 11 | | | |
| 26 | | | | | | | | | | | |
| 27 | Objective to maximize | | | | | | | | | | |
| 28 | Total employees | 23 | | | | | | | | | |

*Multiple optimal solutions have different values in the changing cells, but they all have the same objective value.*

Another interesting aspect of this problem is that if you solve this problem on your own PC, you might get a *different* schedule that is still optimal—that is, a solution that still uses a total of 23 employees and meets all constraints. This is a case of **multiple optimal solutions,** not at all uncommon in LP problems. In fact, it is typically good news for a manager, who can then choose among the optimal solutions using other, possibly nonquantitative criteria.[3]

### Technical Tip: *Solver Tolerance Setting*

*When working with integer constraints, you should be aware of Solver's Tolerance setting.*

*Set Solver's Tolerance to zero to ensure that you get the optimal integer solution. Be aware, however, that this can incur significant extra computing time for larger models.*

*The idea is as follows. As Solver searches for the best integer solution, it is often able to find a "good" solution fairly quickly, but it often has to spend a lot of time finding slightly better solutions. A nonzero tolerance setting allows it to quit early. The default tolerance setting is 5 (percent). This means that if Solver finds a feasible solution that is guaranteed to have an objective value no more than 5% from the optimal value, it will quit and report this good solution (which might even be the optimal solution). Therefore, if you keep this default tolerance value, your integer solutions will sometimes not be optimal, but they will be close. If you want to ensure that you get an optimal solution, you can change the Solver tolerance value to zero. (In Excel 2010, this setting is directly under the Solver Options on the All Methods tab.)*

### Sensitivity Analysis

*To run some sensitivity analyses with SolverTable, you need to modify the original model slightly to incorporate the effect of the input being varied.*

The most obvious type of sensitivity analysis in this example is to analyze the effect of worker requirements on the optimal solution. Specifically, let's suppose the number of employees needed on each day of the week increases by two, four, or six. How does this change the total number of employees needed? You can answer this with SolverTable, but you must first modify the model slightly, as shown in Figure 4.14. The problem is that we want to increase *each* of the daily minimal required values by the same amount. The trick is to enter the original requirements in row 12, enter a trial value for the extra number

---

[3] It is usually difficult to tell whether there are multiple optimal solutions. You typically discover this by rerunning Solver from different starting solutions.

## Figure 4.14  Modified Worker Scheduling Model

| | A | B | C | D | E | F | G | H | I | J | K |
|---|---|---|---|---|---|---|---|---|---|---|---|
| 1 | Worker scheduling model | | | | | | | | Range names used | | |
| 2 | | | | | | | | | Employees_available | =Model!$B$23:$H$23 | |
| 3 | Decision variables: number of employees starting their five-day shift on various days | | | | | | | | Employees_required | =Model!$B$25:$H$25 | |
| 4 | Mon | 2 | | | | | | | Employees_Starting | =Model!$B$4:$B$10 | |
| 5 | Tue | 3 | | | | | | | Total_employees | =Model!$B$28 | |
| 6 | Wed | 3 | | | | | | | | | |
| 7 | Thu | 7 | | | | | | | | | |
| 8 | Fri | 0 | | | | | | | | | |
| 9 | Sat | 4 | | | | | | | | | |
| 10 | Sun | 4 | | | | | | | | | |
| 11 | | | | | | | | | | | |
| 12 | Employees required (original values) | 17 | 13 | 15 | 19 | 14 | 16 | 11 | | Extra required each day | 0 |
| 13 | | | | | | | | | | | |
| 14 | Result of decisions: number of employees working on various days (along top) who started their shift on various days (along side) | | | | | | | | | | |
| 15 | | Mon | Tue | Wed | Thu | Fri | Sat | Sun | | | |
| 16 | Mon | 2 | 2 | 2 | 2 | 2 | | | | | |
| 17 | Tue | | 3 | 3 | 3 | 3 | 3 | | | | |
| 18 | Wed | | | 3 | 3 | 3 | 3 | 3 | | | |
| 19 | Thu | 7 | | | 7 | 7 | 7 | 7 | | | |
| 20 | Fri | 0 | 0 | | | 0 | 0 | 0 | | | |
| 21 | Sat | 4 | 4 | 4 | | | 4 | 4 | | | |
| 22 | Sun | 4 | 4 | 4 | 4 | | | 4 | | | |
| 23 | | | | | | | | | | | |
| 24 | Constraint on worker availabilities | | | | | | | | | | |
| 25 | Employees available | 17 | 13 | 16 | 19 | 15 | 17 | 18 | | | |
| 26 | | >= | >= | >= | >= | >= | >= | >= | | | |
| 27 | Employees required | 17 | 13 | 15 | 19 | 14 | 16 | 11 | | | |
| 28 | | | | | | | | | | | |
| 29 | Objective to maximize | | | | | | | | | | |
| 30 | Total employees | 23 | | | | | | | | | |

required per day in cell K12, enter the formula =B12+$K$12 in cell B27, and then copy this formula across to cell H27. Now you can use the one-way SolverTable option, using cell K12 as the single input, letting it vary from 0 to 6 in increments of 2, and specifying the Total_employees cell as the single output cell.

The results appear in Figure 4.15. When the requirement increases by two each day, only two extra employees are necessary (scheduled appropriately). However, when the requirement increases by four each day, *more* than four extra employees are necessary. The same is true when the requirement increases by six each day. This might surprise you at first, but there is an intuitive reason: Each extra worker works only five days of the week.

## Figure 4.15  Sensitivity to Number of Extra Workers Required per Day

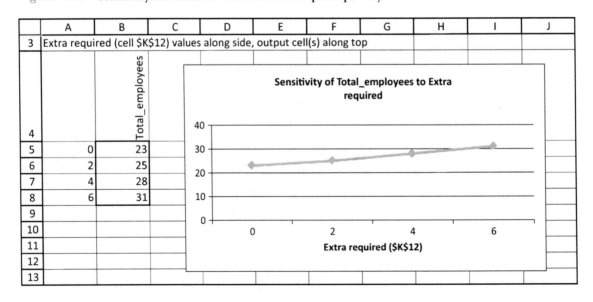

Note that we did not use Solver's sensitivity report here for two reasons. First, Solver does not offer a sensitivity report for models with integer constraints. Second, even if the integer constraints are deleted, Solver's sensitivity report does not answer questions about *multiple* input changes, as we have asked here. It can be used only for questions about one-at-a-time changes to inputs, such as a change to a *specific* day's worker requirement. In this sense, SolverTable is a more flexible tool. ▨

## MODELING ISSUES

1. The postal employee scheduling example is called a *static* scheduling model because we assume that the post office faces the same situation each week. In reality, demands change over time, workers take vacations in the summer, and so on, so the post office does not face the same situation each week. A *dynamic* scheduling model (not covered here) is necessary for such problems.

*Heuristic solutions are often close to optimal, but they are never guaranteed to be optimal.*

2. In a weekly scheduling model for a supermarket or a fast-food restaurant, the number of decision variables can grow quickly and optimization software such as Solver will have difficulty finding an optimal solution. In such cases, heuristic methods (essentially clever trial-and-error algorithms) have been used to find good solutions to the problem. Love and Hoey (1990) indicate how this was done for a particular staff scheduling problem.

3. Our model can easily be expanded to handle part-time employees, the use of overtime, and alternative objectives such as maximizing the number of weekend days off received by employees. You are asked to explore such extensions in the problems. ▨

## ADDITIONAL APPLICATIONS

### Scheduling Employees in Quebec's Liquor Stores

The SAQ is a public corporation of the Province of Quebec that is responsible for distributing and selling alcohol-based products through a large network of more than 400 stores and warehouses. Every week, the SAQ has to schedule more than 3000 employees. Until 2002, the scheduling of these employees was done manually, incurring an annual expense of about Can $1,300,000. Gendron (2005) developed an integer programming model that is estimated to have saved the SAQ about Can $1,000,000 annually. The model has to deal with complex union rules. For example, there is a rule that shifts of six hours or more can be split between two employees, but it must be coupled with another rule that forces employees to take one-hour unpaid lunch or dinner breaks. ■

## PROBLEMS

### Skill-Building Problems

**7.** Modify the post office model so that employees are paid $10 per hour on weekdays and $15 per hour on weekends. Change the objective so that you now minimize the weekly payroll. (You can assume that each employee works eight hours per day.) Is the previous optimal solution still optimal?

**8.** How much influence can the worker requirements for one, two, or three days have on the weekly schedule in

the post office example? Explore this in the following questions:

**a.** Let Monday's requirements change from 17 to 25 in increments of 1. Use SolverTable to see how the total number of employees changes.

**b.** Suppose the Monday and Tuesday requirements can each, independently of one another, increase from 1 to 8 in increments of 1. Use a two-way SolverTable to see how the total number of employees changes.

**c.** Suppose the Monday, Tuesday, and Wednesday requirements each increase by the *same* amount, where this increase can be from 1 to 8 in increments of 1. Use a one-way SolverTable to investigate how the total number of employees changes.

**9.** In the post office example, suppose that each full-time employee works eight hours per day. Thus, Monday's requirement of 17 workers can be viewed as a requirement of 8(17) = 136 hours. The post office can meet its daily labor requirements by using both full-time and part-time employees. During each week, a full-time employee works eight hours a day for five consecutive days, and a part-time employee works four hours a day for five consecutive days. A full-time employee costs the post office $15 per hour, whereas a part-time employee (with reduced fringe benefits) costs the post office only $10 per hour. Union requirements limit part-time labor to 25% of weekly labor requirements.
  **a.** Modify the model as necessary, and then use Solver to minimize the post office's weekly labor costs.
  **b.** Use SolverTable to determine how a change in the part-time labor limitation (currently 25%) influences the optimal solution.

Skill-Extending Problems

**10.** In the post office example, suppose the employees want more flexibility in their schedules. They want to be allowed to work five consecutive days followed by two days off *or* to work three consecutive days followed by a day off, followed by two consecutive days followed by another day off. Modify the original model (with integer constraints) to allow this flexibility. Might this be a good deal for management as well as labor? Explain.

**11.** Suppose the post office has 25 full-time employees and is not allowed to hire or fire any of them. Determine a schedule that maximizes the number of weekend days off received by these employees.

**12.** In the post office example, suppose that the post office can force employees to work one day of overtime each week on the day immediately following this five-day shift. For example, an employee whose regular shift is Monday to Friday can also be required to work on Saturday. Each employee is paid $100 a day for each of the first five days worked during a week and $124 for the overtime day (if any). Determine how the post office can minimize the cost of meeting its weekly work requirements.

## 4.4 AGGREGATE PLANNING MODELS

In this section, the production planning model discussed in Example 3.3 of the previous chapter is extended to include a situation where the number of workers available influences the possible production levels. The workforce level is allowed to change each period through the hiring and firing of workers. Such models, where we determine workforce levels and production schedules for a multiperiod time horizon, are called **aggregate planning** models. There are many versions of aggregate planning models, depending on the detailed assumptions we make. The following example is a fairly simple version that you will have a chance to modify in the "Problems" section.

---

**EXAMPLE** **4.3 WORKER AND PRODUCTION PLANNING AT SURESTEP**

During the next four months the SureStep Company must meet (on time) the following demands for pairs of shoes: 3000 in month 1; 5000 in month 2; 2000 in month 3; and 1000 in month 4. At the beginning of month 1, 500 pairs of shoes are on hand, and SureStep has 100 workers. A worker is paid $1500 per month. Each worker can work up to 160 hours a month before he or she receives overtime. A worker can work up to 20 hours of overtime per month and is paid $13 per hour for overtime labor. It takes four hours of labor and $15 of raw material to produce a pair of shoes. At the beginning of each month, workers can be hired or fired. Each hired worker costs $1600, and each fired worker costs $2000. At the end of each month, a holding cost of $3 per pair of shoes left in inventory is incurred. Production in a given month can be used to meet that month's demand. SureStep wants to use LP to determine its optimal production schedule and labor policy.

**Objective** To develop an LP spreadsheet model that relates workforce and production decisions to monthly costs, and to find the minimum-cost solution that meets forecasted demands on time and stays within limits on overtime hours and production capacity.

There are a number of required inputs for this type of problem. Some, including initial inventory, holding costs, and demands, are similar to requirements for Example 3.3 in the previous chapter, so we won't discuss them again here. Others might be obtained as follows:

- The data on the current number of workers, the regular hours per worker per month, the regular hourly wage rates, and the overtime hourly rate, should be well known. The maximum number of overtime hours per worker per month is probably either the result of a policy decision by management or a clause in the workers' contracts.

- The costs for hiring and firing a worker are not trivial. The hiring cost includes training costs and the cost of decreased productivity due to the fact that a new worker must learn the job. The firing cost includes severance costs and costs due to loss of morale. Neither the hiring nor the firing cost would be simple to estimate accurately, but the human resources department should be able to estimate their values.

- The unit production cost is a combination of two inputs: the raw material cost per pair of shoes and the labor hours per pair of shoes. The raw material cost is the going rate from the supplier(s). The labor per pair of shoes represents the "production function"—the average labor required to produce a unit of the product. The operations managers should be able to supply this number.

## Solution

*The key to this model is choosing the correct changing cells—the decision variables that determine all outputs.*

The variables and constraints for this aggregate planning model are listed in Table 4.5. As you see, there are a lot of variables to keep track of. In fact, the most difficult aspect of modeling this problem is knowing which variables the company gets to choose—the decision variables—and which variables are *determined* by these decisions. It should be clear that the company gets to choose the number of workers to hire and fire and the number of shoes to produce. Also, because management sets only an upper limit on overtime hours, it gets to decide how many overtime hours to use within this limit. But once it decides the values of these variables, everything else is determined. We will show how these are determined through detailed cell formulas, but you should mentally go through the list of "Other calculated variables" in the table and deduce how they are determined by the decision variables. Also, you should convince yourself that the three constraints listed are the ones, and the only ones, that are required.

**Table 4.5    Variables and Constraints for Aggregate Planning Model**

| | |
|---|---|
| **Input variables** | Initial inventory of shoes, initial number of workers, number and wage rate of regular hours, maximum number and wage rate of overtime hours, hiring and firing costs, data for unit production and holding costs, forecasted demands |
| **Decision variables (changing cells)** | Monthly values for number of workers hired and fired, number of shoes produced, and overtime hours used |
| **Objective cell** | Total cost |
| **Other calculated variables** | Monthly values for workers on hand before and after hiring/firing, regular hours available, maximum overtime hours available, total production hours available, production capacity, inventory on hand after production, ending inventory, and various costs |
| **Constraints** | Overtime labor hours used ≤ Maximum overtime hours allowed<br>Production ≤ Capacity<br>Inventory on hand after production ≥ Demand |

The spreadsheet model appears in Figure 4.16. (See the file Aggregate Planning 1.xlsx.) It can be developed as follows.

**1** **Inputs and range names.** Enter the input data and create the range names listed.

**2** **Production, hiring and firing plan.** Enter *any* trial values for the number of pairs of shoes produced each month, the overtime hours used each month, the workers hired each month, and the workers fired each month. These four ranges, in rows 18, 19, 23, and 30, comprise the changing cells.

*This is common in multiperiod problems. You usually have to relate a beginning value in one period to an ending value from the previous period.*

**3** **Workers available each month.** In cell B17 enter the initial number of workers available with the formula

=B5

Because the number of workers available at the beginning of any other month (before hiring and firing) is equal to the number of workers from the previous month, enter the formula

=B20

Figure 4.16 **Aggregate Planning Model**

| | A | B | C | D | E | F | G | H | I |
|---|---|---|---|---|---|---|---|---|---|
| 1 | SureStep aggregate planning model | | | | | | | | |
| 2 | | | | | | | | | |
| 3 | Input data | | | | | | Range names used: | | |
| 4 | Initial inventory of shoes | 500 | | | | | Forecasted_demand | =Model!$B$36:$E$36 | |
| 5 | Initial number of workers | 100 | | | | | Inventory_after_production | =Model!$B$34:$E$34 | |
| 6 | Regular hours/worker/month | 160 | | | | | Maximum_overtime_labor_hours_available | =Model!$B$25:$E$25 | |
| 7 | Maximum overtime hours/worker/month | 20 | | | | | Overtime_labor_hours_used | =Model!$B$23:$E$23 | |
| 8 | Hiring cost/worker | $1,600 | | | | | Production_capacity | =Model!$B$32:$E$32 | |
| 9 | Firing cost/worker | $2,000 | | | | | Shoes_produced | =Model!$B$30:$E$30 | |
| 10 | Regular wages/worker/month | $1,500 | | | | | Total_cost | =Model!$F$46 | |
| 11 | Overtime wage rate/hour | $13 | | | | | Workers_fired | =Model!$B$19:$E$19 | |
| 12 | Labor hours/pair of shoes | 4 | | | | | Workers_hired | =Model!$B$18:$E$18 | |
| 13 | Raw material cost/pair of shoes | $15 | | | | | | | |
| 14 | Holding cost/pair of shoes in inventory/month | $3 | | | | | | | |
| 15 | | | | | | | | | |
| 16 | Worker plan | Month 1 | Month 2 | Month 3 | Month 4 | | | | |
| 17 | Workers from previous month | 100 | 94 | 93 | 50 | | | | |
| 18 | Workers hired | 0 | 0 | 0 | 0 | | | | |
| 19 | Workers fired | 6 | 1 | 43 | 0 | | | | |
| 20 | Workers available after hiring and firing | 94 | 93 | 50 | 50 | | | | |
| 21 | | | | | | | | | |
| 22 | Regular-time hours available | 15040 | 14880 | 8000 | 8000 | | | | |
| 23 | Overtime labor hours used | 0 | 80 | 0 | 0 | | | | |
| 24 | | <= | <= | <= | <= | | | | |
| 25 | Maximum overtime labor hours available | 1880 | 1860 | 1000 | 1000 | | | | |
| 26 | | | | | | | | | |
| 27 | Total hours for production | 15040 | 14960 | 8000 | 8000 | | | | |
| 28 | | | | | | | | | |
| 29 | Production plan | Month 1 | Month 2 | Month 3 | Month 4 | | | | |
| 30 | Shoes produced | 3760 | 3740 | 2000 | 1000 | | | | |
| 31 | | <= | <= | <= | <= | | | | |
| 32 | Production capacity | 3760 | 3740 | 2000 | 2000 | | | | |
| 33 | | | | | | | | | |
| 34 | Inventory after production | 4260 | 5000 | 2000 | 1000 | | | | |
| 35 | | >= | >= | >= | >= | | | | |
| 36 | Forecasted demand | 3000 | 5000 | 2000 | 1000 | | | | |
| 37 | Ending inventory | 1260 | 0 | 0 | 0 | | | | |
| 38 | | | | | | | | | |
| 39 | Monetary outputs | Month 1 | Month 2 | Month 3 | Month 4 | Totals | | | |
| 40 | Hiring cost | $0 | $0 | $0 | $0 | $0 | | | |
| 41 | Firing cost | $12,000 | $2,000 | $86,000 | $0 | $100,000 | | | |
| 42 | Regular-time wages | $141,000 | $139,500 | $75,000 | $75,000 | $430,500 | | | |
| 43 | Overtime wages | $0 | $1,040 | $0 | $0 | $1,040 | | | |
| 44 | Raw material cost | $56,400 | $56,100 | $30,000 | $15,000 | $157,500 | | | |
| 45 | Holding cost | $3,780 | $0 | $0 | $0 | $3,780 | | | |
| 46 | Totals | $213,180 | $198,640 | $191,000 | $90,000 | $692,820 | ← Objective to minimize | | |

in cell C17 and copy it to the range D17:E17. Then in cell B20 calculate the number of workers available in month 1 (after hiring and firing) with the formula

=B17+B18-B19

and copy this formula to the range C20:E20 for the other months.

④ **Overtime capacity.** Because each available worker can work up to 20 hours of overtime in a month, enter the formula

=$B$7*B20

in cell B25 and copy it to the range C25:E25.

⑤ **Production capacity.** Because each worker can work 160 regular-time hours per month, calculate the regular-time hours available in month 1 in cell B22 with the formula

=$B$6*B20

and copy it to the range C22:E22 for the other months. Then calculate the total hours available for production in cell B27 with the formula

=SUM(B22:B23)

and copy it to the range C27:E27 for the other months. Finally, because it takes four hours of labor to make a pair of shoes, calculate the production capacity in month 1 with the formula

=B27/$B$12

in cell B32 and copy it to the range C32:E32.

⑥ **Inventory each month.** Calculate the inventory after production in month 1 (which is available to meet month 1 demand) with the formula

=B4+B30

in cell B34. For any other month, the inventory after production is the previous month's ending inventory plus that month's production, so enter the formula

=B37+C30

in cell C34 and copy it to the range D34:E34. Then calculate the month 1 ending inventory in cell B37 with the formula

=B34-B36

and copy it to the range C37:E37.

⑦ **Monthly costs.** Calculate the various costs shown in rows 40 through 45 for month 1 by entering the formulas

=$B$8*B18

=$B$9*B19

=$B$10*B20

=$B$11*B23

=$B$13*B30

=$B$14*B37

in cells B40 through B45. Then copy the range B40:B45 to the range C40:E45 to calculate these costs for the other months.

⑧ **Totals.** In row 46 and column F, use the SUM function to calculate cost totals, with the value in F46 being the overall total cost to minimize.

*In Example 3.3 from the previous chapter, production capacities were given inputs. Now they are based on the size of the workforce, which itself is a decision variable.*

*A common operation in spreadsheet models is to calculate row and column sums for a rectangular range, as we did for costs in step 8. There is a very quick way to do this. Highlight the row and column where the sums will go (remember to press the Ctrl key to highlight nonadjacent ranges) and click on the summation (Σ) toolbar button. This enters all of the sums automatically. It even calculates the "grand sum" in the corner (cell F46 in the example) if you highlight this cell.*

## Using Solver

The Solver dialog box should be filled in as shown in Figure 4.17. Note that the changing cells include four separate named ranges. To enter these in the dialog box, drag the four ranges, keeping your finger on the Ctrl key. (Alternatively, you can drag a range, type a comma, drag a second range, type another comma, and so on.) As usual, you should also check the Non-Negative option and select the Simplex LP method before optimizing.

Note that there are integer constraints on the numbers hired and fired. You could also constrain the numbers of shoes produced to be integers. However, integer constraints typically require longer solution times. Therefore, it is often best to omit such constraints, especially when the optimal values are fairly large, such as the production quantities in this model. If the solution then has noninteger values, you can usually round them to integers for a solution that is at least close to the optimal integer solution.

**Figure 4.17**

**Solver Dialog Box for Aggregate Planning Model**

## Discussion of the Solution

The optimal solution is given in Figure 4.16. Observe that SureStep should never hire any workers, and it should fire six workers in month 1, one worker in month 2, and 43 workers in month 3. Eighty hours of overtime are used, but only in month 2. The company produces over 3700 pairs of shoes during each of the first two months, 2000 pairs in month 3, and 1000 pairs in month 4. A total cost of $692,820 is incurred. The model will recommend overtime hours only when regular-time production capacity is exhausted. This is because overtime labor is more expensive.

Again, you would probably not force the number of pairs of shoes produced each month to be an integer. It makes little difference whether the company produces 3760 or 3761 pairs of shoes during a month, and forcing each month's shoe production to be an integer can greatly increase the time Solver needs to find an optimal solution. On the other hand, it is somewhat more important to ensure that the number of workers hired and fired each month is an integer, given the relatively small numbers of workers involved.

Finally, if you want to ensure that Solver finds the optimal solution in a problem where some or all of the changing cells must be integers, you should go into Options (in the Solver dialog box) and set the tolerance to zero. Otherwise, Solver might stop when it finds a solution that is only *close* to optimal.

*Because integer constraints make a model more difficult to solve, use them sparingly—only when they are really needed.*

## Sensitivity Analysis

There are many possible sensitivity analyses for this SureStep model. We illustrate one of them with SolverTable, where we see how the overtime hours used and the total cost vary with the overtime wage rate.[4] The results appear in Figure 4.18. As you can see, when the wage rate is really low, the company uses considerably more overtime hours, whereas when it is sufficiently large, the company uses no overtime hours. It is not surprising that the company uses much more overtime when the overtime rate is $7 or $9 per hour. The *regular*-time wage rate is $9.375 per hour (= 1500/160). Of course, the company would never pay *less* per hour for overtime than for regular time.

**Figure 4.18**

Sensitivity to Overtime Wage Rate

| | A | B | C | D | E | F | G |
|---|---|---|---|---|---|---|---|
| 3 | Overtime rate (cell $B$11) values along side, output cell(s) along top | | | | | | |
| 4 | | Overtime_labor_hours_used_1 | Overtime_labor_hours_used_2 | Overtime_labor_hours_used_3 | Overtime_labor_hours_used_4 | Total_cost | |
| 5 | $7 | 1620 | 1660 | 0 | 0 | $684,755 | |
| 6 | $9 | 80 | 1760 | 0 | 0 | $691,180 | |
| 7 | $11 | 0 | 80 | 0 | 0 | $692,660 | |
| 8 | $13 | 0 | 80 | 0 | 0 | $692,820 | |
| 9 | $15 | 0 | 80 | 0 | 0 | $692,980 | |
| 10 | $17 | 0 | 80 | 0 | 0 | $693,140 | |
| 11 | $19 | 0 | 0 | 0 | 0 | $693,220 | |
| 12 | $21 | 0 | 0 | 0 | 0 | $693,220 | |

[4]Solver's sensitivity report isn't even available here because of the integer constraints.

## The Rolling Planning Horizon Approach

In reality, an aggregate planning model is usually implemented via a rolling planning horizon. To illustrate, we assume that SureStep works with a four-month planning horizon. To implement the SureStep model in the rolling planning horizon context, we view the demands as forecasts and solve a four-month model with these forecasts. However, the company would implement only the month 1 production and work scheduling recommendation. Thus (assuming that the numbers of workers hired and fired in a month must be integers) the company would hire no workers, fire six workers, and produce 3760 pairs of shoes with regular-time labor in month 1. Next, the company would observe month 1's *actual* demand. Suppose it is 2950. Then SureStep would begin month 2 with 1310 (= 4260 − 2950) pairs of shoes and 94 workers. It would now enter 1310 in cell B4 and 94 in cell B5 (referring to Figure 4.16). Then it would replace the demands in the Demand range with the updated forecasts for the *next* four months. Finally, SureStep would rerun Solver and use the production levels and hiring and firing recommendations in column B as the production level and workforce policy for month 2.

### Model with Backlogging Allowed

In many situations, backlogging of demand is allowed—that is, customer demand can be met at a later date. We now show how to modify the SureStep model to include the option of backlogging demand. We assume that at the end of each month a cost of $20 is incurred for each unit of demand that remains unsatisfied at the end of the month. This is easily modeled by allowing a month's ending inventory to be negative. For example, if month 1's ending inventory is −10, a shortage cost of $200 (and no inventory holding cost) is incurred. To ensure that SureStep produces any shoes at all, we constrain the ending inventory in month 4 to be nonnegative. This implies that all demand is *eventually* satisfied by the end of the four-month planning horizon. We now need to modify the monthly cost calculations to incorporate costs due to backlogging.

There are actually several modeling approaches to this backlogging problem. We show the most natural approach in Figure 4.19. (See the file Aggregate Planning 2.xlsx.) To begin, enter the per-unit monthly shortage cost in cell B15. (A new row was inserted for this cost input.) Note in row 38 how the ending inventory in months 1 through 3 can be positive (leftovers) or negative (shortages). You can account correctly for the resulting costs with IF functions in rows 46 and 47. For holding costs, enter the formula

=IF(B38>0,$B$14*B38,0)

in cell B46 and copy it across. For shortage costs, enter the formula

=IF(B38<0,−$B$15*B38,0)

in cell B47 and copy it across. (The minus sign makes this a *positive* cost.)

Although these formulas accurately compute holding and shortage costs, the IF functions make the objective cell a *nonlinear* function of the changing cells, and Solver's GRG Nonlinear method must be used, as indicated in Figure 4.20.[5] (How do you know the model is nonlinear? Although there is a mathematical reason, it is easier to try running Solver with the Simplex LP method. Solver will then *inform* you that the model is nonlinear.)

We ran Solver with this setup from a variety of initial solutions in the changing cells, and it always found the solution shown in Figure 4.19. It turns out that this is

---

[5]GRG stands for generalized reduced gradient. This is a technical term for the mathematical algorithm used. The other algorithm available in Solver (starting with Excel 2010) is the Evolutionary algorithm. It can handle IF functions, but we will not discuss this algorithm here. It is discussed in detail in Chapter 8.

## Figure 4.19 Nonlinear Aggregate Planning Model Using IF Functions

| | A | B | C | D | E | F | G | H | I |
|---|---|---|---|---|---|---|---|---|---|
| 1 | SureStep aggregate planning model with backlogging: a nonsmooth model Solver might not handle correctly | | | | | | | | |
| 2 | | | | | | | | | |
| 3 | Input data | | | | | | Range names used: | | |
| 4 | Initial inventory of shoes | 500 | | | | | Forecasted_demand_4 | =Model!$E$37 | |
| 5 | Initial number of workers | 100 | | | | | Inventory_after_production_4 | =Model!$E$35 | |
| 6 | Regular hours/worker/month | 160 | | | | | Maximum_overtime_labor_hours_available | =Model!$B$26:$E$26 | |
| 7 | Maximum overtime hours/worker/month | 20 | | | | | Overtime_labor_hours_used | =Model!$B$24:$E$24 | |
| 8 | Hiring cost/worker | $1,600 | | | | | Production_capacity | =Model!$B$33:$E$33 | |
| 9 | Firing cost/worker | $2,000 | | | | | Shoes_produced | =Model!$B$31:$E$31 | |
| 10 | Regular wages/worker/month | $1,500 | | | | | Total_cost | =Model!$F$48 | |
| 11 | Overtime wage rate/hour | $13 | | | | | Workers_fired | =Model!$B$20:$E$20 | |
| 12 | Labor hours/pair of shoes | 4 | | | | | Workers_hired | =Model!$B$19:$E$19 | |
| 13 | Raw material cost/pair of shoes | $15 | | | | | | | |
| 14 | Holding cost/pair of shoes in inventory/month | $3 | | | | | | | |
| 15 | Shortage cost/pair of shoes/month | $20 | | | | | | | |
| 16 | | | | | | | | | |
| 17 | Worker plan | Month 1 | Month 2 | Month 3 | Month 4 | | | | |
| 18 | Workers from previous month | 100 | 94 | 93 | 38 | | | | |
| 19 | Workers hired | 0 | 0 | 0 | 0 | | | | |
| 20 | Workers fired | 6 | 1 | 55 | 0 | | | | |
| 21 | Workers available after hiring and firing | 94 | 93 | 38 | 38 | | | | |
| 22 | | | | | | | | | |
| 23 | Regular-time hours available | 15040 | 14880 | 6080 | 6080 | | | | |
| 24 | Overtime labor hours used | 0 | 0 | 0 | 0 | | | | |
| 25 | | <= | <= | <= | <= | | | | |
| 26 | Maximum overtime labor hours available | 1880 | 1860 | 760 | 760 | | | | |
| 27 | | | | | | | | | |
| 28 | Total hours for production | 15040 | 14880 | 6080 | 6080 | | | | |
| 29 | | | | | | | | | |
| 30 | Production plan | Month 1 | Month 2 | Month 3 | Month 4 | | | | |
| 31 | Shoes produced | 3760 | 3720 | 1520 | 1500 | | | | |
| 32 | | <= | <= | <= | <= | | | | |
| 33 | Production capacity | 3760 | 3720 | 1520 | 1520 | | | | |
| 34 | | | | | | | | | |
| 35 | Inventory after production | 4260 | 4980 | 1500 | 1000 | | | | |
| 36 | | | | | >= | | | | |
| 37 | Forecasted demand | 3000 | 5000 | 2000 | 1000 | | | | |
| 38 | Ending inventory | 1260 | -20 | -500 | 0 | | | | |
| 39 | | | | | | | | | |
| 40 | Monetary outputs | Month 1 | Month 2 | Month 3 | Month 4 | Totals | | | |
| 41 | Hiring cost | $0 | $0 | $0 | $0 | | | | |
| 42 | Firing cost | $12,000 | $2,000 | $110,000 | $0 | $124,000 | | | |
| 43 | Regular-time wages | $141,000 | $139,500 | $57,000 | $57,000 | $394,500 | | | |
| 44 | Overtime wages | $0 | $0 | $0 | $0 | | | | |
| 45 | Raw material cost | $56,400 | $55,800 | $22,800 | $22,500 | $157,500 | | | |
| 46 | Holding cost | $3,780 | $0 | $0 | $0 | $3,780 | | | |
| 47 | Shortage cost | $0 | $400 | $10,000 | $0 | $10,400 | | | |
| 48 | Totals | $213,180 | $197,700 | $199,800 | $79,500 | $690,180 | ← Objective to minimize | | |

Note that we use IF functions in rows 46 and 47 to capture the holding and shortage costs. These IF functions make the model nonlinear (and "nonsmooth"), and Solver can't handle these functions in a predictable manner. We just got lucky here! Try changing the unit shortage cost in cell B15 to $40 and rerun Solver. Then you won't be so lucky -- Solver will converge to a solution that is pretty far from optimal.

## Figure 4.20

Solver Dialog Box for the GRG Nonlinear Method

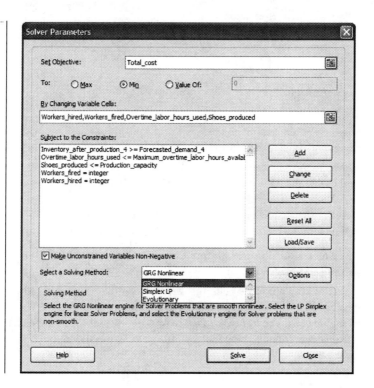

indeed the optimal solution, but we were lucky. When certain functions, including IF, MIN, MAX, and ABS, are used to relate the objective cell to the changing cells, the resulting model becomes not only nonlinear but *nonsmooth*. Essentially, nonsmooth functions can have sharp edges or discontinuities. Solver's GRG nonlinear algorithm can handle "smooth" nonlinearities, as you will see in Chapter 7, but it has trouble with nonsmooth functions. Sometimes it gets lucky, as it did here, and other times it finds a nonoptimal solution that is not even close to the optimal solution. For example, we changed the unit shortage cost from $20 to $40 and reran Solver. Starting from a solution where all changing cells contain zero, Solver stopped at a solution with total cost $726,360, even though the optimal solution has total cost $692,820. In other words, we weren't so lucky this time.

The moral is that you should avoid these nonsmooth functions in optimization models if at all possible. If you *do* use them, as we have done here, you should run Solver several times, starting from different initial solutions. There is still no guarantee that you will get the optimal solution, but you will see more evidence of how Solver is progressing. Alternatively, you can use Frontline Systems's Evolutionary Solver, which became available in Excel's Solver in Excel 2010 and is discussed in detail in Chapter 8.

---

### FUNDAMENTAL INSIGHT

#### Nonsmooth Functions and Solver

Excel's Solver, as well as most other commercial optimization software packages, has trouble with nonlinear functions that are not smooth. These nonsmooth functions typically have sharp edges or discontinuities that make them difficult to handle in optimization models, and (in Excel) they are typically implemented with functions such as IF, MAX, MIN, ABS, and a few others. There is nothing *wrong* with using such functions to implement complex logic in Excel optimization models. The only problem is that Solver cannot handle models with these functions predictably. This is not really the fault of Solver. Such problems are inherently difficult.

---

### Linearizing the Backlogging Model

Although this nonlinear model with IF functions is "natural," the fact that it is not guaranteed to find the optimal solution is disturbing. Fortunately, it is possible to handle shortages with a *linear* model. The method is illustrated in Figure 4.21. (See the file Aggregate Planning 3.xlsx.) To develop this modified spreadsheet model, starting from the original model in the Aggregate Planning 1.xlsx file, follow these steps:

**1** **Enter shortage cost.** Insert a new row below row 14 and enter the shortage cost per pair of shoes per month in cell B15.

**2** **Rows for amounts held and short.** Insert five new rows (which will now be rows 38 through 42) between the Demand and Ending inventory rows. The range B39:E40 will be changing cells. The Leftover range in row 39 contains the amounts left in inventory (if any), whereas the Shortage range in row 40 contains the shortages (if any). Enter *any* values in these ranges.

**Figure 4.21** Linear Model of Backlogging

| | A | B | C | D | E | F | G | H |
|---|---|---|---|---|---|---|---|---|
| 1 | SureStep aggregate planning model with backlogging: a nonsmooth model Solver might not handle correctly | | | | | | | |
| 2 | | | | | | | | |
| 3 | Input data | | | | | | Range names used: | |
| 4 | Initial inventory of shoes | 500 | | | | | Ending_inventory | =Model!$B$43:$E$43 |
| 5 | Initial number of workers | 100 | | | | | Forecasted_demand_4 | =Model!$E$37 |
| 6 | Regular hours/worker/month | 160 | | | | | Inventory_after_production_4 | =Model!$E$35 |
| 7 | Maximum overtime hours/worker/month | 20 | | | | | Maximum_overtime_labor_hours_available | =Model!$B$26:$E$26 |
| 8 | Hiring cost/worker | $1,600 | | | | | Overtime_labor_hours_used | =Model!$B$24:$E$24 |
| 9 | Firing cost/worker | $2,000 | | | | | Production_capacity | =Model!$B$33:$E$33 |
| 10 | Regular wages/worker/month | $1,500 | | | | | Shoes_produced | =Model!$B$31:$E$31 |
| 11 | Overtime wage rate/hour | $13 | | | | | Total_cost | =Model!$F$53 |
| 12 | Labor hours/pair of shoes | 4 | | | | | Units_left_over | =Model!$B$39:$E$39 |
| 13 | Raw material cost/pair of shoes | $15 | | | | | Units_left_over_minus_units_short | =Model!$B$41:$E$41 |
| 14 | Holding cost/pair of shoes in inventory/month | $3 | | | | | Units_short | =Model!$B$40:$E$40 |
| 15 | Shortage cost/pair of shoes/month | $20 | | | | | Workers_fired | =Model!$B$20:$E$20 |
| 16 | | | | | | | Workers_hired | =Model!$B$19:$E$19 |
| 17 | Worker plan | Month 1 | Month 2 | Month 3 | Month 4 | | | |
| 18 | Workers from previous month | 100 | 94 | 93 | 38 | | | |
| 19 | Workers hired | 0 | 0 | 0 | 0 | | | |
| 20 | Workers fired | 6 | 1 | 55 | 0 | | | |
| 21 | Workers available after hiring and firing | 94 | 93 | 38 | 38 | | | |
| 22 | | | | | | | | |
| 23 | Regular-time hours available | 15040 | 14880 | 6080 | 6080 | | | |
| 24 | Overtime labor hours used | 0 | 0 | 0 | 0 | | | |
| 25 | | <= | <= | <= | <= | | | |
| 26 | Maximum overtime labor hours available | 1880 | 1860 | 760 | 760 | | | |
| 27 | | | | | | | | |
| 28 | Total hours for production | 15040 | 14880 | 6080 | 6080 | | | |
| 29 | | | | | | | | |
| 30 | Production plan | Month 1 | Month 2 | Month 3 | Month 4 | | | |
| 31 | Shoes produced | 3760 | 3720 | 1520 | 1500 | | | |
| 32 | | <= | <= | <= | <= | | | |
| 33 | Production capacity | 3760 | 3720 | 1520 | 1520 | | | |
| 34 | | | | | | | | |
| 35 | Inventory after production | 4260 | 4980 | 1500 | 1000 | | | |
| 36 | | | | | >= | | | |
| 37 | Forecasted demand | 3000 | 5000 | 2000 | 1000 | | | |
| 38 | | | | | | | | |
| 39 | Leftover | 1260 | 0 | 0 | 0 | | | |
| 40 | Shortage | 0 | 20 | 500 | 0 | | | |
| 41 | Leftover minus shortage | 1260 | -20 | -500 | 0 | | | |
| 42 | | = | = | = | = | | | |
| 43 | Ending inventory | 1260 | -20 | -500 | 0 | | | |
| 44 | | | | | | | | |
| 45 | Monetary outputs | Month 1 | Month 2 | Month 3 | Month 4 | Totals | | |
| 46 | Hiring cost | $0 | $0 | $0 | $0 | $0 | | |
| 47 | Firing cost | $12,000 | $2,000 | $110,000 | $0 | $124,000 | | |
| 48 | Regular-time wages | $141,000 | $139,500 | $57,000 | $57,000 | $394,500 | | |
| 49 | Overtime wages | $0 | $0 | $0 | $0 | $0 | | |
| 50 | Raw material cost | $56,400 | $55,800 | $22,800 | $22,500 | $157,500 | | |
| 51 | Holding cost | $3,780 | $0 | $0 | $0 | $3,780 | | |
| 52 | Shortage cost | $0 | $400 | $10,000 | $0 | $10,400 | | |
| 53 | Totals | $213,180 | $197,700 | $199,800 | $79,500 | $690,180 | ← Objective to minimize | |

Text box (near rows 33–42):

There is a somewhat unintuitive trick to making this backlogging model linear, without using any IF functions. The trick is to create new changing cells in rows 39 and 40 for the amounts leftover and short. The purpose of these is to enable simple linear formulas in rows 51 and 52 for the holding and shortage costs. However, because they are changing cells, they can freely vary. To make sure they have "sensible" values, we need to constrain them. This is done by equating rows 41 and 43. Essentially, these two rows evaluate ending inventory in two different ways: (1) as Leftover minus Shortage (row 41) and (2) as Inventory after production minus Forecasted demand (row 43). These two should be the same, so we add a constraint to force them to be equal.

---

**3** **Ending inventory (positive or negative).** The key observation is the following. Let $L_t$ be the amount of leftover inventory at the end of month $t$, and let $S_t$ be the amount short at the end of month $t$. Then $L_t = 0$ if $S_t \geq 0$, and $S_t = 0$ if $L_t \geq 0$. So ending inventory can be written as

$$I_t = L_t - S_t$$

For example, if $I_2 = 6$, then $L_2 = 6$ and $S_2 = 0$, indicating that SureStep has six pairs of shoes left over at the end of month 2. But if $I_2 = -3$, then $L_2 = 0$ and $S_2 = 3$, indicating that SureStep has a shortage of three pairs of shoes at the end of month 2. To incorporate this into the model, enter the formula

=B39-B40

in cell B41 and copy it to the range C41:E41.

**4** **Monthly costs.** Insert a new row (which will be row 52) below the holding cost row. Modify the holding cost for month 1 by entering the formula

=$B$14*B39

in cell B51. Calculate the shortage cost for month 1 in cell B52 with the formula

=$B$15*B40

Then copy the range B51:B52 to the range C51:E52 for the other months. Make sure the totals in row 53 and column F are updated to include the shortage costs.

## USING SOLVER FOR THE BACKLOG MODEL

The changes from the original Solver setup are as follows.

**1 Extra changing cells.** Add the Leftover and Shortage ranges as changing cells. This allows Solver to adjust each month's amount leftover and amount short to be consistent with the desired ending inventory for the month.

**2 Constraint on last month's inventory.** Change the constraints that were previously listed as **Inventory_after_production>=Forecasted_demand** to **Inventory_after_ production_4>=Forecasted_demand_4**. This allows months 1 through 3 to have negative ending inventory, but it ensures that all demand is met by the end of month 4.

**3 Logical constraint on ending inventory.** Add the constraint **Leftover_minus_shortage=Ending_inventory**. If you study the model closely, you will notice that ending inventory is calculated in two different ways (in rows 41 and 43). This constraint ensures that both ways produce the same values.

**4 Optimize.** Make sure the Simplex LP method is selected, and click on Solve to obtain the optimal solution shown in Figure 4.21.

Note that this solution is the same as the one in Figure 4.19 that was obtained with the "IF function" model. So this time, Solver handled the IF function correctly, but it will not always do so. Admittedly, the linearized version in Figure 4.21 involves a somewhat unintuitive trick, but it does guarantee a linear model, which means that Solver will find the optimal solution. ▪

## MODELING ISSUES

1. Silver et al. (1998) recommend that when demand is seasonal, the planning horizon should extend beyond the next seasonal peak.

2. Beyond a certain point, the cost of using extra hours of overtime labor increases because workers become less efficient. We haven't modeled this type of behavior, but it would make the model nonlinear. ▪

## PROBLEMS

### Skill-Building Problems

**13.** Extend SureStep's original no-backlogging aggregate planning model from four to six months. Try several different values for demands in months 5 and 6, and run Solver for each. Is your optimal solution for the *first* four months the same as the one in the example?

**14.** SureStep is currently getting 160 regular-time hours from each worker per month. This is actually calculated from 8 hours per day times 20 days per month. For this, they are paid $9.375 per hour (=1500/160). Suppose workers can change their contract so that they only have to work 7.5 hours per day regular-time—everything above this becomes overtime—and their regular-time wage rate increases to $10 per hour. They will still work 20 days per month. Will this change the optimal no-backlogging solution?

15. The current solution to SureStep's no-backlogging aggregate planning model requires a lot of firing. Run a one-way SolverTable with the firing cost as the input variable and the numbers fired as the outputs. Let the firing cost increase from its current value to double that value in increments of $400. Do high firing costs eventually induce the company to fire fewer workers?

16. Suppose SureStep could begin a machinery upgrade and training program to increase its worker productivity. This program would result in the following values of labor hours per pair of shoes over the next four months: 4, 3.9, 3.8, and 3.8. How much would this new program be worth to SureStep, at least for this four-month planning horizon with no backlogging? How might you evaluate the program's worth *beyond* the next four months?

## Skill-Extending Problems

17. In the current no-backlogging problem, SureStep doesn't hire any workers and uses almost no overtime. This is evidently because of low demand. Change the demands to 6000, 8000, 5000, and 3000, and reoptimize. Is there now hiring and overtime? With this new demand pattern, explore the trade-off between hiring and overtime by running a two-way SolverTable. As inputs, use the hiring cost per worker and the maximum overtime hours allowed per worker per month, varied as you see fit. As outputs, use the total number of workers hired over the four months and the total number of overtime hours used over the four months. Write up your results in a short memo to SureStep management.

18. In the SureStep no-backlogging problem, change the demands so that they become 6000, 8000, 5000, 3000. Also, change the problem slightly so that newly hired workers take six hours to produce a pair of shoes during their first month of employment. After that, they take only four hours per pair of shoes. Modify the model appropriately, and use Solver to find the optimal solution.

19. We saw that the natural way to model SureStep's backlogging model, with IF functions, leads to a nonsmooth model that Solver has difficulty handling. Another version of the problem is also difficult for Solver. Suppose SureStep wants to meet all demand on time (no backlogging), but it wants to keep its employment level as constant across time as possible. To induce this, it charges a cost of $1000 each month on the absolute difference between the beginning number of workers and the number after hiring and firing—that is, the absolute difference between the values in rows 17 and 20 of the original spreadsheet model. Implement this extra cost in the model in the natural way, using the ABS function. Using demands of 6000, 8000, 5000, and 3000, see how well Solver does in trying to solve this nonsmooth model. Try several initial solutions, and see whether Solver gets the same optimal solution from each of them.

## 4.5 BLENDING MODELS

In many situations, various inputs must be blended together to produce desired outputs. In many of these situations, linear programming can find the optimal combination of outputs as well as the mix of inputs that are used to produce the desired outputs. Some examples of blending problems are given in Table 4.6.

Table 4.6  Examples of Blending Problems

| Inputs | Outputs |
| --- | --- |
| Meat, filler, water | Different types of sausage |
| Various types of oil | Heating oil, gasolines, aviation fuels |
| Carbon, iron, molybdenum | Different types of steel |
| Different types of pulp | Different kinds of recycled paper |

The following example illustrates how to model a typical blending problem in Excel. Although this example is small relative to blending problems in real applications, it is still probably too complex for you to guess the optimal solution.

EXAMPLE | **4.4 BLENDING AT CHANDLER OIL**

Chandler Oil has 5000 barrels of crude oil 1 and 10,000 barrels of crude oil 2 available. Chandler sells gasoline and heating oil. These products are produced by blending the two crude oils together. Each barrel of crude oil 1 has a "quality level" of 10 and each barrel of crude oil 2 has a quality level of 5.[6] Gasoline must have an average quality level of at least 8, whereas heating oil must have an average quality level of at least 6. Gasoline sells for $75 per barrel, and heating oil sells for $60 per barrel. We assume that demand for heating oil and gasoline is unlimited, so that all of Chandler's production can be sold. Chandler wants to maximize its revenue from selling gasoline and heating oil.

**Objective**   To develop an LP spreadsheet model for finding the revenue-maximizing plan that meets quality constraints and stays within limits on crude oil availabilities.

### WHERE DO THE NUMBERS COME FROM?

Most of the inputs for this problem should be easy to obtain.

- The selling prices for outputs are dictated by market pressures.
- The availabilities of inputs are based on crude supplies from the suppliers.
- The quality levels of crude oils are known from chemical analysis, whereas the required quality levels for outputs are specified by Chandler, probably in response to competitive or regulatory pressures.

### Solution

*In typical blending problems, the correct decision variables are the amounts of each input blended into each output.*

The variables and constraints required for this blending model are listed in Table 4.7. The key is the selection of the appropriate decision variables. Many students, when asked what decision variables should be used, specify the amounts of the two crude oils used and the amounts of the two products produced. However, this is not enough. The problem is that this information doesn't tell Chandler how to *make* the outputs from the inputs. The company instead requires a blending plan: how much of each input to use in the production of a barrel of each output. Once you understand that this blending plan is the basic decision, all other output variables follow in a straightforward manner.

Table 4.7   Variables and Constraints for Blending Model

| | |
|---|---|
| **Input variables** | Unit selling prices, availabilities of inputs, quality levels of inputs, required quality levels of outputs |
| **Decision variables (changing cells)** | Barrels of each input used to produce each output |
| **Objective cell** | Revenue from selling gasoline and heating oil |
| **Other calculated variables** | Barrels of inputs used, barrels of outputs produced (and sold), quality obtained and quality required for outputs |
| **Constraints** | Barrels of inputs used ≤ Barrels available |
| | Quality of outputs obtained ≥ Quality required |

A secondary, but very important, issue in typical blending models is how to implement the quality constraints. (The constraints here are in terms of quality. In other blending

---

[6]To avoid being overly technical, we use the generic term *quality level*. In real oil blending, qualities of interest might be octane rating, viscosity, and others.

problems they are often expressed in terms of percentages of some ingredient(s). For example, a typical quality constraint might be that some output can contain no more than 2% sulfur.) When we explain how to develop the spreadsheet model, we will discuss the preferred way to implement quality constraints.

### DEVELOPING THE SPREADSHEET MODEL

The spreadsheet model for this problem appears in Figure 4.22. (See the file Blending Oil.xlsx.) To set it up, proceed as follows.

**1** **Inputs and range names.** Enter the unit selling prices, quality levels for inputs, required quality levels for outputs, and availabilities of inputs in the blue cells. Then name the ranges as indicated.

**2** **Inputs blended into each output.** As discussed, the quantities Chandler must specify are the barrels of each input used to produce each output. Enter *any* trial values for these quantities in the Blending_plan range. For example, the value in cell B16 is the amount of crude oil 1 used to make gasoline and the value in cell C16 is the amount of crude oil 1 used to make heating oil. The Blending_plan range contains the changing cells.

**3** **Inputs used and outputs sold.** Calculate the row sums (in column D) and column sums (in row 18) of the Blending_plan range. There is a quick way to do this. Highlight both the row and column where the sums will go (highlight one, then hold down the Ctrl key and highlight the other), and click on the Summation ($\Sigma$) button on the Home ribbon. This creates SUM formulas in each highlighted cell.

*From here on, the solutions shown are optimal. However, remember that you can start with any solution. It doesn't even have to be feasible.*

---

Figure 4.22    Oil Blending Model

| | A | B | C | D | E | F | G | H |
|---|---|---|---|---|---|---|---|---|
| 1 | Chandler oil blending model | | | | | Range names used | | |
| 2 | | | | | | Barrels_available | =Model!$F$16:$F$17 | |
| 3 | Monetary inputs | Gasoline | Heating oil | | | Barrels_sold | =Model!$B$18:$C$18 | |
| 4 | Selling price/barrel | $75 | $60 | | | Barrels_used | =Model!$D$16:$D$17 | |
| 5 | | | | | | Blending_plan | =Model!$B$16:$C$17 | |
| 6 | Quality level per barrel of crudes | | | | | Quality_points_obtained | =Model!$B$22:$C$22 | |
| 7 | Crude oil 1 | 10 | | | | Quality_points_required | =Model!$B$24:$C$24 | |
| 8 | Crude oil 2 | 5 | | | | Revenue | =Model!$B$27 | |
| 9 | | | | | | | | |
| 10 | Required quality level per barrel of product | | | | | | | |
| 11 | | Gasoline | Heating oil | | | | | |
| 12 | | 8 | 6 | | | | | |
| 13 | | | | | | | | |
| 14 | Blending plan (barrels of crudes in each product) | | | | | | | |
| 15 | | Gasoline | Heating oil | Barrels used | | Barrels available | | |
| 16 | Crude oil 1 | 3000 | 2000 | 5000 | <= | 5000 | | |
| 17 | Crude oil 2 | 2000 | 8000 | 10000 | <= | 10000 | | |
| 18 | Barrels sold | 5000 | 10000 | | | | | |
| 19 | | | | | | | | |
| 20 | Constraints on quality | | | | | | | |
| 21 | | Gasoline | Heating oil | | | | | |
| 22 | Quality points obtained | 40000 | 60000 | | | | | |
| 23 | | >= | >= | | | | | |
| 24 | Quality points required | 40000 | 60000 | | | | | |
| 25 | | | | | | | | |
| 26 | Objective to maximize | | | | | | | |
| 27 | Revenue | $975,000 | | | | | | |

**4** **Quality achieved.** Keep track of the quality level of gasoline and heating oil in the Quality_points_obtained range as follows. Begin by calculating for each output the number of quality points (QP) in the inputs used to produce this output:

QP in gasoline = 10 * Oil 1 in gasoline + 5 * Oil 2 in gasoline
QP in heating oil = 10 * Oil 1 in heating oil + 5 * Oil 2 in heating oil

The gasoline quality constraint is then

$$\text{QP in gasoline} \geq 8 * \text{Gasoline sold} \qquad (4.1)$$

Similarly, the heating oil quality constraint is

$$\text{QP in heating oil} \geq 6 * \text{Heating oil sold} \qquad (4.2)$$

To implement Inequalities (4.1) and (4.2), calculate the QP for gasoline in cell B22 with the formula

```
=SUMPRODUCT(B16:B17, $B$7:$B$8)
```

and copy this formula to cell C22 to generate the QP for heating oil.

**5** **Quality required.** Calculate the required quality points for gasoline and heating oil in cells B24 and C24. Specifically, determine the required quality points for gasoline in cell B24 with the formula

```
=B12*B18
```

and copy this formula to cell C24 for heating oil.

**6** **Revenue.** Calculate the total revenue in cell B27 with the formula

```
=SUMPRODUCT(B4:C4,B18:C18)
```

## Using Solver

To solve Chandler's problem with Solver, fill out the main Solver dialog box as shown in Figure 4.23. As usual, check the Non-Negative option and specify the Simplex LP method before optimizing. You should obtain the optimal solution shown in Figure 4.22.

### Discussion of the Solution

The optimal solution implies that Chandler should make 5000 barrels of gasoline with 3000 barrels of crude oil 1 and 2000 barrels of crude oil 2. The company should also make 10,000 barrels of heating oil with 2000 barrels of crude oil 1 and 8000 barrels of crude oil 2. With this blend, Chandler will obtain a revenue of $975,000. As stated previously, this problem is sufficiently complex to defy intuition. Clearly, gasoline is more profitable per barrel than heating oil, but given the crude availability and the quality constraints, it turns out that Chandler should sell twice as much heating oil as gasoline. This would have been difficult to guess ahead of time.

### Sensitivity Analysis

We perform two typical sensitivity analyses on this blending model. In each, we see how revenue and the amounts of the outputs produced (and sold) vary. In the first analysis, we use the unit selling price of gasoline as the input and let it vary from $50 to $90 in increments of $5. The SolverTable results appear in Figure 4.24. Two things are

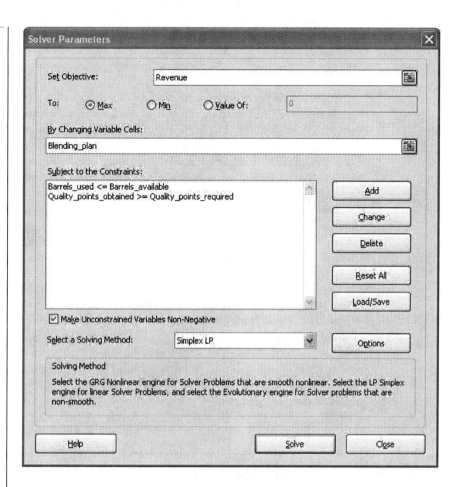

Figure 4.23

Solver Dialog Box for Blending Model

Figure 4.24

Sensitivity to the Selling Price of Gasoline

| | A | B | C | D | E | F | G |
|---|---|---|---|---|---|---|---|
| 1 | **Oneway analysis for Solver model in Model worksheet** | | | | | | |
| 2 | | | | | | | |
| 3 | Selling price gasoline (cell $B$4) values along side, output cell(s) along top | | | | | | |
| 4 | | Barrels_sold_1 | Barrels_sold_2 | Revenue | Increase | | |
| 5 | $50 | 0 | 15000 | $900,000 | | | |
| 6 | $55 | 0 | 15000 | $900,000 | $0 | | |
| 7 | $60 | 5000 | 10000 | $900,000 | $0 | | |
| 8 | $65 | 5000 | 10000 | $925,000 | $25,000 | | |
| 9 | $70 | 5000 | 10000 | $950,000 | $25,000 | | |
| 10 | $75 | 5000 | 10000 | $975,000 | $25,000 | | |
| 11 | $80 | 5000 | 10000 | $1,000,000 | $25,000 | | |
| 12 | $85 | 5000 | 10000 | $1,025,000 | $25,000 | | |
| 13 | $90 | 5000 | 10000 | $1,050,000 | $25,000 | | |

of interest. First, as the price of gasoline increases from $55 to $65, Chandler starts producing gasoline and less heating oil, exactly as you would expect. Second, the revenue can only increase or stay the same, as the changes in column E (calculated manually) indicate.

In the second sensitivity analysis, we vary the availability of crude 1 from 2000 barrels to 20,000 barrels in increments of 1000 barrels. The resulting SolverTable output appears in Figure 4.25. These results make sense if you analyze them carefully. First, the revenue increases, but at a decreasing rate, as more crude 1 is available. This is a common occurrence in LP models. As more of a resource is made available, revenue can only increase or remain the same, but each extra unit of the resource produces less (or at least no more) revenue than the previous unit. Second, the amount of gasoline produced increases, whereas the amount of heating oil produced decreases. Here's why: Crude 1 has a higher quality than crude 2, and gasoline requires higher quality. Gasoline also sells for a higher price. Therefore, as more crude 1 is available, Chandler can produce more gasoline, receive more revenue, and still meet quality standards.

Could these sensitivity questions also be answered with Solver's sensitivity report, shown in Figure 4.26? Consider the sensitivity to the change in the price of gasoline. The first and third rows of the top table in this report are for sensitivity to the objective coefficients of decision variables involving gasoline. The problem is that when the price of gasoline changes, *both* of these coefficients change. The reason is that the objective includes the sum of these two decision variables, multiplied by the unit price of gasoline. However, Solver's sensitivity report is valid only for one-at-a-time coefficient changes. Therefore, it cannot answer our question.

**Figure 4.25**

Sensitivity to the Availability of Crude 1

| | A | B | C | D | E | F | G |
|---|---|---|---|---|---|---|---|
| 1 | Oneway analysis for Solver model in Model worksheet | | | | | | |
| 2 | | | | | | | |
| 3 | Barrels available crude 1 (cell $F$16) values along side, output cell(s) along top | | | | | | |
| 4 | | Barrels_sold_1 | Barrels_sold_2 | Revenue | Increase | | |
| 5 | 2000 | 0 | 10000 | $600,000 | | | |
| 6 | 3000 | 1000 | 12000 | $795,000 | $195,000 | | |
| 7 | 4000 | 3000 | 11000 | $885,000 | $90,000 | | |
| 8 | 5000 | 5000 | 10000 | $975,000 | $90,000 | | |
| 9 | 6000 | 7000 | 9000 | $1,065,000 | $90,000 | | |
| 10 | 7000 | 9000 | 8000 | $1,155,000 | $90,000 | | |
| 11 | 8000 | 11000 | 7000 | $1,245,000 | $90,000 | | |
| 12 | 9000 | 13000 | 6000 | $1,335,000 | $90,000 | | |
| 13 | 10000 | 15000 | 5000 | $1,425,000 | $90,000 | | |
| 14 | 11000 | 17000 | 4000 | $1,515,000 | $90,000 | | |
| 15 | 12000 | 19000 | 3000 | $1,605,000 | $90,000 | | |
| 16 | 13000 | 21000 | 2000 | $1,695,000 | $90,000 | | |
| 17 | 14000 | 23000 | 1000 | $1,785,000 | $90,000 | | |
| 18 | 15000 | 25000 | 0 | $1,875,000 | $90,000 | | |
| 19 | 16000 | 26000 | 0 | $1,950,000 | $75,000 | | |
| 20 | 17000 | 27000 | 0 | $2,025,000 | $75,000 | | |
| 21 | 18000 | 28000 | 0 | $2,100,000 | $75,000 | | |
| 22 | 19000 | 29000 | 0 | $2,175,000 | $75,000 | | |
| 23 | 20000 | 30000 | 0 | $2,250,000 | $75,000 | | |

## Figure 4.26  Sensitivity Report for Blending Model

| | Cell | Name | Final Value | Reduced Cost | Objective Coefficient | Allowable Increase | Allowable Decrease |
|---|---|---|---|---|---|---|---|
| 6 | **Adjustable Cells** | | | | | | |
| 7 | | | Final | Reduced | Objective | Allowable | Allowable |
| 8 | Cell | Name | Value | Cost | Coefficient | Increase | Decrease |
| 9 | $B$16 | Crude oil 1 Gasoline | 3000 | 0 | 75 | 175 | 25 |
| 10 | $C$16 | Crude oil 1 Heating oil | 2000 | 0 | 60 | 25 | 175 |
| 11 | $B$17 | Crude oil 2 Gasoline | 2000 | 0 | 75 | 262.5 | 18.75 |
| 12 | $C$17 | Crude oil 2 Heating oil | 8000 | 0 | 60 | 18.75 | 43.75 |
| 13 | | | | | | | |
| 14 | **Constraints** | | | | | | |
| 15 | | | Final | Shadow | Constraint | Allowable | Allowable |
| 16 | Cell | Name | Value | Price | R.H. Side | Increase | Decrease |
| 17 | $D$16 | Crude oil 1 Barrels used | 5000 | 90 | 5000 | 10000 | 2500 |
| 18 | $D$17 | Crude oil 2 Barrels used | 10000 | 53 | 10000 | 10000 | 6666.666667 |
| 19 | $B$22 | Quality points obtained Gasoline | 40000 | -7 | 0 | 5000 | 20000 |
| 20 | $C$22 | Quality points obtained Heating oil | 60000 | -7 | 0 | 10000 | 6666.666667 |

In contrast, the first row of the bottom table in Figure 4.26 complements the SolverTable sensitivity analysis on the availability of crude 1. It shows that if the availability increases by no more than 10,000 barrels or decreases by no more than 2500 barrels, the shadow price remains $90 per barrel—that is, the same $90,000 increase in profit per 1000 barrels in Figure 4.25. Beyond that range, the sensitivity report indicates only that the shadow price will change. The SolverTable results indicate *how* it changes. For example, when crude 1 availability increases beyond 15,000 barrels, the SolverTable results indicate that the shadow price decreases to $75 per barrel.

### A Caution About Blending Constraints

*Blending models usually have various quality constraints, often expressed as required percentages of various ingredients. To keep these models linear (and avoid dividing by zero), it is important to clear denominators.*

Before concluding this example, we discuss why the model is linear. The key is the implementation of the quality constraints, shown in Inequalities (4.1) and (4.2). To keep a model linear, each side of an inequality constraint must be a constant, the product of a constant and a variable, or a sum of such products. If the quality constraints are implemented as in Inequalities (4.1) and (4.2), the constraints are indeed linear. However, it is arguably more natural to rewrite this type of constraint by dividing through by the amount sold. For example, the modified gasoline constraint becomes

$$\frac{QP \text{ in gasoline}}{\text{Gasoline sold}} \geq 8 \qquad (4.3)$$

Although this form of the constraint is perfectly valid—and is possibly more natural to many people—it suffers from two drawbacks. First, it makes the model nonlinear. This is because the left side is no longer a sum of products; it involves a quotient. We prefer linear models whenever possible. Second, suppose it turns out that Chandler's optimal solution calls for *no* gasoline at all. Then Inequality (4.3) includes division by zero, and this causes an error in Excel. Because of these two drawbacks, it is best to "clear denominators" in all such blending constraints. ▪

## MODELING ISSUES

In reality, a company using a blending model would run the model periodically (each day, say) and set production on the basis of the current inventory of inputs and the current forecasts of demands and prices. Then the forecasts and the input levels would be updated, and the model would be run again to determine the next day's production. ▪

## ADDITIONAL APPLICATIONS

### Blending at Texaco

Texaco, in DeWitt et al. (1989), uses a nonlinear programming model (OMEGA) to plan and schedule its blending applications. Texaco's model is nonlinear because blend volatilities and octanes are nonlinear functions of the amount of each input used to produce a particular gasoline.

### Blending in the Oil Industry

Many oil companies use LP to optimize their refinery operations. Magoulas and Marinos-Kouris (1988) discuss one such blending model that has been used to maximize a refinery's profit. ▪

## PROBLEMS

### Skill-Building Problems

**20.** Use SolverTable in Chandler's blending model to see whether, by increasing the selling price of gasoline, you can get an optimal solution that produces only gasoline, no heating oil. Then use SolverTable again to see whether, by increasing the selling price of heating oil, you can get an optimal solution that produces only heating oil, no gasoline.

**21.** Use SolverTable in Chandler's blending model to find the shadow price of crude oil 1—that is, the amount Chandler would be willing to spend to acquire more crude oil 1. Does this shadow price change as Chandler keeps getting more of crude oil 1? Answer the same questions for crude oil 2.

**22.** How sensitive is the optimal solution (barrels of each output sold and profit) to the required quality points?

Answer this by running a two-way SolverTable with these three outputs. You can choose the values of the two inputs to vary.

**23.** In Chandler's blending model, suppose a chemical ingredient called CI is needed by both gasoline and heating oil. At least 3% of every barrel of gasoline must be CI, and at least 5% of every barrel of heating oil must be CI. Suppose that 4% of all crude oil 1 is CI, and 6% of all crude oil 2 is CI. Modify the model to incorporate the constraints on CI, and then optimize. Don't forget to clear denominators.

**24.** In the current blending model, a barrel of any input results in a barrel of output. However, in a real blending problem, there can be losses. Suppose a barrel of input results in only a fraction of a barrel of output. Specifically, each barrel of either crude oil used for gasoline results in only 0.95 barrel of gasoline, and each barrel

of either crude used for heating oil results in only 0.97 barrel of heating oil. Modify the model to incorporate these losses, and reoptimize.

Skill-Extending Problem

**25.** We warned you about clearing denominators in the quality constraints. This problem illustrates what can happen if you don't do so.
   **a.** Implement the quality constraints as indicated in Inequality (4.3) of the text. Then run Solver with the Simplex LP method. What happens? What if you use the GRG Nonlinear method instead?
   **b.** Repeat part **a**, but increase the selling price of heating oil to $120 per barrel. What happens now? Does it matter whether you use the Simplex LP method, as opposed to the GRG Nonlinear method? Why?

## 4.6 PRODUCTION PROCESS MODELS

LP is often used to determine the optimal method of operating a production process. In particular, many oil refineries use LP to manage their production operations. The models are often characterized by the fact that some of the products produced are *inputs* to the production of other products. The following example is typical.

### EXAMPLE 4.5 DRUG PRODUCTION AT REPCO

Repco produces three drugs, A, B, and C, and can sell these drugs in unlimited quantities at unit prices $8, $70, and $100, respectively. Producing a unit of drug A requires one hour of labor. Producing a unit of drug B requires two hours of labor and two units of drug A. Producing one unit of drug C requires three hours of labor and one unit of drug B. Any drug A that is used to produce drug B cannot be sold separately, and any drug B that is used to produce drug C cannot be sold separately. A total of 4000 hours of labor are available. Repco wants to use LP to maximize its sales revenue.

**Objective** To develop an LP spreadsheet model that relates production decisions to amounts required for production and amounts available for selling, and to use Solver to maximize sales revenue, subject to limited labor hours.

#### WHERE DO THE NUMBERS COME FROM?

The inputs for this problem should be easy to obtain:

▧ The company sets its selling prices, which are probably dictated by the market.

▧ The available labor hours are based on the size of the current workforce assigned to production of these drugs. These might be flexible quantities, depending on whether workers could be diverted from other duties to work on these drugs and whether new labor could be hired.

▧ The labor and drug usage inputs for producing the various drugs are probably well known, based on productivity levels and chemical requirements.

## Solution

The decision variables should be the smallest set of variables that determines everything else. After the company decides how much of each drug to produce, there is really nothing left to decide.

The variables and constraints required to model this problem are listed in Table 4.8. The key to the model is understanding which variables can be chosen—the decision variables—and which variables are determined by this choice. It is probably clear that Repco must decide how much of each drug to produce. However, it might not be clear why the amounts used for production of other drugs and the amounts sold are *not* decision variables. The idea is that as soon as Repco decides to produce, say, 10 units of drug B, it automatically knows that it must produce at least 20 units of drug A. In fact, it cannot decide to produce just *any* quantities of the three drugs. For example, it can't produce 10 units of drug B and only 15 units of drug A. Therefore, the drugs required for producing other drugs put automatic constraints on the production quantities. Note that any drugs not used in production of other drugs are sold.

**Table 4.8  Variables and Constraints for the Production Process Model**

| | |
|---|---|
| **Input variables** | Labor inputs to drug production, drugs required for production of other drugs, selling prices of drugs, labor hours available |
| **Decision variables (changing cells)** | Units of drugs to produce |
| **Objective (target cell)** | Revenue from sales |
| **Other calculated variables** | Units of drugs used to make other drugs, units of drugs left over to sell |
| **Constraints** | Drugs produced $\geq$ Drugs required for production of other drugs |
| | Labor hours used $\leq$ Labor hours available |

### DEVELOPING THE SPREADSHEET MODEL

The key to the spreadsheet model is that everything produced is used in some way. Either it is used as an input to the production of some other drug, or it is sold. Therefore, the following *balance equation* holds for each product:

$$\text{Amount produced} = \text{Amount used to produce other drugs} + \text{Amount sold} \quad \textbf{(4.4)}$$

This balance equation can be implemented in three steps:

**1** Specify the amounts produced in changing cells.

**2** Calculate the amounts used to produce other drugs based on the way the production process works.

**3** Calculate the amounts sold from Equation (4.4) by subtraction. Then impose a constraint that Equation (4.4) must be satisfied.

The spreadsheet model for Repco appears in Figure 4.27. (See the file Production Process.xlsx.) To proceed, carry out the following steps:

**1** **Inputs and range names.** Enter the inputs in the shaded blue ranges. For example, the 2 in cell C7 indicates that two units of drug A are needed to produce each unit of drug B, and the 0s in this range indicate which drugs are not needed to produce other drugs. (Note, however, the 0 in cell D7, which could be misleading. Drug A is required to make drug B, and drug B is required to make drug C. Therefore, drug A is required

Figure 4.27 Repco Production Process Model

| | A | B | C | D | E | F | G | H | I | J |
|---|---|---|---|---|---|---|---|---|---|---|
| 1 | Repco production process model | | | | | Range names used: | | | | |
| 2 | | | | | | Hours_available | =Model!$D$23 | | | |
| 3 | Inputs used (along side) to make one unit of product (along top) | | | | | Hours_used | =Model!$B$23 | | | |
| 4 | | Drug A | Drug B | Drug C | | Revenue_from_sales | =Model!$B$25 | | | |
| 5 | Labor hours | 1 | 2 | 3 | | Units_produced | =Model!$B$16:$D$16 | | | |
| 6 | | | | | | Units_sold | =Model!$B$19:$D$19 | | | |
| 7 | Drug A | 0 | 2 | 0 | | Units_used_in_production | =Model!$B$18:$D$18 | | | |
| 8 | Drug B | 0 | 0 | 1 | | | | | | |
| 9 | Drug C | 0 | 0 | 0 | | | | | | |
| 10 | | | | | | | | | | |
| 11 | Unit selling prices | Drug A | Drug B | Drug C | | | | | | |
| 12 | | $8 | $70 | $100 | | | | | | |
| 13 | | | | | | | | | | |
| 14 | Production and sales plan | | | | | Units of products used (along side) to make products (along top) | | | | |
| 15 | | Drug A | Drug B | Drug C | | | Drug A | Drug B | Drug C | Total used |
| 16 | Units produced | 2000 | 1000 | 0 | | Drug A | 0 | 2000 | 0 | 2000 |
| 17 | | >= | >= | >= | | Drug B | 0 | 0 | 0 | 0 |
| 18 | Units used in production | 2000 | 0 | 0 | | Drug C | 0 | 0 | 0 | 0 |
| 19 | Units sold | 0 | 1000 | 0 | | | | | | |
| 20 | | | | | | | | | | |
| 21 | Labor hour constraint | | | | | | | | | |
| 22 | | Hours used | | Hours available | | | | | | |
| 23 | | 4000 | <= | 4000 | | | | | | |
| 24 | | | | | | | | | | |
| 25 | Revenue from sales | $70,000 | ◄——— | Objective to maximize | | | | | | |

indirectly to make drug C. However, this indirect effect is accounted for by the values in cells C7 and D8, so the 0 in cell D7 is appropriate.) Then create the range names indicated.

**2** **Units produced.** Enter *any* trial values for the number of units produced in the Units_produced range. This range contains the only changing cells.

**3** **Units used to make other products.** In the range G16:I18, calculate the total number of units of each product that are used to produce other products. Begin by calculating the amount of A used to produce A in cell G16 with the formula

```
=B7*B$16
```

and copy this formula to the range G16:I18 for the other combinations of products. For example, in the solution shown, 10 units of drug B are produced, so 2000 units of drug A are required, as calculated in cell H16. Then calculate the row totals in column J with the SUM function. Then it is convenient to transfer these sums in column J to the B18:D18 range. There are two ways to do this, that is, to make a column into a row or vice versa. The easiest way is to copy the range J16:J18, then select cell B18, select the Edit/Paste Special menu item, and check the Transpose option. Unfortunately, this method doesn't copy formulas correctly. The second way uses Excel's TRANSPOSE function. To copy the formulas correctly, highlight the B18:D18 range, type the formula

```
=TRANSPOSE(J16:J18)
```

and press Ctrl+Shift+Enter (all three keys at once).

**Excel Tool: *Paste Special Transpose***
*To copy a row range to a column range, copy the row range, select the first cell in the column range, and select Transpose from the Paste dropdown menu on the Home ribbon. The*

*same method can be used to copy a column range to a row range. However, this method doesn't copy formulas correctly.*

**Excel Function: *TRANSPOSE and Other Array Functions***
*The TRANSPOSE function is useful for linking a row to a column or vice versa. It has the syntax =TRANSPOSE(Range). To implement it, highlight the row or column range where the results will go, type the formula, and press Ctrl+Shift+Enter. This function is one of several* array *functions in Excel, which means that it fills an entire range, not just a single cell, all at once. All array formulas require you to highlight the entire range where the results will go, type the formula, and then press Ctrl+Shift+Enter. After you do this, you will notice curly brackets around the formula in the Formula Bar. You should* not *actually type these curly brackets. They simply indicate the presence of an array function.*

**4** **Units sold.** Referring to Equation (4.4), determine the units sold of each drug by subtraction. Specifically, enter the formula

=B16-B18

in cell B19 and copy it to the range C19:D19.

**5** **Labor hours used.** Calculate the total number of labor hours used in cell B23 with the formula

=SUMPRODUCT(B5:D5,Units_produced)

**6** **Total revenue.** Calculate Repco's revenue from sales in cell B25 with the formula

=SUMPRODUCT(B12:D12,Units_sold)

## USING SOLVER

To use Solver to maximize Repco's revenue, fill in the Solver dialog box as shown in Figure 4.28. As usual, check the Non-Negative option and select the Simplex LP method before optimizing. Note that the drugs produced are constrained to be greater than or equal to the drugs used in production of other drugs. An equivalent alternative is to constrain the units sold to be nonnegative.

**Figure 4.28**

**Solver Dialog Box for Repco Model**

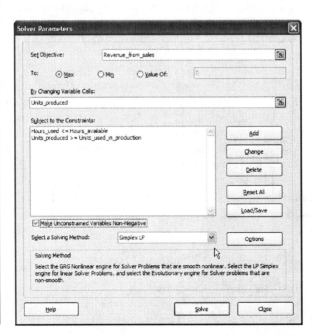

## Discussion of the Solution

The optimal solution in Figure 4.27 indicates that Repco obtains a revenue of $70,000 by producing 2000 units of drug A, all of which are used to produce 1000 units of drug B. All units of drug B produced are sold. Even though drug C has the highest selling price, Repco produces none of drug C, evidently because of the large labor requirement for drug C.

## Sensitivity Analysis

Drug C is not produced at all, even though its selling price is by far the highest. How high would this selling price have to be to induce Repco to produce drug C? You can use SolverTable to answer this, using drug C selling price as the input variable, letting it vary from $100 to $200 in increments of $10, and keeping track of the total revenue, the units produced of each drug, and the units used (row 18) of each drug. The results are shown in Figure 4.29.

**Figure 4.29**

Sensitivity to Selling Price of Drug C

| | A | B | C | D | E | F | G | H |
|---|---|---|---|---|---|---|---|---|
| 1 | Oneway analysis for Solver model in Model worksheet | | | | | | | |
| 2 | | | | | | | | |
| 3 | Drug C selling price (cell $D$12) values along side, output cell(s) along top | | | | | | | |
| 4 | | Units_produced_1 | Units_produced_2 | Units_produced_3 | Units_used_in_production_1 | Units_used_in_production_2 | Units_used_in_production_3 | Revenue_from_sales |
| 5 | $100 | 2000 | 1000 | 0 | 2000 | 0 | 0 | $70,000 |
| 6 | $110 | 2000 | 1000 | 0 | 2000 | 0 | 0 | $70,000 |
| 7 | $120 | 2000 | 1000 | 0 | 2000 | 0 | 0 | $70,000 |
| 8 | $130 | 1142.857 | 571.4286 | 571 | 1143 | 571 | 0 | $74,286 |
| 9 | $140 | 1142.857 | 571.4286 | 571 | 1143 | 571 | 0 | $80,000 |
| 10 | $150 | 1142.857 | 571.4286 | 571 | 1143 | 571 | 0 | $85,714 |
| 11 | $160 | 1142.857 | 571.4286 | 571 | 1143 | 571 | 0 | $91,429 |
| 12 | $170 | 1142.857 | 571.4286 | 571 | 1143 | 571 | 0 | $97,143 |
| 13 | $180 | 1142.857 | 571.4286 | 571 | 1143 | 571 | 0 | $102,857 |
| 14 | $190 | 1142.857 | 571.4286 | 571 | 1143 | 571 | 0 | $108,571 |
| 15 | $200 | 1142.857 | 571.4286 | 571 | 1143 | 571 | 0 | $114,286 |

As you can see, until the drug C selling price reaches $130, Repco uses the same solution as before.[7] However, when it increases to $130 and beyond, 571.4 units of drug C are produced. This in turn requires 571.4 units of drug B, which requires 1142.9 units of drug A, but only drug C is actually sold. Of course, Repco would like to produce even more of drug C (which would require more production of drugs A and B), but the labor hour constraint does not allow it. Therefore, further increases in the selling price of drug C have no effect on the solution—other than increasing revenue.

Because available labor imposes an upper limit on the production of drug C even when it is very profitable, it is interesting to see what happens when the selling price of drug C *and* the labor hours available both increase. Here you can use a two-way SolverTable, selecting selling price of drug C and labor hour availability as the two inputs with reasonable values, and selecting the amount produced of drug C as the single output. The results from SolverTable appear in Figure 4.30.

[7] If you obtain Solver's sensitivity report, you will see that the change actually occurs when the price of drug C reaches $122.50. Our SolverTable grid of prices is too coarse to detect this exact changeover point.

| | A | B | C | D | E | F | G | H |
|---|---|---|---|---|---|---|---|---|
| 1 | Twoway analysis for Solver model in Model worksheet | | | | | | | |
| 2 | | | | | | | | |
| 3 | Selling price drug C (cell $D$12) values along side, Hours available (cell $D$23) values along top | | | | | | | |
| 4 | Units_produced_3 | 4000 | 5000 | 6000 | 7000 | 8000 | 9000 | 10000 |
| 5 | $100 | 0.0 | 0.0 | 0.0 | 0.0 | 0.0 | 0.0 | 0.0 |
| 6 | $110 | 0.0 | 0.0 | 0.0 | 0.0 | 0.0 | 0.0 | 0.0 |
| 7 | $120 | 0.0 | 0.0 | 0.0 | 0.0 | 0.0 | 0.0 | 0.0 |
| 8 | $130 | 571.4 | 714.3 | 857.1 | 1000.0 | 1142.9 | 1285.7 | 1428.6 |
| 9 | $140 | 571.4 | 714.3 | 857.1 | 1000.0 | 1142.9 | 1285.7 | 1428.6 |
| 10 | $150 | 571.4 | 714.3 | 857.1 | 1000.0 | 1142.9 | 1285.7 | 1428.6 |
| 11 | $160 | 571.4 | 714.3 | 857.1 | 1000.0 | 1142.9 | 1285.7 | 1428.6 |
| 12 | $170 | 571.4 | 714.3 | 857.1 | 1000.0 | 1142.9 | 1285.7 | 1428.6 |
| 13 | $180 | 571.4 | 714.3 | 857.1 | 1000.0 | 1142.9 | 1285.7 | 1428.6 |
| 14 | $190 | 571.4 | 714.3 | 857.1 | 1000.0 | 1142.9 | 1285.7 | 1428.6 |
| 15 | $200 | 571.4 | 714.3 | 857.1 | 1000.0 | 1142.9 | 1285.7 | 1428.6 |

This table again shows that no drug C is produced, regardless of labor hour availability, until the selling price of drug C reaches $130. (Of course, the actual breakpoint is probably *between* $120 and $130. You can't tell from the grid of input values used in the table.) The effect of increases in labor hour availability is to let Repco produce more of drug C. Specifically, Repco produces as much of drug C as possible, given that one unit of drug B, and hence two units of drug A, are required for each unit of drug C.

Before leaving this example, we provide further insight into the sensitivity behavior in Figure 4.29. Specifically, why should Repco start producing drug C when its unit selling price increases to some value between $120 and $130? There is a straightforward answer to this question because the model contains a *single* resource constraint: the labor hour constraint. (The analysis would be more complicated with multiple resources.)

Consider the production of one unit of drug B, which requires two labor hours plus two units of drug A, each of which requires one labor hour, for a total of four labor hours. It returns $70 in revenue. Therefore, revenue per labor hour when producing drug B is $17.50. To be eligible as a "winner," drug C has to beat this. Note that each unit of drug C requires seven labor hours (three for itself and four for the unit of drug B it requires). To beat the $17.50 revenue per labor hour of drug B, the unit selling price of drug C must be at least $122.50 [= 17.50(7)]. If its selling price is below this, for example, $121, Repco will sell all drug B and no drug C. If its selling price is above this, for example, $127, Repco will sell all drug C and no drug B. ■

# PROBLEMS

## Skill-Building Problems

**26.** Run a one-way sensitivity analysis on the optimal solution to the unit selling price of drug A in the Repco problem. If this price is high enough, will Repco start selling drug A in addition to producing it? Then run a similar one-way sensitivity analysis on the optimal solution to the price of drug B. If this price gets low enough, what happens to the optimal solution?

**27.** Suppose there is a fourth drug, drug D, that Repco can produce and sell. Each unit of drug D requires four labor hours, one unit of drug A, and one unit of drug C to produce, and it sells for $150 per unit.

Modify the current model to incorporate drug D and reoptimize. If drug D isn't produced in the optimal solution, use sensitivity analysis to see how much higher its selling price would have to be before Repco would produce it. If drug D is produced in the optimal solution, use sensitivity analysis to see how much lower its selling price would have to be before Repco would stop producing it.

**28.** We claimed that the Repco model could either constrain the units produced to be greater than or equal to the units used by production or constrain the units sold to be nonnegative. Modify the model to implement the latter (deleting the former), and verify that you get the same optimal solution.

**29.** In a production process model such as Repco's, certain inputs make no sense in the usage table (the range B7:D9 of the model). For example, suppose that, in addition to current usages, each unit of drug A requires one unit of drug C. Why does this result in a nonsensical problem? What happens if you run Solver on it anyway? What happens if you run Solver on it after adding a constraint that the sum of the units produced (over all three drugs) must be at least 1?

---

## 4.7 FINANCIAL MODELS

The majority of optimization examples described in management science textbooks are in the area of operations: scheduling, blending, logistics, aggregate planning, and others. This is probably warranted, because many of the most successful management science applications in the real world have been in these areas. However, optimization and other management science methods have also been applied successfully in a number of financial areas, and they deserve recognition. Several of these applications are discussed throughout this book. In this section, we begin the discussion with two typical applications of LP in finance. The first involves investment strategy. The second involves pension fund management.

---

### EXAMPLE | 4.6 FINDING AN OPTIMAL INVESTMENT STRATEGY AT BARNEY-JONES

At the present time, the beginning of year 1, the Barney-Jones Investment Corporation has $100,000 to invest for the next four years. There are five possible investments, labeled A through E. The timing of cash outflows and cash inflows for these investments is somewhat irregular. For example, to take part in investment A, cash must be invested at the beginning of year 1, and for every dollar invested, there are returns of $0.50 and $1.00 at the beginnings of years 2 and 3. Information for the other investments follows, where all returns are per dollar invested:

- Investment B: Invest at the beginning of year 2, receive returns of $0.50 and $1.00 at the beginnings of years 3 and 4

- Investment C: Invest at the beginning of year 1, receive return of $1.20 at the beginning of year 2

- Investment D: Invest at the beginning of year 4, receive return of $1.90 at the beginning of year 5

- Investment E: Invest at the beginning of year 3, receive return of $1.50 at the beginning of year 4

We assume that any amounts can be invested in these strategies and that the returns are the same for each dollar invested. However, to create a diversified portfolio, Barney-Jones wants to limit the amount put into any investment to $75,000. The company wants an investment strategy that maximizes the amount of cash on hand at the beginning of year 5. At the beginning of any year, it can invest only cash on hand, which includes returns from previous investments. Any cash not invested in any year can be put in a short-term money market account that earns 3% annually.

**Objective** To develop an LP spreadsheet model that relates investment decisions to total ending cash, and to use Solver to find the strategy that maximizes ending cash and invests no more than a given amount in any one investment.

There is no mystery here. We assume that the terms of each investment are spelled out, so that Barney-Jones knows exactly when money must be invested and what the amounts and timing of returns will be. Of course, this would not be the case for many real-world investments, such as money put into the stock market, where considerable uncertainty is involved. We consider one such example of investing with uncertainty when we study portfolio optimization in Chapter 7.

## Solution

*There are often multiple equivalent ways to state a constraint. You can choose the one that is most natural for you.*

The variables and constraints for this investment model are listed in Table 4.9. On the surface, this problem appears to be very straightforward. You must decide how much to invest in the available investments at the beginning of each year, using only the cash available. If you try modeling this problem without our help, however, we suspect that you will have some difficulty. It took us a few tries to get a model that is easy to read and generalizes to other similar investment problems. Note that the second constraint in the table can be expressed in two ways. It can be expressed as shown, where the cash on hand *after* investing is nonnegative, or it can be expressed as "cash invested in any year must be less than or equal to cash on hand at the beginning of that year." These are equivalent. The one you choose is a matter of taste.

**Table 4.9** Variables and Constraints for Investment Model

| | |
|---|---|
| **Input variables** | Timing of investments and returns, initial cash, maximum amount allowed in any investment, money market rate on cash |
| **Decision variables (changing cells)** | Amounts to invest in investments |
| **Objective cell** | Ending cash at the beginning of year 5 |
| **Other calculated variables** | Cash available at the beginning of years 2–4 |
| **Constraints** | Amount in any investment ≤ Max investment amount |
| | Cash on hand after investing each year ≥ 0 |

### DEVELOPING THE SPREADSHEET MODEL

The spreadsheet model for this investment problem appears in Figure 4.31. (See the file Investing.xlsx.) To set up this spreadsheet, proceed as follows.

*Note how the two input tables allow you to create copyable SUMPRODUCT formulas for cash outflows and inflows. Careful spreadsheet planning can often greatly simplify the necessary formulas.*

**1  Inputs and range names.** As usual, enter the given inputs in the blue cells and name the ranges indicated. Pay particular attention to the two shaded tables. This is probably the first model you have encountered where model development is affected significantly by the way you enter the inputs, specifically, the information about the investments. We suggest separating cash outflows from cash inflows, as shown in the two ranges B11:F14 and B19:F23. The top table indicates when investments can be made, where $0.00 indicates no possible investment, and $1.00 indicates a dollar of investment. The bottom table then indicates the amounts and timing of returns per dollar invested.

**2  Investment amounts.** Enter *any* trial values in the Dollars_invested range. This range contains the changing cells. Also put a link to the maximum investment amount per investment by entering the formula

=$B$5

in cell B28 and copying it across.

Figure 4.31    Investment Model

| | A | B | C | D | E | F | G | H | I | J |
|---|---|---|---|---|---|---|---|---|---|---|
| 1 | Investments with irregular timing of returns | | | | | | | Range names used | | |
| 2 | | | | | | | | Cash_after_investing | =Model!$E$32:$E$35 | |
| 3 | Inputs | | | | | | | Dollars_invested | =Model!$B$26:$F$26 | |
| 4 | Initial amount to invest | $100,000 | | | | | | Final_cash | =Model!$B$38 | |
| 5 | Maximum per investment | $75,000 | | | | | | Maximum_per_investment | =Model!$B$28:$F$28 | |
| 6 | Interest rate on cash | 3% | | | | | | | | |
| 7 | | | | | | | | | | |
| 8 | Cash outlays on investments (all incurred at beginning of year) | | | | | | | | | |
| 9 | | Investment | | | | | | | | |
| 10 | Year | A | B | C | D | E | | | | |
| 11 | 1 | $1.00 | $0.00 | $1.00 | $0.00 | $0.00 | | | | |
| 12 | 2 | $0.00 | $1.00 | $0.00 | $0.00 | $0.00 | | | | |
| 13 | 3 | $0.00 | $0.00 | $0.00 | $0.00 | $1.00 | | | | |
| 14 | 4 | $0.00 | $0.00 | $0.00 | $1.00 | $0.00 | | | | |
| 15 | | | | | | | | | | |
| 16 | Cash returns from investments (all incurred at beginning of year) | | | | | | | | | |
| 17 | | Investment | | | | | | | | |
| 18 | Year | A | B | C | D | E | | | | |
| 19 | 1 | $0.00 | $0.00 | $0.00 | $0.00 | $0.00 | | | | |
| 20 | 2 | $0.50 | $0.00 | $1.20 | $0.00 | $0.00 | | | | |
| 21 | 3 | $1.00 | $0.50 | $0.00 | $0.00 | $0.00 | | | | |
| 22 | 4 | $0.00 | $1.00 | $0.00 | $0.00 | $1.50 | | | | |
| 23 | 5 | $0.00 | $0.00 | $0.00 | $1.90 | $0.00 | | | | |
| 24 | | | | | | | | | | |
| 25 | Investment decisions | | | | | | | | | |
| 26 | Dollars invested | $64,286 | $75,000 | $35,714 | $75,000 | $75,000 | | | | |
| 27 | | <= | <= | <= | <= | <= | | | | |
| 28 | Maximum per investment | $75,000 | $75,000 | $75,000 | $75,000 | $75,000 | | | | |
| 29 | | | | | | | | | | |
| 30 | Constraints on cash balance | | | | | | | | | |
| 31 | Year | Beginning cash | Returns from investments | Cash invested | Cash after investing | | | | | |
| 32 | 1 | $100,000 | $0 | $100,000 | $0 | >= | 0 | | | |
| 33 | 2 | $0 | $75,000 | $75,000 | $0 | >= | 0 | | | |
| 34 | 3 | $0 | $101,786 | $75,000 | $26,786 | >= | 0 | | | |
| 35 | 4 | $27,589 | $187,500 | $75,000 | $140,089 | >= | 0 | | | |
| 36 | 5 | $144,292 | $142,500 | | | | | | | |
| 37 | | | | | | | | | | |
| 38 | Final cash | $256,792 | ← | Objective to maximize: final cash at beginning of year 5 | | | | | | |

**③ Cash balances and flows.** The key to the model is the section in rows 32 through 36. For each year, you need to calculate the beginning cash held from the previous year, the returns from investments that are due in that year, the investments made in that year, and cash balance after investments. Begin by entering the initial cash in cell B32 with the formula

=B4

Moving across, calculate the return due in year 1 in cell C32 with the formula

=SUMPRODUCT(B19:F19,Dollars_invested)

Admittedly, no returns come due in year 1, but this formula can be copied down column C for other years. Next, calculate the total amount invested in year 1 in cell D32 with the formula

=SUMPRODUCT(B11:F11,Dollars_invested)

Now find the cash balance after investing in year 1 in cell E32 with the formula

=B32+C32-D32

The only other required formula is the formula for the cash available at the beginning of year 2. Because any cash not invested earns 3% interest, enter the formula

=E32*(1+$B$6)

in cell B33. This formula, along with those in cells C32, D32, and E32, can now be copied down. (The zeros in column G are entered manually as a reminder of the nonnegativity constraint on cash after investing.)

**④ Ending cash.** The ending cash at the beginning of year 5 is the sum of the amount in the money market and any returns that come due in year 5. Calculate this sum with the formula

=SUM(B36:C36)

in cell B38. (*Note*: Here is the type of error to watch out for. We originally failed to calculate the return in cell C36 and mistakenly used the beginning cash in cell B36 as the objective cell. We realized our error when the optimal solution called for no money in investment D, which is clearly an attractive investment. The moral is that you can often catch errors by looking at the *plausibility* of the outputs.)

### Review of the Model

Take a careful look at this model and how it has been set up. There are undoubtedly many alternative ways to model this problem, but the attractive feature of this model is the way the tables of inflows and outflows in rows 11 through 14 and 19 through 23 create *copyable* formulas for returns and investment amounts in columns C and D of rows 32 through 35. In fact, this same model setup, with only minor modifications, will work for *any* set of investments, regardless of the timing of investments and their returns. Generalizability is a quality you should strive for in your spreadsheet models.

### USING SOLVER

To find the optimal investment strategy, fill in the Solver dialog box as shown in Figure 4.32. Note that the explicit nonnegativity constraint in Figure 4.32 is necessary, even though the Non-Negative option is checked. Again, this is because the Non-Negative option covers only the changing cells. If you want other output cells to be nonnegative, you must add such constraints explicitly.

Figure 4.32

**Solver Dialog Box
for Investment
Model**

## Discussion of the Results

The optimal solution appears in Figure 4.31. Let's follow the cash. The company spends all of its cash in year 1 on the two available investments, A and C ($64,286 in A, $35,714 in C). A total of $75,000 in returns from these investments is available in year 2, and all of this is invested in investment B. At the beginning of year 3, a total of $101,786 is available from investment A and B returns, and $75,000 of this is invested in investment E. This leaves $26,786 for the money market, which grows to $27,589 at the beginning of year 4. In addition, returns totaling $187,500 from investments B and E come due in year 4. Of this total cash of $215,089, $75,000 is invested in investment D, and the rest, $140,089, is put in the money market. The return from investment D, $142,500, plus the money available from the money market, $144,292, equals the final cash in the objective cell, $286,792.

## Sensitivity Analysis

A close look at the optimal solution in Figure 4.31 indicates that Barney-Jones is penalizing itself by imposing a maximum of $75,000 per investment. This upper limit is forcing the company to put cash into the money market fund, despite this fund's low rate of return. Therefore, a natural sensitivity analysis is to see how the optimal solution changes as this maximum value changes. You can perform this sensitivity analysis with a one-way SolverTable, shown in Figure 4.33.[8] The maximum in cell B5 is the input cell, varied from $75,000 to $225,000 in increments of $25,000, and the optimal changing cells and objective cell are outputs. As you can see, the final cash (column G) grows steadily as the maximum allowable investment amount increases. This is because the company can take greater advantage of the attractive investments and put less in the money market account.

Figure 4.33

Sensitivity of Optimal Solution to Maximum Investment Amount

| | A | B | C | D | E | F | G |
|---|---|---|---|---|---|---|---|
| 3 | Max per investment (cell $B$5) values along side, output cell(s) along top | | | | | | |
| 4 | | Dollars_invested_1 | Dollars_invested_2 | Dollars_invested_3 | Dollars_invested_4 | Dollars_invested_5 | Final_cash |
| 5 | $75,000 | $64,286 | $75,000 | $35,714 | $75,000 | $75,000 | $286,792 |
| 6 | $100,000 | $61,538 | $76,923 | $38,462 | $100,000 | $100,000 | $320,731 |
| 7 | $125,000 | $100,000 | $50,000 | $0 | $125,000 | $125,000 | $353,375 |
| 8 | $150,000 | $100,000 | $50,000 | $0 | $150,000 | $125,000 | $375,125 |
| 9 | $175,000 | $100,000 | $50,000 | $0 | $175,000 | $125,000 | $396,875 |
| 10 | $200,000 | $100,000 | $50,000 | $0 | $200,000 | $125,000 | $418,625 |
| 11 | $225,000 | $100,000 | $50,000 | $0 | $225,000 | $125,000 | $440,375 |

To perform sensitivity on an output variable not calculated explicitly in your spreadsheet model, calculate it in some unused portion of the spreadsheet before running SolverTable.

You can go one step further with the two-way SolverTable in Figure 4.34. Now both the maximum investment amount and the money market rate are inputs, and the maximum amount ever put in the money market fund is the single output. Because this latter amount is not calculated in the spreadsheet model, you need to calculate it with the formula =MAX(Cash_after_investing) in an unused cell before using it as the output cell for SolverTable. In every case, even with a large maximum investment amount and a low money market rate, the company puts *some* money into the money market account. The reason is simple. Even when the maximum investment amount is $225,000, the company evidently has more cash than this to invest at some point (probably at the beginning of year 4). Therefore, it will have to put some of it in the money market. ▓

[8]Because Solver's sensitivity reports do not help answer our specific sensitivity questions in this example or the next example, we discuss only SolverTable results.

Figure 4.34    Sensitivity of Maximum in Money Market to Two Inputs

| | A | B | C | D | E | F | G | H | I |
|---|---|---|---|---|---|---|---|---|---|
| 3 | Interest on cash (cell $B$6) values along side, Max per investment (cell $B$5) values along top, output cell in corner | | | | | | | | |
| 4 | Maximum_in_money_market | $75,000 | $100,000 | $125,000 | $150,000 | $175,000 | $200,000 | $225,000 | |
| 5 | 0.5% | $139,420 | $126,923 | $112,500 | $87,500 | $62,500 | $37,500 | $12,500 | |
| 6 | 1.0% | $139,554 | $126,923 | $112,500 | $87,500 | $62,500 | $37,500 | $12,500 | |
| 7 | 1.5% | $139,688 | $126,923 | $112,500 | $87,500 | $62,500 | $37,500 | $12,500 | |
| 8 | 2.0% | $139,821 | $126,923 | $112,500 | $87,500 | $62,500 | $37,500 | $12,500 | |
| 9 | 2.5% | $139,955 | $126,923 | $112,500 | $87,500 | $62,500 | $37,500 | $12,500 | |
| 10 | 3.0% | $140,089 | $126,923 | $112,500 | $87,500 | $62,500 | $37,500 | $12,500 | |
| 11 | 3.5% | $140,223 | $126,923 | $112,500 | $87,500 | $62,500 | $37,500 | $12,500 | |
| 12 | 4.0% | $140,357 | $126,923 | $112,500 | $87,500 | $62,500 | $37,500 | $12,500 | |
| 13 | 4.5% | $140,491 | $126,923 | $112,500 | $87,500 | $62,500 | $37,500 | $12,500 | |

The following example illustrates a common situation where fixed payments are due in the future and current funds must be allocated and invested so that their returns are sufficient to make the payments. We place this in a pension fund context.

EXAMPLE | **4.7 MANAGING A PENSION FUND AT ARMCO**

James Judson is the financial manager in charge of the company pension fund at Armco Incorporated. James knows that the fund must be sufficient to make the payments listed in Table 4.10. Each payment must be made on the first day of each year. James is going to finance these payments by purchasing bonds. It is currently January 1, 2010, and three bonds are available for immediate purchase. The prices and coupons for the bonds are as follows. (All coupon payments are received on January 1 and arrive in time to meet cash demands for the date on which they arrive.)

- Bond 1 costs $980 and yields a $60 coupon in the years 2011 through 2014 and a $1060 payment on maturity in the year 2015.
- Bond 2 costs $970 and yields a $65 coupon in the years 2011 through 2020 and a $1065 payment on maturity in the year 2021.
- Bond 3 costs $1050 and yields a $75 coupon in the years 2011 through 2023 and a $1075 payment on maturity in the year 2024.

James must decide how much cash to allocate (from company coffers) to meet the initial $11,000 payment and buy enough bonds to make future payments. He knows that any excess cash on hand can earn an annual rate of 4% in a fixed-rate account. How should he proceed?

Table 4.10    Payments for Pension Example

| Year | Payment | Year | Payment | Year | Payment |
|---|---|---|---|---|---|
| 2010 | $11,000 | 2015 | $18,000 | 2020 | $25,000 |
| 2011 | $12,000 | 2016 | $20,000 | 2021 | $30,000 |
| 2012 | $14,000 | 2017 | $21,000 | 2022 | $31,000 |
| 2013 | $15,000 | 2018 | $22,000 | 2023 | $31,000 |
| 2014 | $16,000 | 2019 | $24,000 | 2024 | $31,000 |

**Objective** To develop an LP model that relates initial allocation of money and bond purchases to future cash availabilities, and to minimize the initialize allocation of money required to meet all future pension fund payments.

WHERE DO THE NUMBERS COME FROM?

As in the previous financial example, the inputs are fairly easy to obtain. A pension fund has known liabilities that must be met in future years, and information on bonds and fixed-rate accounts is widely available.

## Solution

The variables and constraints required for this pension fund model are listed in Table 4.11. When modeling this problem, there is a new twist that involves the money James must allocate now for his funding problem. It is clear that he must decide how many bonds of each type to purchase now (note that no bonds are purchased in the *future*), but he must also decide how much money to allocate from company coffers. This allocated money has to cover the initial pension payment this year *and* the bond purchases. In addition, James wants to find the *minimum* allocation that will suffice. Therefore, this initial allocation serves two roles in the model. It is a decision variable *and* it is the objective to minimize. In terms of spreadsheet modeling, it is perfectly acceptable to make the objective cell one of the changing cells, and this is done here. You will not see this in many models—because the objective typically involves a linear combination of several decision variables—but it is occasionally the most natural way to proceed.

**Table 4.11** Variables and Constraints for Pension Model

| | |
|---|---|
| **Input variables** | Pension payments, information on bonds, fixed interest rate on cash |
| **Decision variables (changing cells)** | Money to allocate now, numbers of bonds to purchase now |
| **Object cell** | Money to allocate in now (minimize) |
| **Other calculated variables** | Cash available to meet pension payments each year |
| **Constraints** | Cash available for payments $\geq$ Required payments |

### FUNDAMENTAL INSIGHT

#### The Objective as a Changing Cell

In all optimization models, the objective cell has to be a function of the changing cells, that is, the objective value should change as values in the changing cells change. It is perfectly consistent with this requirement to have the objective cell *be* one of the changing cells. This doesn't occur in very many optimization models, but it is sometimes useful, even necessary.

DEVELOPING THE SPREADSHEET MODEL

The completed spreadsheet model is shown in Figure 4.35. (See the file Pension Fund Management.xlsx.) You can create it with the following steps.

Figure 4.35    Pension Fund Management Model

| | A | B | C | D | E | F | G | H | I | J | K | L | M | N | O | P |
|---|---|---|---|---|---|---|---|---|---|---|---|---|---|---|---|---|
| 1 | Pension fund management | | | | | | | | | | | | | | | |
| 2 | | | | | | | | | | | | | | | | |
| 3 | Costs (now) and income (in other years) from bonds | | | | | | | | | | | | | | | |
| 4 | Year | 2010 | 2011 | 2012 | 2013 | 2014 | 2015 | 2016 | 2017 | 2018 | 2019 | 2020 | 2021 | 2022 | 2023 | 2024 |
| 5 | Bond 1 | $980 | $60 | $60 | $60 | $60 | $1,060 | | | | | | | | | |
| 6 | Bond 2 | $970 | $65 | $65 | $65 | $65 | $65 | $65 | $65 | $65 | $65 | $65 | $1,065 | | | |
| 7 | Bond 3 | $1,050 | $75 | $75 | $75 | $75 | $75 | $75 | $75 | $75 | $75 | $75 | $75 | $75 | $75 | $1,075 |
| 8 | | | | | | | | | | | | | | | | |
| 9 | Interest rate | 4% | | | | | | | | | | | | | | |
| 10 | | | | | | | | | | | | | | | | |
| 11 | Number of bonds (allowing fractional values) to purchase now | | | | | | | | | | | | | | | |
| 12 | Bond 1 | 73.69 | | | | | | | | | | | | | | |
| 13 | Bond 2 | 77.21 | | | | | | | | | | | | | | |
| 14 | Bond 3 | 28.84 | | | | | | | | | | | | | | |
| 15 | | | | | | | | | | | | | | | | |
| 16 | Money allocated | $197,768 | ← | Objective to minimize, also a changing cell | | | | | | | | | | | | |
| 17 | | | | | | | | | | | | | | | | |
| 18 | Constraints to meet payments | | | | | | | | | | | | | | | |
| 19 | Year | 2010 | 2011 | 2012 | 2013 | 2014 | 2015 | 2016 | 2017 | 2018 | 2019 | 2020 | 2021 | 2022 | 2023 | 2024 |
| 20 | Amount available | $20,376 | $21,354 | $21,332 | $19,228 | $16,000 | $85,298 | $77,171 | $66,639 | $54,646 | $41,133 | $25,000 | $84,390 | $58,728 | $31,000 | $31,000 |
| 21 | | >= | >= | >= | >= | >= | >= | >= | >= | >= | >= | >= | >= | >= | >= | >= |
| 22 | Amount required | $11,000 | $12,000 | $14,000 | $15,000 | $16,000 | $18,000 | $20,000 | $21,000 | $22,000 | $24,000 | $25,000 | $30,000 | $31,000 | $31,000 | $31,000 |
| 23 | | | | | | | | | | | | | | | | |
| 24 | Range names used: | | | | | | | | | | | | | | | |
| 25 | Amount_available | =Model!$B$20:$P$20 | | | | | | | | | | | | | | |
| 26 | Amount_required | =Model!$B$22:$P$22 | | | | | | | | | | | | | | |
| 27 | Bonds_purchased | =Model!$B$12:$B$14 | | | | | | | | | | | | | | |
| 28 | Money_allocated | =Model!$B$16 | | | | | | | | | | | | | | |

The value in cell B16 is the money allocated to make the current payment and buy bonds now. It is both a changing cell and the target cell to minimize.

**①  Inputs and range names.** Enter the given data and name the ranges as indicated. Note that the bond costs in the range B5:B7 have been entered as *positive* quantities. Some financial analysts might prefer that they be entered as negative numbers, indicating outflows. It doesn't really matter, however, as long as you are careful with the Excel formulas later on.

*Always document your spreadsheet conventions as clearly as possible.*

**②  Money allocated and bonds purchased.** As discussed previously, the money allocated in the current year and the numbers of bonds purchased now are both decision variables, so enter *any* values for these in the Money_allocated and Bonds_purchased ranges. Note that the color-coding convention for the Money_allocated cell have to be modified. Because it is both a changing cell and the objective cell, we colored it red but added a note to emphasize that it is the objective to minimize.

**③  Cash available to make payments.** In the current year, the only cash available is the money initially allocated minus cash used to purchase bonds. Calculate this quantity in cell B20 with the formula

=Money_allocated-SUMPRODUCT(Bonds_purchased,B5:B7)

For all other years, the cash available comes from two sources: excess cash invested at the fixed interest rate the year before and payments from bonds. Calculate this quantity for 2011 in cell C20 with the formula

=(B20-B22)*(1+$B$9)+SUMPRODUCT(Bonds_purchased,C5:C7)

and copy it across row 20 for the other years.

As you can see, this model is fairly straightforward to develop once you understand the role of the amount allocated in cell B16. However, we have often given this problem as an assignment to our students, and many fail to deal correctly with the amount allocated. (They usually forget to make it a changing cell.) So make sure you understand what we have done, and why we have done it this way.

The main Solver dialog box should be filled out as shown in Figure 4.36. Once again, notice that the Money_allocated cell is both the objective cell and one of the changing cells.

Figure 4.36

Solver Dialog Box
for Pension Fund
Model

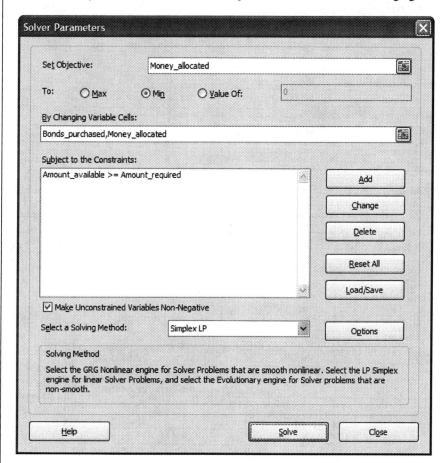

### Discussion of the Solution

The optimal solution appears in Figure 4.35. You might argue that the numbers of bonds purchased should be constrained to integer values. We tried this and the optimal solution changed very little: The optimal numbers of bonds to purchase changed to 74, 79, and 27, and the optimal money to allocate increased to $197,887. With this integer solution, shown in Figure 4.37, James sets aside $197,887 initially. Any less than this would not work—he couldn't make enough from bonds to meet future pension payments. All but $20,387 of this (see cell B20) is spent on bonds, and of the $20,387, $11,000 is used to make the current pension payment. After this, the amounts in row 20, which are always sufficient to make the payments in row 22, are composed of returns from bonds and cash, with interest, from the previous year. Even more so than in previous examples, there is no way to guess this optimal solution. The timing of bond returns and the irregular pension payments make a spreadsheet optimization model absolute necessary.

### Sensitivity Analysis

Because the bond information and pension payments are evidently fixed, there is only one obvious direction for sensitivity analysis: on the fixed interest rate in cell B9. We tried this,

*Constraints always have the potential to penalize the objective to some extent. SolverTable is a perfect tool for finding the magnitude of this penalty.*

Figure 4.37 Optimal Integer Solution for Pension Fund Model

| | A | B | C | D | E | F | G | H | I | J | K | L | M | N | O | P |
|---|---|---|---|---|---|---|---|---|---|---|---|---|---|---|---|---|
| 1 | Pension fund management | | | | | | | | | | | | | | | |
| 2 | | | | | | | | | | | | | | | | |
| 3 | Costs (now) and income (in other years) from bonds | | | | | | | | | | | | | | | |
| 4 | Year | 2010 | 2011 | 2012 | 2013 | 2014 | 2015 | 2016 | 2017 | 2018 | 2019 | 2020 | 2021 | 2022 | 2023 | 2024 |
| 5 | Bond 1 | $980 | $60 | $60 | $60 | $60 | $1,060 | | | | | | | | | |
| 6 | Bond 2 | $970 | $65 | $65 | $65 | $65 | $65 | $65 | $65 | $65 | $65 | $65 | $1,065 | | | |
| 7 | Bond 3 | $1,050 | $75 | $75 | $75 | $75 | $75 | $75 | $75 | $75 | $75 | $75 | $75 | $75 | $75 | $1,075 |
| 8 | | | | | | | | | | | | | | | | |
| 9 | Interest rate | 4% | | | | | | | | | | | | | | |
| 10 | | | | | | | | | | | | | | | | |
| 11 | Number of bonds (allowing fractional values) to purchase now | | | | | | | | | | | | | | | |
| 12 | Bond 1 | 74.00 | | | | | | | | | | | | | | |
| 13 | Bond 2 | 79.00 | | | | | | | | | | | | | | |
| 14 | Bond 3 | 27.00 | | | | | | | | | | | | | | |
| 15 | | | | | | | | | | | | | | | | |
| 16 | Money allocated | $197,887 | ← | Objective to minimize, also a changing cell | | | | | | | | | | | | |
| 17 | | | | | | | | | | | | | | | | |
| 18 | Constraints to meet payments | | | | | | | | | | | | | | | |
| 19 | Year | 2010 | 2011 | 2012 | 2013 | 2014 | 2015 | 2016 | 2017 | 2018 | 2019 | 2020 | 2021 | 2022 | 2023 | 2024 |
| 20 | Amount available | $20,387 | $21,363 | $21,337 | $19,231 | $16,000 | $85,600 | $77,464 | $66,923 | $54,919 | $41,396 | $25,252 | $86,422 | $60,704 | $32,917 | $31,019 |
| 21 | | >= | >= | >= | >= | >= | >= | >= | >= | >= | >= | >= | >= | >= | >= | >= |
| 22 | Amount required | $11,000 | $12,000 | $14,000 | $15,000 | $16,000 | $18,000 | $20,000 | $21,000 | $22,000 | $24,000 | $25,000 | $30,000 | $31,000 | $31,000 | $31,000 |

Figure 4.38

**Sensitivity to Fixed Interest Rate**

| | A | B | C | D | E | F |
|---|---|---|---|---|---|---|
| 3 | Interest rate (cell $B$9) values along side, output cell(s) along top | | | | | |
| 4 | | Bonds_purchased_1 | Bonds_purchased_2 | Bonds_purchased_3 | Money_allocated | |
| 5 | 2.0% | 77.12 | 78.71 | 28.84 | $202,010 | |
| 6 | 2.4% | 76.41 | 78.40 | 28.84 | $201,145 | |
| 7 | 2.8% | 75.72 | 78.10 | 28.84 | $200,288 | |
| 8 | 3.2% | 75.03 | 77.80 | 28.84 | $199,439 | |
| 9 | 3.6% | 74.36 | 77.50 | 28.84 | $198,600 | |
| 10 | 4.0% | 73.69 | 77.21 | 28.84 | $197,768 | |
| 11 | 4.4% | 73.04 | 76.92 | 28.84 | $196,946 | |
| 12 | 4.8% | 72.40 | 76.63 | 28.84 | $196,131 | |
| 13 | 5.2% | 71.77 | 76.34 | 28.84 | $195,325 | |
| 14 | 5.6% | 71.15 | 76.06 | 28.84 | $194,527 | |
| 15 | 6.0% | 70.54 | 75.78 | 28.84 | $193,737 | |

allowing this rate to vary from 2% to 6% in increments of 0.5% and keeping track of the optimal changing cells, including the objective cell. The results appear in Figure 4.38 (without the integer constraints). They indicate that as the interest rate increases, James can get by with fewer bonds of types 1 and 2, and he can allocate less money for the problem. The reason is that he is making more interest on excess cash. ▨

## ADDITIONAL APPLICATIONS

### Using LP to Optimize Bond Portfolios

Many Wall Street firms buy and sell bonds. Rohn (1987) developed a bond selection model that maximizes profit from bond purchases and sales subject to constraints that minimize the firm's risk exposure. The method used to model this situation is closely related to the method used to model the Barney-Jones problem. ∎

# PROBLEMS

## Skill-Building Problems

**30.** In the Barney-Jones investment model, increase the maximum amount allowed in any investment to $150,000. Then run a one-way sensitivity analysis to the money market rate on cash. Capture one output variable: the maximum amount of cash ever put in the money market. You can choose any reasonable range for varying the money market rate.

**31.** Modify the Barney-Jones investment model so that a minimum amount must be put into any investment, although this minimum can vary by investment. For example, the minimum amount for investment A might be $0, whereas the minimum amount for investment D might be $50,000. These minimum amounts should be inputs; you can make up any values you like. Run Solver on your modified model.

**32.** We claimed that our model for Barney-Jones is generalizable. Try generalizing it to the case where there are two more potential investments, F and G. Investment F requires a cash outlay in year 2 and returns $0.50 in *each* of the next four years for every dollar invested. Investment G requires a cash outlay in year 3 and returns $0.75 in each of years 5, 6, and 7 for every dollar invested. Modify the model as necessary, making the objective the final cash after year 7.

**33.** In the Barney-Jones investment model, we ran investments across columns and years down rows. Many financial analysts seem to prefer the opposite. Modify the spreadsheet model so that years go across columns and investments go down rows. Run Solver to ensure that your modified model is correct. (There are two possible ways to do this, and you can experiment to see which you prefer. First, you could basically start over on a blank worksheet. Second, you could use Excel's TRANSPOSE function.)

**34.** In the pension fund model, suppose there is an upper limit of 60 on the number of bonds of any particular type that can be purchased. Modify the model to incorporate this extra constraint and then reoptimize. How much more money does James need to allocate initially?

**35.** In the pension fund model, suppose there is a fourth bond, bond 4. Its unit cost in 2010 is $1020, it returns coupons of $70 in years 2011 to 2014 and a payment of $1070 in 2015. Modify the model to incorporate this extra bond and reoptimize. Does the solution change—that is, should James purchase any of bond 4?

**36.** In the pension fund model, suppose James has been asked to see how the optimal solution will change if the required payments in years 2015 to 2024 all increase by the same percentage, where this percentage could be anywhere from 5% to 25%. Use an appropriate one-way SolverTable to help him out, and write a memo describing the results.

**37.** The pension fund model is streamlined, perhaps too much. It does all of the calculations concerning cash flows in row 20. James decides he would like to break these out into several rows of calculations: Beginning cash (for 2010, this is the amount allocated; for other years, it is the unused cash, plus interest, from the previous year), Amount spent on bonds (positive in 2010 only), Amount received from bonds (positive for years 2011 to 2024 only), Cash available for making pension fund payments, and (below the Amount required row) Cash left over (amount invested in the fixed interest rate). Modify the model by inserting these rows, enter the appropriate formulas, and run Solver. You should obtain the same result but get more detailed information.

## Skill-Extending Problems

**38.** Suppose the investments in the Barney-Jones model sometimes require cash outlays in more than one year. For example, a $1 investment in investment B might require $0.25 to be spent in year 1 and $0.75 to be spent in year 2. Does the current model easily accommodate such investments? Try it with some cash outlay data you make up, run Solver, and interpret the results.

**39.** In the pension fund model, if the amount of money initially is *less* than the amount found by Solver, then James will not be able to meet all of the pension fund payments. Use the current model to demonstrate that this is true. To do so, enter a value less than the optimal value into cell B16. Then run Solver, but remove the Money_allocated cell as a changing cell and as the target cell. (If there is no target cell, Solver simply tries to find a solution that satisfies all of the constraints.) What do you find?

**40.** Continuing the previous problem in a slightly different direction, continue to use the Money_allocated cell as a changing cell, and add a constraint that it must be less than or equal to any value, such as $195,000, that is less than its current optimal value. With this constraint, James will not be able to meet all of the pension fund payments. Create a new target cell to minimize the total amount of payments not met. The easiest way to do this is with IF functions. Unfortunately, this makes the model nonsmooth, and Solver might have trouble finding the optimal solution. Try it and see.

# 4.8 DATA ENVELOPMENT ANALYSIS (DEA)

The **data envelopment analysis** (DEA) method can be used to determine whether a university, hospital, restaurant, or other business is operating efficiently. Specifically, DEA can be used by inefficient organizations to benchmark efficient and best-practice organizations. According to Sherman and Ladino (1995):

> Many managers of service organizations would describe benchmarking and best practice analysis as basic, widely accepted concepts already used in their businesses. Closer examination indicates that the traditional techniques used to identify and promulgate best practices are not very effective, largely because the operations of these service organizations are too complex to allow them to identify best practices accurately. DEA provides an objective way to identify best practices in these service organizations and has consistently generated new insights that lead to substantial productivity gains that were not otherwise identifiable.

The following example illustrates DEA and is based on Callen (1991). See also Norton (1994b).

---

EXAMPLE | **4.8 DEA IN THE HOSPITAL INDUSTRY**

Consider a group of three hospitals. To keep the model small, assume that each hospital uses two inputs to produce three outputs. (In a real DEA, there are typically many more inputs and outputs.) The two inputs used by each hospital are

> input 1 = capital (measured by hundreds of hospital beds)
>
> input 2 = labor (measured by thousands of labor hours used in a month)

The outputs produced by each hospital are

output 1 = hundreds of patient-days during month for patients under age 14

output 2 = hundreds of patient-days during month for patients between 14 and 65

output 3 = hundreds of patient-days for patients over 65

The inputs and outputs for these hospitals are given in Table 4.12. Which of these three hospitals is efficient in terms of using its inputs to produce outputs?

Table 4.12   Input and Output for the Hospital Example

|  | **Inputs** | | **Outputs** | | |
|---|---|---|---|---|---|
|  | 1 | 2 | 1 | 2 | 3 |
| Hospital 1 | 5 | 14 | 9 | 4 | 16 |
| Hospital 2 | 8 | 15 | 5 | 7 | 10 |
| Hospital 3 | 7 | 12 | 4 | 9 | 13 |

**Objective**   To develop an LP spreadsheet model, using the DEA methodology, to determine whether each hospital is efficient in terms of using its inputs to produce its outputs.

In a general DEA analysis, the organization's inputs and outputs must first be defined. Then for each input or output, a unit of measurement must be selected. Neither of these is necessarily an easy task, because organizations such as hospitals, banks, and schools consume a variety of inputs and produce a variety of outputs that can be measured in alternative ways. However, after the list of inputs and outputs has been chosen and units of measurement have been selected, accounting data can be used to find the required data for the model, as in Table 4.12.

## Solution

The idea is that each hospital should be shown in its best possible light. That is, the inputs and outputs should be valued in such a way that a given hospital looks as good as possible relative to the other hospitals. Specifically, to determine whether a hospital is efficient, the model determines a price per unit of each output and a cost per unit of each input. Then the efficiency of a hospital is defined as

$$\text{Efficiency of hospital} = \frac{\text{Value of hospital's outputs}}{\text{Value of hospital's inputs}}$$

The DEA approach uses the following four ideas to determine whether a hospital is efficient.

* No hospital can be more than 100% efficient. Therefore, the efficiency of each hospital is constrained to be less than or equal to 1. To make this a *linear* constraint, it is expressed in the form

  Value of hospital's outputs ≤ Value of hospital's inputs

* When determining whether a hospital is efficient, it is useful to scale input prices so that the value of the hospital's inputs equals 1. Any other value would suffice, but using 1 causes the efficiency of the hospital to be equal to the value of the hospital's outputs.

* To put a given hospital in its best light, the input costs and output prices should be chosen to maximize this hospital's efficiency. If the hospital's efficiency equals 1, the hospital is efficient; if the hospital's efficiency is less than 1, the hospital is inefficient.

* All input costs and output prices must be nonnegative.

Putting these ideas together, the variables required for the DEA model are summarized in Table 4.13. Note the reference to "selected hospital." The model is actually analyzed three times, once for each hospital. So the selected hospital each time is the one currently in focus.

---

Table 4.13  Variables and Constraints for the DEA Model

| | |
|---|---|
| **Input variables** | Inputs used, outputs produced for each hospital |
| **Decision variables** (changing cells) | Unit costs of inputs, unit prices of outputs for selected hospital |
| **Objective (target cell)** | Total output value of selected hospital |
| **Other calculated variables** | Total input cost, total output value (for each hospital) |
| **Constraints** | Total input cost ≥ Total output value (for each hospital) |
| | Total cost for selected hospital = 1 |

---

Figure 4.39 contains the DEA spreadsheet model used to determine the efficiency of hospital 1. (See the file Hospital DEA.xlsx.) To develop this model, proceed as follows.

Figure 4.39　DEA Model for Hospital 1

| | A | B | C | D | E | F | G | H | I | J | K |
|---|---|---|---|---|---|---|---|---|---|---|---|
| 1 | DEA model for checking efficiency of a selected hospital | | | | | | | | | Range names used | |
| 2 | | | | | | | | | | Input_costs | =Model!$B$14:$B$16 |
| 3 | Selected hospital | 1 | | | | | | | | Output_values | =Model!$D$14:$D$16 |
| 4 | | | | | | | | | | Selected_hospital | =Model!$B$3 |
| 5 | Inputs used | Input 1 | Input 2 | | Outputs produced | Output 1 | Output 2 | Output 3 | | Selected_hospital_input_cost | =Model!$B$19 |
| 6 | Hospital 1 | 5 | 14 | | Hospital 1 | 9 | 4 | 16 | | Selected_hospital_output_value | =Model!$B$22 |
| 7 | Hospital 2 | 8 | 15 | | Hospital 2 | 5 | 7 | 10 | | Unit_costs_of_inputs | =Model!$B$10:$C$10 |
| 8 | Hospital 3 | 7 | 12 | | Hospital 3 | 4 | 9 | 13 | | Unit_prices_of_outputs | =Model!$F$10:$H$10 |
| 9 | | | | | | | | | | | |
| 10 | Unit costs of inputs | 0.000 | 0.071 | | Unit prices of outputs | 0.0000 | 0.0000 | 0.063 | | | |
| 11 | | | | | | | | | | | |
| 12 | Constraints that input costs must cover output values | | | | | | | | | | |
| 13 | | Hospital | Input costs | | Output values | | | | | | |
| 14 | | 1 | 1.000 | >= | 1.000 | | | | | | |
| 15 | | 2 | 1.071 | >= | 0.625 | | | | | | |
| 16 | | 3 | 0.857 | >= | 0.813 | | | | | | |
| 17 | | | | | | | | | | | |
| 18 | Constraint that selected hospital's input cost must equal a nominal value of 1 | | | | | | | | | | |
| 19 | Selected hospital input cost | 1.000 | = | 1 | | | | | | | |
| 20 | | | | | | | | | | | |
| 21 | Maximize selected hospital's output value (to see if it is 1, hence efficient) | | | | | | | | | | |
| 22 | Selected hospital output value | 1.000 | | | | | | | | | |

**①　Input given data and name ranges.** Enter the input and output information for each hospital in the ranges B6:C8 and F6:H8 and name the various ranges as indicated.

**②　Selected hospital.** Enter 1, 2, or 3 in cell B3, depending on which hospital you want to analyze. (You will eventually analyze all three.)

**③　Unit input costs and output prices.** Enter *any* trial values for the input costs and output prices in the Unit_costs_of_inputs and Unit_prices_of_outputs ranges.

**④　Total input costs and output values.** In the Input_costs range, calculate the cost of the inputs used by each hospital. To do this, enter the formula

=SUMPRODUCT(Unit_costs_of_inputs,B6:C6)

in cell B14 for hospital 1, and copy this to the rest of the Input_costs range for the other hospitals. Similarly, calculate the output values by entering the formula

=SUMPRODUCT(Unit_prices_of_outputs,F6:H6)

in cell D14 and copying it to the rest of the Output_values range. Note that even though the focus is currently on hospital 1's efficiency, you still need to calculate input costs and output values for the other hospitals so that you have something to compare hospital 1 to.

**⑤　Total input cost and output value for the selected hospital.** In row 19, constrain the total input cost of the *selected* hospital to be 1 by entering the formula

=VLOOKUP(Selected_hospital,A14:B16,2)

in cell B19, and enter a 1 in cell D19. Similarly, enter the formula

=VLOOKUP(Selected_hospital,A14:D16,4)

in cell B22. (Make sure you understand how these VLOOKUP functions work.) Remember that because the selected hospital's input cost is constrained to be 1, its output value in cell B22 is automatically its efficiency.

## USING SOLVER TO DETERMINE WHETHER HOSPITAL 1 IS EFFICIENT

To determine whether hospital 1 is efficient, use Solver as follows. When you are finished, the Solver dialog box should appear as shown in Figure 4.40.

**Figure 4.40**

Solver Dialog Box
for the DEA Model

**① Objective.** Select cell B22 as the target cell to maximize. Because the cost of hospital 1 inputs is constrained to be 1, this causes Solver to maximize the efficiency of hospital 1.

**② Changing cells.** Choose the Unit_costs_of_inputs and Unit_prices_of_outputs ranges as the changing cells.

**③ Selected hospital's input cost constraint.** Add the constraint Selected_hospital_input_cost=1. This sets the total value of hospital 1's inputs equal to 1.

**④ Efficiency constraint.** Add the constraint Input_costs>=Output_values. This ensures that no hospital is more than 100% efficient.

**⑤ Specify nonnegativity and optimize.** Check the Non-Negative option and the Simplex LP method, and then solve to obtain the optimal solution shown in Figure 4.39.

The 1 in cell B22 of this solution means that hospital 1 *is* efficient. In words, Solver has found a set of unit costs for the inputs and the unit prices for the outputs such that the total value of hospital 1's outputs equals the total cost of its inputs.

**Figure 4.41  DEA Model for Hospital 2**

| | A | B | C | D | E | F | G | H | I | J | K |
|---|---|---|---|---|---|---|---|---|---|---|---|
| 1 | DEA model for checking efficiency of a selected hospital | | | | | | | | | Range names used | |
| 2 | | | | | | | | | | Input_costs | =Model!$B$14:$B$16 |
| 3 | Selected hospital | 2 | | | | | | | | Output_values | =Model!$D$14:$D$16 |
| 4 | | | | | | | | | | Selected_hospital | =Model!$B$3 |
| 5 | Inputs used | Input 1 | Input 2 | | Outputs produced | Output 1 | Output 2 | Output 3 | | Selected_hospital_input_cost | =Model!$B$19 |
| 6 | Hospital 1 | 5 | 14 | | Hospital 1 | 9 | 4 | 16 | | Selected_hospital_output_value | =Model!$B$22 |
| 7 | Hospital 2 | 8 | 15 | | Hospital 2 | 5 | 7 | 10 | | Unit_costs_of_inputs | =Model!$B$10:$C$10 |
| 8 | Hospital 3 | 7 | 12 | | Hospital 3 | 4 | 9 | 13 | | Unit_prices_of_outputs | =Model!$F$10:$H$10 |
| 9 | | | | | | | | | | | |
| 10 | Unit costs of inputs | 0.000 | 0.067 | | Unit prices of outputs | 0.0800 | 0.0533 | 0.000 | | | |
| 11 | | | | | | | | | | | |
| 12 | Constraints that input costs must cover output values | | | | | | | | | | |
| 13 | | Hospital | Input costs | | Output values | | | | | | |
| 14 | | 1 | 0.933 | >= | 0.933 | | | | | | |
| 15 | | 2 | 1.000 | >= | 0.773 | | | | | | |
| 16 | | 3 | 0.800 | >= | 0.800 | | | | | | |
| 17 | | | | | | | | | | | |
| 18 | Constraint that selected hospital's input cost must equal a nominal value of 1 | | | | | | | | | | |
| 19 | Selected hospital input cost | 1.000 | = | 1 | | | | | | | |
| 20 | | | | | | | | | | | |
| 21 | Maximize selected hospital's output value (to see if it is 1, hence efficient) | | | | | | | | | | |
| 22 | Selected hospital output value | 0.773 | | | | | | | | | |

## Determining Whether Hospitals 2 and 3 Are Efficient

To determine whether hospital 2 is efficient, simply replace the value in cell B3 by 2 and rerun Solver. The Solver settings do not need to be modified. The optimal solution appears in Figure 4.41. From the value of 0.773 in cell B22, you can see that hospital 2 is *not* efficient. Similarly, you can determine that hospital 3 *is* efficient by replacing the value in cell B3 by 3 and rerunning Solver (see Figure 4.42).

**Figure 4.42  DEA Model for Hospital 3**

| | A | B | C | D | E | F | G | H | I | J | K |
|---|---|---|---|---|---|---|---|---|---|---|---|
| 1 | DEA model for checking efficiency of a selected hospital | | | | | | | | | Range names used | |
| 2 | | | | | | | | | | Input_costs | =Model!$B$14:$B$16 |
| 3 | Selected hospital | 3 | | | | | | | | Output_values | =Model!$D$14:$D$16 |
| 4 | | | | | | | | | | Selected_hospital | =Model!$B$3 |
| 5 | Inputs used | Input 1 | Input 2 | | Outputs produced | Output 1 | Output 2 | Output 3 | | Selected_hospital_input_cost | =Model!$B$19 |
| 6 | Hospital 1 | 5 | 14 | | Hospital 1 | 9 | 4 | 16 | | Selected_hospital_output_value | =Model!$B$22 |
| 7 | Hospital 2 | 8 | 15 | | Hospital 2 | 5 | 7 | 10 | | Unit_costs_of_inputs | =Model!$B$10:$C$10 |
| 8 | Hospital 3 | 7 | 12 | | Hospital 3 | 4 | 9 | 13 | | Unit_prices_of_outputs | =Model!$F$10:$H$10 |
| 9 | | | | | | | | | | | |
| 10 | Unit costs of inputs | 0.000 | 0.083 | | Unit prices of outputs | 0.1000 | 0.0667 | 0.000 | | | |
| 11 | | | | | | | | | | | |
| 12 | Constraints that input costs must cover output values | | | | | | | | | | |
| 13 | | Hospital | Input costs | | Output values | | | | | | |
| 14 | | 1 | 1.167 | >= | 1.167 | | | | | | |
| 15 | | 2 | 1.250 | >= | 0.967 | | | | | | |
| 16 | | 3 | 1.000 | >= | 1.000 | | | | | | |
| 17 | | | | | | | | | | | |
| 18 | Constraint that selected hospital's input cost must equal a nominal value of 1 | | | | | | | | | | |
| 19 | Selected hospital input cost | 1.000 | = | 1 | | | | | | | |
| 20 | | | | | | | | | | | |
| 21 | Maximize selected hospital's output value (to see if it is 1, hence efficient) | | | | | | | | | | |
| 22 | Selected hospital output value | 1.000 | | | | | | | | | |

In summary, the Solver results imply that hospitals 1 and 3 are efficient, but hospital 2 is inefficient.

## What Does It Mean to Be Efficient or Inefficient?

This idea of efficiency or inefficiency might still be a mystery, so let's consider it further. A hospital is efficient if the inputs and outputs can be priced in such a way that this hospital gets out all of the value that it puts in. The pricing scheme depends on the hospital. Each hospital tries to price inputs and outputs to put its operations in the best possible light. In the example, hospital 1 attaches 0 prices to input 1 (hospital beds) and output 3 (patient-days for patients over 65), and it attaches positive prices to the rest. This makes hospital 1 look efficient. Hospital 3, which is also efficient, also attaches 0 prices to input 1 and output 3, but its prices for the others are somewhat different from hospital 1's prices.

If DEA finds that a hospital is inefficient, there is no pricing scheme where that hospital can recover its entire input costs in output values. Actually, it can be shown that if a hospital is inefficient, then a combination of the efficient hospitals can be found that uses no more inputs than the inefficient hospital, yet produces at least as much of each output as the inefficient hospital. In this sense, the hospital is inefficient.

To see how this combination can be found, consider the spreadsheet model in Figure 4.43. Begin by entering any positive weights in the Weights range. For any such weights (they don't even need to sum to 1), consider the combination hospital as a fraction of hospital 1 and another fraction of hospital 3. For example, with the weights shown, the combination hospital uses about 26% of the inputs and produces about 26% of the outputs of hospital 1, and it uses about 66% of the inputs and produces about 66% of the outputs of hospital 3. When they are combined in row 6 with the SUMPRODUCT function [for example, the formula in cell D6 is =SUMPRODUCT(Weights,D4:D5)], you can see the quantities of inputs this combination hospital uses and the quantities of outputs it produces.

To find weights where the combination hospital is better than hospital 2, it suffices to find any *feasible* solution to the inequalities indicated in rows 6 to 8, and this can be done by using the Solver setup in Figure 4.44. (The weights in Figure 4.43 do the job.) Note that there is no objective to maximize or minimize; all you want is a solution that satisfies the constraints. Furthermore, there is guaranteed to be a feasible solution because hospital 2 has already been identified as inefficient.

Figure 4.43

Illustrating How Hospital 2 Is Inefficient

| | A | B | C | D | E | F | G | H | I |
|---|---|---|---|---|---|---|---|---|---|
| 1 | Comparing combination of hospitals 1 and 3 to inefficient hospital 2 | | | | | | | | |
| 2 | | | | | | | | | |
| 3 | | Weights | | Input 1 | Input 2 | | Output 1 | Output 2 | Output 3 |
| 4 | Hospital 1 | 0.2615 | | 5 | 14 | | 9 | 4 | 16 |
| 5 | Hospital 2 | 0.6615 | | 7 | 12 | | 4 | 9 | 13 |
| 6 | Combination | | | 5.938 | 11.6 | | 5 | 7 | 12.785 |
| 7 | | | | <= | <= | | >= | >= | >= |
| 8 | Hospital 2 | | | 8 | 15 | | 5 | 7 | 10 |

Figure 4.44

Solver Setup for Finding an Inefficiency

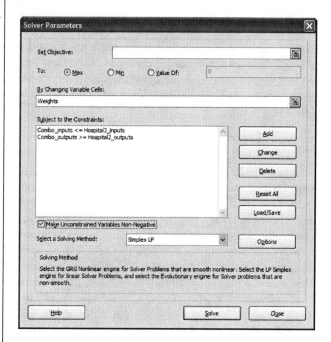

In reality, after DEA analysis identifies an organizational unit as being inefficient, this unit should consider benchmarking itself relative to the competition to see where it can make more efficient use of its inputs. ▮

## MODELING ISSUES

1. The ratio (input $i$ cost)/(input $j$ cost) can be interpreted as the marginal rate of substitution (at the optimal solution) of input $i$ for input $j$. That is, the same level of outputs can be maintained if the use of input $i$ decreases by a small amount $\Delta$ and the use of input $j$ increases by [(input $i$ cost)/(input $j$ cost)] $\Delta$. For example, for hospital 2, (input 2 cost/input 1 cost) = 6700. This implies that if the use of input 2 decreases by a small amount $\Delta$, hospital 2 can maintain its current output levels if the usage of input 1 increases by $6700\Delta$.

2. The ratio *(output $i$ price)/(output $j$ price)* can be interpreted as the marginal rate of substitution (at the optimal solution) of output $i$ for output $j$. That is, the same level

of input usage can be maintained if the production of output $i$ decreases by a small amount $\Delta$ and the production of output $j$ increases by [(output $i$ price)/(output $j$ price)]$\Delta$. For example, for hospital 2, (output 2 price)/(output 1 price) = 0.67. This implies that if the use of output 2 decreases by a small amount $\Delta$, hospital 2 can maintain its current resource usage if the production of output 1 increases by $0.67\Delta$.  ▨

## ADDITIONAL APPLICATIONS

### DEA for Evaluating School Bus Transportation

Sexton et al. (1994) used DEA to evaluate the efficiency of school bus transportation for the counties of North Carolina. For each county, they used two inputs: buses used and total operating expense. They used a single output: pupils transported per day. However, they noted a problem with traditional DEA. Consider two counties (county 1 and county 2) that use exactly the same inputs and produce the same outputs. Suppose that county 1 is very sparsely populated and county 2 is densely populated. Clearly, county 1 is transporting pupils more efficiently than county 2, but a DEA conducted by the method described will not show this. Realizing this, the authors developed a method to adjust the output of county 2 downward and the output of county 1 upward to compensate for this problem. The North Carolina Department of Education penalized the inefficient counties by reducing their budgetary appropriations. Since the time DEA was performed, most counties have greatly increased their efficiency.

### DEA in the Banking Industry

Sherman and Ladino (1995) used DEA to identify the most and least efficient branches in a banking firm with 33 branch banks. They found efficiency ratings that varied from 37% to 100%, with 23 of the 33 branches rated below 100% and 10 below 70%. Each of the inefficient branches was compared to a reference set of best-practice branches—efficient branches that offered the same types of services as the inefficient branch. This allowed them to make specific suggestions as to how the inefficient branches could improve. For example, they showed that branch 1 should be able to provide its current level and mix of services with 4.5 fewer customer-service personnel, 1.8 fewer sales service personnel, 0.3 fewer managers, $222,928 less in operating expenses, and 1304 fewer square feet. They also indicated the added amount of service that the inefficient branches could provide, in addition to resource savings, if these branches could become as efficient as the best-practice branches. For example, branch 1 could handle (per year) about 15,000 additional deposits, withdrawals, and checks cashed; 2000 added bank checks, bonds, and travelers' checks; 8 additional night deposits, while reducing the resources needed, if it attained the efficiency level of the best-practice branches. See the May–June 1999 issue of *Interfaces* for more applications of DEA in the banking industry.  ■

## PROBLEMS

### Skill-Building Problems

**1.** Pine Valley Bank has three branches. You have been asked to evaluate the efficiency of each. The following inputs and outputs are to be used for the study:

- input 1 = labor hours used (hundreds per month)
- input 2 = space used (in hundreds of square feet)
- input 3 = supplies used per month (in dollars)

- output 1 = loan applications per month
- output 2 = deposits processed per month (in thousands)
- output 3 = checks processed per month (in thousands)

The relevant information is given in the file P04_41.xlsx. Use these data to determine whether any bank branches are inefficient.

**42.** The Salem Board of Education wants to evaluate the efficiency of the town's four elementary schools. The three outputs of the schools are
- output 1 = average reading score
- output 2 = average mathematics score
- output 3 = average self-esteem score

The three inputs to the schools are
- input 1 = average educational level of mothers (defined by highest grade completed: 12 = high school graduate; 16 = college graduate, and so on)
- input 2 = number of parent visits to school (per child)
- input 3 = teacher-to-student ratio

The relevant information for the four schools is given in the file P04_42.xlsx. Determine which (if any) schools are inefficient.

**43.** You have been asked to evaluate the efficiency of the Port Charles Police Department. Three precincts are to be evaluated. The inputs and outputs for each precinct are as follows:
- input 1 = number of policemen
- input 2 = number of vehicles used
- output 1 = number of patrol units responding to service requests (thousands per year)
- output 2 = number of convictions obtained each year (in hundreds)

You are given the data in the file P04_43.xlsx. Use this information to determine which precincts, if any, are inefficient.

**44.** You have been commissioned by Indiana University to evaluate the relative efficiency of four degree-granting units: Business, Education, Arts and Sciences, and Health, Physical Education, and Recreation (HPER). You are given the information in the file P04_44.xlsx. Use DEA to identify all inefficient units.

## 4.9 CONCLUSION

In this chapter, we have presented LP spreadsheet models of many diverse situations. Although there is no standard procedure that can be used to attack all problems, there are several keys you should use with most spreadsheet optimization models:

- Determine the changing cells, the cells that contain the values of the decision variables. These cells should contain the values the decision maker has direct control over, and they should determine all other outputs, either directly or indirectly. For example, in blending models, the changing cells should contain the amount of each input used to produce each output; in employee scheduling models, the changing cells should contain the number of employees who work each possible five-day shift.

- Set up the spreadsheet model so that you can easily calculate what you want to maximize or minimize (usually profit or cost). For example, in the aggregate planning model, a good way to compute total cost is to compute the monthly cost of operation in each row.

- Set up the spreadsheet model so that the relationships between the cells in the spreadsheet and the problem constraints are readily apparent. For example, in the post office scheduling example, it is convenient to calculate the number of employees working each day of the week near the number of employees needed for each day of the week.

- Make your spreadsheet readable. Use descriptive labels, use range names, use cell comments and text boxes for explanations, and plan your model layout before you dive in. This might not be too important for small, straightforward models, but it is crucial for large, complex models. Just remember that *other* people are likely to be examining your spreadsheet models.

- Keep in mind that LP models tend to fall into categories, but they are definitely not all alike. For example, a problem might involve a combination of the ideas discussed in the worker scheduling, blending, and production process examples of this chapter. Each new model presents new challenges, and you must be flexible and imaginative to meet these challenges. It takes practice and perseverance.

## Summary of Key Management Science Terms

| Term | Explanation | Page |
|------|-------------|------|
| Dual-objective model | Model with two competing objectives; usual strategy is to constrain one of them and optimize the other | 121 |
| Integer constraints | Constraints that limit (some) changing cells to integer values | 123 |
| Multiple optimal solutions | Case where several solutions have the same optimal value of the objective | 129 |
| Heuristic | An educated guess solution, not guaranteed to be optimal but usually quick and easy to obtain | 131 |
| Nonsmooth problems | Nonlinear models with "sharp edges" or discontinuities that make them difficult to solve | 140 |
| DEA (Data Envelopment Analysis) | Method for determining whether organizational units are efficient in terms of using their inputs to produce their outputs | 168 |

## Summary of Key Excel Terms

| Term | Explanation | Excel | Page |
|------|-------------|-------|------|
| Range name shortcut | Quick way to create range names, using labels in adjacent cells | Use Create from Selection on Formulas ribbon | 117 |
| Solver integer constraints | Constraints on changing cells forcing them to be integers | Specify in Add Constraint dialog box with Solver | 123 |
| Row, column sums shortcut | Quick way of getting row and/or column sums from a table | Highlight row under table and column to right of table, click on Σ buttom | 136 |
| Nonsmooth functions with Solver | Avoid use of functions such as IF, MIN, MAX, and ABS in Solver models; Solver can't handle them predictably (except with its Evolutionary algorithm, the topic of Chapter 8) | | 140 |
| TRANSPOSE function | Useful function for transferring column range to row range, or vice versa | Highlight result range, type **=TRANSPOSE(*range*)**, press Ctrl+Shift+Enter | 153 |
| Array functions | Excel functions such as TRANSPOSE that fill a whole range at once | Highlight result range, type formula, press Ctrl+Shift+Enter | 154 |

## PROBLEMS

### Skill-Building Problems

45. A bus company believes that it will need the following numbers of bus drivers during each of the next five years: 60 drivers in year 1; 70 drivers in year 2; 50 drivers in year 3; 65 drivers in year 4; 75 drivers in year 5. At the beginning of each year, the bus company must decide how many drivers to hire or fire. It costs $4000 to hire a driver and $2000 to fire a driver. A driver's salary is $10,000 per year. At the beginning of year 1, the company has 50 drivers. A driver hired at the beginning of a year can be used to meet the current year's requirements and is paid full salary for the current year.

**a.** Determine how to minimize the bus company's salary, hiring, and firing costs over the next five years.

**b.** Use SolverTable to determine how the total number hired, total number fired, and total cost change as the unit hiring and firing costs *each* increase by the same percentage.

46. During each four-hour period, the Smalltown police force requires the following number of on-duty police officers: eight from midnight to 4 A.M.; seven from 4 A.M. to 8 A.M.; six from 8 A.M. to noon; six from noon to 4 P.M.; five from 4 P.M. to 8 P.M.; and four from 8 P.M. to midnight. Each police officer works two consecutive four-hour shifts.

**a.** Determine how to minimize the number of police officers needed to meet Smalltown's daily requirements.

**b.** Use SolverTable to see how the number of police officers changes as the number of officers needed from midnight to 4 A.M. changes.

47. Shoemakers of America forecasts the following demand for the next six months: 5000 pairs in month 1; 6000 pairs in month 2; 7000 pairs in month 3; 9000 pairs in month 4; 6000 pairs in month 5; 5000 pairs in month 6. It takes a shoemaker 20 minutes to produce a pair of shoes. Each shoemaker works 150 hours per month plus up to 40 hours per month of overtime. A shoemaker is paid a regular salary of $2000 per month plus $20 per hour for overtime. At the beginning of each month, Shoemakers can either hire or fire workers. It costs the company $1000 to hire a worker and $1200 to fire a worker. The monthly holding cost per pair of shoes is 5% of the cost of producing a pair of shoes with regular-time labor. The raw materials in a pair of shoes cost $10. At the beginning of month 1, Shoemakers has 15 workers and 500 pairs of shoes in inventory. Determine how to minimize the cost of meeting (on time) the demands of the next six months.

48. NewAge Pharmaceuticals produces the drug NasaMist from four chemicals. Today, the company must produce 1000 pounds of the drug. The three active ingredients in NasaMist are A, B, and C. By weight, at least 8% of NasaMist must consist of A, at least 4% of B, and at least 2% of C. The cost per pound of each chemical and the amount of each active ingredient in one pound of each chemical are given in the file P04_48.xlsx. At least 100 pounds of chemical 2 must be used.

**a.** Determine the cheapest way of producing today's batch of NasaMist.

**b.** Use SolverTable to see how much the percentage of requirement of A is really costing NewAge. Let the percentage required vary from 6% to 12%.

49. You have decided to enter the candy business. You are considering producing two types of candies: Slugger candy and Easy Out candy, both of which consist solely of sugar, nuts, and chocolate. At present, you have in stock 10,000 ounces of sugar, 2000 ounces of nuts, and 3000 ounces of chocolate. The mixture used to make Easy Out candy must contain at least 20% nuts. The mixture used to make Slugger candy must contain at least 10% nuts and 10% chocolate. Each ounce of Easy Out candy can be sold for $1.20, and each ounce of Slugger candy for $1.40.

**a.** Determine how you can maximize your revenue from candy sales.

**b.** Use SolverTable to determine how changes in the price of Easy Out change the optimal solution.

**c.** Use SolverTable to determine how changes in the amount of available sugar change the optimal solution.

50. Sunblessed Juice Company sells bags of oranges and cartons of orange juice. Sunblessed grades oranges on a scale of 1 (poor) to 10 (excellent). At present, Sunblessed has 100,000 pounds of grade 9 oranges and 120,000 pounds of grade 6 oranges on hand. The average quality of oranges sold in bags must be at least 7, and the average quality of the oranges used to produce orange juice must be at least 8. Each pound of oranges that is used for juice yields a revenue of $1.50 and incurs a variable cost (consisting of labor costs, variable overhead costs, inventory costs, and so on) of $1.05. Each pound of oranges sold in bags yields a revenue of $1.50 and incurs a variable cost of $0.70.

**a.** Determine how Sunblessed can maximize its profit.

**b.** Use SolverTable to determine how a change in the cost per bag of oranges changes the optimal solution.

**c.** Use SolverTable to determine how a change in the amount of grade 9 oranges available affects the optimal solution.

**d.** Use SolverTable to determine how a change in the required average quality required for juice changes the optimal solution.

51. A bank is attempting to determine where its assets should be invested during the current year. At present, $500,000 is available for investment in bonds, home loans, auto loans, and personal loans. The annual rates of return on each type of investment are known to be the following: bonds, 10%; home loans, 16%; auto loans, 13%; personal loans, 20%. To ensure that the bank's portfolio is not too risky, the bank's investment manager has placed the following three restrictions on the bank's portfolio:

- The amount invested in personal loans cannot exceed the amount invested in bonds.
- The amount invested in home loans cannot exceed the amount invested in auto loans.
- No more than 25% of the total amount invested can be in personal loans.

Help the bank maximize the annual return on its investment portfolio.

52. Young MBA Erica Cudahy can invest up to $15,000 in stocks and loans. Each dollar invested in stocks yields $0.10 profit, and each dollar invested in a loan yields $0.15 profit. At least 30% of all money invested must be in stocks, and at least $6000 must be in loans. Determine how Erica can maximize the profit earned on her investments.

53. A fertilizer company blends silicon and nitrogen to produce two types of fertilizers. Fertilizer 1 must be at least 40% nitrogen and sells for $70 per pound. Fertilizer 2 must be at least 70% silicon and sells for $40 per pound. The company can purchase up to 8000 pounds of nitrogen at $15 per pound and up to 10,000 pounds of silicon at $10 per pound.
   a. Assuming that all fertilizer produced can be sold, determine how the company can maximize its profit.
   b. Use SolverTable to explore the effect on profit of changing the minimum percentage of nitrogen required in fertilizer 1.
   c. Suppose the availabilities of nitrogen and silicon both increase by the same percentage from their current values. Use SolverTable to explore the effect of this change on profit.

54. A chemical manufacturer uses chemicals 1 and 2 to produce two drugs. Drug 1 must be at least 70% chemical 1, and drug 2 must be at least 60% chemical 2. Up to 50,000 ounces of drug 1 can be sold at $30 per ounce; up to 60,000 ounces of drug 2 can be sold at $25 per ounce. Up to 45,000 ounces of chemical 1 can be purchased at $15 per ounce, and up to 55,000 ounces of chemical 2 can be purchased at $18 per ounce. Determine how to maximize the manufacturer's profit.

55. Hiland's Appliances stocks laptops, TVs, refrigerators, microwave ovens, and ranges. These products compete for floor space, tie up different amounts of capital, and have different profit margins. The company has also specified minimum percentages of these products it wants to stock (out of the total of all items stocked). The relevant data are listed in the file P04_55.xlsx. Hiland's wants no more than $750,000 to be tied up in inventory of these products, and it has only 10,000 square feet of floor space for them.
   a. Assuming that the value of the company's inventory is the sum of all profit margins of all items, how many units of each product should the company stock to maximize its value?
   b. If the company could obtain an extra 2500 square feet of floor space, how much would it be worth in terms of extra value? Is the value from 5000 extra square feet twice as much as the value from 2500 extra square feet?

56. Many Wall Street firms use LP models to select a desirable bond portfolio. The following is a simplified version of such a model. Solodrex is considering investing in four bonds; $1 million is available for investment. The expected annual return, the worst-case annual return on each bond, and the *duration* of each bond are given in the file P04_56.xlsx. (The duration of a bond is a measure of the bond's sensitivity to interest rates.) Solodrex wants to maximize the expected return from its bond investments, subject to three constraints:
   ■ The worst-case return of the bond portfolio must be at least 8%.
   ■ The average duration of the portfolio must be at most 6. For example, a portfolio that invests $600,000 in bond 1 and $400,000 in bond 4 has an average duration of [600,000(3) + 400,000(9)]/1,000,000 = 5.4.
   ■ Because of diversification requirements, at most 40% of the total amount invested can be invested in a single bond.

Determine how Solodrex can maximize the expected return on its investment.

57. A coal company produces coal at three mines and ships it to four customers. The cost per ton of producing coal, the ash and sulfur content (per ton) of the coal, and the production capacity (in tons) for each mine are given in the file P04_57.xlsx. The number of tons of coal demanded by each customer and the cost (in dollars) of shipping a ton of coal from a mine to each customer are also provided in this same file. The amount of coal shipped to each customer must contain at most 6% ash and at most 3.5% sulfur. Show the company how to minimize the cost of meeting customer demands.

58. A furniture company manufactures tables and chairs. A table requires 40 board feet of wood, and a chair requires 30 board feet of wood. Wood can be purchased at a cost of $1.50 per board foot, and 40,000 board feet of wood are available for purchase. It takes two hours of skilled labor to manufacture an unfinished table or an unfinished chair. Three more hours of skilled labor will turn an unfinished table into a finished table, and two more hours of skilled labor will turn an unfinished chair into a finished chair. A total of 5000 hours of skilled labor is available (and have already been paid for). All furniture produced can be sold at the following unit prices: an unfinished table, $130; a finished table, $220; an unfinished chair, $80; a finished chair, $175.
   a. Determine how to maximize the company's profit from manufacturing tables and chairs.
   b. Use a two-way SolverTable to see how the numbers of unfinished products (both chairs and tables) sold depend on the selling prices of these unfinished products. Of course, neither

unfinished selling price should be as large as the corresponding finished selling price.

**59.** A chemical company produces three products, A, B, and C, and can sell these products in unlimited quantities at the following unit prices: A, $10; B, $55; C, $100. Producing a unit of A requires one hour of labor; a unit of B, two hours of labor plus two units of A; and a unit of C, three hours of labor plus one unit of B. Any A that is used to produce B cannot be sold. Similarly, any B that is used to produce C cannot be sold. A total of 4000 hours of labor is available. Only as many as 500 units of product C can be sold. Determine how to maximize the company's revenue.

**60.** Abotte Products produces three products, A, B, and C. The company can sell up to 300 pounds of each product at the following prices (per pound): product A, $10; product B, $12; product C, $20. Abotte purchases raw material at $5 per pound. Each pound of raw material can be used to produce either one pound of A or one pound of B. For a cost of $3 per pound processed, product A can be converted to 0.6 pound of product B and 0.4 pound of product C. For a cost of $2 per pound processed, product B can be converted to 0.8 pound of product C. Determine how Abotte can maximize its profit.

**61.** An investor has $100,000 to invest right now (the beginning of year 1). The cash flows associated with five available investments are listed in the file P04_61.xlsx. For example, every dollar invested in A in year 1 yields $1.40 in year 4. In addition to these investments, the investor can invest as much money each year as he wants in CDs, which pay 3% interest. The investor wants to maximize his available cash in year 4. Assuming that he can put no more than $50,000 in any investment, develop an LP model to help the investor achieve his goal.

**62.** At the beginning of year 1, you have $10,000. Investments A and B are available; their cash flows are shown in the file P04_62.xlsx. Assume that any money not invested in A or B earns interest at an annual rate of 3%.
  **a.** Determine how to maximize your cash on hand in year 4.
  **b.** Use SolverTable to determine how a change in the year 3 yield for investment A changes the optimal solution to the problem.
  **c.** Use SolverTable to determine how a change in the year 4 yield of investment B changes the optimal solution to the problem.

**63.** You now have $10,000, and the following investment plans are available to you during the next three years:
  ■ **Investment A:** Every dollar invested now yields $0.10 a year from now and $1.30 three years from now.
  ■ **Investment B:** Every dollar invested now yields $0.20 a year from now and $1.10 two years from now.

  ■ **Investment C:** Every dollar invested a year from now yields $1.50 three years from now.

During each year, you can place uninvested cash in money market funds that yield 3% interest per year. However, you can invest at most $5000 in any one of plans A, B, or C. Determine how to maximize your cash on hand three years from now.

**64.** An oil company processes oil into aviation fuel and heating oil. It costs $65,000 to purchase each 1000 barrels of oil, which is then distilled and yields 500 barrels of aviation fuel and 500 barrels of heating oil. Output from the distillation can be sold directly or processed in the catalytic cracker. If sold after distillation without further processing, aviation fuel sells for $80,000 per 1000 barrels, and heating oil sells for $65,000 per 1000 barrels. It takes one hour to process 1000 barrels of aviation fuel in the catalytic cracker, and these 1000 barrels can be sold for $145,000. It takes 45 minutes to process 1000 barrels of heating oil in the cracker, and these 1000 barrels can be sold for $125,000. Each day at most 20,000 barrels of oil can be purchased, and eight hours of cracker time are available. Determine how to maximize the company's profit.

**65.** All steel manufactured by Allied Steel must meet the following requirements: between 3.2% and 3.5% carbon; between 1.8% and 2.5% silicon; between 0.9% and 1.2% nickel; tensile strength of at least 45,000 pounds per square inch (psi). The company manufactures steel by combining two alloys. The cost and properties of each alloy are given in the file P04_65.xlsx. Assume that the tensile strength of a mixture of the two alloys can be determined by averaging the tensile strength of the alloys that are mixed together. For example, a one-ton mixture that is 40% alloy 1 and 60% alloy 2 has a tensile strength of 0.4(42,000) + 0.6(50,000). Determine how to minimize the cost of producing a ton of steel.

**66.** United Steel manufactures two types of steel at three different steel mills. During a given month, each steel mill has 200 hours of blast furnace time available. Because of differences in the furnaces at each mill, the time and cost to produce a ton of steel differ for each mill, as listed in the file P04_66.xlsx. Each month, the company must manufacture at least 500 tons of steel 1 and 600 tons of steel 2. Determine how United Steel can minimize the cost of manufacturing the desired steel.

**67.** Based on Heady and Egbert (1964). Walnut Orchard has two farms that grow wheat and corn. Because of differing soil conditions, there are differences in the yields and costs of growing crops on the two farms. The yields and costs are listed in the file P04_67.xlsx. Each farm has 100 acres available for cultivation; 11,000 bushels of wheat and 7000 bushels of corn must be grown.

**a.** Determine a planting plan that will minimize the cost of meeting these requirements.

**b.** Use SolverTable to see how the total cost changes if the requirements for wheat and corn both change by the *same* percentage, where this percentage change can be as low as $-50\%$ or as high as $+50\%$.

**68.** Candy Kane Cosmetics (CKC) produces Leslie Perfume, which requires chemicals and labor. Two production processes are available. Process 1 transforms one unit of labor and two units of chemicals into three ounces of perfume. Process two transforms two units of labor and three units of chemicals into five ounces of perfume. It costs CKC $3 to purchase a unit of labor and $2 to purchase a unit of chemicals. Each year up to 20,000 units of labor and 35,000 units of chemicals can be purchased. In the absence of advertising, CKC believes it can sell 1000 ounces of perfume. To stimulate demand for Leslie, CKC can hire the beautiful model Jenny Nelson. Jenny is paid $100 per hour. Each hour Jenny works for the company is estimated to increase the demand for Leslie Perfume by 200 ounces. Each ounce of Leslie Perfume sells for $5. Determine how CKC can maximize its profit.

**69.** Federated Oil has refineries in Los Angeles and Chicago. The Los Angeles refinery can refine up to two million barrels of oil per year, and the Chicago refinery up to three million. After the oil is refined, it is shipped to two distribution points, Houston and New York City. Federated Oil estimates that each distribution point can sell up to five million barrels per year. Because of differences in shipping and refining costs, the profit earned (in dollars) per million barrels of oil shipped depends on where the oil was refined and on the point of distribution. This information is listed in the file P04_69.xlsx. The company is considering expanding the capacity of each refinery. Each million barrels of annual refining capacity that is added will cost $120,000 for the Los Angeles refinery and $150,000 for the Chicago refinery. Determine how Federated Oil can maximize its profit (including expansion costs) over a 10-year period.

**70.** A feed company produces two types of cattle feed, both consisting totally of wheat and alfalfa. Feed 1 must contain at least 80% wheat, and feed 2 must contain at least 60% alfalfa. Feed 1 sells for $1.50 per pound, and feed 2 sells for $1.30 per pound. The company can purchase up to 1000 pounds of wheat at $0.50 per pound and up to 800 pounds of alfalfa at $0.40 per pound. Demand for each type of feed is unlimited. Determine how to maximize the company's profit.

**71.** Carrington Oil produces gas 1 and gas 2 from two types of crude oil: crude 1 and crude 2. Gas 1 is allowed to contain up to 4% impurities, and gas 2 is allowed to contain up to 3% impurities. Gas 1 sells for $72 per barrel, whereas gas 2 sells for $84 per barrel. Up to 4200 barrels of gas 1 and up to 4300 barrels of gas 2 can be sold. The cost per barrel of each crude, their availability, and the level of impurities in each crude are listed in the file P04_71.xlsx. Before blending the crude oil into gas, any amount of each crude can be "purified" for a cost of $3.50 per barrel. Purification eliminates half of the impurities in the crude oil.

**a.** Determine how to maximize profit.

**b.** Use SolverTable to determine how an increase in the availability of crude 1 affects the optimal profit.

**c.** Use SolverTable to determine how an increase in the availability of crude 2 affects the optimal profit.

**d.** Use SolverTable to determine how a change in the price of gas 2 changes the optimal profit and the types of gas produced.

**72.** Based on Thomas (1971). A toy company produces toys at two plants and sells them in three regions. The current demands at these regions are given in the file P04_72.xlsx. Each plant can produce up to 2500 units. Each toy sells for $10, and the cost of producing and shipping a toy from a given plant to a region is given in the same file. The company can advertise locally and nationally. Each $1 spent on a local ad raises sales in a region by 0.5 units, whereas each $1 spent advertising nationally increases sales in each region by 0.3 units.

**a.** Determine how the company can maximize its profit.

**b.** If sales stimulated by advertising exhibits diminishing returns, how would you change your model?

**73.** A company produces two products: A and B. Product A sells for $11 per unit and product B sells for $23 per unit. Producing a unit of product A requires two hours on assembly line 1 and one unit of raw material. Producing a unit of product B requires two units of raw material, one unit of A, and two hours on assembly line 2. On line 1, 1300 hours of time are available, and 500 hours are available on line 2. A unit of raw material can be bought (for $5 a unit) or produced (at no cost) by using two hours of time on line 1.

**a.** Determine how to maximize profit.

**b.** The company will stop buying raw material when the price of raw material exceeds what value? (Use SolverTable.)

**74.** A bank needs exactly two employees working each hour from 9 A.M. to 5 P.M. Workers can work the shifts and are paid the wages listed in the file P04_74.xlsx. For example, a worker working 9 A.M. to 2 P.M. is paid $42.00. Find an assignment of workers that provides enough workers at minimum cost.

**75.** Based on Gaballa and Pearce (1979). Northwest Airlines has determined that it needs the number of ticket agents during each hour of the day listed in the file P04_75.xlsx. Workers work nine-hour shifts, one hour of which is for lunch. The lunch hour can be either the fourth or fifth hour of their shift. What is the minimum number of workers needed by Northwest?

**76.** A rock company uses five types of rocks to fill four orders. The phosphate content, availability of each type of rock, and the production cost per pound for each rock are listed in the file P04_76.xlsx, as well as the size of each order and the minimum and maximum phosphate percentage in each order. What is the cheapest way to fill the orders?

**77.** An automobile manufacturer needs to plan its production for the next year. Demands for the next 12 months are forecasted to be 940, 790, 360, 720, 270, 130, 160, 300, 990, 290, 280, and 790. Other relevant information is as follows:
- Workers are paid $5000 per month.
- It costs $500 to hold a car in inventory for a month. The holding cost is based on each month's ending inventory.
- It costs $4000 to hire a worker.
- It costs $6000 to fire a worker.
- Each worker can make up to eight cars a month.
- Workers are hired and fired at the beginning of each month.
- At the beginning of month 1 there are 500 cars in inventory and 60 workers.

How can the company minimize the cost of meeting demand for cars on time?

**78.** An oil company produces gasoline from five inputs. The cost, density, viscosity, and sulfur content, and the number of barrels available of each input are listed in the file P04_78.xlsx. Gasoline sells for $72 per barrel. Gasoline can have a density of at most 0.98 units per barrel, a viscosity of at most 37 units per barrel, and a sulfur content of at most 3.7 units per barrel.
  **a.** How can the company maximize its profit?
  **b.** Describe how the optimal solution to the problem changes as the price of gasoline ranges from $65 to $80 per barrel.

**79.** The HiTech company produces Blu-Ray disc players. Estimated demands for the next four quarters are 5000, 10,000, 8000, and 2000. At the beginning of quarter 1, HiTech has 60 workers. It costs $2000 to hire a worker and $4000 to fire a worker. Workers are paid $10,000 per quarter plus $80 for each unit they make during overtime. A new hire can make up to 60 units per quarter during regular-time, whereas a previously hired worker can make up to 90 units per quarter. Any worker can make up to 20 units per quarter during overtime. Each disc player is sold for $160. It costs $20 to hold a disc player in inventory for a quarter.

Assume workers are hired and fired at the beginning of each quarter and that all of a quarter's production is available to meet demand for that quarter. Initial inventory at the beginning of quarter 1 is 1000 disc players. How can the company maximize its profit? Assume that demand is lost if insufficient stock is available. That is, there is no backlogging of demand (and there is no requirement that HiTech must satisfy all of its demand).

## Skill-Extending Problems

**80.** MusicTech manufactures and sells a portable music device called an mTune (similar to an iPod). At beginning of month 1, the company has $100,000 and 15 employees. Each machine the company owns has the capacity to make up to 900 mTunes per month, and each worker can make up to 600 mTunes per month. The company cannot use more labor or machine capacity than is available in any given month. Also, the company wants to have a nonnegative cash balance at all points in time. The company's costs are the following:
- Holding cost of $2 each month per mTune in ending inventory
- Cost in month 1 of buying machines ($3000 per machine)
- Raw material cost of $6 per mTune
- Monthly worker wage of $3500
- Hiring cost of $4000 per worker
- Firing cost of $5000 per worker

In the absence of advertising, the monthly demands in months 1 through 6 are forecasted to be 5000, 8000, 7000, 6000, 5000, and 5000. However, MusicTech can increase demand each month by advertising. Every $10 (up to a maximum of $50,000 per month) spent on advertising during a month increases demand for that month by one mTune. The devices are sold for $75 each. The sequence of events in any month is that the company buys machines (month 1 only), hires and fires workers, makes the mTunes, advertises, pays all costs for the month, and collects revenues for the month. Develop a model to maximize profit (total revenue minus total costs) earned during the next six months.

**81.** You want to take out a $300,000 loan on a 20-year mortgage with end-of-month payments. The annual rate of interest is 6%. Twenty years from now, you will need to make a $40,000 ending balloon payment. Because you expect your income to increase, you want to structure the loan so at the beginning of each year, your monthly payments increase by 2%.
  **a.** Determine the amount of each year's monthly payment. You should use a lookup table to look up each year's monthly payment and to look up the year based on the month (e.g., month 13 is year 2, etc.).

**b.** Suppose payment each month is to be the same, and there is no balloon payment. Show that the monthly payment you can calculate from your spreadsheet matches the value given by the Excel PMT function PMT(0.06/12,240,−300000,0,0).

82. A graduated payment mortgage (GPM) enables the borrower to have lower payments earlier in the mortgage and increased payments later on. The assumption is the borrower's income will increase over time so that it will be easier for the borrower to meet all payments. Suppose you borrow $60,000 on a 30-year monthly mortgage. You obtain a GPM where monthly payments increase 7.5% per year through year 5 and then remain constant from year 5 through year 30. For annual interest rates of 10%, 11%, 12%, 13%, and 14%, use Solver to find the amount of each year's monthly payment.

83. Suppose you are planning for retirement. At the beginning of this year and each of the next 39 years, you plan to contribute some money to your retirement fund. Each year, you plan to increase your retirement contribution by $500. When you retire in 40 years, you plan to withdraw $100,000 at the beginning of each year for the next 20 years. You assume the following about the yields of your retirement investment portfolio:
   ■ During the first 20 years, your investments will earn 10% per year.
   ■ During all other years, your investments will earn 5% per year.

All contributions and withdrawals occur at the beginnings of the respective years.
   **a.** Given these assumptions, what is the least amount of money you can contribute this year and still have enough to make your retirement withdrawals?
   **b.** How does your answer change if inflation is 2% per year and your goal is to withdraw $100,000 per year (in today's dollars) for 20 years?

84. Based on Brams and Taylor (2000). Suppose that Eli Lilly and Pfizer are going to merge. Merger negotiations must settle the following issues:
   ■ What will the name of the merged corporation be?
   ■ Will corporate headquarters be in Indianapolis (Lilly wants this) or New York (Pfizer wants this)?
   ■ Which company's chairperson will be chairperson of the merged corporation?
   ■ Which company gets to choose the CEO?
   ■ On the issue of layoffs, what percentage of each company's view will prevail?

Brams developed a remarkably simple method for the two adversaries to settle their differences. (This same method could be used to settle differences between other adversaries, such as a husband and wife in a divorce, Arab and Israel in Middle East, and so on.) Each adversary allocates 100 points between all of the issues. These allocations are listed in the file P04_84.xlsx. For example, Lilly believes headquarters is worth 25 points, whereas Pfizer thinks headquarters is only worth 10 points. Layoffs may be divided (for example, Lilly might get 70% of the say in layoffs and Pfizer 30%), but on all other issues, only one company gets its way. The **adjusted winner procedure** says that the best way to make decisions on each issue is to:
   ■ give each adversary the same number of points;
   ■ ensure that each company prefers its allocation to the allocation of its opponent;
   ■ maximize the number of points received by either participant.

Such a solution is equitable (because each party receives the same number of points) and is envy-free (because neither side prefers what its opponent receives to what it receives). It can also be shown that the adjusted winner procedure yields a Pareto optimal solution. This means that no other allocation can make one player better off without making the other player worse off. Find the adjusted winner solution to the merger example. Also show that the adjusted winner solution for this example is Pareto optimal.

85. AdminaStar processes Medicare claims. At the beginning of month 1 they have a backlog of 40,000 difficult claims and 60,000 easy claims. The predicted claim volume for months 1 through 8 is listed in the file P04_85.xlsx. At the beginning of month 1, AdminaStar has 70 experienced claim processors. Each month it can hire up to 10 trainees. At the end of each month, 5% of experienced employees quit, and 20% of trainees are fired. Each worker is available for 160 hours per month. The number of minutes needed by each worker to process each type of claim is listed in this same file. AdminaStar wants ending inventory for months 2 through 7 to be no greater than 50,000 of each type of claim. All claims must be processed by the end of month 8. What is the minimum number of trainees that need to be hired during months 1 to 8? (*Note:* Trainees must be integers. Experienced workers will probably end up being fractional. You have two options. First, you can ignore the fractional values. Second, you can use the ROUND function to round them to the nearest integers. However, this makes the model nonlinear, so you won't be able to use Solver's Simplex LP method. Try this second option.)

86. Based on Charnes and Cooper (1955). A small company is trying to determine employee salary based on the following attributes: effectiveness, responsibility, initiative, experience, education, self-expression, planning ability, intelligence, and the ability to get things done. Each of the company's seven executives has been rated on each of these attributes, with the ratings shown in the file P04_86.xlsx. The company wants to set each executive's salary

by multiplying a weight for each attribute by the executive's score on each attribute. The salaries must satisfy the following constraints:

- The salary of a lower-numbered executive must be at least as large as the salary of a higher-numbered executive.
- Executive 1's salary can be at most $160,000 and executive 7's salary must be at least $40,000.
- The salaries of executives 1, 5, and 7 should match $160,000, $100,000, and $40,000, respectively, as closely as possible.
- All attribute weights must be nonnegative.

Develop a method for setting salaries. [*Hint*: For executives 1, 5, and 7, define "over" and "under" changing cells and add a constraint such as Executive 5 salary + (Amount executive 5 salary under $100,000) − (Amount executive 5 salary over $100,000) = $100,000. Then the target cell to minimize is the sum of over and under changing cells for positions 1, 5, and 7. If you did not include the over and under changing cells, why would your model fail to be linear?]

**87.** During the next four quarters, Dorian Auto must meet (on time) the following demands for cars: 4000 in quarter 1; 2000 in quarter 2; 5000 in quarter 3; 1000 in quarter 4. At the beginning of quarter 1, there are 300 autos in stock. The company has the capacity to produce at most 3000 cars per quarter. At the beginning of each quarter, the company can change production capacity. It costs $100 to increase quarterly production capacity by one unit. For example, it would cost $10,000 to increase capacity from 3000 to 3100. It also costs $50 per quarter to maintain each unit of production capacity (even if it is unused during the current quarter). The variable cost of producing a car is $2000. A holding cost of $150 per car is assessed against each quarter's ending inventory. At the end of quarter 4, plant capacity must be at least 4000 cars.
  **a.** Determine how to minimize the total cost incurred during the next four quarters.
  **b.** Use SolverTable to determine how much the total cost increases as the required capacity at the end of quarter 4 increases (from its current value of 4000).

**88.** The Internal Revenue Service (IRS) has determined that during each of the next 12 months it will need the numbers of supercomputers given in the file P04_88.xlsx. To meet these requirements, the IRS rents supercomputers for a period of one, two, or three months. It costs $1000 to rent a supercomputer for one month, $1800 for two months, and $2500 for three months. At the beginning of month 1, the IRS has no supercomputers.
  **a.** Determine the rental plan that meets the requirements for the next 12 months at minimum cost.

You can assume that fractional rentals are allowed. Thus, if your solution says to rent 140.6 computers for one month, you can round this up to 141 or down to 140 without much effect on the total cost.
  **b.** Suppose the monthly requirement increases anywhere from 10% to 50% each month. (Assume that whatever the percentage increase is, it is the *same* each month.) Use SolverTable to see whether the total rental cost increases by this same percentage.

**89.** You own a wheat warehouse with a capacity of 20,000 bushels. At the beginning of month 1, you have 6000 bushels of wheat. Each month, wheat can be bought and sold at the prices per bushel listed in the file P04_89.xlsx. The sequence of events during each month is as follows:
- You observe your initial stock of wheat.
- You can sell any amount of wheat up to your initial stock at the current month's selling price.
- You can buy as much wheat as you want, subject to the limitation of warehouse size.
  **a.** Determine how to maximize the profit earned over the next 10 months.
  **b.** Use SolverTable to determine how a change in the capacity of the warehouse affects the optimal solution.

**90.** You can calculate the *risk index* of an investment by taking the absolute values of percentage changes in the value of the investment for each year and averaging them. Suppose you are trying to determine the percentages of your money to invest in several potential investments. The file P04_90.xlsx lists the annual returns (percentage changes in value) for these investments for a 20-year period. Let the risk index of a portfolio be the weighted average of the risk indices of these investments, where the weights are the fractions of the portfolio assigned to the investments. Suppose that the amount of each investment must be between 10% and 40% of the total invested. You would like the risk index of your portfolio to equal 0.16, and your goal is to maximize the expected return on your portfolio. Determine the maximum expected return on your portfolio, subject to the stated constraints. Use the average return earned by each investment during the 20-year period as your estimate of expected return.

**91.** Based on Magoulas and Marinos-Kouris (1988). An oil company produces two products: regular and premium gasoline. Each product contains 0.15 gram of lead per liter. The two products are produced from these six inputs: reformate, fluid catalytic cracker gasoline (FCG), isomerate (ISO), polymer (POL), methyl tertiary butyl ether (MTBE), and butane (BUT). Each input has four attributes: research octane number (RON), Reid vapor pressure (RVP), ASTM volatility at 70 degrees Celsius, and ASTM volatility at 130 degrees Celsius. (ASTM is the American Society for Testing and Materials.) The attributes and daily availability (in liters) of each input are listed in the file P04_91.xlsx. The requirements for each output are also listed in this file. The daily demand (in thousands of liters) for each product must be met, but more can be produced if desired. The RON and ASTM requirements are minimums; the RVP requirement is a maximum. Regular gasoline sells for $0.754 per liter; premium gasoline for $0.819. Before each product is ready for sale, 0.15 gram per liter of lead must be removed. The cost of removing 0.1 gram per liter is $0.213. At most, 38% of each type of gasoline can consist of FCG. How can the company maximize its daily profit?

92. Capsule Drugs manufactures two drugs. The drugs are produced by blending two chemicals. By weight, drug 1 must contain at least 65% chemical 1, and drug 2 must contain at least 55% chemical 1. Drug 1 sells for $6 per ounce, and drug 2 sells for $4 per ounce. Chemicals 1 and 2 can be produced by one of two production processes. Running process 1 for an hour requires 7 ounces of raw material and 2 hours skilled labor, and it yields 3 ounces of each chemical. Running process 2 for an hour requires 5 ounces of raw material and 3 hours of skilled labor, and it yields 3 ounces of chemical 1 and 1 ounce of chemical 2. A total of 3000 hours of skilled labor and 5000 ounces of raw material are available. Determine how to maximize Capsule's sales revenues.

93. Molecular Products produces three chemicals: B, C, and D. The company begins by purchasing chemical A for a cost of $650 per 100 liters. For an additional cost of $320 and the use of three hours of skilled labor, 100 liters of A can be transformed into 40 liters of C and 60 liters of B. Chemical C can either be sold or processed further. It costs $130 and one hour of skilled labor to process 100 liters of C into 60 liters of D and 40 liters of B. For each chemical, the selling price per 100 liters and the maximum amount (in 100s of liters) tha can be sold are listed in the file P04_93.xlsx. A maximum of 200 labor hours is available. Determine how Molecular can maximize its profit.

94. Bexter Labs produces three products: A, B, and C. Bexter can sell up to 3000 units of product A, up to 2000 units of product B, and up to 2000 units of product C. Each unit of product C uses two units of A and three units of B and incurs $5 in processing costs. Products A and B are produced from either raw material 1 or raw material 2. It costs $6 to purchase and process one unit of raw material 1. Each processed unit of raw material 1 yields two units of A and three units of B. It costs $3 to purchase and process a unit of raw material 2. Each processed unit of raw material 2 yields one unit of A and two units of B. The unit

prices for the products are A, $5; B, $4; C, $25. The quality levels of each product are: A, 8; B, 7; C, 6. The average quality level of the units sold must be at least 7. Determine how to maximize Bexter's profit.

95. Mondo Motorcycles is determining its production schedule for the next four quarters. Demands for motorcycles are forecasted to be 400 in quarter 1; 700 in quarter 2; 500 in quarter 3; 200 in quarter 4. Mondo incurs four types of costs, as described here:
- It costs Mondo $800 to manufacture each motorcycle.
- At the end of each quarter, a holding cost of $100 per motorcycle left in inventory is incurred.
- When production is increased from one quarter to the next, a cost is incurred, primarily for training employees. If the increase in production is $x$ motorcycles, the cost is $700x$.
- When production is decreased from one quarter to the next, a cost is incurred, primarily for severance pay and decreased morale. If the decrease in production is $x$ motorcycles, the cost is $600x$.

All demands must be met on time, and a quarter's production can be used to meet demand for the current quarter (as well as future quarters). During the quarter immediately preceding quarter 1, 500 Mondos were produced. Assume that at the beginning of quarter 1, no Mondos are in inventory.
a. Determine how to minimize Mondo's total cost during the next four quarters.
b. Use SolverTable to determine how Mondo's optimal production schedule would be affected by a change in the cost of increasing production from one quarter to the next.
c. Use SolverTable to determine how Mondo's optimal production schedule would be affected by a change in the cost of decreasing production from one quarter to the next.

96. An automobile manufacturing company has a $1,500,000 advertising budget. To increase its automobile sales, the company is considering advertising in newspapers and on television. The more the company uses a particular medium, the less effective each additional ad is. The file P04_96.xlsx lists the number of new customers reached by each ad. Each newspaper ad costs $1000, and each television ad costs $10,000. At most, 30 newspaper ads and 15 television ads can be placed. How can the company maximize the number of new customers created by advertising?

97. Broker Sonya Wong is currently trying to maximize her profit in the bond market. Four bonds are available for purchase and sale at the bid and ask prices shown in the file P04_97.xlsx. Sonya can buy up to 1000 units of each bond at the ask price or sell up to 1000 units of each bond at the bid price. During each of the next three years, the person who sells a bond will pay

the owner of the bond the cash payments listed in the same file. Sonya's goal is to maximize her revenue from selling bonds minus her payment for buying bonds, subject to the constraint that after each year's payments are received, her current cash position (due only to cash payments from bonds and not purchases or sales of bonds) is nonnegative. Note that her current cash position can depend on past coupons and that cash accumulated at the end of each year earns 5.25% annual interest. Determine how to maximize net profit from buying and selling bonds, subject to the constraints previously described. Why do you think we limit the number of units of each bond that can be bought or sold?

**98.** Budget Auto produces inexpensive cars. Each car is sold for $7900. The raw material in a car costs $5000. Labor time and robot time are needed to produce cars. A worker can do the needed labor on, at most, 100 cars per month; a robot can complete the needed work on, at most, 200 cars per month. The company currently has four workers. Each worker receives a monthly salary of $6000. It costs $2500 to hire a worker and $1000 to fire a worker. Hired workers are fully productive during the month they are hired. Robots must be bought at the beginning of month 1 at a cost of $15,000 per robot. The (assumed known) demand for cars is listed in the file P04_98.xlsx. At the end of each month, the company incurs a holding cost of $200 per car. How can the company maximize the profit earned during the next six months?

**99.** The ZapCon Company is considering investing in three projects. If it fully invests in a project, the realized cash flows (in millions of dollars) will be as listed in the file P04_99.xlsx. For example, project 1 requires a cash outflow of $3 million today and returns $5.5 million three years from now. Today Zap-Con has $2 million in cash. At each time point (0, 0.5, 1, 1.5, 2, and 2.5 years from today), the company can, if desired, borrow up to $2 million at 3.5% (per six months) interest. Leftover cash earns 3% (per six months) interest. For example, if after borrowing and investing at time 0, ZapCon has $1 million, it would receive $30,000 in interest at time 0.5 year. The company's goal is to maximize cash on hand after cash flows three years from now are accounted for. What investment and borrowing strategy should it use? Assume that the company can invest in a fraction of a project. For example, if it invests in 0.5 of project 3, it has, for example, cash outflows of −$1 million at times 0 and 0.5.

**100.** You are a CFA (chartered financial analyst). An overextended client has come to you because she needs help paying off her credit card bills. She owes the amounts on her credit cards listed in the file

P04_100.xlsx. The client is willing to allocate up to $5000 per month to pay off these credit cards. All cards must be paid off within 36 months. The client's goal is to minimize the total of all her payments. To solve this problem, you must understand how interest on a loan works. To illustrate, suppose the client pays $5000 on Saks during month 1. Then her Saks balance at the beginning of month 2 is $20,000 − [$5000 − 0.005(20,000)]. This follows because she incurs 0.005(20,000) in interest charges on her Saks card during month 1. Help the client solve her problem. After you have solved this problem, give an intuitive explanation of the solution found by Solver.

**101.** Aluminaca produces 100-foot-long, 200-foot-long, and 300-foot-long ingots for customers. This week's demand for ingots is listed in the file P04_101.xlsx. Aluminaca has four furnaces in which ingots can be produced. During one week, each furnace can be operated for 50 hours. Because ingots are produced by cutting up long strips of aluminum, longer ingots take less time to produce than shorter ingots. If a furnace is devoted completely to producing one type of ingot, the number it can produce in one week is listed in the same file. For example, furnace 1 could produce 350 300-foot ingots per week. The material in an ingot costs $10 per foot. A customer who wants a 100-foot or 200-foot ingot will accept an ingot of that length or longer. How can Aluminaca minimize the material costs incurred in meeting required weekly demands?

**102.** Each day, Eastinghouse produces capacitors during three shifts: 8 A.M. to 4 P.M., 4 P.M. to 12 A.M., and 12 A.M. to 8 A.M. The hourly salary paid to the employees on each shift, the price charged for each capacitor made during each shift, and the number of defects in each capacitor produced during a given shift are listed in the file P04_102.xlsx. The company can employ up to 125 workers, and each worker can be assigned to one of the three shifts. A worker produces 10 capacitors during a shift, but due to machinery limitations, no more than 50 workers can be assigned to any shift. Each capacitor produced can be sold, but the average number of defects per capacitor for the day's production cannot exceed 3. Determine how Eastinghouse can maximize its daily profit.

**103.** During the next three months, a heating and cooling company must meet (on time) the following demands for air conditioners: month 1, 300; month 2, 400; month 3, 500. Air conditioners can be produced in either New York or Los Angeles. It takes 1.5 hours of skilled labor to produce an air conditioner in Los Angeles, and it takes 2 hours in New York. It costs $400 to produce an air conditioner in Los Angeles, and it costs $350 in New York. During each month, each city has 420 hours of skilled labor available. It costs

$100 to hold an air conditioner in inventory for a month. At the beginning of month 1, the company has 200 air conditioners in stock. Determine how the company can minimize the cost of meeting air conditioner demands for the next three months.

104. Gotham City National Bank is open Monday through Friday from 9 A.M. to 5 P.M. From past experience, the bank knows that it needs the numbers of tellers listed in the file P04_104.xlsx. Gotham City Bank hires two types of tellers. Full-time tellers work 9 A.M. to 5 P.M. five days a week, with one hour off each day for lunch. The bank determines when a full-time employee takes his or her lunch hour, but each teller must go between 12 P.M. and 1 P.M. or between 1 P.M. and 2 P.M. Full-time employees are paid (including fringe benefits) $15 per hour, which includes payment for lunch hour. The bank can also hire part-time tellers. Each part-time teller must work exactly four consecutive hours each day. A part-time teller is paid $9 per hour and receives no fringe benefits. To maintain adequate quality of service, the bank has decided that, at most, five part-time tellers can be hired. Determine how to meet the bank's teller requirements at minimum cost.

105. Based on Rothstein (1973). The Springfield City Police Department employs 30 police officers. Each officer works five days per week. The crime rate fluctuates with the day of the week, so the number of police officers required each day depends on the day of the week, as follows: Saturday, 28; Sunday, 18; Monday, 18; Tuesday, 24; Wednesday, 25; Thursday, 16; Friday, 21. The police department wants to schedule police officers to minimize the number whose days off are *not* consecutive. Determine how to accomplish this goal.

106. Based on Charnes and Cooper (1955). Alex Cornby makes his living buying and selling corn. On January 1, he has 5000 bushels of corn and $10,000 in cash. On the first day of each month, Alex can buy corn at the forecasted prices per bushel listed in the file P04_106.xlsx. On the last day of each month, Alex can sell corn at the forecasted prices listed in the same file. Alex stores his corn in a warehouse that can hold 10,000 bushels of corn. He must be able to pay cash for all corn at the time of purchase. Determine how Alex can maximize his cash on hand at the end of April.

107. City 1 produces 500 tons of waste per day, and city 2 produces 400 tons of waste per day. Waste must be incinerated at incinerator 1 or 2, and each incinerator can process up to 500 tons of waste per day. The cost to incinerate waste is $40 per ton at incinerator 1 and $30 per ton at incinerator 2. Incineration reduces each ton of waste to 0.2 ton of debris, which must be dumped at one of two landfills. Each landfill can receive at most 200 tons of debris per day. It costs $3 per mile to transport a ton of material (either debris or waste). Distances (in miles) between locations are listed in the file P04_107.xlsx. Determine how to minimize the total cost of disposing of the waste from both cities.

108. Based on Smith (1965). Silicon Valley Corporation (Silvco) manufactures transistors. An important aspect of the manufacture of transistors is the melting of the element germanium (a major component of a transistor) in a furnace. Unfortunately, the melting process yields germanium of highly variable quality. Two methods can be used to melt germanium. Method 1 costs $50 per transistor, and method 2 costs $70 per transistor. The qualities of germanium obtained by methods 1 and 2 are listed in the file P04_108.xlsx. Silvco can refire melted germanium in an attempt to improve its quality. It costs $25 to refire the melted germanium for one transistor. The results of the refiring process are also listed in the same file. For example, if grade 3 germanium is refired, half of the resulting germanium will be grade 3, and the other half will be grade 4. Silvco has sufficient furnace capacity to melt or refire germanium for at most 20,000 transistors per month. Silvco's monthly demands are for 1000 grade 4 transistors, 2000 grade 3 transistors, 3000 grade 2 transistors, and 3000 grade 1 transistors. Determine how to minimize the cost of producing the needed transistors.

109. The Fresh Turkey Company produces two types of turkey cutlets for sale to fast-food restaurants. Each type of cutlet consists of white meat and dark meat. Cutlet 1 sells for $2.79 per pound and must consist of at least 70% white meat. Cutlet 2 sells for $1.89 per pound and must consist of at least 60% white meat. At most, 10,000 pounds of cutlet 1 and 4000 pounds of cutlet 2 can be sold. The two types of turkey used to manufacture the cutlets are purchased from a turkey farm. Each type 1 turkey costs $8.99 and yields six pounds of white meat and two pounds of dark meat. Each type 2 turkey costs $5.99 and yields three pounds of white meat and three pounds of dark meat. Determine how to maximize Fresh Turkey's profit.

110. The production line employees at Grummins Engine work four days a week, 10 hours a day. Each day of the week, the following minimum numbers of line employees are needed: Monday through Friday, 70 employees; Saturday and Sunday, 30 employees. Grummins employs 110 line employees. Determine how to maximize the number of consecutive days off received by these employees. For example, a worker who gets Sunday, Monday, and Wednesday off receives two consecutive days off.

111. Based on Lanzenauer et al. (1987). To process income tax forms, the IRS first sends each form

through the data preparation (DP) department, where information is coded for computer entry. Then the form is sent to data entry (DE), where it is entered into the computer. During the next 3 weeks, the following quantities of forms will arrive: week 1, 40,000; week 2, 30,000; week 3, 60,000. All employees work 40 hours per week and are paid $500 per week. Data preparation of a form requires 15 minutes, and data entry of a form requires 10 minutes. Each week, an employee is assigned to either data entry or data preparation. The IRS must complete processing all forms by the end of week 5 and wants to minimize the cost of accomplishing this goal. Assume that all workers are full-time employees and that the IRS will have the same number of employees each week. Assume that all employees are capable of performing data preparation and data entry. Determine how many workers should be working and how the workers should allocate their hours during the next five weeks.

112. Based on Robichek et al. (1965). The Korvair Department Store has $100,000 in available cash. At the beginning of each of the next six months, Korvair will receive revenues and pay bills as listed in the file P04_112.xlsx. It is clear that Korvair will have a short-term cash flow problem until the store receives revenues from the Christmas shopping season. To solve this problem, Korvair must borrow money. At the beginning of July, the company takes out a six-month loan. Any money borrowed for a six-month period must be paid back at the end of December along with 9% interest (early payback does not reduce the total interest of the loan). Korvair can also meet cash needs through month-to-month borrowing. Any money borrowed for a one-month period incurs an interest cost of 4% per month. Determine how Korvair can minimize the cost of paying its bills on time.

113. Mackk Engine produces diesel trucks. New government emission standards have dictated that the average pollution emissions of all trucks produced in the next three years cannot exceed 10 grams per truck. Mackk produces two types of trucks. Each type 1 truck sells for $20,000, costs $15,000 to manufacture, and emits 15 grams of pollution. Each type 2 truck sells for $17,000, costs $14,000 to manufacture, and emits 5 grams of pollution. Production capacity limits total truck production during each year to at most 320 trucks. The maximum numbers of each truck type that can be sold during each of the next three years are listed in the file P04_113.xlsx. Demand can be met from previous production or the current year's production. It costs $2000 to hold one truck (of any type) in inventory for one year. Determine how Mackk can maximize its profit during the next three years.

114. Each hour from 10 A.M. to 7 P.M., Bank One receives checks and must process them. Its goal is to process all checks the same day they are received. The bank has 13 check processing machines, each of which can process up to 500 checks per hour. It takes one worker to operate each machine. Bank One hires both full-time and part-time workers. Full-time workers work 10 A.M. to 6 P.M., 11 A.M. to 7 P.M., or 12 P.M. to 8 P.M. and are paid $160 per day. Part-time workers work either 2 P.M. to 7 P.M. or 3 P.M. to 8 P.M. and are paid $75 per day. The numbers of checks received each hour are listed in the file P04_114.xlsx. In the interest of maintaining continuity, Bank One believes that it must have at least three full-time workers under contract. Develop a work schedule that processes all checks by 8 P.M. and minimizes daily labor costs.

115. Owens-Wheat uses two production lines to produce three types of fiberglass mat. The demand requirements (in tons) for each of the next four months are shown in the file P04_115.xlsx. If it were dedicated entirely to the production of one product, a line 1 machine could produce either 20 tons of type 1 mat or 30 tons of type 2 mat during a month. Similarly, a line 2 machine could produce either 25 tons of type 2 mat or 28 tons of type 3 mat. It costs $5000 per month to operate a machine on line 1 and $5500 per month to operate a machine on line 2. A cost of $2000 is incurred each time a new machine is purchased, and a cost of $1000 is incurred if a machine is retired from service. At the end of each month, Owens would like to have at least 50 tons of each product in inventory. At the beginning of month 1, Owens has five machines on line 1 and eight machines on line 2. Assume the per-ton cost of holding either product in inventory for one month is $5.
   a. Determine a minimum cost production schedule for the next four months.
   b. There is an important aspect of this situation that cannot be modeled by linear programming. What is it? (Hint: If Owens makes product 1 and product 2 on line 1 during a month, is this as efficient as making just product 1 on line 1?)

116. Rylon Corporation manufactures Brute cologne and Chanelle perfume. The raw material needed to manufacture each type of fragrance can be purchased for $60 per pound. Processing 1 pound of raw material requires 1 hour of laboratory time. Each pound of processed raw material yields 3 ounces of Regular Brute cologne and 4 ounces of Regular Chanelle perfume. Regular Brute can be sold for $140 per ounce and Regular Chanelle for $120 per ounce. Rylon also has the option of further processing Regular Brute and Regular Chanelle to produce Luxury Brute, sold at $360 per ounce, and Luxury Chanelle, sold at $280 per ounce. Each ounce of Regular Brute

processed further requires an additional 3 hours of laboratory time and a $40 processing cost and yields 1 ounce of Luxury Brute. Each ounce of Regular Chanelle processed further requires an additional 2 hours of laboratory time and a $40 processing cost and yields 1 ounce of Luxury Chanelle. Each year, Rylon has 6000 hours of laboratory time available and can purchase up to 4000 pounds of raw material.

   a. Determine how Rylon can maximize its profit. Assume that the cost of the laboratory hours is a fixed cost (so that it can be ignored for this problem).

   b. Suppose that 1 pound of raw material can be used to produce either 3 ounces of Brute or 4 ounces of Chanelle. How does your answer to part **a** change?

   c. Use SolverTable to determine how a change in the price of Luxury Chanelle changes the optimal profit.

   d. Use SolverTable to determine how simultaneous changes in lab time and raw material availability change the optimal profit.

   e. Use SolverTable to determine how a change in the extra lab time required to process Luxury Brute changes the optimal profit.

117. Sunco Oil has three different processes that can be used to manufacture various types of gasoline. Each process involves blending oils in the company's catalytic cracker. Running process 1 for an hour costs $20 and requires two barrels of crude oil 1 and three barrels of crude oil 2. The output from running process 1 for an hour is two barrels of gas 1 and one barrel of gas 2. Running process 2 for an hour costs $30 and requires one barrel of crude 1 and three barrels of crude 2. The output from running process 2 for an hour is three barrels of gas 2. Running process 3 for an hour costs $14 and requires two barrels of crude 2 and three barrels of gas 2. The output from running process 3 for an hour is two barrels of gas 3. Each month, 4000 barrels of crude 1, at $45 per barrel, and 7000 barrels of crude 2, at $55 per barrel, can be purchased. All gas produced can be sold at the following per-barrel prices: gas 1, $85; gas 2, $90; gas 3, $95. Determine how to maximize Sunco's profit (revenues less costs). Assume that only 2500 hours of time on the catalytic cracker are available each month.

118. Flexco produces six products in the following manner. Each unit of raw material purchased yields 4 units of product 1, 2 units of product 2, and 1 unit of product 3. Up to 1200 units of product 1 can be sold, and up to 300 units of product 2 can be sold. Demand for products 3 and 4 is unlimited. Each unit of product 1 can be sold or processed further. Each unit of product 1 that is processed further yields 1 unit of product 4. Each unit of product 2 can be

sold or processed further. Each unit of product 2 that is processed further yields 0.8 unit of product 5 and 0.3 unit of product 6.

   Up to 1000 units of product 5 can be sold, and up to 800 units of product 6 can be sold. Up to 3000 units of raw material can be purchased at $6 per unit. Leftover units of products 5 and 6 must be destroyed. It costs $4 to destroy each leftover unit of product 5 and $3 to destroy each leftover unit of product 6. Ignoring raw material purchase costs, the unit price and production cost for each product are listed in the file P04_118.xlsx. Determine a profit-maximizing production schedule for Flexco.

119. Each week, Chemco can purchase unlimited quantities of raw material at $6 per pound. Each pound of purchased raw material can be used to produce either input 1 or input 2. Each pound of raw material can yield 2 ounces of input 1, requiring 2 hours of processing time and incurring $2 in processing costs. Each pound of raw material can yield 3 ounces of input 2, requiring 2 hours of processing time and incurring $4 in processing costs. Two production processes are available. It takes 2 hours to run process 1, requiring 2 ounces of input 1 and 1 ounce of input 2. It costs $1 to run process 1. Each time process 1 is run, 1 ounce of product A and 1 ounce of liquid waste are produced. Each time process 2 is run requires 3 hours of processing time, 2 ounces of input 2, and 1 ounce of input 1. Each process 2 run yields 1 ounce of product B and 0.8 ounce of liquid waste. Process 2 incurs $8 in costs. Chemco can dispose of liquid waste in the Port Charles River or use the waste to produce product C or product D. Government regulations limit the amount of waste Chemco is allowed to dump into the river to 5000 ounces per week.

   Each ounce of product C costs $4 to produce and sells for $18. Producing 1 ounce of product C requires 1 hour of processing time, 2 ounces of input 1, and 0.8 ounce of liquid waste. Each ounce of product D costs $5 to produce and sells for $12. Producing 1 ounce of product D requires 1 hour of processing time, 2 ounces of input 2, and 1.2 ounces of liquid waste. At most, 7000 ounces of product A and 5000 ounces of product B can be sold each week, but weekly demand for products C and D is unlimited. Product A sells for $22 per ounce and product B sells for $24 per ounce. Each week, 25,000 hours of processing time are available. Determine how Chemco can maximize its weekly profit.

120. Bexter Labs produces three products: A, B, and C. Bexter can sell up to 2000 units of product A, up to 2500 units of product B, and up to 800 units of product C. Each unit of product C uses two units of A and three units of B and incurs $5 in processing costs. Products A and B are produced from either raw material 1 or raw material 2. It costs $6 to purchase and

process one unit of raw material 1. Each processed unit of raw material 1 yields two units of A and three units of B. It costs $3 to purchase and process a unit of raw material 2. Each processed unit of raw material 2 yields one unit of A and two units of B. The unit prices for the products are A, $5; B, $4; C, $25. The quality levels of each product are A, 8; B, 7; C, 6. The average quality level of the units sold must be at least 7. Determine how to maximize Bexter's profit.

121. Based on Franklin and Koenigsberg (1973). The city of Busville contains three school districts. The numbers of minority and nonminority students in each district are given in the file P04_121.xlsx. The local court has decided that each of the town's two high schools (Cooley High and Walt Whitman High) must have approximately the same percentage of minority students (within 5%) as the entire town. The distances (in miles) between the school districts and the high schools are also given in the same file. Each high school must have an enrollment of 300 to 500 students. Determine an assignment of students to schools that minimizes the total distance students must travel to school.

122. Based on Carino and Lenoir (1988). Brady Corporation produces cabinets. Each week, Brady requires 90,000 cubic feet of processed lumber. The company can obtain lumber in two ways. First, it can purchase lumber from an outside supplier and then dry it at the Brady kiln. Second, Brady can chop down trees on its land, cut them into lumber at its sawmill, and then dry the lumber at its kiln. The company can purchase grade 1 or grade 2 lumber. Grade 1 lumber costs $3 per cubic foot and when dried yields 0.7 cubic foot of useful lumber. Grade 2 lumber costs $7 per cubic foot and when dried yields 0.9 cubic foot of useful lumber. It costs the company $3 to chop down a tree. After being cut and dried, a log yields 0.8 cubic feet of lumber. Brady incurs costs of $4 per cubic foot of lumber it dries. It costs $2.50 per cubic foot of logs sent through the sawmill. Each week, the sawmill can process up to 35,000 cubic feet of lumber. Each week, up to 40,000 cubic feet of grade 1 lumber and up to 60,000 cubic feet of grade 2 lumber can be purchased. Each week, 40 hours of time are available for drying lumber. The time it takes to dry one cubic foot of lumber is as follows: grade 1, 2 seconds; grade 2, 0.8 second; log, 1.3 seconds. Determine how Brady can minimize the weekly cost of meeting its demand for processed lumber.

123. Based on Dobson and Kalish (1988). Chandler Enterprises produces two competing products, A and B. The company wants to sell these products to two groups of customers. The values each customer places on a unit of A and B are shown in the file P04_123.xlsx. Each customer will buy either product A or product B, but not both. A customer is willing to buy product A if she believes that the premium of product A is greater than or equal to the premium of product B and premium of product A is greater than or equal to 0. Here, the "premium" of a product is its value minus its price. Similarly, a customer is willing to buy B if she believes the premium of product B is greater than or equal to the premium of product A and the premium of product B is greater than or equal to 0. Group 1 has 1000 members, and group 2 has 1500 members. Chandler wants to set prices for each product to ensure that group 1 members purchase product A and group 2 members purchase product B. Determine how Chandler can maximize its revenue.

124. Based on Robichek et al. (1965). At the beginning of month 1, Finco has $4500 in cash. At the beginning of months 1, 2, 3, and 4, Finco receives certain revenues, after which it pays bills. (See the file P04_124.xlsx.) Any money left over can be invested for one month at the interest rate of 0.25% per month; for two months at 0.28% per month; for three months at 0.33% per month; or for four months at 0.37% per month. Determine an investment strategy that maximizes cash on hand at the beginning of month 5.

125. During each six-hour period of the day, the Bloomington Police Department needs at least the number of police officers shown in the file P04_125.xlsx. Police officers can be hired to work either 12 consecutive hours or 18 consecutive hours. Police officers are paid $15 per hour for each of the first 12 hours they work in a day and $23 per hour for each of the next six hours they work in a day. Determine how to minimize the cost of meeting Bloomington's daily police requirements.

126. Based on Glassey and Gupta (1978). A paper recycling plant processes box board, tissue paper, newsprint, and book paper into pulp that can be used to produce three grades of recycled paper. The prices per ton and the pulp contents of the four inputs are shown in the file P04_126.xlsx.

Two methods, de-inking and asphalt dispersion, can be used to process the four inputs into pulp. It costs $20 to de-ink a ton of any input. The process of de-inking removes 10% of the input's pulp, leaving 90% of the original pulp. It costs $15 to apply asphalt dispersion to a ton of material. The asphalt dispersion process removes 20% of the input's pulp. At most, 3000 tons of input can be run through the asphalt dispersion process or the de-inking process. Grade 1 paper can be produced only with newsprint or book paper pulp; grade 2 paper only with book paper, tissue paper, or box board pulp; and grade 3 paper only with newsprint, tissue paper, or box board pulp. To meet its current demands, the company needs 500 tons of pulp for grade 1 paper, 500 tons of pulp for grade 2 paper, and 600 tons of pulp for grade 3 paper. Determine how to minimize the cost of meeting the demands for pulp.

127. At the beginning of month 1, GE Capital has 50 million accounts. Of these, 40 million are paid up (0-due), 4 million are 1 month overdue (1-due), 4 million are 2 months overdue (2-due), and 2 million are 3 months overdue (3-due). After an account is more than 3 months overdue, it is written off as a bad debt. For each overdue account, GE Capital can either phone the cardholder, send a letter, or do nothing. A letter requires an average of 0.05 hour of labor, whereas a phone call requires an average of 0.10 hour of labor. Each month 500,000 hours of labor are available. We assume that the average amount of a monthly payment is $30. Thus, if a 2-due account remains 2-due, it means that 1 month's payment ($30) has been received, and if a 2-due account becomes 0-due, it means that 3 months' payments ($90) have been received. On the basis of thousands of accounts, DMMs (Delinquency Movement Matrices) shown in the file P04_127.xlsx have been estimated. For example, the top-left 0.60 entry in the first table means that 60% of all 1-due accounts that receive a letter become 0-due by the next month. The 0.10 and 0.30 values in this same row mean that 10% of all 1-due accounts remain 1-due after receiving a letter, and 30% of all 1-due accounts become 2-due after receiving a letter. Your goal is to determine how to allocate your workforce over the next four months to maximize the expected collection revenue received during that time. (*Note:* 0-due accounts are never contacted, which accounts for the lack of 0-due rows in the first two tables.)

128. Three bonds, as listed in the file P04_128.xlsx, are currently for sale. Each bond has a face value of $100. Every six months, starting six months from the current date and ending at the expiration date, each bond pays 0.5*(coupon rate)*(Face value). At the expiration date the face value is paid. For example, the second bond pays

- $2.75 six months from now
- $102.75 a year from now

Given the current price structure, the question is whether there is a way to make an infinite amount of money. To answer this, you need to look for an arbitrage. An *arbitrage* exists if there is a combination of bond sales and purchases today that yields

- a positive cash flow today
- nonnegative cash flows at all future dates

If such a strategy exists, then it is possible to make an infinite amount of money. For example, if buying 10 units of bond 1 today and selling 5 units of bond 2 today yielded, say, $1 today and nothing at all future

dates, you could make $k by purchasing 10k units of bond 1 today and selling 5k units of bond 2 today. You could also cover all payments at future dates from money received on those dates.

a. Show that an arbitrage opportunity exists for the bonds in the file P04_128.xlsx. (*Hint:* Set up an LP that maximizes today's cash flow subject to constraints that cash flow at each future date is nonnegative. You should get a "no convergence" message from Solver.)

b. Usually bonds are bought at an ask price and sold at a bid price. Consider the same three bonds as before and suppose the ask and bid prices are as listed in the same file. Show that these bond prices admit no arbitrage opportunities.

## Modeling Problems

129. You have been assigned to develop a model that can be used to schedule employees at a local fast-food restaurant. Assume that computer technology has advanced to the point where very large problems can be solved on a PC at the restaurant.

a. What data would you collect as inputs to your model?

b. Describe in words several appropriate objective functions for your model.

c. Describe in words the constraints needed for your model.

130. You have been assigned to develop a model that can be used to schedule the nurses working in a maternity ward.

a. What data would you collect as inputs to your model?

b. Describe in words several appropriate objective functions for your model.

c. Describe in words the constraints needed for your model.

131. Keefer Paper produces recycled paper from paper purchased from local offices and universities. The company sells three grades of paper: high-brightness paper, medium-brightness paper, and low-brightness paper. The high-brightness paper must have a brightness level of at least 90, the medium-brightness paper must have a brightness level of between 80 and 90, and the low-brightness paper must have a brightness level no greater than 80. Discuss how Keefer might use a blending model to maximize its profit.

132. In this chapter, we give you the cost of producing a product and other inputs that are used in the analysis. Do you think most companies find it easy to determine the cost of producing a product? What difficulties might arise?

133. Discuss how the aggregate planning model could be extended to handle a company that produces

several products on several types of machines. What information would you need to model this type of problem?

**134.** A large CPA firm currently has 100 junior staff members and 20 partners. In the long run—say, 20 years from now—the firm would like to consist of 130 junior staff members and 20 partners. During a given year, 10% of all partners and 30% of all junior staff members leave the firm. The firm can control the number of hires each year and the fraction of junior employees who are promoted to partner each year. Can you develop a personnel strategy that would meet the CPA firm's goals?

**135.** The worker scheduling model in this chapter was purposely made small (only seven changing cells). What would make a similar problem for a company like McDonald's much harder? What types of constraints would be required? How many changing cells (approximately) might there be?

**136.** Explain why it is problematic to include a constraint such as the following in an LP model for a blending problem:

$$\frac{\text{Total octane in gasoline 1 blend}}{\text{Barrels of gasoline 1 blended daily}} \geq 10$$

Saudi Arabia is a kingdom in the Middle East with an area of 865,000 square miles, occupying about four-fifths of the Arabian Peninsula. With a population of about 10 million, this Muslim and Arab state is generally recognized as being formed in 1927 when Ibn Sa'ud united the country and was acknowledged as the sovereign independent ruler. Summer heat is intense in the interior, reaching 124°F, but it is dry and tolerable in contrast to coastal regions and some highlands, which have high humidity during the summer. Winters (December through February) are cool, with the coldest weather occurring at high altitudes and in the far north. A minimum temperature recorded at at-Turayf in 1950 was 10°F, and it was accompanied by several inches of snow and an inch of ice on ponds. Average winter temperatures are 74°F at Jidda and 58°F at Riyadh (the capital city), which has an annual precipitation of 2.5 to 3 inches.

After oil was discovered in Bahrain in 1932, many companies turned to Saudi Arabia and started exploring. Thus, in 1937, the American Arabian Oil Company, Inc. (AMARCO), was formed as a joint venture between Standard Oil Company of California (SOCAL) and the Government of Saudi Arabia to explore, produce, and market any petroleum found in the country. The year before, a geologist from SOCAL had discovered a small quantity of oil in the Eastern Province at Dammam Dome, on which the oil company town of Dhahran is now built. It was just beginning to be developed when another discovery was made—of what was to prove to be the largest oil field in the world. Called the Ghamar field, it would start Saudi Arabia on the road to becoming a highly developed country in just a generation. Located about 50 miles inland from the western shores of the Persian Gulf, the Ghamar field is a structural accumulation along 140 miles of a north–south anticline. The productive area covers approximately 900 square miles, and the vertical oil column is about 1,300 feet. It is generally considered to have recoverable reserves of about 75 billion barrels of oil. Total proven reserves in Saudi Arabia are estimated at more than 500 billion barrels, enough for more than a hundred years of production.

[9] This case was written by William D. Whisler, California State University, Hayward.

Since 1950, Saudi Arabia has experienced greater and more rapid changes than it had in the several preceding centuries. For example, during this time, as skilled nationals became available, more and more of the exploration, drilling, refining, and other production activities came under the control of the country. SOCAL was left primarily with the marketing and transportation functions outside the country.

During the 1960s, AMARCO increased its profitability substantially by hiring Dr. George Dantzig, then of the University of California, as a consultant. He supervised the development and implementation of LP models to optimize the production of different types of crude oils, their refining, and the marketing of some of their principal products. As a result of this effort, an operations research (OR) department was started in the company with the responsibility of continuing to review the firm's operations to find other areas where costs might be decreased or profits increased by applications of OR.

Now attention is being focused on another aspect of one of the company's small California refinery operations: the production of three types of aviation gasoline from the Saudi Arabian crude oil available. Recently, the marketing of petroleum products to the airline industry has become a rather substantial portion of AMARCO's business. As shown in Figure 4.45, the three aviation gasolines, A, B, and C, are made by blending four feedstocks: Alkylate, Catalytic Cracked Gasoline, Straight Run Gasoline, and Isopentane.

In Table 4.14, TEL stands for tetraethyl lead, which is measured in units of milliliters per gallon (ml/gal). Thus, a TEL of 0.5 means there is 0.5 milliliter of tetraethyl lead per gallon of feedstock. Table 4.14 shows that TEL does influence the octane number but does not influence the Reid vapor pressure.

Each type of aviation gasoline has a maximum permissible Reid vapor pressure of 7. Aviation gasoline A has a TEL level of 0.5 ml/gal and has a minimum octane number of 80. The TEL level of aviation gasolines B and C is 4 ml/gal, but the former has a minimum octane number of 91, whereas the latter has a minimum of 100.

Assume that all feedstocks going into aviation gasoline A are leaded at a TEL level of 0.5 ml/gal and that those going into aviation gasolines B and C are leaded at a TEL level of 4 ml/gal. Table 4.15 gives the aviation gasoline data. A final condition is that marketing requires that the amount of aviation gas A produced be at least as great as the amount of aviation gas B.

Figure 4.45

**The Production of Aviation Gasoline**

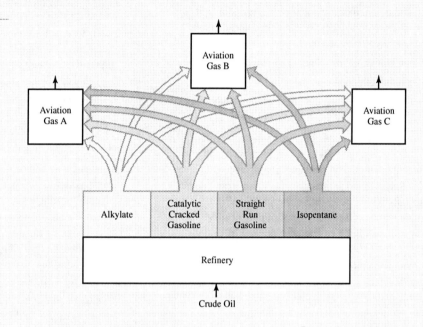

Table 4.14 Stock Availabilities[a]

| | | Feedstock | | |
| Characteristic | Alkylate | Catalytic Cracked Gasoline | Straight Run Gasoline | Isopentane |
|---|---|---|---|---|
| Reid Vapor Pressure | 5 | 8 | 4 | 20 |
| Octane Number | | | | |
|   If TEL is 0.5 | 94 | 83 | 74 | 95 |
|   If TEL is 4.0 | 107.5 | 93 | 87 | 108 |
| Available (Bbl/day) | 14,000 | 13,000 | 14,000 | 11,000 |
| Value ($/Bbl) | 17.00 | 14.50 | 13.50 | 14.00 |

[a]Some of the data in this case have been adapted from Walter W. Garvin, *Introduction to Linear Programming* (New York: McGraw-Hill, 1960), Chapter 5.

Table 4.15 Aviation Gasoline Data

| | Aviation Gasoline | | |
| Characteristic | A | B | C |
|---|---|---|---|
| Minimum requirements (Bbl/day) | 12,000 | 13,000 | 12,000 |
| Price ($/Bbl) | 15.00 | 16.00 | 16.50 |

## Questions

1. AMARCO's planners want to determine how the three grades of aviation gasoline should be blended from the available input streams so that the specifications are met and income is maximized. Develop an LP spreadsheet model of the company's problem.

2. Solve the linear programming model developed in Question 1.

*The following questions should be attempted only after Questions 1 and 2 have been answered correctly.*

3. Suppose that a potential supply shortage of Saudi Arabian petroleum products exists in the near future due to possible damage to AMARCO's oil production facilities from Iraqi attacks. This could cause the prices of the three types of aviation gasolines to double (while the values of the stocks remain the same, because they are currently on hand). How would this affect the refinery's operations? If, after current stocks are exhausted, additional quantities must be obtained at values double those given in Table 4.14, how might AMARCO's plans be affected?

4. Suppose that because of the new Iraqi crisis, the supply of alkylate is decreased by 1,800 bbl/day, catalytic cracked gas is decreased by 2,000 bbl/day, and straight run gasoline is decreased by 5,000 bbl/day. How does this affect AMARCO's operations?

5. AMARCO is considering trying to fill the aviation gasoline shortage created by the new Iraqi crisis by increasing its own production. If additional quantities of alkylate, catalytic cracked gasoline, straight run gasoline, and isopentane are available, should they be processed? If so, how much of them should be processed, and how do their values affect the situation?

6. Due to the uncertainty about both the U.S. economy and the world economy resulting from the Iraqi crisis, AMARCO's economists are considering doing a new market research study to reestimate the minimum requirement forecasts. With the economy continually weakening, it is felt that demand will decrease, possibly drastically, in the future. However, because such marketing research is expensive, management is wondering whether it would be worthwhile. That is, do changes in the minimum requirements have a significant effect on AMARCO's operations? What is the change in profit from an increase or a decrease in the minimum requirements? Over what ranges of demand do these profit changes apply?

7. Suppose that the Middle East crisis ends and a flood of oil fills the marketplace, causing the prices of aviation gasoline to drop to $10.00, $11.00, and $11.50, respectively, for A, B, and C. How would this affect the company's plans?

8. Suppose that the U.S. government is considering mandating the elimination of lead from aviation gasoline to decrease air pollution. This law would be based on new technology that allows jet engines to burn unleaded gasoline efficiently at any octane level. Thus, there would no longer be any need for constraints on octane level. How would such a new law affect AMARCO?

9. The Environmental Protection Agency is proposing regulations to decrease air pollution. It plans to improve the quality of aviation gasolines by decreasing the requirement on Reid vapor pressure from 7 to 6. Management is concerned about this regulation and wonders how it might affect AMARCO's profitability. Analyze and make a recommendation.

10. The Marketing Department indicates that AMARCO will be able to increase its share of the market substantially with a new contract being negotiated with a new customer. The difficulty is that this contract will require that the amount of aviation gas A plus the amount of B must be at least as great as the amount of C produced. Because aviation gasolines A and B are least profitable of the three, this could cause a big decrease in profit for the company. However, marketing indicates that this is a short-run view, because the "large" increase in market share with the concomitant long-run profit increases will more than offset the "temporary small decrease" in profits because of the additional restriction. What do you recommend? Why? ▥

American Office Systems, Inc., was established by the late R. J. Miller, Sr., in 1939. It started as an office supply store in Mountain View, California, and expanded slowly over the years into the manufacture of small office equipment, overhead projectors, and bookkeeping machines. In the 1950s, computers started eroding its market for bookkeeping machines, so the company diversified into the copy machine market. However, it never captured a large market share because bigger firms such as Xerox, Canon, Sharp, and A. B. Dick were so firmly entrenched.

A few years ago, American Office Systems' engineering staff developed an adapter that links a standard copy machine to personal computers, allowing a copy machine to be used as a laser printer, scanner, and fax. The adapters show great promise for both home and office use. However, the company is not well known by either the financial community or the copy machine market, principally due to its small size and rather lackluster record, so it could secure only $15 million in initial financial backing for the adapters. The $15 million was used to finance the construction of a small production facility and of administrative offices in 1994, and in 1995 production and sales began. Two versions of the adapter exist, one for PCs and one for Apple computers. The former sells for $175 and the latter for $200.

At the beginning of December 1995, Dr. R. J. Miller, II, the president, convened a meeting about the coming year's plans for the adapters. Rob Olsen, Vice President of Production, argued that production facilities should be expanded: "Until we have sufficient capacity to produce the adapters," he said, "there is no use advertising." Sue Williams, Director of Marketing, replied, "On the contrary, without any demand for the adapters, there is no reason to produce them. We need to focus on advertising first." J.T. Howell, the Comptroller, pointed out that Olsen and Williams were talking about the situation as if it only involved a decision between production and marketing: "Yes, funds need to be allocated between production and advertising. However, more important than both is the cash flow difficulty that the company has been experiencing. As you know, it was only yesterday that,

finally, I was able to secure a $750,000 line of credit for the coming year from Citibank. I might add that it is at a very favorable interest rate of 16%. This will partially solve our cash flow problems and it will have a big effect on both production and advertising decisions. In addition, there are financial and accounting factors that must be allowed for in any decision about the adapters." Olsen interjected, "Wow, this is more complicated than I anticipated originally. Before we make a decision, I think we ought to use some modern management science techniques to be sure that all the relevant factors are considered. Last week I hired Carlos Garcia from Stanford. He has a Master's degree in Operations Research. I think this would be a good project for him." However, Williams said that she thinks that an executive, judgmental decision would be much better. "Let's not get carried away with any of the quantitative mumbo-jumbo that Rob is always suggesting. Besides, his studies always take too much time and are so technical that no one can understand them. We need a decision by the end of next week." After listening to the discussion, Miller decided to appoint an executive action team to study the problem and make a recommendation at next week's meeting. "Rob and Sue, I want both of you to document your arguments in more detail. J.T., be more precise with your comments about the cash flow, accounting, and financial problems. And, by the way Rob, have Carlos look into a model to see if it might produce some insights."

Most of the $15 million initial financing was used to build a five-story building in Mountain View, south of San Francisco. Although currently only about 90% complete, it is being used. The first floor contains the production and shipping facilities plus a small storage area. A larger warehouse, already owned by the company, is located across the street. The other four floors of the building are for the engineering department (second floor), a research lab (third floor), and administration (top two floors). The production facility operates two shifts per day and has a production capacity of 30 PC adapters and 10 Apple adapters per hour. Olsen uses 20 production days per month in his planning. Usually there are a few more, but these are reserved for maintenance and repairs. The last stage of the initial construction will be finished by the beginning of the fourth quarter,

[10] This case was written by William D. Whisler, California State University, Hayward.

making the building 100% finished. This will increase the production capacity rates by 10%.

Howell normally does the company's financial planning monthly, and he assumes that cash flows associated with all current operating expenses, sales revenues (taking collections into account), advertising costs, loans from the line of credit, investments of excess cash in short-term government securities, and so forth, occur at the end of the corresponding month. Because he needs information for the meeting next week, however, he decides to do a rough plan on a quarterly basis. This means that all the just mentioned cash flows, and so on, will be assumed to occur at the end of the quarter. After the meeting, when more time is available, the plan will be expanded to a monthly basis. To get started, one of his senior financial analysts prepares the list of quarterly fixed operating expenses shown in Table 4.16. In addition, the accounting department calculates that the variable costs of the adapters are $100 each for the PC version and $110 each for the Apple version.

Table 4.16    Quarterly Fixed Operating Expenses

| Expense | Cost |
| --- | --- |
| Administrative expense | $1,500,000 |
| Fixed manufacturing costs | 750,000 |
| Sales agents' salaries | 750,000 |
| Depreciation | 100,000 |

At present, American Office Systems is experiencing a cash flow squeeze due to the large cash requirements of the startup of the adapter production, advertising, and sales costs. If excess cash is available in any quarter, however, Howell says that the company policy is to invest it in short-term government securities, such as treasury bills. He estimates that during the coming year these investments will yield a return of 6%.

Olsen asks Garcia to look into the production and inventory aspects of the situation first, because this area was his specialty at Stanford. Then he says that he wants him to think about a programming model that might integrate all components of the problem—production, sales, advertising, inventory,

accounting, and finance. A mixed-integer programming model appears to be the most appropriate; however, he asks Garcia to use linear programming as an approximation due to the time limitations and Williams's concern about his ideas always being too technical. "There will be more time after next week's meeting to refine the model," he says.

After discussions with Olsen and Williams, Garcia feels that something needs to be done to help the company handle the uncertainty surrounding future sales of the adapters. He points out that it is impossible to guarantee that the company will never be out of stock. However, it is possible to decrease shortages so that any difficulties associated with them would be small and not cause major disruptions or additional management problems, such as excess time and cost spent expediting orders. Thus, Garcia formulates an inventory model. To be able to solve the model, he has to check the inventory levels of the adapters currently on hand in the warehouse. From these quantities, he calculates that there will be 10,000 PC and 5,000 Apple adapters on hand at the beginning of 1996. Based on the results of the model, he recommends that a simple rule of thumb be used: production plus the end-of-period inventory for the adapters should be at least 10% larger than the estimated sales for the next period. This would be a safety cushion to help prevent shortages of the adapters. In addition, to provide a smooth transition to 1997, the inventory level plus production at the end of the fourth quarter of 1996 should be at least twice the maximum expected sales for that quarter. Garcia says that using these rules of thumb will minimize annual inventory costs. When explaining the inventory model to Olsen, Garcia emphasizes the importance of including inventory carrying costs as part of any analysis, even though such costs frequently are not out-of-pocket. He says that his analysis of data provided by the accounting department yielded a 1% per month inventory carry cost, and this is what he used in his model.

Sales during the first year (1995) for the adapters are shown in Table 4.17. Next year's sales are uncertain. One reason for the uncertainty is that they depend on the advertising. To begin the analysis,

Williams asks her marketing research analyst, Debra Lu, to estimate the maximum sales levels for the coming four quarters if no advertising is done. Since last year's sales of both models showed a steady increase throughout the year, Lu projects a continuation of the trend. She forecasts that the company will be able to sell any number of adapters up to the maximum expected sales amounts shown in Table 4.17.

Table 4.17   1995 Adapter Sales and Maximum Expected 1996 Sales

|  | 1995 Sales | | 1996 Maximum Expected Sales | |
| Quarter | PC Adapters | Apple Adapters | PC Adapters | Apple Adapters |
| --- | --- | --- | --- | --- |
| 1 | 5,000 | 1,000 | 9,000 | 1,800 |
| 2 | 6,000 | 1,200 | 10,000 | 2,000 |
| 3 | 7,000 | 1,400 | 11,000 | 2,200 |
| 4 | 8,000 | 1,600 | 12,000 | 2,400 |

Miller suggests that advertising in magazines such as *PC World* and *Home Office* will increase consumer awareness of both the company and the adapters. The next day, Williams has a meeting with several staff members of a San Francisco advertising agency. They show her recommendations for two types of ads (one for the PC adapters and one for the Apple adapters), give her cost information, and the estimated effectiveness of an advertising campaign. Armed with this information and some data from Lu, Williams prepares a brief report for Miller setting out her reasons for thinking that each $10 spent on advertising will sell an additional PC adapter; the same relationship holds true for the Apple adapter.

Based on an analysis of 1995 sales and accounts receivable, the accounting department determines that collection experience is as shown in Table 4.18. For example, 75% of the PC adapters sold in a quarter are paid for during the quarter, 20% are paid for during the following quarter, and 3% are paid for during the third quarter. The remaining 2% are written off and sold to a collection agency for $0.50 on the dollar.

Table 4.18   Collections

| Quarter | PC Adapters | Apple Adapters |
| --- | --- | --- |
| 1 | 0.75 | 0.80 |
| 2 | 0.20 | 0.11 |
| 3 | 0.03 | 0.05 |

## Questions

1.  Suppose that you are Garcia. Develop an LP spreadsheet model of the situation to help the executive action team make a decision about how to allocate funds between production and advertising so that all the cash flow, financial, accounting, marketing, inventory, and production considerations are taken into account and American Office Systems' profits are maximized. Use the data collected and the estimates made by the members of the executive action team.

2.  Solve the LP model formulated in Question 1.

*The executive action team has assembled to reconsider the plans for the adapters for the coming year. Garcia, who developed the LP model, concludes his presentation by saying, "As everyone can see, the model gives the optimal solution that maximizes profits. Since I have incorporated the estimates and assumptions that all of you made, clearly it is the best solution. No other alternative can give a higher profit." Even Williams, who initially was skeptical of using quantitative models for making executive-level decisions, is impressed and indicates that she will go along with the results.*

*Miller says, "Good work, Carlos! This is a complex problem but your presentation made it all seem so simple. However, remember that those figures you used were based on estimates made by all of us. Some were little better than guesses. What happens if they are wrong? In other words, your presentation has helped me get a handle on the problem we are facing, and I know that models are useful where hard, accurate data exist. However, with all the uncertainty in our situation and the many rough estimates made, it seems to me that I will still have to make a judgment call when it comes down to making a final decision. Also, there has been a new development. J.T. tells me that we might be able to get another $1 million* line of credit from a Bahamian bank. It will take a while to work out the details and maybe it will cost us a little. I am wondering if it is worth it. What would we do with the $1 million if we got it?" J. T. responds, "We really need the $1 million. But it is a drop in the bucket. My analysis shows that we really need another $8 million line of credit."

Analyze, as Garcia is going to do, the effect of uncertainty and errors on the results of Questions 1 and 2 by answering the following questions. They should be attempted only after Questions 1 and 2 have been answered correctly.

3. One area where assumptions were made is adapter price.

   a. What happens if the prices for the adapters are a little weak and they decrease to $173 for the PC version and $198 for the Apple version? Does this make any difference?

   b. What about decreases to $172 and $197, respectively, for the PC and Apple versions? Explain the answers in terms that Miller will understand.

   c. Suppose that American Office Systems can increase the price of the adapters to $180 and $205. How would this affect the original solution?

4. Another potential variable is adapter production cost.

   a. Suppose that an error was made in determining the costs of the adapters and that they really should have been $102 for the PC version and $112 for the Apple version. What is the effect of this error?

   b. What about costs of $105 and $115? Explain the answers in terms that Miller will understand.

5. Howell notes that one of the contributing factors to American Office Systems' cash squeeze is the slow collection of accounts receivable. He is considering adopting a new collection procedure recommended by a consulting company. It will cost $100,000 and will change the collection rates to those given in Table 4.19.

   a. Analyze the effect of this new collection policy and make a recommendation to Howell

about whether to implement the new procedure. As before, any accounts receivable not collected by the end of the third quarter will be sold to a collection agency for $0.50 on the dollar.

   b. Howell wonders whether switching to selling adapters for all cash is worth the effort. This would ameliorate the cash squeeze because it would eliminate not only the slow collections but also the use of the collection agency for accounts that remain unpaid after nine months. It would cost about $90,000 more than at present to implement the all-cash policy because the accounting system would need to be modified and personnel would have to be retrained. Analyze this possibility and make a recommendation to Howell.

Table 4.19   New Collections

| Quarter | PC Adapters | Apple Adapters |
|---------|-------------|----------------|
| 1 | 0.90 | 0.92 |
| 2 | 0.07 | 0.03 |
| 3 | 0.01 | 0.01 |

6. Yet another variable is advertising effectiveness.

   a. Suppose that Williams overestimated the effectiveness of advertising. It now appears that $100 is needed to increase sales by one adapter. How will this affect the original solution? Explain the answer in terms that Miller will understand.

   b. What happens if the required advertising outlay is $12.50 per additional adapter sold?

7. Suppose that the line of credit from Citibank that Howell thought he had arranged did not work out because of the poor financial situation of the company. The company can obtain one for the same amount from a small local bank; however, the interest rate is much higher, 24%. Analyze how this change affects American Office Systems.

8. The safety cushion for inventory is subject to revision.

   a. Suppose that Garcia finds a bug in his original inventory model. Correcting it results in a safety cushion of 15% instead of the 10% he suggested previously. Determine whether this is important.

b. What if the error is 20%? Explain the answers in terms that Miller will understand.

9. Production capacity is scheduled to increase by 10% in the fourth quarter.

a. Suppose that Miller is advised by the construction company that the work will not be finished until the following year. How will this delay affect the company's plans?

b. In addition to the delay in part a, suppose that an accident in the production facility damages some of the equipment so that the capacity is decreased by 10% in the fourth quarter. Analyze how this will affect the original solution.

10. Williams is worried about the accuracy of Lu's 1996 maximum expected sales forecasts. If errors in these forecasts have a big effect on the company profits, she is thinking about hiring a San Francisco marketing research firm to do a more detailed analysis. They would charge $50,000 for a study. Help Williams by analyzing what would happen if Lu's forecasts are in error by 1,000 for PC adapters and 200 for Apple adapters each quarter. Should she hire the marketing research firm?

11. a. To determine whether the extra $1 million line of credit is needed, analyze its effect on the original solution given in Question 2.

b. To fully understand the ramifications of the extra $1,000,000 line of credit, redo (1) Question 3b, (2) Question 4b, (3) Question 6a, and (4) Question 8b. Summarize your results.

c. What about Howell's claim that an extra $8,000,000 line of credit is necessary? Use that adjustment and redo Question 6a. ▨

akefield Corporation's oil trading desk buys and sells oil products (crude oil and refined fuels), options, and futures in international markets. The trading desk is responsible for buying raw material for Lakefield's refining and blending operations and for selling final products. In addition to trading for the company's operations, the desk also takes speculative positions. In speculative trades, the desk attempts to profit from its knowledge and information about conditions in the global oil markets.

One of the traders, Lisa Davies, is responsible for transactions in the cash market (as opposed to the futures or options markets). Lisa has been trading for several years and has seen the prices of oil-related products fluctuate tremendously. Figure 4.46 shows the prices of heating oil #2 and unleaded gasoline from January 1986 through July 1992. Although excessive volatility of oil prices is undesirable for most businesses, Lakefield's oil trading desk often makes substantial profits in periods of high volatility.

The prices of various oil products tend to move together over long periods of time. Because finished oil products are refined from crude oil, the prices of all finished products tend to rise if the price of crude increases. Because finished oil products are not perfect substitutes, the prices of individual products do not move in lockstep. In fact, over short time periods, the price movements of two products can have a low correlation. For example, in late 1989 and early 1990, there was a severe cold wave in the northeastern United States. The price of heating oil rose from $0.60 per gallon to over $1 per gallon. In the same time period, the price of gasoline rose just over $0.10 per gallon.

Davies believes that some mathematical analysis might be helpful to spot trading opportunities in the cash markets. The next section provides background about a few important characteristics of fuel oils, along with a discussion of the properties of blended fuels and some implications for pricing.

## Characteristics of Hydrocarbon Fuels

The many varieties of hydrocarbon fuels include heating oil, kerosene, gasoline, and diesel oil. Each type of fuel has many characteristics, for example, heat content, viscosity, freezing point, luminosity,

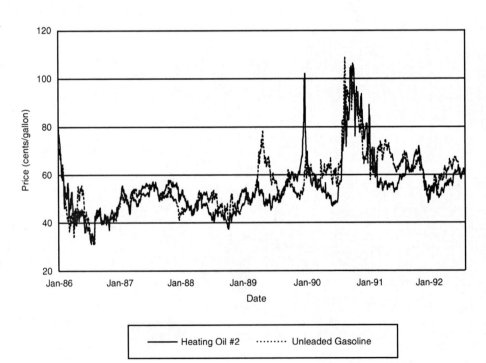

Figure 4.46

Price of Heating
Oil #2 and Unleaded
Gasoline

volatility (speed of vaporization), and so on. The relative importance of each characteristic depends on the intended use of the fuel. For example, octane rating is one of the most important characteristics of gasoline. Octane is a measure of resistance to ignition under pressure. An engine burning low-octane fuel is susceptible to "engine knock," which reduces its power output. Surprisingly, octane rating is more important than heat content for gasoline. In contrast, the most important characteristic of kerosene jet fuel is its heat content, but viscosity is also important. High-viscosity fuels do not flow as smoothly through fuel lines.

For the types of fuels Lisa Davies usually trades, the most important characteristics are density, viscosity, sulfur content, and flash point, which are described next. When trading and blending other fuels, characteristics besides these four are important to consider.

**Density**   The density of a substance is its mass per unit volume (e.g., grams per cubic centimeter). The density of water is 1 g/cc. A related measure is American Petroleum Institute gravity (API), which is measured in degrees. API is related to density by

$$API = \frac{141.5}{D} - 131.5$$

where $D$ is density measured in g/cc. Water has an API of $10°$. Note that density and API are *inversely* related.

The specifications for kerosene jet fuel are nearly identical for all civilian airlines worldwide. Kerosene jet fuel should have an API gravity between $37°$ and $51°$. Diesel fuel and heating oil are required to have an API not less than $30°$. API is important for controlling the flow of fuel in a combustion engine. It can also be used to limit the concentration of heavy hydrocarbon compounds in the fuel.

**Viscosity**   Viscosity refers to the resistance of a liquid to flow. A highly viscous liquid, such as ketchup or molasses, does not pour easily. Viscosity is measured by the amount of time a specified volume of liquid takes to flow through a tube of a certain diameter. It is commonly measured in units of centistokes (hundredths of stokes). Most fuel

specifications place upper limits on viscosity. Less viscous fuel flows easily through lines and atomizes easily for efficient combustion. More viscous fuels must be heated initially to reduce viscosity.

**Sulfur Content**   The content of sulfur is measured in percentage of total sulfur by weight. For example, a fuel with 2% sulfur content has 2 grams of sulfur for every 100 grams of fuel. Sulfur causes corrosion and abrasion of metal surfaces. Low sulfur content is important for maintaining the proper operation of equipment.

**Flash Point**   The flash point of a substance is the lowest temperature at which the substance ignites when exposed to a flame. The product description of kerosene jet fuel from the American Society for Testing and Materials specifies a flash point of at least $100°F$. The New York Mercantile Exchange futures contract for heating oil #2 specifies a flash point of at least $130°F$. Flash-point restrictions are often prescribed for safety reasons.

Table 4.20 gives a description of some fuels and their prices on a given day. In Table 4.20, the units of viscosity are centistokes, sulfur is given in percentage by weight, and flash point is in degrees Fahrenheit. For convenience, all prices in Table 4.20 are given in dollars per barrel. In practice, the prices of heating oil, gasoline, and kerosene jet fuel are typically quoted in cents per gallon. (There are 42 gallons in a barrel.)

### Blending Fuels

Because hydrocarbon fuels are made of similar compounds and have similar characteristics, a certain degree of substitutability exists among fuels. Different fuels can also be blended to form a new fuel. Next we describe how the characteristics of the individual fuels combine in the blended fuel.

Sulfur combines linearly by weight. This means, for example, that mixing equal weights of a 1% sulfur oil with a 3% sulfur oil produces a 2% sulfur oil. To a close approximation, sulfur combines linearly by volume (because the densities of oils are not very different). That is, combining 0.5 barrel of 1% sulfur oil with 0.5 barrel of 3% sulfur oil gives 1 barrel of very nearly 2% sulfur oil.

Table 4.20    Description of Available Fuels

| | Fuel 1<br>1% Sulfur<br>Fuel Oil | Fuel 2<br>3% Sulfur<br>Fuel Oil | Fuel 3<br>0.7% Sulfur<br>Fuel Oil | Fuel 4<br>Heating<br>Oil | Fuel 5<br>1% Vacuum<br>Gas Oil | Fuel 6<br>2% Vacuum<br>Gas Oil |
|---|---|---|---|---|---|---|
| API | 10.50 | 10.50 | 10.50 | 34.00 | 25.00 | 25.00 |
| Viscosity | 477.00 | 477.00 | 477.00 | 3.50 | 25.00 | 25.00 |
| Sulfur | 1.00 | 3.00 | 0.70 | 0.20 | 1.00 | 2.00 |
| Flash point | 140.00 | 140.00 | 140.00 | 130.00 | 200.00 | 200.00 |
| Price | 16.08 | 13.25 | 17.33 | 24.10 | 20.83 | 20.10 |

| | Fuel 7<br>0.5% Vacuum<br>Gas Oil | Fuel 8<br>Straight Run<br>(Low Sulfur) | Fuel 9<br>Straight Run<br>(High Sulfur) | Fuel 10<br>Kerosene<br>Jet Fuel | Fuel 11<br>Diesel<br>Fuel | Fuel 12<br><br>Slurry |
|---|---|---|---|---|---|---|
| API | 25.00 | 21.00 | 17.00 | 46.000 | 35.00 | −4.50 |
| Viscosity | 25.00 | 212.00 | 212.00 | 1.500 | 2.50 | 261.00 |
| Sulfur | 0.50 | 0.30 | 2.75 | 0.125 | 0.20 | 2.37 |
| Flash point | 200.00 | 250.00 | 250.00 | 123.000 | 150.00 | 109.00 |
| Price | 21.46 | 21.00 | 20.00 | 25.520 | 24.30 | 11.50 |

In general, to say that a certain property of oil combines linearly (by volume) means the following: Suppose $x_j$ barrels of oil $j$ (for $j = 1, 2, \ldots, n$) are blended together to form one barrel of oil; that is, $\sum_{j=1}^{n} x_j = 1$. Also suppose that $c_j$ is the measure of the property of oil $j$. Then if the property combines linearly, the measure of the property for the blended oil is a linear combination of the $c_j$'s; that is, $\sum_{j=1}^{n} c_j x_j$.

API gravity does not combine linearly, but density does combine linearly. For example, consider blending 0.5 barrel of oil that has a density of 0.8 g/cc with 0.5 barrel of oil with a density of 1.2 g/cc. The resulting barrel of oil has a density of 1.0 ($= 0.8[0.5] + 1.2[0.5]$). The 0.8 g/cc density oil has an API of 45.38 , and the 1.2 g/cc density oil has an API of $-13.58°$. If API combined linearly, the blended barrel of oil would have an API of $15.90°(= 45.38$ $[0.5] - 13.58 [0.5])$. However, an API of 15.90 corresponds to a density of 0.96 g/cc, not 1.0 g/cc.[11]

Viscosity, measured in centistokes, does not combine linearly. However, chemical engineers have

determined that viscosity can be transformed to another measure, called linear viscosity, which (nearly) combines linearly.[12] Similarly, flash points measured in degrees Fahrenheit do not combine linearly. But chemical engineers defined a new measure, termed linear flash point, which does combine linearly.[13] Table 4.21 summarizes the properties of the 12 fuels measured in units that combine linearly.

## Implications for Pricing

Sulfur in oil is a contaminant. Therefore, oil with a low sulfur content is more valuable than oil with a higher sulfur content, all other characteristics being equal. This relationship can be seen in Table 4.20 by comparing the prices of fuels 1, 2, and 3 and fuels 5,

---

[11] To convert API to density, use $D = 141.5/(API + 131.5)$.

[12] Let $vs$ represent viscosity measured in centistokes. Then linear viscosity, denoted $v$, is defined $v = \ln(\ln[vs + 0.08])$.

[13] Let $fp$ denote flash point measured in degrees Fahrenheit. Then linear flash point is defined $f = 10^{42}(fp + 460)^{-14.286}$. Empirical analysis of oil blending data confirms that the measure $f$ combines nearly linearly.

| | Fuel 1 1% Sulfur Fuel Oil | Fuel 2 3% Sulfur Fuel Oil | Fuel 3 0.7% Sulfur Fuel Oil | Fuel 4 Heating Oil | Fuel 5 1% Vacuum Gas Oil | Fuel 6 2% Vacuum Gas Oil |
|---|---|---|---|---|---|---|
| Density | 0.996 | 0.996 | 0.996 | 0.855 | 0.904 | 0.904 |
| Linear visc. | 1.819 | 1.819 | 1.819 | 0.243 | 1.170 | 1.170 |
| Sulfur | 1.000 | 3.000 | 0.700 | 0.200 | 1.000 | 2.000 |
| Linear flash | 204.800 | 204.800 | 204.800 | 260.400 | 52.500 | 52.500 |
| Price | 16.080 | 13.250 | 17.330 | 24.100 | 20.830 | 20.100 |

| | Fuel 7 0.5% Vacuum Gas Oil | Fuel 8 Straight Run (Low Sulfur) | Fuel 9 Straight Run (High Sulfur) | Fuel 10 Kerosene Jet Fuel | Fuel 11 Diesel Fuel | Fuel 12 Slurry |
|---|---|---|---|---|---|---|
| Density | 0.904 | 0.928 | 0.953 | 0.797 | 0.850 | 1.114 |
| Linear visc. | 1.170 | 1.678 | 1.678 | −.782 | −.054 | 1.716 |
| Sulfur | 0.500 | 0.300 | 2.750 | 0.125 | 0.200 | 2.370 |
| Linear flash | 52.500 | 18.500 | 18.500 | 308.800 | 161.700 | 437.000 |
| Price | 21.460 | 21.000 | 20.000 | 25.520 | 24.300 | 11.500 |

6, and 7. Lower-density oils are generally preferred to higher-density oils, because energy per unit mass is higher for low-density fuels, which reduces the weight of the fuel. Lower-viscosity oils are preferred because they flow more easily through fuel lines than oils with higher viscosities. High flash points are preferred for safety reasons. However, because flash point and linear flash point are inversely related, this means that oils with lower linear flash point are preferred to oils with higher linear flash point.

That fuels can be blended cheaply to form new fuels affects price as well. For example, fuel 2 and fuel 3 from Table 4.20 can be blended to form a fuel with the same API, viscosity, sulfur, and flash point as fuel 1. In particular, 0.1304 barrel of fuel 2 and 0.8696 barrel of fuel 3 can be blended to form one barrel of a new fuel, which, in terms of the four main characteristics, is identical to fuel 1. Because the cost of blending is small, prices combine nearly linearly. The cost to create the blended fuel is $16.80 per barrel ($16.80 = 0.1304[13.25] + 0.8696[17.33]). If the price of fuel 1 were greater than $16.80, say $17.10, Lisa Davies could create an arbitrage. She could buy fuels 2 and 3 in the appropriate proportions,

Lakefield Corporation could blend them together, and Davies could sell the blend at the price of fuel 1. The profit would be $0.30 per barrel minus any blending and transaction costs. However, the actual price of fuel 1 is $16.08, so this plan does not represent an arbitrage opportunity.

The no-arbitrage pricing principle is simply a generalization of the previous example. No arbitrage means that the price of any fuel must be less than or equal to the cost of any blend of fuels of equal or better quality. As mentioned earlier, better means larger API, lower viscosity, lower sulfur content, and higher flash point. In terms of linear properties, better means lower density, lower linear viscosity, lower sulfur content, and lower linear flash point. Any number of fuels (not just two) can be blended together.

Davies would like to develop a system that automatically checks the no-arbitrage pricing condition for all of the fuels. If the condition is violated, she would like to know the appropriate amounts of the fuels to buy to create the arbitrage, the profit per barrel of the blended fuel, and the characteristics of the blended fuel.

1. Suppose that 0.3 barrel of fuel 2, 0.3 barrel of fuel 3, and 0.4 barrel of fuel 4 are blended together. What is the cost of the blended fuel? What are the (linear) properties of the blended fuel (i.e., density, linear viscosity, sulfur content, and linear flash point)?

2. Using the data from Table 4.21, check whether any of the fuels violate the no-arbitrage pricing condition. If no fuel violates the condition, which fuel's price comes the closest to the no-arbitrage upper bound? If there is a violation, give the explicit recipe.

3. What modifications would you make to the analysis to account for blending costs?

4. What would be the important issues or steps involved in creating a real system for this problem? ▨

Daily trading volume in the foreign exchange markets often exceeds $1 trillion. Participants trade in the spot currency markets, forward markets, and futures markets. In addition, currency options, currency swaps, and other derivative contracts are traded. For simplicity, this case focuses on the spot currency market only. A spot currency transaction is simply an agreement to buy some amount of one currency using another currency.[14] For example, a British company might need to pay a Japanese supplier 150 million yen. Suppose that the spot yen/pound rate is 134.33. Then the British company could use the spot currency market to buy 150 million yen at a cost of 1,116,653 (=150,000,000/134.33) British pounds. A sample of today's cross-currency spot rates is given in the file Currency Rates.xlsx.

To continue the example, suppose the company canceled the order from the supplier and wanted to convert the 150 million yen back into British pounds. If the pound/yen spot rate is 0.00743, the company could use the 150 million yen to buy 1,114,500 (=150,000,000 × 0.00743) pounds. Note that the 1,114,500 pounds is less than the original 1,116,653 pounds. The difference is the result of the bid-offer spread: The price to buy yen (the bid price) is greater than the price to sell yen (the offer price). The bid-offer spread represents a transaction cost to the company.

Occasionally, market prices may become "out of line" in the sense that there are arbitrage opportunities. In this context, arbitrage means that there is a set of spot currency transactions that creates positive wealth but does not require any funds to initiate—that is, it is a "money pump." When such pure arbitrage opportunities exist, supply and demand forces will generally move prices to eliminate the opportunities. Hence, it is desirable to quickly identify arbitrage opportunities when they do exist and to take advantage of them to the greatest extent possible.

## Questions

1. Develop an LP model to determine whether there are any arbitrage opportunities with the spot currency rates given in the file. Note that an arbitrage opportunity could involve several currencies. If there is an arbitrage opportunity, your model should specify the exact set of transactions to achieve it.

2. Find the cross-currency rates in a recent newspaper—for example, in the *Wall Street Journal*—or on the Web at http://www.oanda.com/convert/classic. Check the numbers for an arbitrage opportunity. If you find one, do you think it represents a real arbitrage opportunity? Why or why not? ▩

---

[14]A spot transaction agreed to today is *settled* (i.e., the money changes hands) two business days from today. By contrast, a three-month forward transaction agreed to today is settled (approximately) three months from today.

# Optimization Models with Integer Variables

© JOSHUA GATES WEISBERG/EPA/Landov

## U.S. AIR FORCE SPACE COMMAND'S LONG-TERM INVESTMENT IN SPACE SYSTEMS

The U.S. Air Force created Space Command in 1982 to enhance defense in the United States through space superiority and to protect the country from weapons of mass destruction. Space Command spends billions of dollars each year procuring and deploying launch vehicles and space systems required for mission area tasks. Space Command included a space and missile optimization analysis (SAMOA) group to determine the best use of funds to satisfy requirements over a 24-year time horizon. Brown et al. (2003) describe their role within SAMOA to develop a strategic plan that was presented to Congress in 1999 as part of the military's overall strategic plan. The authors of the plan developed an integer programming model, similar to the capital budgeting model in this chapter but *much* larger in scale, to determine the best set of space projects to undertake over the planning horizon. This plan tries to achieve the various missions of Space Command as fully as possible while staying within budget. Like everything in the military, the model has an acronym, SCOUT (space command optimizer of utility toolkit).

The overall planning process within SAMOA is extremely complex. The process consists of five steps: (1) mission area assessment, (2) mission needs analysis, (3) mission solution analysis, (4) portfolio selection, and (5) refined portfolio selection. The first three steps are essentially steps 1 and 2 of the seven-step modeling process described in Chapter 1. They define the tasks that Space Command needs to accomplish to achieve its missions, the current and future needs—over and above what already exists—to accomplish these tasks, and the required data on candidate systems being considered. This data includes (1) scores for how each system, or combination of systems, accomplishes various tasks; (2) possible starting and ending times for the system (where the possible starting times can be several years in the future, due to the time required for R&D); (3) expected system costs, including development and operating costs over a multiyear period; (4) various precedence relations and side constraints (for example, system B can't be selected unless project A is selected); (5) launch requirements and per-launch costs; and (6) budgetary restrictions.

The last two steps build the integer programming model and then refine it, based on nonquantitative considerations such as political pressures. The model itself has a large number of integer decision variables. There is a binary variable for each combination of system and starting and ending years. For example, if a given system can be started any year from 2005 until 2010 and then end 12 years later, there will be six binary variables, one for each potential starting year. There are also integer variables for the number of launches by each selected system each year. The constraints are mostly of the "logical" type. For example, they enforce all precedence relations and side constraints, and they allow a given system to be selected for only one start-end time combination. The authors use a "penalty" type of objective. That is, the objective is total discounted penalty dollars, with penalties for not completely achieving task performance and for violating budget constraints. This allows solutions to violate constraints slightly (they can be slightly over budget, say), which provides more flexibility. The discounting is done in the usual financial sense, to make violations in the distant future less important.

The strategic master plan, the result of the SCOUT model and its refinements, was submitted to Congress in 1999. The plan included planned investments totaling about $310 billion. As the authors state, "This planning effort is the best-staffed and most scrupulously managed example of optimization-based capital planning that we have ever seen." Since 1999, Space Command and several other military units have used SAMOA to help create their strategic master plans. We recommend both this article and a somewhat more general article about military capital planning by Brown et al. (2004). They are both excellent examples of how integer programming can be used to make important and costly capital budgeting decisions. They also indicate the differences between capital budgeting in the military versus capital budgeting in civilian organizations. ∎

## 6.1 INTRODUCTION

In this chapter, we show how many complex problems can be modeled using 0–1 variables and other variables that are constrained to have integer values. A **0–1 variable** is a decision variable that must equal 0 or 1. Usually a 0–1 variable corresponds to an activity that either is or is not undertaken. If the 0–1 variable corresponding to the activity equals 1, the activity is undertaken; if it equals 0, the activity is not undertaken. A 0–1 variable is also called a **binary variable.**

Optimization models in which some or all of the variables must be integers are known as **integer programming** (IP) models.[1] In this chapter, we illustrate many of the modeling techniques that are needed to formulate IP models of complex situations. You should be aware that any optimization software, including Excel's Solver, typically has a much

---

[1] Many problems in the literature are described as mixed integer linear programming (MILP) models, which indicates that some of the changing cells are constrained to be integers and others are not. Although we do use this acronym, some of our models are of this type.

harder time solving an IP problem than an LP problem. In fact, optimization software is sometimes unable to solve an IP problem, even if the IP problem has an optimal solution. The reason is that these problems are inherently difficult to solve, no matter what software package is used. However, as you will see in this chapter, your ability to *model* complex problems increases tremendously when you use binary variables.

IP models come in many forms. You saw examples in Chapter 4 where the decision variables are naturally integer-valued. For example, when scheduling postal workers (Example 4.2), it is natural to require the numbers of workers to be integers. In examples like this, where you do not want certain decision variables to have fractional values, the problems are basically LP models with integer constraints added at the last minute. In many such examples, if you ignore the integer constraints, optimize with Solver, and then round to the nearest integers, the resulting integer solution will probably be close to optimal—although admittedly the rounded solution is sometimes not optimal.

The "integer" models in Chapter 4 are not the types of IP models discussed in this chapter. If it were simply a matter of adding integer constraints to decision variables, such as the numbers of workers, this chapter wouldn't be necessary. However, many inherently *nonlinear* problems can be transformed into linear models with the use of binary variables. These are the types of models discussed here. The clever use of binary variables allows you to solve many interesting and difficult problems that LP algorithms are incapable of solving.

*Except for binary or integer constraints on some changing cells, all models in this chapter are linear.*

All the models we analyze in this chapter are, aside from binary or integer changing cells, *linear* models. As in previous chapters, this means that the target cell is ultimately a sum of products of constants and changing cells. The same goes for both sides of all constraints. In other words, the models in this chapter *look* much like the models in the previous three chapters. The only difference is that some of the changing cells are now constrained to be binary or integer. Although the basic algorithm that Solver uses for such models is fundamentally different—because of the binary or integer variables—it still helps that the models are linear. They would present even more of a challenge to Solver if they were nonlinear.

## 6.2 OVERVIEW OF OPTIMIZATION WITH INTEGER VARIABLES

When Excel's Solver solves a linear model without integer constraints, it uses a very efficient algorithm, the simplex method, to perform the optimization. As discussed in Chapter 3, this method examines the "corner" points of the feasible region and returns the best corner point as the optimal solution. The simplex method is efficient because it typically examines only a very small fraction of the hundreds, thousands, or even millions of possible corner points before determining the best corner point.

*The branch and bound algorithm is a general approach to searching through all of the possibly millions of solutions in an efficient manner.*

The main difference between LP and IP models is that LP models allow fractional values, such as 0.137 and 5.3246, in the changing cells, whereas IP models allow only integer values in integer-constrained changing cells. In fact, if changing cells are constrained to be binary, the only allowable values are 0 and 1. This suggests that IP models should be easier to solve. After all, there are many fewer integer values in a given region than there are continuous values, so searching through the integers should be quicker—especially if their only possible values are 0 and 1. However, IP models are actually *much* more difficult to solve than LP models. Although several solution methods have been suggested by researchers—and new methods for specialized problems are still being developed—the solution procedure used by Solver is called **branch and bound.** Although we do not go into the details of the algorithms, we discuss briefly what Solver is doing. This way you can appreciate some of the difficulties with IP models, and you might also understand some of the messages you see in the status bar as Solver performs its optimization.

## Branch and Bound Algorithm

Consider a model with 100 changing cells, all constrained to be binary. Because there are
only two values for each binary variable—0 and 1—there are potentially $2^{100}$ feasible solutions, although many of these might not satisfy all of the constraints. Unfortunately, $2^{100}$ is
an *extremely* large number, so it would take even a very fast computer a long time to check
each one of them. Therefore, the naive method of **complete enumeration** of all possible
solutions—look at each solution and select the best—is usually impractical. However,
**implicit enumeration** is often very practical. This approach examines only a fraction of
all $2^{100}$ potential solutions, hopefully a very small fraction, and in doing so, it guarantees
that solutions not examined have no chance of being optimal. To see how this works, suppose you find a feasible solution with a profit of $500. If you can somehow guarantee that
each solution in a particular subset of solutions has profit *less* than $500, you can ignore
this entire subset because it cannot possibly contain the profit-maximizing solution.

This general idea is the essence of the branch and bound method used by Solver in IP
models. The *branching* part means that the algorithm systematically searches through the
set of all feasible integer solutions, creating branches, or subsets, of solutions as it goes.
For example, if $x_1$ is a binary variable, one branch might have $x_1 = 0$ and another branch
might have $x_1 = 1$. Then if $x_2$ is another binary variable, two branches might be created off
the $x_1 = 0$ branch—one with $x_2 = 0$ and one with $x_2 = 1$. By forming enough branches, all
possible integer solutions are eventually examined.

The key, however, is the *bounding* part of the algorithm. Suppose, for the sake of argument, that the objective is to maximize profit. Also, suppose that partway through the solution procedure, the *best* feasible integer solution so far has a profit of $500. This is called
the **incumbent** solution—the best so far. Its profit represents a *lower bound* on the optimal
profit. That is, the optimal solution must have a profit of at least $500 because a feasible
solution with a profit of $500 has already been found. This is the easy part of the bounding
procedure. The best profit found so far is a lower bound on the optimal profit.

The hard part is finding suitable *upper* bounds. Suppose you are considering the
branch where $x_1 = 0$ and $x_2 = 1$. If you can somehow show that *any* solution that has $x_1 = 0$
and $x_2 = 1$ can have profit at most $490 (or any number less than the incumbent, $500),
then you can ignore this entire branch. Therefore, the goal is to find an upper bound for
each branch that (1) is easy to find in terms of computing time and (2) is as low as possible. Why should it be as low an upper bound as possible? Suppose the upper bound you
find for the $x_1 = 0$ and $x_2 = 1$ branch is instead $515. Then because the incumbent's profit
is only $500, this branch might have some potential. That is, it might contain a solution
with profit greater than the incumbent. Therefore, you have to pursue it, which costs computer

time. The lower the upper bounds you can produce, the quicker you can "prune" branches and the faster the algorithm will be.

The procedures used to find good upper bounds for branches are beyond the level of this book. Fortunately, Solver takes care of the details. However, you should now understand some of the messages you will see in the status bar when you run Solver on IP models. For example, try running Solver on the cutting stock model in Example 6.7 with a tolerance of 0% (see below). You will see plenty of these messages, where the incumbent objective value and the current subproblem (or branch) quickly flash by. For this particular cutting stock model, Solver quickly finds an incumbent solution that is optimal, but it must examine literally thousands of branches before it can *guarantee* that the incumbent is optimal. After a minute or two of computing, we had seen results for 10,000 branches, and there was no end in sight.

## The Solver Tolerance Setting

The Solver Options dialog box contains a Tolerance setting, which is relevant for integer-constrained models. Excel's default tolerance is 5%. In Excel 2010, this setting, listed as Integer Optimality (%), is found under Solver Options in the dialog box shown in Figure 6.1. (In earlier versions, it was also under Solver Options but in a slightly different dialog box.) To explain the Tolerance option, we must first define the **LP relaxation** of an IP model. This is the same model as the IP model, except that all integer constraints are omitted. In particular, cells that are originally constrained to be binary are allowed under the LP relaxation to have *any* fractional values between 0 and 1 (including 0 and 1). The LP relaxation is typically easy to solve (using the simplex method), and it provides a bound for the IP model. For example, consider a maximization problem where the optimal solution to the LP relaxation has an optimal objective value of $48,214. Then the optimal objective for the original integer-constrained problem can be no larger than $48,214, so this value represents an upper bound for the original problem.

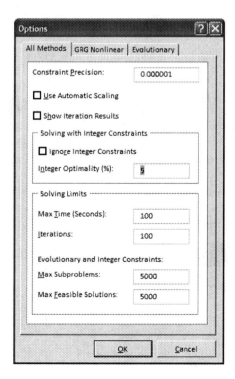

Figure 6.1

**Solver Tolerance Setting**

A tolerance setting of 5% means that Solver stops as soon as it finds a feasible (integer) solution to the IP model that is within 5% of the current upper bound. Initially, the optimal objective value of the LP relaxation serves as the upper bound. As Solver proceeds to find solutions that satisfy the integer constraints, it keeps updating the upper bound. The exact details need not concern you. The important point is that when Solver stops, it guarantees an integer solution that is within at least 5% of the optimal integer solution.

The implication is that if you set the tolerance to 0%, Solver will (in theory) run until it finds the *optimal* integer solution. So why isn't a tolerance setting of 0% always used? The reason is that for many IP models, especially large models, it can take Solver a long time to find the optimal solution (or guarantee that the best solution found so far *is* optimal). On the other hand, a solution that is *close* to optimal—within 5%, say—can often be found quickly. This explains why Frontline Systems, the developer of Solver, chose the default tolerance setting of 5%.

We use a tolerance of 0% for all the models in this chapter, simply to guarantee an optimal solution. Therefore, if you use the default tolerance of 5%, you *might* get a solution that is slightly worse than ours.

*To guarantee an optimal integer solution, change the Solver tolerance setting to 0%. The disadvantage of this approach is that Solver can run considerably longer on large models.*

### Solver Messages

Until now, the only Solver message you have probably seen is the final one that says an optimal solution has been found. When you run Solver on some of the difficult problems in this chapter, however, you might see a few other messages, such as those in Figures 6.2 and 6.3. These are due to Solver running a long time and bumping into the limits in the Options dialog box in Figure 6.1. If you see one of these types of messages, you have two options. First, you can change the options in Figure 6.1. (You would have to make this change before the Solver run.) For example, you could increase the Max Subproblems setting to a number greater than 5000. Second, you can simply click on Continue to let Solver run

**Figure 6.2**

Max Subproblems Warning

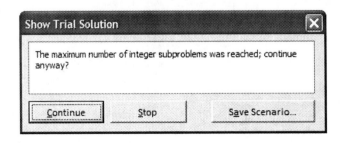

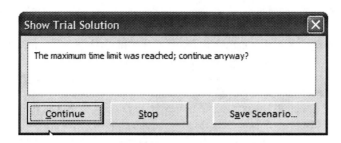

Figure 6.3

**Time Limit Warning**

**Show Trial Solution** ☒

The maximum time limit was reached; continue anyway?

Continue    Stop    Save Scenario...

longer. We recommend the second option. Actually, if you are tired of waiting and believe the incumbent solution is good enough, you can also click on Stop, in which case Solver gives you the option of saving the best solution so far.

## 6.3 CAPITAL BUDGETING MODELS

Perhaps the simplest binary IP model is the following capital budgeting example, which illustrates the go/no-go nature of many IP models.

**EXAMPLE**    **6.1 SELECTING INVESTMENTS AT TATHAM**

The Tatham Company is considering seven investments. The cash required for each investment and the net present value (NPV) each investment adds to the firm are listed in Table 6.1. The cash available for investment is $15,000. Tatham wants to find the investment policy that maximizes its NPV. The crucial assumption here is that if Tatham wants to take part in any of these investments, it must go all the way. It cannot, for example, go halfway in investment 1 by investing $2500 and realizing an NPV of $8000. In fact, if partial investments were allowed, you wouldn't need IP; you could use LP.

Table 6.1    Data for the Capital Budgeting Example

| Investment | Cash Required | NPV |
|:---:|:---:|:---:|
| 1 | $5,000 | $16,000 |
| 2 | $2,500 | $8,000 |
| 3 | $3,500 | $10,000 |
| 4 | $6,000 | $19,500 |
| 5 | $7,000 | $22,000 |
| 6 | $4,500 | $12,000 |
| 7 | $3,000 | $7,500 |

**Objective**    To use binary IP to find the set of investments that stays within budget and maximizes total NPV.

### WHERE DO THE NUMBERS COME FROM?

The initial required cash and the available budget are easy to obtain. Obtaining the NPV for each investment is undoubtedly harder. A time sequence of anticipated cash inflows from the investments and a discount factor are required. Simulation might even be used to estimate these NPVs. In any case, financial analysts must provide the estimations of the required NPVs.

## Solution

The variables and constraints required for this model are listed in Table 6.2. The most important part is that the decision variables must be binary, where a 1 means that an investment is chosen and a 0 means that it isn't. These variables cannot have fractional values such as 0.5, because partial investments are not allowed—the company has to go all the way or not at all. Note that the binary restriction is shown in the second row of the table, not the last row. This is done throughout the chapter. However, when you set up the Solver dialog box, you must add explicit binary constraints in the Constraints section.

Table 6.2   Variables and Constraints for the Capital Budgeting Model

| Input variables | Initial cash required for investments, NPVs from investments, budget |
|---|---|
| Decision variables (changing cells) | Whether to invest (binary variables) |
| Objective (target cell) | Total NPV |
| Other calculated variables | Total initial cash required |
| Constraints | Total initial cash required ≤ Budget |

### DEVELOPING THE SPREADSHEET MODEL

To form the spreadsheet model, which is shown in Figure 6.4, proceed as follows. (See the file Capital Budgeting 1.xlsx.)

Figure 6.4   Capital Budgeting Model

| | A | B | C | D | E | F | G | H | I | J | K | L | M |
|---|---|---|---|---|---|---|---|---|---|---|---|---|---|
| 1 | Tatham capital budgeting model | | | | | | | | | | Range names used: | | |
| 2 | | | | | | | | | | | Amount_invested | =Model!$B$14 | |
| 3 | Input data on potential investments | | | | | | | | | | Budget | =Model!$D$14 | |
| 4 | Investment | 1 | 2 | 3 | 4 | 5 | 6 | 7 | | | Investment_levels | =Model!$B$10:$H$10 | |
| 5 | Investment cost | $5,000 | $2,500 | $3,500 | $6,000 | $7,000 | $4,500 | $3,000 | | | Total_NPV | =Model!$B$17 | |
| 6 | NPV | $16,000 | $8,000 | $10,000 | $19,500 | $22,000 | $12,000 | $7,500 | | | | | |
| 7 | NPV per investment dollar | 3.20 | 3.20 | 2.86 | 3.25 | 3.14 | 2.67 | 2.50 | | | | | |
| 8 | | | | | | | | | | | | | |
| 9 | Decisions: whether to invest | | | | | | | | | | | | |
| 10 | Investment levels | 1 | 1 | 0 | 0 | 1 | 0 | 0 | | | | | |
| 11 | | | | | | | | | | | | | |
| 12 | Budget constraint | | | | | | | | | | | | |
| 13 | | Amount invested | | Budget | | | | | | | | | |
| 14 | | $14,500 | <= | $15,000 | | | | | | | | | |
| 15 | | | | | | | | | | | | | |
| 16 | Objective to maximize | | | | | | | | | | | | |
| 17 | Total NPV | $46,000 | | | | | | | | | | | |

**①  Inputs.** Enter the initial cash requirements, the NPVs, and the budget in the shaded ranges.

**②  0–1 values for investments.** Enter *any* trial 0–1 values for the investments in the Investment_levels range. Actually, you can even enter fractional values such as 0.5 in these cells. Solver's binary constraints will eventually force them to be 0 or 1.

**③  Cash invested.** Calculate the total cash invested in cell B14 with the formula

=SUMPRODUCT(B5:H5,Investment_levels)

Note that this formula sums the costs *only* for those investments with 0–1 variables equal to 1. To see this, think how the SUMPRODUCT function works when one of its ranges is a 0–1 range. It effectively sums the cells in the other range corresponding to the 1s.

**④  NPV contribution.** Calculate the NPV contributed by the investments in cell B17 with the formula

=SUMPRODUCT(B6:H6,Investment_levels)

Again, this sums only the NPVs of the investments with 0–1 variables equal to 1.

*A SUMPRODUCT formula, where one of the ranges is a 0–1 range, just sums the values in the other range that correspond to the 1s.*

The Solver dialog box appears in Figure 6.5. The objective is to maximize the total NPV, subject to staying within the budget. However, the changing cells must be *constrained* to be 0–1. Fortunately, Solver makes this simple, as shown in Figure 6.6. You add a constraint with Investments_levels in the left box and choose the *bin* option in the middle box. The word "binary" in the right box is then added automatically. Note that if *all* changing cells are binary, you do not need to check the Non-Negative option (because 0 and 1 are certainly nonnegative), but you should still choose the Simplex LP method if the model is linear, as it is here.[2]

### Discussion of the Solution

The optimal solution in Figure 6.4 indicates that Tatham can obtain a maximum NPV of $46,000 by selecting investments 1, 2, and 5. These three investments consume only $14,500 of the available budget, with $500 left over. However, this $500 is not enough—because of the "investing all the way" requirement—to invest in any of the remaining investments.

If Tatham's investments are ranked on the basis of NPV per dollar invested (see row 7 of Figure 6.4), the ranking from best to worst is 4, 1, 2, 5, 3, 6, 7. Using your economic

---

[2] All the models in this chapter satisfy two of the three properties of linear models in Chapter 3: proportionality and additivity. Even though they clearly violate the third assumption, divisibility, which precludes integer constraints, they are still considered linear by Solver. Therefore, you should still choose the Simplex LP method.

intuition, you might expect the investments to be chosen in this order—until the budget runs out. However, the optimal solution does not do this. It selects the second-, third-, and fourth-best investments, but it ignores the best. To understand why it does this, imagine investing in the order from best to worst, according to row 7, until the budget allows no more. By the time you have invested in investments 4, 1, and 2, you will have consumed $13,500 of the budget, and the remainder, $1500, is not sufficient to invest in any of the rest. This strategy provides an NPV of only $43,500. A smarter strategy, the optimal solution from Solver, gains you an extra $2500 in NPV.

## Sensitivity Analysis

SolverTable can be used on models with binary variables exactly as you have used it in previous models.[3] Here you can use it to see how the total NPV varies as the budget increases. Select the Budget cell as the single input cell, allow it to vary from $15,000 to $25,000 in increments of $1000, and keep track of the total NPV, the amount of the budget used, and the binary variables. The results are given in Figure 6.7. Clearly, Tatham can achieve a larger NPV with a larger budget, but as the numbers and the chart show, each extra $1000 of budget does *not* have the same effect on total NPV. The first $1000 increase to the budget adds $3500 to total NPV, the next two $1000 increases add $4000 each, the next two

Figure 6.7

Sensitivity to Budget

| | A | B | C | D | E | F | G | H | I | J |
|---|---|---|---|---|---|---|---|---|---|---|
| 1 | Oneway analysis for Solver model in Model worksheet | | | | | | | | | |
| 2 | | | | | | | | | | |
| 3 | Budget (cell $D$14) values along side, output cell(s) along top | | | | | | | | | |
| 4 | | Investment_levels_1 | Investment_levels_2 | Investment_levels_3 | Investment_levels_4 | Investment_levels_5 | Investment_levels_6 | Investment_levels_7 | Amount_invested | Total_NPV |
| 5 | $15,000 | 1 | 1 | 0 | 0 | 1 | 0 | 0 | $14,500 | $46,000 |
| 6 | $16,000 | 0 | 1 | 0 | 1 | 1 | 0 | 0 | $15,500 | $49,500 |
| 7 | $17,000 | 1 | 1 | 1 | 1 | 0 | 0 | 0 | $17,000 | $53,500 |
| 8 | $18,000 | 1 | 0 | 0 | 1 | 1 | 0 | 0 | $18,000 | $57,500 |
| 9 | $19,000 | 0 | 1 | 1 | 1 | 1 | 0 | 0 | $19,000 | $59,500 |
| 10 | $20,000 | 0 | 1 | 0 | 1 | 1 | 1 | 0 | $20,000 | $61,500 |
| 11 | $21,000 | 1 | 1 | 0 | 1 | 1 | 0 | 0 | $20,500 | $65,500 |
| 12 | $22,000 | 1 | 0 | 1 | 1 | 1 | 0 | 0 | $21,500 | $67,500 |
| 13 | $23,000 | 1 | 0 | 0 | 1 | 1 | 1 | 0 | $22,500 | $69,500 |
| 14 | $24,000 | 1 | 1 | 1 | 1 | 1 | 0 | 0 | $24,000 | $75,500 |
| 15 | $25,000 | 1 | 1 | 0 | 1 | 1 | 1 | 0 | $25,000 | $77,500 |
| 16 | | | | | | | | | | |
| 17 | | | | | | | | | | |

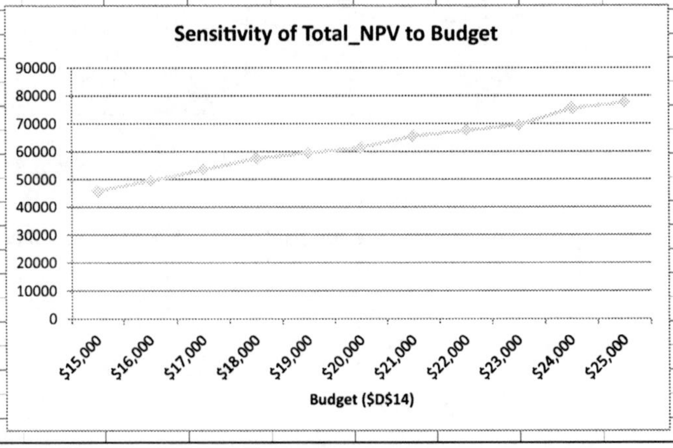

[3] As mentioned in Chapter 4, Solver's sensitivity report is not even available for models with integer constraints because the mathematical theory behind the report changes significantly when variables are constrained to be integers.

$1000 increases add $2000 each, and so on. Note also how the selected investments vary a lot as the budget increases. This somewhat strange behavior is due to the "lumpiness" of the inputs and the all-or-nothing nature of the problem.

**Effect of Solver Tolerance Setting**

When the Tolerance setting is 5% instead of 0%, Solver's solution might not be optimal, but it will be close.

To illustrate the effect of the Solver Tolerance setting, compare the SolverTable results in Figure 6.8 with those in Figure 6.7. Each is for the Tatham capital budgeting model, but Figure 6.8 uses Solver's default tolerance of 5%, whereas Figure 6.7 uses a tolerance of 0%. The three shaded cells in Figure 6.8 indicate *lower* total NPVs than the corresponding cells in Figure 6.7. In these three cases, Solver stopped short of finding the true optimal solutions because it found solutions within the 5% tolerance and then quit. (You might get slightly different results. It depends on the starting solution in your model.)

**Figure 6.8**

**Results with Tolerance at 5%**

| | A | B | C | D | E | F | G | H | I | J |
|---|---|---|---|---|---|---|---|---|---|---|
| 1 | Oneway analysis for Solver model in Model worksheet | | | | | | | | | |
| 2 | | | | | | | | | | |
| 3 | Budget (cell $D$14) values along side, output cell(s) along top | | | | | | | | | |
| 4 | | Investment_levels_1 | Investment_levels_2 | Investment_levels_3 | Investment_levels_4 | Investment_levels_5 | Investment_levels_6 | Investment_levels_7 | Amount_invested | Total_NPV |
| 5 | $15,000 | 1 | 1 | 0 | 0 | 1 | 0 | 0 | $14,500 | $46,000 |
| 6 | $16,000 | 0 | 1 | 0 | 1 | 1 | 0 | 0 | $15,500 | $49,500 |
| 7 | $17,000 | 1 | 1 | 1 | 1 | 0 | 0 | 0 | $17,000 | $53,500 |
| 8 | $18,000 | 1 | 0 | 0 | 1 | 1 | 0 | 0 | $18,000 | $57,500 |
| 9 | $19,000 | 0 | 1 | 1 | 1 | 1 | 0 | 0 | $19,000 | $59,500 |
| 10 | $20,000 | 1 | 0 | 1 | 0 | 1 | 1 | 0 | $20,000 | $60,000 |
| 11 | $21,000 | 1 | 1 | 0 | 1 | 1 | 0 | 0 | $20,500 | $65,500 |
| 12 | $22,000 | 1 | 1 | 0 | 1 | 1 | 0 | 0 | $20,500 | $65,500 |
| 13 | $23,000 | 0 | 1 | 0 | 1 | 1 | 1 | 1 | $23,000 | $69,000 |
| 14 | $24,000 | 1 | 1 | 1 | 1 | 1 | 0 | 0 | $24,000 | $75,500 |
| 15 | $25,000 | 1 | 1 | 0 | 1 | 1 | 1 | 0 | $25,000 | $77,500 |
| 16 | | | | | | | | | | |
| 17 | | | | | This is with Solver's tolerance at 5%. The | | | | | |
| 18 | | | | | three gray cells are *larger* than on the | | | | | |
| 19 | | | | | previous sheet, which indicates that they | | | | | |
| 20 | | | | | are not optimal. | | | | | |

## MODELING ISSUES

1. The following modifications of the capital budgeting example can be handled easily. You are asked to explore similar modifications in the problems.

   ▨ Suppose that at most two projects can be selected. In this case, you should add a constraint that the sum of the 0–1 variables for the investments is less than or equal to 2. This constraint is satisfied if zero, one, or two investments are chosen, but it is violated if three or more investments are chosen.

   ▨ Suppose that if investment 2 is selected, then investment 1 must also be selected. In this case, you should add a constraint saying that the 0–1 variable for investment 1 is greater than or equal to the 0–1 variable for investment 2. This constraint rules out the one possibility that is not allowed—where investment 2 is selected but investment 1 is not.

   ▨ Suppose that either investment 1 or investment 3 (or both) *must* be selected. In this case, you should add a constraint that the *sum* of the 0–1 variables for investments

1 and 3 must be greater than or equal to 1. This rules out the one possibility that is not allowed—where both of these 0–1 variables are 0, so that neither investment is selected.

2. Capital budgeting models with multiple periods can also be handled. Figure 6.9 shows one possibility. (See the Capital Budgeting 2.xlsx file.) The costs in rows 5 and 6 are *both* incurred if any given investment is selected. Now there are two budget constraints, one in each year, but otherwise the model is exactly as before. Note that some investments can have a cost of 0 in year 1 and a positive cost in year 2. This effectively means that these investments are undertaken in year 2 rather than year 1. Also, it is easy to modify the model to incorporate costs in years 3, 4, and so on.

**Figure 6.9  A Two-Period Capital Budgeting Model**

| | A | B | C | D | E | F | G | H | I | J | K | L |
|---|---|---|---|---|---|---|---|---|---|---|---|---|
| 1 | Tatham two-period capital budgeting model | | | | | | | | | Range names used: | | |
| 2 | | | | | | | | | | Amount_invested | =Model!$B$14:$B$15 | |
| 3 | Input data on potential investments | | | | | | | | | Budget | =Model!$D$14:$D$15 | |
| 4 | Investment | 1 | 2 | 3 | 4 | 5 | 6 | 7 | | Investment_levels | =Model!$B$10:$H$10 | |
| 5 | Year 1 cost | $5,000 | $2,500 | $3,500 | $6,500 | $7,000 | $4,500 | $3,000 | | Total_NPV | =Model!$B$18 | |
| 6 | Year 2 cost | $2,000 | $1,500 | $2,000 | $0 | $500 | $1,500 | $0 | | | | |
| 7 | NPV | $16,000 | $8,000 | $10,000 | $20,000 | $22,000 | $12,000 | $8,000 | | | | |
| 8 | | | | | | | | | | | | |
| 9 | Decisions: whether to invest | | | | | | | | | | | |
| 10 | Investment levels | 1 | 1 | 0 | 1 | 0 | 0 | 0 | | | | |
| 11 | | | | | | | | | | | | |
| 12 | Budget constraints | | | | | | | | | | | |
| 13 | | Amount invested | | Budget | | | | | | | | |
| 14 | | $14,000 | <= | $14,000 | | | | | | | | |
| 15 | | $3,500 | <= | $4,500 | | | | | | | | |
| 16 | | | | | | | | | | | | |
| 17 | Objective to maximize | | | | | | | | | | | |
| 18 | Total NPV | $44,000 | | | | | | | | | | |

3. If Tatham could choose a *fractional* amount of an investment, you could maximize its NPV by deleting the binary constraint. The optimal solution to the resulting LP model has a total NPV of $48,714. All of investments 1, 2, and 4, and 0.214 of investment 5 are chosen.[4] Note that there is no way to round the changing cell values from this LP solution to obtain the optimal IP solution. Sometimes the solution to an IP model *without* the integer constraints bears little resemblance to the optimal IP solution.

4. Any IP model involving 0–1 variables with only one constraint is called a **knapsack problem.** Think of the problem faced by a hiker going on an overnight hike. For example, imagine that the hiker's knapsack can hold only 14 pounds, and she must choose which of several available items to take on the hike. The benefit derived from each item is analogous to the NPV of each project, and the weight of each item is analogous to the cash required by each investment. The single constraint is analogous to the budget constraint—that is, only 14 pounds can fit in the knapsack. In a knapsack problem, the goal is to get the most value in the knapsack without overloading it. ▨

## ADDITIONAL APPLICATIONS

### Impact of Check Sequencing on NSF (Not Sufficient Funds) Fees

Apte et al. (2004) report an interesting application in the banking industry that can be modeled very much like the classical knapsack problem. When a bank receives checks on a customer's account, it can process these in any order. If the total of these checks is greater

---

[4]If you try this with the Capital Budgeting 1.xlsx file, delete the binary constraint, but don't forget to constrain the Investment_levels range to be nonnegative and less than or equal to 1.

than the customer's checking balance, the order in which the checks are processed can affect the *number* of checks that cannot be honored. For each such check that bounces, the bank charges the customer an NSF fee of about $20 on average. For example, suppose the customer's balance is $200, and checks in the amounts $150, $100, $75, and $25 are presented. If the bank processes them in low-to-high order, then there is only one NSF fee, for the $150 check. However, if it processes them in high-to-low order, there is an NSF fee for each of the three smallest checks. This is *not* a small problem. There is some evidence that by using high-to-low order rather than the opposite, the banking industry stands to gain as much as $1.5 *billion* annually in extra NSF fees. At the time of the article, banks were involved in several lawsuits brought by customers who claimed that the deliberate use of high-to-low order is an unfair practice. ∎

## PROBLEMS

*Solutions for problems whose numbers appear within a colored box can be found in the Student Solutions Files. Refer to this book's preface for purchase information.*

### Skill-Building Problems

1. In the capital budgeting model in Figure 6.4, we supplied the NPV for each investment. Suppose instead that you are given only the streams of cash inflows from each investment shown in the file P06_01.xlsx. This file also shows the cash requirements and the budget. You can assume that (1) all cash outflows occur at the beginning of year 1, (2) all cash inflows occur at the ends of their respective years, and (3) the company uses a 10% discount rate for calculating its NPVs. Which investments should the company select?

2. Solve the previous problem using the input data in the file P06_02.xlsx.

3. Solve Problem 1 with the extra assumption that the investments can be grouped naturally as follows: 1–4, 5–8, 9–12, 13–16, and 17–20.
   a. Find the optimal investments when at most one investment from each group can be selected.
   b. Find the optimal investments when at least one investment from each group must be selected. (If the budget isn't large enough to permit this, increase the budget to a larger value.)

4. Solve the following modifications of the capital budgeting model in Figure 6.4. (Solve each part independently of the others.)
   a. Suppose that at most two of projects 1 through 5 can be selected.
   b. Suppose that if investment 1 is selected, then investment 3 must also be selected.
   c. Suppose that at least one of investments 6 and 7 *must* be selected.
   d. Suppose that investment 2 can be selected only if *both* investments 1 and 3 are selected.

5. In the capital budgeting model in Figure 6.4, investment 4 has the largest ratio of NPV to cash requirement, but it is not selected in the optimal solution. How much NPV will be lost if Tatham is *forced* to select investment 4? Answer by solving a suitably modified model.

6. As it currently stands, investment 7 in the capital budgeting model in Figure 6.4 has the lowest ratio of NPV to cash requirement, 2.5. Keeping this same ratio, can you change the cash requirement and NPV for investment 7 so that it *is* selected in the optimal solution? Does this lead to any general insights? Explain.

7. Suppose in the capital budgeting model in Figure 6.4 that each investment requires $2000 during year 2, and only $5000 is available for investment during year 2.
   a. Assuming that available money uninvested at the end of year 1 cannot be used during year 2, what combination of investments maximizes NPV?
   b. Suppose that any uninvested money at the end of year 1 is available for investment in year 2. Does your answer to part **a** change?

8. Expand and then solve the capital budgeting model in Figure 6.4 so that 20 investments are now possible. You can make up the data on cash requirements, NPVs, and the budget, but use the following guidelines:
   - The cash requirements and NPVs for the various investments can vary widely, but the ratio of NPV to cash requirement should be between 2.5 and 3.5 for each investment.
   - The budget should allow somewhere between 5 and 10 of the investments to be selected.

### Skill-Extending Problems

9. The models in this chapter are often called *combinatorial* models because each solution is a combination of the various 0–1 values, and only a finite number of such combinations exist. For the capital budgeting model in Figure 6.4, there are seven investments, so there are $2^7 = 128$ possible solutions (some of which are infeasible). This is a fairly large number, but not *too* large. Solve the model *without* Solver by listing all 128 solutions. For each, calculate the total cash requirement and

total NPV for the model. Then manually choose the one that stays within the budget and has the largest NPV.

10. Make up an example, as described in Problem 8, with 20 possible investments. However, do it so the ratios of NPV to cash requirement are in a very tight range, from 3.0 to 3.2. Then use Solver to find the optimal solution when the Solver tolerance is set to its default value of 5%, and record the solution. Next, solve again with the tolerance set to 0%. Do you get the same solution? Try this on a few more instances of the model, where you keep changing the inputs. The question is whether the tolerance setting matters in these types of "close call" problems.

## 6.4 FIXED-COST MODELS

In many situations, a cost is incurred if an activity is undertaken at any *positive* level. This cost is independent of the level of the activity and is known as a *fixed cost* (or *fixed charge*). Here are three examples of fixed costs:

- The construction of a warehouse incurs a fixed cost that is the same whether the warehouse is built with a low- or a high-capacity level.

- A cash withdrawal from a bank incurs a fixed cost, independent of the size of the withdrawal.

- A machine that is used to produce several products must be set up for the production of each product. Regardless of the batch size produced, the same fixed cost (lost production due to the setup time) is incurred.

In these examples, a fixed cost is incurred if an activity is undertaken at any positive level, whereas no fixed cost is incurred if the activity is not undertaken at all. Although it might not be obvious, this feature makes the problem inherently *nonlinear*, which means that a straightforward application of LP is not possible. However, a clever use of 0–1 variables can result in a model with linear constraints and a linear objective.

*Unless you use binary variables to handle the logic, fixed-cost models are nonlinear and difficult to solve.*

It is important to realize that the type of model discussed here and throughout the rest of the chapter (except for Example 6.7) is fundamentally different from the previous capital budgeting model and the integer-constrained models in Chapter 4. You do not simply create an LP model and then add integer constraints. Instead, you use 0–1 variables to *model the logic*. The logic in this section is that if a certain activity is done at any *positive* level, a fixed cost is incurred. However, no fixed cost is incurred if the activity is not done at all. Your first instinct might be to handle such logic with IF functions. However, Solver cannot handle IF functions predictably. This is not really a weakness of Solver. These types of problems are inherently difficult. Fortunately, Solver *is* able to handle linear models with binary variables, so this is the approach you should take whenever possible. The appropriate use of 0–1 variables allows you to solve a whole new class of difficult problems. The following example is typical.

### FUNDAMENTAL INSIGHT

#### Binary Variables for Modeling

Binary variables are often used to transform a nonlinear model into a linear (integer) model. For example, a fixed cost is not a linear function of the level of some activity; it is either incurred or it isn't incurred. This type of on-off behavior is difficult for nonlinear solvers to handle. However, this behavior can often be handled easily when binary variables are used to make the model linear. Still, large models with many binary variables can be difficult to solve. One approach is to solve the model without integer constraints and then round fractional values to the nearest integer (0 or 1). Unfortunately, this approach is typically not very good because the rounded solution is often infeasible, and even if it is feasible, its objective value can be considerably worse than the optimal objective value.

EXAMPLE  6.2 TEXTILE MANUFACTURING AT GREAT THREADS

The Great Threads Company is capable of manufacturing shirts, shorts, pants, skirts, and jackets. Each type of clothing requires that Great Threads have the appropriate type of machinery available. The machinery needed to manufacture each type of clothing must be rented at the weekly rates shown in Table 6.3. This table also lists the amounts of cloth and labor required per unit of clothing, as well as the selling price and the unit variable cost for each type of clothing. In a given week, 4000 labor hours and 4500 square yards (sq yd) of cloth are available. The company wants to find a solution that maximizes its weekly profit.

**Table 6.3**  Data for the Great Threads Example

|  | Rental Cost | Labor Hours | Cloth (sq yd) | Selling Price | Unit Variable Cost |
|---|---|---|---|---|---|
| Shirts | $1500 | 2.0 | 3.0 | $35 | $20 |
| Shorts | $1200 | 1.0 | 2.5 | $40 | $10 |
| Pants | $1600 | 6.0 | 4.0 | $65 | $25 |
| Skirts | $1500 | 4.0 | 4.5 | $70 | $30 |
| Jackets | $1600 | 8.0 | 5.5 | $110 | $35 |

**Objective**   To develop a linear model with binary variables that can be used to maximize the company's profit, correctly accounting for fixed costs and staying within resource availabilities.

### WHERE DO THE NUMBERS COME FROM?

Except for the fixed costs, this is the same basic problem as the product mix problem (Examples 3.1 and 3.2) in Chapter 3. Therefore, the same discussion there about input variables applies here. The fixed costs are the given rental rates for the machinery.

## Solution

*Fixed costs imply that the proportionality assumption of linear models no longer holds.*

The variables and constraints required for this model are listed in Table 6.4. First, note that the cost of producing $x$ shirts during a week is 0 if $x = 0$, but it is $1500 + 20x$ if $x > 0$. This cost structure violates the proportionality assumption (discussed in Chapter 3) that is needed for a linear model. If proportionality were satisfied, the cost of making, say, 10 shirts would be double the cost of making 5 shirts. However, because of the fixed cost, the total cost of making 5 shirts is $1600, and the cost of making 10 shirts is only $1700. This violation of proportionality requires you to resort to 0–1 variables to obtain a *linear* model. These 0–1 variables allow you to model the fixed costs correctly.

**Table 6.4**  Variables and Constraints for the Fixed-Cost Model

| Input variables | Fixed rental costs, resource usages (labor hours, cloth) per unit of clothing, selling prices, unit variable costs, resource availabilities |
|---|---|
| Decision variables (changing cells) | Whether to produce any of each type of clothing (binary), how much of each type of clothing to produce |
| Objective (target cell) | Profit |
| Other calculated variables | Resources used, upper limits on amounts to produce, total revenue, total variable cost, total fixed cost |
| Constraints | Amount produced ≤ Logical upper limit (capacity)<br>Resources used ≤ Resources available |

## DEVELOPING THE SPREADSHEET MODEL

The spreadsheet model, shown in Figure 6.10, can be developed as follows. (See the file Fixed Cost Manufacturing.xlsx.)

Figure 6.10   **Fixed-Cost Clothing Model**

| | A | B | C | D | E | F | G | H | I | J | K |
|---|---|---|---|---|---|---|---|---|---|---|---|
| 1 | Great Threads fixed cost clothing model | | | | | | | | Range names used: | | |
| 2 | | | | | | | | | Effective_capacity | =Model!$B$18:$F$18 | |
| 3 | Input data on products | | | | | | | | Rent_equipment | =Model!$B$14:$F$14 | |
| 4 | | Shirts | Shorts | Pants | Skirts | Jackets | | | Profit | =Model!$B$29 | |
| 5 | Labor hours/unit | 2 | 1 | 6 | 4 | 8 | | | Resource_available | =Model!$D$22:$D$23 | |
| 6 | Cloth (sq. yd.)/unit | 3 | 2.5 | 4 | 4.5 | 5.5 | | | Resource_used | =Model!$B$22:$B$23 | |
| 7 | | | | | | | | | Units_produced | =Model!$B$16:$F$16 | |
| 8 | Selling price/unit | $35 | $40 | $65 | $70 | $110 | | | | | |
| 9 | Variable cost/unit | $20 | $10 | $25 | $30 | $35 | | | | | |
| 10 | Fixed cost for equipment | $1,500 | $1,200 | $1,600 | $1,500 | $1,600 | | | | | |
| 11 | | | | | | | | | | | |
| 12 | Production plan, constraints on capacity | | | | | | | | | | |
| 13 | | Shirts | Shorts | Pants | Skirts | Jackets | | | | | |
| 14 | Rent equipment | 0 | 1 | 0 | 0 | 1 | | | | | |
| 15 | | | | | | | | | | | |
| 16 | Units produced | 0 | 965.52 | 0 | 0 | 379.31 | | | | | |
| 17 | | <= | <= | <= | <= | <= | | | | | |
| 18 | Effective capacity | 0.00 | 1800.00 | 0.00 | 0.00 | 500.00 | | | | | |
| 19 | | | | | | | | | | | |
| 20 | Constraints on resources | | | | | | | | | | |
| 21 | | Resource used | | Available | | | | | | | |
| 22 | Labor hours | 4000.00 | <= | 4000 | | | | | | | |
| 23 | Cloth | 4500.00 | <= | 4500 | | | | | | | |
| 24 | | | | | | | | | | | |
| 25 | Monetary outputs | | | | | | | | | | |
| 26 | Revenue | $80,345 | | | | | | | | | |
| 27 | Variable cost | $22,931 | | | | | | | | | |
| 28 | Fixed cost for equipment | $2,800 | | | | | | | | | |
| 29 | Profit | $54,614 | ← Objective to maximize | | | | | | | | |

**①   Inputs.** Enter the given inputs in the blue ranges.

**②   Binary values for clothing types.** Enter *any* trial values for the 0–1 variables for the various clothing types in the Rent_equipment range. For example, if you enter a 1 in cell C14, you are implying that the machinery for making shorts is rented and its fixed cost is incurred.

**③   Production quantities.** Enter *any* trial values for the numbers of the various clothing types produced in the Units_produced range. At this point, you could enter "illegal" values, such as 0 in cell B14 and a positive value in cell B16. (This is illegal because it implies that the company produces some shirts but avoids the fixed cost of the machinery for shirts.) However, Solver will eventually disallow such illegal combinations.

**④   Labor and cloth used.** In cell B22 enter the formula

=SUMPRODUCT(B5:F5,Units_produced)

to calculate total labor hours, and copy this to cell B23 for cloth.

**⑤   Effective capacities.** Now comes the tricky part of the model. You need to ensure that if any of a given type of clothing is produced, its 0–1 variable equals 1. This ensures that the model incurs the fixed cost of renting the machine for this type of clothing. You could easily implement these constraints with IF statements. For example, to implement the constraint for shirts, you could enter the following formula in cell B14:

=IF(B16>0,1,0)

However, Excel's Solver is unable to deal with IF functions predictably. Therefore, you should instead model the fixed-cost constraints as shown in Inequality (6.1).

Shirts produced ≤ Maximum capacity × (0–1 variable for shirts)        **(6.1)**

Similar inequalities exist for the other types of clothing.

Here is the logic behind Inequality (6.1). If the 0–1 variable for shirts is 0, then the right-hand side of the inequality is 0, which means that the left-hand side must be 0—no shirts can be produced. That is, if the 0–1 variable for shirts is 0 so that no fixed cost for shirts is incurred, Inequality (6.1) does not allow Great Threads to "cheat" and produce a positive number of shirts. On the other hand, if the 0–1 variable for shirts is 1, the inequality is certainly true and is essentially redundant. It simply states that the number of shirts produced must be no greater than the *maximum* number that could be produced. Inequality (6.1) rules out the one case it should rule out—namely, that Great Threads produces shirts but avoids the fixed cost.

To implement Inequality (6.1), you need a maximum capacity—an upper limit on the number of shirts that *could* be produced. To obtain this, suppose the company puts all of its resources into producing shirts. Then the number of shirts that can be produced is limited by the smaller of

$$\frac{\text{Available labor hours}}{\text{Labor hours per shirt}}$$

and

$$\frac{\text{Available square yards of cloth}}{\text{Square yards of cloth per shirt}}$$

Therefore, the smaller of these—the most limiting—can be used as the maximum needed in Inequality (6.1).

To Implement this logic, calculate the effective capacity for shirts in cell B18 with the formula

`=B14*MIN($D$22/B5,$D$23/B6)`

Then copy this formula to the range C18:F18 for the other types of clothing.[5] By the way, this MIN formula causes no problems for Solver because it involves only input cells, not *changing* cells.

**⑥ Monetary values.** Calculate the total sales revenue and the total variable cost by entering the formula

`=SUMPRODUCT(B8:F8,Units_produced)`

in cell B26 and copying it to cell B27. Then calculate the total fixed cost in cell B28 with the formula

`=SUMPRODUCT(B10:F10,Rent_equipment)`

Note that this formula sums the fixed costs only for those products with 0–1 variables equal to 1. Finally, calculate the total profit in cell B29 with the formula

`=B26-B27-B28`

## USING SOLVER

The Solver dialog box is shown in Figure 6.11. The objective is to maximize profit, subject to using no more labor hours or cloth than are available and ensuring that production is less than or equal to effective capacity. The key is that this effective capacity is 0 if the machinery for a given type of clothing is not rented. As usual, you should check the Non-Negative option, select the Simplex LP method, and set the tolerance to 0 (under Solver Options).

---

[5] Why not set the upper limit on shirts equal to a huge number like 1,000,000? The reason is that Solver works most efficiently when the upper limit is as tight—that is, as low—as possible. A tighter upper limit means fewer potential feasible solutions for Solver to search through. Here's an analogy. If you were trying to locate a criminal, which would be easier: (1) if you were told that he was somewhere in Texas, or (2) if you were told he was somewhere in Dallas?

Figure 6.11

Solver Dialog Box
for the Fixed-Cost
Model

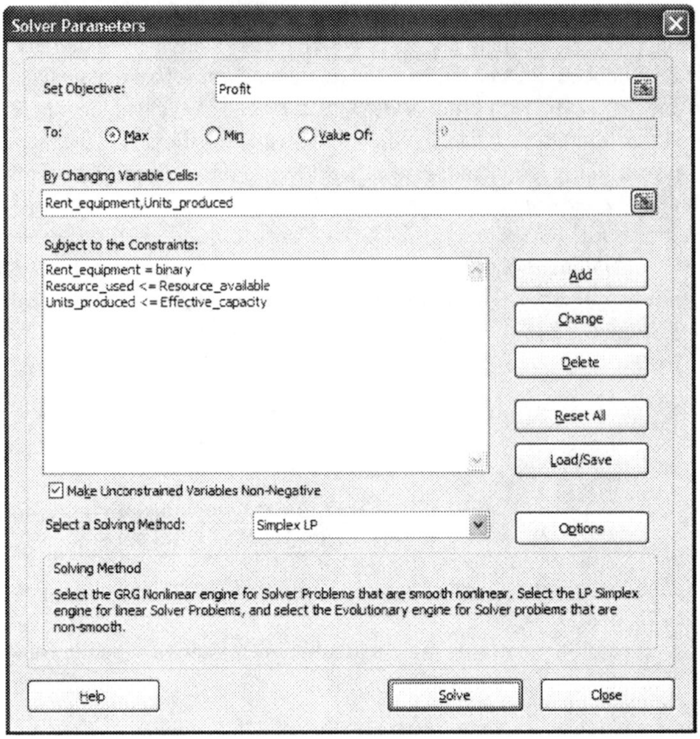

Although Solver finds the optimal solution automatically, you should understand the effect of the logical upper bound constraint on production. It rules out a solution such as the one shown in Figure 6.12. This solution calls for a positive production level of pants but does not incur the fixed cost of the pants equipment. The logical upper bound constraint rules this out because it prevents a positive value in row 16 if the corresponding binary value in row 14 is 0. In other words, if the company wants to produce some pants, the constraint in Inequality (6.1) forces the associated binary variable to be 1, thus incurring the fixed cost for pants.

Note that Inequality (6.1) does *not* rule out the situation you see for skirts in Figure 6.12, where the binary value is 1 and the production level is 0. However, Solver will never choose this type of solution as optimal. Solver recognizes that the binary value in this case can be changed to 0, so that no skirt equipment is rented and its fixed cost is not incurred.

*There is no point to set-
ting a binary variable
equal to 1—and Solver
will never do it—unless
there is positive produc-
tion of that product.*

### Discussion of the Solution

The optimal solution in Figure 6.10 indicates that Great Threads should produce about 966 shorts and 379 jackets, but no shirts, pants, or skirts. The total profit is $54,614. Note that the 0–1 variables for shirts, pants, and skirts are all 0, which forces production of these products to be 0. However, the 0–1 variables for shorts and jackets, the products that are produced, are 1. This ensures that the fixed cost of producing shorts and jackets is included in the total cost.

It might be helpful to think of this solution as occurring in two stages. In the first stage, Solver determines which products to produce—in this case, shorts and jackets only. Then in the second stage, Solver determines how *many* shorts and jackets to produce. If you know that the company plans to produce shorts and jackets only, you could then ignore the fixed costs and determine the best production quantities with the same types of product mix models discussed in Chapter 3. Of course, these two stages—deciding which products

Figure 6.12   An Illegal (and Nonoptimal) Solution

|   | A | B | C | D | E | F |
|---|---|---|---|---|---|---|
| 1 | **Great Threads fixed cost clothing model** | | | | | |
| 2 | | | | | | |
| 3 | **Input data on products** | | | | | |
| 4 | | Shirts | Shorts | Pants | Skirts | Jackets |
| 5 | Labor hours/unit | 2 | 1 | 6 | 4 | 8 |
| 6 | Cloth (sq. yd.)/unit | 3 | 2.5 | 4 | 4.5 | 5.5 |
| 7 | | | | | | |
| 8 | Selling price/unit | $35 | $40 | $65 | $70 | $110 |
| 9 | Variable cost/unit | $20 | $10 | $25 | $30 | $35 |
| 10 | Fixed cost for equipment | $1,500 | $1,200 | $1,600 | $1,500 | $1,600 |
| 11 | | | | | | |
| 12 | **Production plan, constraints on capacity** | | | | | |
| 13 | | Shirts | Shorts | Pants | Skirts | Jackets |
| 14 | Rent equipment | 0 | 1 | 0 | 1 | 1 |
| 15 | | | | | | |
| 16 | Units produced | 0 | 500.00 | 450.00 | 0 | 100.00 |
| 17 | | <= | <= | <= | <= | <= |
| 18 | Effective capacity | 0.00 | 1800.00 | 0.00 | 1000.00 | 500.00 |
| 19 | | | | | | |
| 20 | **Constraints on resources** | | | | | |
| 21 | | Resource used | | Available | | |
| 22 | Labor hours | 4000.00 | <= | 4000 | | |
| 23 | Cloth | 3600.00 | <= | 4500 | | |
| 24 | | | | | | |
| 25 | **Monetary outputs** | | | | | |
| 26 | Revenue | $60,250 | | | | |
| 27 | Variable cost | $19,750 | | | | |
| 28 | Fixed cost for equipment | $4,300 | | | | |
| 29 | Profit | $36,200 | ← | Objective to maximize | | |

*Because of fixed costs, the optimal solution might call for only a small subset of products to be produced. Only extra side constraints can force more products to be produced.*

to produce and how many of each to produce—are interrelated, and Solver determines both of them in its solution process.

The Great Threads management might not be too excited about producing shorts and jackets only. Suppose the company wants to ensure that at least three types of clothing are produced at positive levels. One approach is to add another constraint—namely, that the sum of the 0–1 values in row 14 is greater than or equal to 3. You can check, however, that when this constraint is added and Solver is run, the 0–1 variable for skirts becomes 1, but no skirts are produced. Shorts and jackets are more profitable than skirts, so only shorts and jackets are produced (see Figure 6.13). The new constraint forces Great Threads to rent an extra piece of machinery (for skirts), but it doesn't force the company to use it. To force the company to produce some skirts, you also need to add a constraint on the value in E16, such as E16>=100. Any of these additional constraints will cost Great Threads money, but if, as a matter of policy, the company wants to produce more than two types of clothing, this is its only option.

## Sensitivity Analysis

Because the optimal solution currently calls for only shorts and jackets to be produced, an interesting sensitivity analysis is to see how much incentive is required for other products to be produced. One way to check this is to increase the selling price for a nonproduced product such as skirts in a one-way SolverTable. We did this, keeping track of all binary variables and profit, with the results shown in Figure 6.14. When the selling price for skirts is $85 or less,

Figure 6.13 **The Great Threads Model with Extra Constraint**

| | A | B | C | D | E | F | G | H | I |
|---|---|---|---|---|---|---|---|---|---|
| 1 | Great Threads fixed cost clothing model | | | | | | | | |
| 2 | | | | | | | | | |
| 3 | Input data on products | | | | | | | | |
| 4 | | Shirts | Shorts | Pants | Skirts | Jackets | | | |
| 5 | Labor hours/unit | 2 | 1 | 6 | 4 | 8 | | | |
| 6 | Cloth (sq. yd.)/unit | 3 | 2.5 | 4 | 4.5 | 5.5 | | | |
| 7 | | | | | | | | | |
| 8 | Selling price/unit | $35 | $40 | $65 | $70 | $110 | | | |
| 9 | Variable cost/unit | $20 | $10 | $25 | $30 | $35 | | | |
| 10 | Fixed cost for equipment | $1,500 | $1,200 | $1,600 | $1,500 | $1,600 | | | |
| 11 | | | | | | | | | |
| 12 | Production plan, constraints on capacity | | | | | | | | |
| 13 | | Shirts | Shorts | Pants | Skirts | Jackets | Sum | | Required |
| 14 | Rent equipment | 0 | 1 | 0 | 1 | 1 | 3 | >= | 3 |
| 15 | | | | | | | | | |
| 16 | Units produced | 0 | 965.52 | 0 | 0 | 379.31 | | | |
| 17 | | <= | <= | <= | <= | <= | | | |
| 18 | Effective capacity | 0.00 | 1800.00 | 0.00 | 1000.00 | 500.00 | | | |
| 19 | | | | | | | | | |
| 20 | Constraints on resources | | | | | | | | |
| 21 | | Resource used | | | Available | | | | |
| 22 | Labor hours | 4000.00 | <= | | 4000 | | | | |
| 23 | Cloth | 4500.00 | <= | | 4500 | | | | |
| 24 | | | | | | | | | |
| 25 | Monetary outputs | | | | | | | | |
| 26 | Revenue | $80,345 | | | | | | | |
| 27 | Variable cost | $22,931 | | | | | | | |
| 28 | Fixed cost for equipment | $4,300 | | | | | | | |
| 29 | Profit | $53,114 | ← | | Objective to maximize | | | | |

Figure 6.14

**Sensitivity of Binary Variables to Unit Revenue of Skirts**

| | A | B | C | D | E | F | G |
|---|---|---|---|---|---|---|---|
| 1 | Oneway analysis for Solver model in Model worksheet | | | | | | |
| 2 | | | | | | | |
| 3 | Selling price skirts (cell $E$8) values along side, output cell(s) along top | | | | | | |
| 4 | | Rent_Equipment_1 | Rent_Equipment_2 | Rent_Equipment_3 | Rent_Equipment_4 | Rent_Equipment_5 | Profit |
| 5 | $70 | 0 | 1 | 0 | 0 | 1 | $54,614 |
| 6 | $75 | 0 | 1 | 0 | 0 | 1 | $54,614 |
| 7 | $80 | 0 | 1 | 0 | 0 | 1 | $54,614 |
| 8 | $85 | 0 | 1 | 0 | 0 | 1 | $54,614 |
| 9 | $90 | 0 | 0 | 0 | 1 | 0 | $58,500 |
| 10 | $95 | 0 | 0 | 0 | 1 | 0 | $63,500 |
| 11 | $100 | 0 | 0 | 0 | 1 | 0 | $68,500 |

the company continues to produce only shorts and jackets. However, when the selling price is $90 or greater, the company stops producing shorts and jackets and produces *only* skirts. You can check that the optimal production quantity of skirts is 1000 when the selling price of skirts is any value $90 or above. The only reason that the profits in Figure 6.14 increase from row 37 down is that the revenues from these 1000 skirts keep increasing.

## A Model with IF Functions

In case you are still not convinced that the binary variable approach is required, and you think IF functions could be used instead, take a look at last worksheet in the finished version

Figure 6.15

Solver Dialog Box
When IF Functions
Are Used

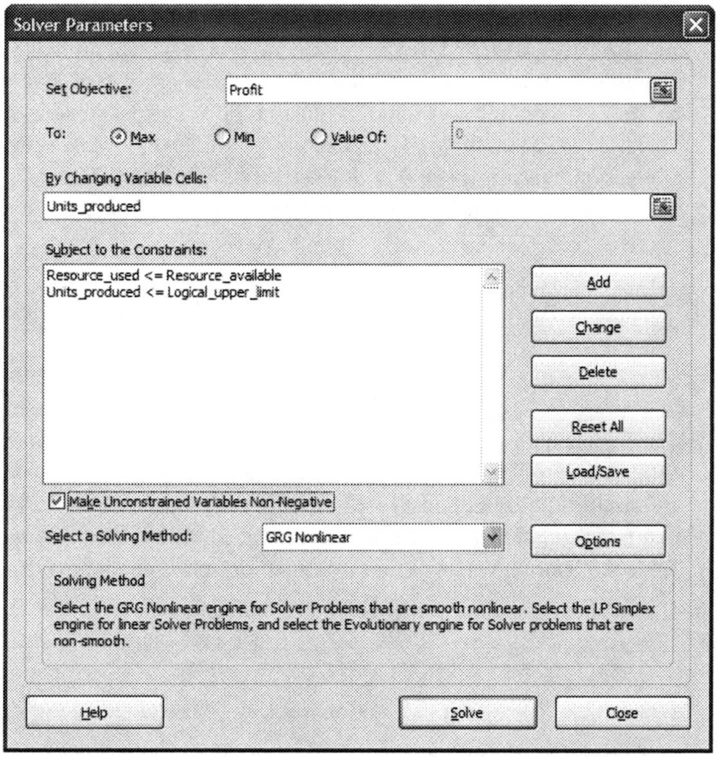

of the file. The resulting model *looks* the same as in Figure 6.11, but it incorporates the following changes:

- The binary range is no longer part of the changing cells range. Instead, cell B14 contains the formula =IF(B16>0,1,0), which is copied across to cell F14. Logically, this probably appears more natural. If a production quantity is positive, a 1 is entered in row 14, which means that the fixed cost is incurred.

- The effective capacities in row 18 are modeled with IF functions. Specifically, cell B18 contains the formula =IF(B16>0,MIN($D$22/B5,$D$23/B6),0), which is copied across to cell F18. (Actually, this constraint isn't even necessary now. Why?)

- The Solver dialog box is now set up as shown in Figure 6.15. The Rent_equipment range is not part of the changing cells range, and there is no binary constraint. The GRG Nonlinear method is selected because the IF functions make the model nonlinear.

*You can try modeling the logic with IF functions, but, depending on the initial values in the changing cells, Solver is likely to get the wrong solution.*

When we ran Solver on this modified model, we found inconsistent results, depending on the initial production quantities entered in row 16. For example, when we entered initial values all equal to 0, the Solver solution was exactly that—all 0s. Of course, this solution is *terrible* because it leads to a profit of $0. However, when we entered initial production quantities all equal to 100, Solver found the correct optimal solution, the same as in Figure 6.10. Was this just lucky? To check, we tried another initial solution, where the production quantities for shorts and jackets were 0, and the production quantities for shirts, pants, and skirts were all 500. In this case, Solver found a solution where only skirts are produced. Of course, we know this is not optimal.

The moral is that the IF-function approach is not the way to go. Its success depends strongly on the initial values entered in the changing cells, and this requires you to make very good guesses. In contrast, the binary approach ensures that you get the correct solution regardless of the initial values in the changing cells. ▦

The following example is similar to the Great Threads example in that there is a fixed cost for any positive level of production of a given product. However, an additional requirement states that if the company produces *any* of a given product, then (possibly because of economies of scale) it must produce at least some minimal level such as 1000. This is a typical example of a problem with **either–or constraints:** The company's level of production must either be 0 or at least 1000. In the next example, we show how the use of binary variables allows you to model the either–or constraints in a linear manner.

EXAMPLE  **6.3 MANUFACTURING AT DORIAN AUTO**

Dorian Auto is considering manufacturing three types of cars (compact, midsize, and large) and two types of minivans (midsize and large). The resources required and the profit contributions yielded by each type of vehicle are shown in Table 6.5. At present, 6500 tons of steel and 65,000 hours of labor are available. If any vehicles of a given type are produced, production of that type of vehicle is economically feasible only if at least a minimal number of that type are produced. These minimal numbers are also listed in Table 6.5. Dorian wants to find a production schedule that maximizes its profit.

Table 6.5   Data for the Dorian Car Example

| Vehicle Type | Compact Car | Midsize Car | Large Car | Midsize Minivan | Large Minivan |
|---|---|---|---|---|---|
| Steel (tons)/unit | 1.5 | 3 | 5 | 6 | 8 |
| Labor hours/unit | 30 | 25 | 40 | 45 | 55 |
| Minimum production (if any) | 1000 | 1000 | 1000 | 200 | 200 |
| Profit contribution/unit | $2,000 | $2,500 | $3,000 | $5,500 | $7,000 |

**Objective**   To use a binary model to determine which types of vehicles to produce (above their minimal requirements), and in what quantities, to maximize profit.

WHERE DO THE NUMBERS COME FROM?

This is basically a product mix problem, similar to those in Chapter 3. Therefore, the same comments about inputs discussed there apply here as well. The only new inputs in this problem are the minimal production quantities. These might be policy decisions determined by Dorian—management sees no reason to produce midsize minivans unless it can produce at least 200 of them, say—but these policy decisions are undoubtedly based on costs. Presumably, the fixed costs of product design, manufacturing, and marketing are prohibitive unless a minimal number of any vehicle type is produced.

Solution

The variables and constraints for the Dorian model are listed in Table 6.6. Dorian must decide not only how many of each type of vehicle to produce, but also which types to produce. Of course, after it decides to produce midsize minivans, say, then it must produce at least 200 of them. The constraints include the usual resource availability constraints. In addition, there are lower and upper limits on the production quantities of any vehicle type. The lower limit is zero or the minimal production quantity, depending on whether that vehicle type is produced. The upper limit is similar to the upper limit in the Great Thread's fixed-cost model in Example 6.2. That is, it is either zero, if the vehicle type is not produced at all, or it is some suitable large number. As in Example 6.2, this large number can be the number of that type of vehicle that could be produced if *all* of the steel and labor hours were devoted to it alone.

Table 6.6 Variables and Constraints for the Dorian Manufacturing Model

| | |
|---|---|
| Input variables | Resources (steel and labor hours) consumed by each vehicle type, profit contribution for each vehicle type, minimal production quantity for each vehicle type, resource availabilities |
| Decision variables (changing cells) | Whether to produce any of each vehicle type (binary), units produced of each vehicle type |
| Objective (target cell) | Profit |
| Other calculated variables | Logical lower and upper bounds on production quantities, resources used |
| Constraints | Production quantities ≥ Logical lower bounds<br>Production quantities ≤ Logical upper bounds<br>Resources used ≤ Resources available |

## DEVELOPING THE SPREADSHEET MODEL

The example can be modeled with the following steps. (See Figure 6.16 and the file Either Or Manufacturing.xlsx.)

Figure 6.16 The Dorian Auto Production Model

| | A | B | C | D | E | F | G | H | I | J |
|---|---|---|---|---|---|---|---|---|---|---|
| 1 | Dorian Auto production model with either-or constraints | | | | | | | | | |
| 2 | | | | | | | | | | |
| 3 | Inputs | | | | | | | Range names used: | | |
| 4 | Vehicle type | Compact car | Midsize car | Large car | Midsize minivan | Large minivan | | Logical_capacity | =Model!$B$19:$F$19 | |
| 5 | Steel (tons)/unit | 1.5 | 3 | 5 | 6 | 8 | | Minimum_production | =Model!$B$15:$F$15 | |
| 6 | Labor hours/unit | 30 | 25 | 40 | 45 | 55 | | Produce_at_least_minimum | =Model!$B$13:$F$13 | |
| 7 | Minimum production (if any) | 1000 | 1000 | 1000 | 200 | 200 | | Profit | =Model!$B$27 | |
| 8 | | | | | | | | Resource_available | =Model!$D$23:$D$24 | |
| 9 | Profit contribution/unit | $2,000 | $2,500 | $3,000 | $5,500 | $7,000 | | Resource_used | =Model!$B$23:$B$24 | |
| 10 | | | | | | | | Units_produced | =Model!$B$17:$F$17 | |
| 11 | Production plan and bounds on production quantities | | | | | | | | | |
| 12 | Type of car | Compact car | Midsize car | Large car | Midsize minivan | Large minivan | | | | |
| 13 | Produce at least minimum | 1 | 0 | 0 | 1 | 1 | | | | |
| 14 | | | | | | | | | | |
| 15 | Minimum production | 1000 | 0 | 0 | 200 | 200 | | | | |
| 16 | | <= | <= | <= | <= | <= | | | | |
| 17 | Units produced | 1000 | 0 | 0 | 200 | 473 | | | | |
| 18 | | <= | <= | <= | <= | <= | | | | |
| 19 | Logical capacity | 2167 | 0 | 0 | 1083 | 813 | | | | |
| 20 | | | | | | | | | | |
| 21 | Constraints on resources | | | | | | | | | |
| 22 | | Resource used | | Resource available | | | | | | |
| 23 | Steel | 6482 | <= | 6500 | | | | | | |
| 24 | Labor hours | 65000 | <= | 65000 | | | | | | |
| 25 | | | | | | | | | | |
| 26 | Objective to maximize | | | | | | | | | |
| 27 | Profit | $6,409,091 | | | | | | | | |

**1 Inputs.** Enter the input data in the blue ranges.

**2 Number of vehicles produced.** Enter *any* trial values for the number of vehicles of each type produced in the Units_produced range.

**3 Binary variables for minimum production.** Enter *any* trial 0–1 values in the Produce_at_least_minimum range. If a value in this range is 1, this means that Dorian must produce at least the minimum number of the corresponding vehicle type. A value of 0 in this range means that Dorian does not produce any of the corresponding vehicle type.

④ **Lower limits on production.** The either–or constraints are implemented with the binary variables in row 13 and the inequalities indicated in rows 15 through 19. To obtain the lower limits on production, enter the formula

=B7*B13

in cell B15 and copy it across row 15. This lower limit implies that if the binary variable in row 13 is 1, then Dorian must produce at least the minimum number of that vehicle type. However, if the binary variable is 0, then the lower bound in row 15 is 0 and is essentially redundant—it just says that production must be nonnegative.

⑤ **Upper limits on production.** To obtain upper limits on production, enter the formula

B13*MIN($D$23/B5,$D$24/B6)

in cell B19 and copy it across row 19. Note that the MIN term in this formula is the maximum number of compact cars Dorian could make if it devoted *all* of its resources to compact cars. (A similar upper limit was used in the Great Threads model in Example 6.2.) If the binary variable in row 13 is 1, this upper limit is essentially redundant—production can never be greater than this in any case. But if the binary variable is 0, this upper limit is 0, which prevents Dorian from making any vehicles of this type.

To summarize the lower and upper limits, if the binary variable is 1, the production limits become

Minimum production required ≤ Production ≤ Maximum production possible

On the other hand, if the binary variable is 0, the limits become

0 ≤ Production ≤ 0

*The trick is in getting the constraints to allow what we want to allow, but to disallow "illegal" solutions.*

Of course, these latter inequalities imply that production is 0. Exactly one of these cases must hold for each car type, so they successfully implement the either–or constraints. These lower and upper limits are the keys to the model.

⑥ **Steel and labor used.** Calculate the tons of steel and number of labor hours used in the Resources_used range by entering the formula

=SUMPRODUCT(B5:F5,Units_produced)

in cell B23 and copying it to cell B24.

⑦ **Profit.** Calculate the profit in cell B27 with the formula

=SUMPRODUCT(B9:F9,Units_produced)

USING SOLVER

The completed Solver dialog box is shown in Figure 6.17. The objective is to maximize profit, the changing cells are the production quantities and the binary variables, and the constraints specify the production limits and resource availabilities. Note that the production quantities are not constrained to be integers, although you could do so. Extra integer constraints only make the model more difficult to optimize, and if the optimal number of some vehicle type turns out to be 472.7, say, it is probably acceptable to round this up to 473 or down to 472.

### Discussion of the Solution

The optimal solution in Figure 6.16 indicates, by the 0 values in row 13, that Dorian should not produce any midsize or large cars. The number of 1s in this row, however, indicates that Dorian *must* produce at least the minimum number (1000) of compact cars and the

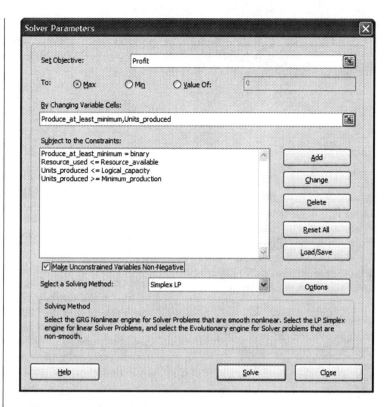

**Figure 6.17** Solver Dialog Box for the Dorian Production Model

minimum number (200) of each type of minivan. More specifically, the company should produce just enough compact cars and midsize minivans to meet the minimal production quantities. These vehicle types are relatively profitable, given the resources they use. However, they are evidently not as profitable as large minivans. The company should make as many of these as it can, after producing the compact cars and midsize minivans, until it runs out of labor hours.

This solution is certainly not intuitive. (For example, if large minivans are so profitable, why doesn't the company produce all large minivans and nothing else? Do you see why?) Also, this solution appears to be very sensitive to the inputs. Although we do not present any formal sensitivity analysis with SolverTable, we urge you to try different values for the minimal production quantities, the unit profit contributions, and/or the resource availabilities. We found that even small changes in these can yield a very different optimal production policy. For example, you can check that if the availability of steel decreases to 6000 tons, only compact cars and midsize minivans are produced, both above their minimal levels, and *no* large minivans are produced. ▧

## ADDITIONAL APPLICATIONS

### Locating Distribution Centers

When Dow Consumer Products (a manufacturer of food-care products) acquired the Texize home-care product lines of Morton Thiokol in 1985 to form DowBrands, Inc., the distribution channels of the two organizations remained, for the most part, separate. Each had its own district and regional distribution centers for storing and then shipping products to the customer regions. This led to possible inefficiencies in a business where keeping logistics costs low is the key to survival. Robinson et al. (1993), acting as consultants for

DowBrands, modeled the problem as a fixed-cost network problem—which distribution centers to keep open and which routes to use to satisfy which customers with which products. The study was highly successful and convinced DowBrands to close a significant number of distribution centers to reduce costs. ■

# PROBLEMS

## Skill-Building Problems

**11.** How difficult is it to expand the Great Threads model to accommodate another type of clothing? Answer by assuming that the company can also produce sweatshirts. The rental cost for sweatshirt equipment is $1100; the variable cost per unit and the selling price are $15 and $45, respectively; and each sweatshirt requires one labor hour and 3.5 square yards of cloth.

**12.** Referring to the previous problem, if it is optimal for the company to produce sweatshirts, use SolverTable to see how much larger the fixed cost of sweatshirt machinery would have to be before the company would *not* produce any sweatshirts. However, if the solution to the previous problem calls for no sweatshirts to be produced, use SolverTable to see how much lower the fixed cost of sweatshirt machinery would have to be before the company would start producing sweatshirts.

**13.** In the Great Threads model, we didn't constrain the production quantities in row 16 to be integers, arguing that any fractional values could be safely rounded to integers. See whether this is true. Constrain these quantities to be integers and then run Solver. Are the optimal integer values the same as the rounded fractional values in Figure 6.10?

**14.** In the optimal solution to the Great Threads model, the labor hour and cloth constraints are both binding—the company is using all it has.
   **a.** Use SolverTable to see what happens to the optimal solution when the amount of available cloth increases from its current value. (You can choose the range of input values to use.) Capture all of the changing cells, the labor hours and cloth used, and the profit as outputs in the table. The real issue here is whether the company can profitably use more cloth when it is already constrained by labor hours.
   **b.** Repeat part **a**, but reverse the roles of labor hours and cloth. That is, use the available labor hours as the input for SolverTable.

**15.** In the optimal solution to the Great Threads model, no pants are produced. Suppose Great Threads has an order for 300 pairs of pants that *must* be produced. Modify the model appropriately and use Solver to find

the new optimal solution. (Is it enough to put a lower bound of 300 on the production quantity in cell D16? Will this automatically force the binary value in cell D14 to be 1? Explain.) How much profit does the company lose because of having to produce pants?

**16.** In the Dorian production model, the optimal solution calls for the minimum number of compact cars and midsize minivans to be produced, but for *more* than the minimum number of large minivans to be produced. If the large minivans are evidently that profitable, why doesn't Dorian discontinue making compact cars and midsize minivans and instead produce even more large minivans?

**17.** As the Dorian production model is currently stated, each vehicle type has a minimum production level; if this type is produced at all, its production quantity must be at least this minimum. Suppose that for large minivans, there is also a *maximum* production level of 400. If large minivans are produced, the production level must be from 200 to 400. Modify the model as necessary and use Solver to find the new optimal solution. How do you know that the current optimal solution is not optimal for the modified model?

**18.** The optimal solution to the Dorian production model appears to be sensitive to the model inputs. For each of the following inputs, create a one-way Solver Table that captures all changing cells and the target cell as outputs. You can choose the ranges of these inputs to make the results interesting. Comment on your results.
   **a.** The steel available
   **b.** The labor hours available
   **c.** The unit profit contribution of large minivans
   **d.** The minimum production level (currently 200) of large minivans
   **e.** The minimum production level (currently 1000) of compact cars

**19.** If Solver could handle IF functions correctly, how would you use them in the Dorian production example to create an arguably more natural model—without binary variables? Run Solver on your modified model. Do you get the correct solution? (*Note:* You will have to use the GRG Nonlinear method.)

**20.** In the Great Threads model, you found an upper bound on production of any clothing type by calculating the amount that could be produced if *all* of the resources were devoted to this clothing type.

  **a.** What if you instead used a very large value such as 1,000,000 for this upper bound? Try it and see whether you get the same optimal solution.

  **b.** Explain why *any* such upper bound is required. Exactly what role does it play in the model developed in this section?

**21.** In the last sheet of the file Fixed Cost Manufacturing.xlsx, we illustrated one way to model the Great Threads problem with IF functions that didn't work. Try a slightly different approach here. Eliminate the binary variables in row 14 altogether, and eliminate the upper bounds in row 18 and the corresponding upper bound constraints in the Solver dialog box. (The only constraints will now be the resource availability constraints.) However, use IF functions to calculate the total fixed cost of renting equipment, so that if the amount of any clothing type is positive, its fixed cost

is added to the total fixed cost. Is Solver able to handle this model? Does it depend on the initial values in the changing cells? (Don't forget to use the GRG Nonlinear method.)

**22.** In the Dorian production model, suppose that the production quantity of compact cars must either be less than or equal to 100 (a small batch) or greater than or equal to 1000 (a large batch). The same statements hold for the other vehicle types as well, except that the small and large batch limits for both sizes of minivans are 50 and 200. Modify the model appropriately and use Solver to find the optimal solution.

**23.** Suppose in the Dorian production model that no minimum production limits are placed on the individual vehicle types. However, minimum production limits are placed on *all* cars and on *all* minivans. Specifically, if Dorian produces *any* cars, regardless of size, it must produce at least 1500 cars total. Similarly, if the company produces *any* minivans, it must produce at least 1000 minivans total. Modify the model appropriately and use Solver to find the optimal solution.

## 6.5 SET-COVERING AND LOCATION-ASSIGNMENT MODELS

Many companies have geographically dispersed customers that they must service in some way. To do this, they create service center facilities at selected locations and then assign each customer to one of the service centers. Various costs are incurred, including (1) fixed costs of locating service centers in particular locations; (2) operating costs, depending on the service centers' locations; and (3) transportation costs, depending on the distances between customers and their assigned service centers. In this section, we illustrate several examples of this basic problem.

We first examine a particular type of location model called a **set-covering** model. In a set-covering model, each member of a given set (set 1) must be "covered" by an acceptable member of another set (set 2). The usual objective in a set-covering problem is to minimize the number of members in set 2 that are needed to cover all the members in set 1. For example, set 1 might consist of all cities in a county, and set 2 might consist of the cities where a fire station is located. A fire station "covers" a city if the fire station is located, say, within 10 minutes of the city. The goal is to minimize the number of fire stations needed to cover all cities. Set-covering models have been applied to areas as diverse as airline crew scheduling, truck dispatching, political redistricting, and capital investment. The following example presents a typical set-covering model.

---

EXAMPLE | **6.4 HUB LOCATION AT WESTERN AIRLINES**

Western Airlines wants to design a hub system in the United States. Each hub is used for connecting flights to and from cities within 1000 miles of the hub. Western runs flights among the following cities: Atlanta, Boston, Chicago, Denver, Houston, Los Angeles, New Orleans, New York, Pittsburgh, Salt Lake City, San Francisco, and Seattle. The company wants to determine the smallest number of hubs it needs to cover all these cities, where a city is covered if it is within 1000 miles of at least one hub. Table 6.7 lists which cities are within 1000 miles of other cities.

Table 6.7    Data for the Western Set-Covering Example

| | Cities Within 1000 Miles |
|---|---|
| Atlanta (AT) | AT, CH, HO, NO, NY, PI |
| Boston (BO) | BO, NY, PI |
| Chicago (CH) | AT, CH, NY, NO, PI |
| Denver (DE) | DE, SL |
| Houston (HO) | AT, HO, NO |
| Los Angeles (LA) | LA, SL, SF |
| New Orleans (NO) | AT, CH, HO, NO |
| New York (NY) | AT, BO, CH, NY, PI |
| Pittsburgh (PI) | AT, BO, CH, NY, PI |
| Salt Lake City (SL) | DE, LA, SL, SF, SE |
| San Francisco (SF) | LA, SL, SF, SE |
| Seattle (SE) | SL, SF, SE |

**Objective**    To develop a binary model to find the minimum number of hub locations that can cover all cities.

## WHERE DO THE NUMBERS COME FROM?

Western has evidently made a policy decision that its hubs will cover only cities within a 1000-mile radius. Then the cities covered by any hub location can be found from a map. (In a later sensitivity analysis, we explore how the solution changes when the coverage distance is allowed to vary.)

## Solution

The variables and constraints for this set-covering model are listed in Table 6.8. The model is straightforward. There is a binary variable for each city to indicate whether a hub is located there. Then the number of hubs that cover each city is constrained to be at least 1. There are no monetary costs in this version of the problem. The objective is simply to minimize the number of hubs.

Table 6.8    Variables and Constraints for the Set-Covering Model

| | |
|---|---|
| Input variables | Cities within 1000 miles of one another |
| Decision variables (changing cells) | Locations of hubs (binary) |
| Objective (target cell) | Number of hubs |
| Other calculated variables | Number of hubs covering each city |
| Constraints | Number of hubs covering a city ≥ 1 |

## DEVELOPING THE SPREADSHEET MODEL

The spreadsheet model for Western is shown in Figure 6.18. (See the file Locating Hubs 1.xlsx.) The model can be developed as follows:

**Figure 6.18   The Airline Hub Set-Covering Model**

| | A | B | C | D | E | F | G | H | I | J | K | L | M | N | O | P | Q |
|---|---|---|---|---|---|---|---|---|---|---|---|---|---|---|---|---|---|
| 1 | Western Airlines hub location model | | | | | | | | | | | | | | | | |
| 2 | | | | | | | | | | | | | | | | | |
| 3 | Input data: which cities are covered by which potential hubs | | | | | | | | | | | | | | Range names used: | | |
| 4 | | Potential hub | | | | | | | | | | | | | Hubs_covered_by | =Model!$B$25:$B$36 | |
| 5 | City | | AT | BO | CH | DE | HO | LA | NO | NY | PI | SL | SF | SE | Total_hubs | =Model!$B$39 | |
| 6 | AT | | 1 | 0 | 1 | 0 | 1 | 0 | 1 | 1 | 1 | 0 | 0 | 0 | Used_as_hub | =Model!$B$21:$M$21 | |
| 7 | BO | | 0 | 1 | 0 | 0 | 0 | 0 | 0 | 1 | 1 | 0 | 0 | 0 | | | |
| 8 | CH | | 1 | 0 | 1 | 0 | 0 | 0 | 1 | 1 | 1 | 0 | 0 | 0 | | | |
| 9 | DE | | 0 | 0 | 0 | 1 | 0 | 0 | 0 | 0 | 0 | 1 | 0 | 0 | | | |
| 10 | HO | | 1 | 0 | 0 | 0 | 1 | 0 | 1 | 0 | 0 | 0 | 0 | 0 | | | |
| 11 | LA | | 0 | 0 | 0 | 0 | 0 | 1 | 0 | 0 | 0 | 1 | 1 | 0 | | | |
| 12 | NO | | 1 | 0 | 1 | 0 | 1 | 0 | 1 | 0 | 0 | 0 | 0 | 0 | | | |
| 13 | NY | | 1 | 1 | 1 | 0 | 0 | 0 | 0 | 1 | 1 | 0 | 0 | 0 | | | |
| 14 | PI | | 1 | 1 | 1 | 0 | 0 | 0 | 0 | 1 | 1 | 0 | 0 | 0 | | | |
| 15 | SL | | 0 | 0 | 0 | 1 | 0 | 1 | 0 | 0 | 0 | 1 | 1 | 1 | | | |
| 16 | SF | | 0 | 0 | 0 | 0 | 0 | 1 | 0 | 0 | 0 | 1 | 1 | 1 | | | |
| 17 | SE | | 0 | 0 | 0 | 0 | 0 | 0 | 0 | 0 | 0 | 1 | 1 | 1 | | | |
| 18 | | | | | | | | | | | | | | | | | |
| 19 | Decisions: which cities to use as hubs | | | | | | | | | | | | | | | | |
| 20 | | | AT | BO | CH | DE | HO | LA | NO | NY | PI | SL | SF | SE | | | |
| 21 | Used as hub | | 0 | 0 | 0 | 0 | 1 | 0 | 0 | 1 | 0 | 1 | 0 | 0 | | | |
| 22 | | | | | | | | | | | | | | | | | |
| 23 | Constraints that each city must be covered by at least one hub | | | | | | | | | | | | | | | | |
| 24 | City | Hubs covered by | | Required | | | | | | | | | | | | | |
| 25 | AT | 2 | >= | 1 | | | | | | | | | | | | | |
| 26 | BO | 1 | >= | 1 | | | | | | | | | | | | | |
| 27 | CH | 1 | >= | 1 | | | | | | | | | | | | | |
| 28 | DE | 1 | >= | 1 | | | | | | | | | | | | | |
| 29 | HO | 1 | >= | 1 | | | | | | | | | | | | | |
| 30 | LA | 1 | >= | 1 | | | | | | | | | | | | | |
| 31 | NO | 1 | >= | 1 | | | | | | | | | | | | | |
| 32 | NY | 1 | >= | 1 | | | | | | | | | | | | | |
| 33 | PI | 1 | >= | 1 | | | | | | | | | | | | | |
| 34 | SL | 1 | >= | 1 | | | | | | | | | | | | | |
| 35 | SF | 1 | >= | 1 | | | | | | | | | | | | | |
| 36 | SE | 1 | >= | 1 | | | | | | | | | | | | | |
| 37 | | | | | | | | | | | | | | | | | |
| 38 | Objective to minimize | | | | | | | | | | | | | | | | |
| 39 | Total hubs | | 3 | | | | | | | | | | | | | | |

Note that there are multiple optimal solutions to this model, all of which require a total of 3 hubs. You might get a different solution from the one shown here.

① **Inputs.** Enter the information from Table 6.7 in the blue range. A 1 in a cell indicates that the column city covers the row city, whereas a 0 indicates that the column city does not cover the row city. For example, the three 1s in row 7 indicate that Boston, New York, and Pittsburgh are the only cities within 1000 miles of Boston.

② **0–1 values for hub locations.** Enter *any* trial 0–1 values in the Used_as_hub range to indicate which cities are used as hubs. These are the changing cells.

*A SUMPRODUCT of two 0–1 ranges just finds the number of matches of 1s in the two ranges. Here it calculates the number of hubs that cover a given city.*

③ **Cities covered by hubs.** Determine the number of hubs that cover each city. Specifically, calculate the total number of hubs within 1000 miles of Atlanta in cell B25 with the formula

=SUMPRODUCT(B6:M6,Used_as_hub)

For any 0–1 values in the changing-cells range, this formula finds the number of hubs that cover Atlanta. Then copy this to the rest of the Hubs_covered_by range. Note that a value in the Hubs_covered_by range can be 2 or greater. This indicates that a city is within 1000 miles of multiple hubs.

④ **Number of hubs.** Calculate the total number of hubs used in cell B39 with the formula

=SUM(Used_as_hub)

The Solver dialog box is shown in Figure 6.19. The objective is to minimize the total number of hubs, subject to covering each city by at least one hub and ensuring that the changing cells are binary. As usual, you should select the Simplex LP method.

Figure 6.19
Solver Dialog Box
for the Set-Covering
Model

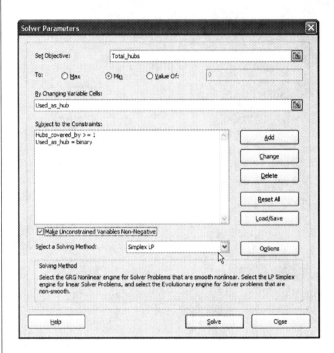

**Figure 6.19**
Solver Dialog Box for the Set-Covering Model

### Discussion of the Solution

Figure 6.20 is a graphical representation of the optimal solution, where the double ovals indicate hub locations and the large circles indicate ranges covered by the hubs. (These large circles are not drawn to scale. In reality, they should be circles of radius 1000 miles centered at the hubs.) Three hubs—in Houston, New York, and Salt Lake City—are needed.[6] Would you have guessed this? The Houston hub covers Houston, Atlanta, and New Orleans. The New York hub covers Atlanta, Pittsburgh, Boston, New York, and Chicago. The Salt Lake City hub covers Denver, Los Angeles, Salt Lake City, San Francisco, and Seattle. Note that Atlanta is the only city covered by two hubs; it can be serviced by New York or Houston.

### Sensitivity Analysis

An interesting sensitivity analysis for Western's problem is to see how the solution is affected by the mile limit. Currently, a hub can service all cities within 1000 miles. What if the limit were 800 or 1200 miles, say? To answer this question, data on actual distances among all the cities must be collected. After you have a matrix of these distances, you can build the 0–1 matrix, corresponding to the range B6:M17 in Figure 6.18, with IF functions.

---

[6] Multiple optimal solutions exist for this model, all requiring three hubs, so you might obtain a different solution from ours.

Figure 6.20

Graphical Solution
to the Set-Covering
Model

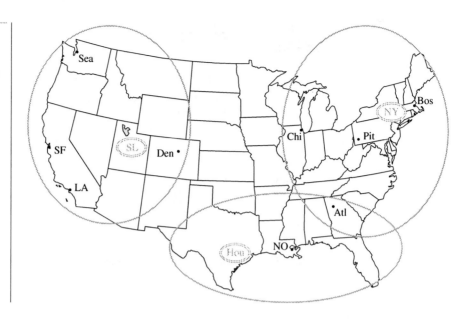

Figure 6.21  **Sensitivity to Mile Limit**

|  | A | B | C | D | E | F | G | H | I | J | K | L | M | N |
|---|---|---|---|---|---|---|---|---|---|---|---|---|---|---|
| 1 | Oneway analysis for Solver model in Model worksheet | | | | | | | | | | | | | |
| 2 | | | | | | | | | | | | | | |
| 3 | Mile limit (cell $B$4) values along side, output cell(s) along top | | | | | | | | | | | | | |
| 4 | | AT | BO | CH | DE | HO | LA | NO | NY | PI | SL | SF | SE | Total_hubs |
| 5 | 800 | 1 | 1 | 0 | 0 | 0 | 0 | 0 | 0 | 0 | 1 | 0 | 1 | 4 |
| 6 | 900 | 1 | 1 | 0 | 0 | 0 | 0 | 0 | 0 | 0 | 1 | 0 | 0 | 3 |
| 7 | 1000 | 1 | 1 | 0 | 0 | 0 | 0 | 0 | 0 | 0 | 1 | 0 | 0 | 3 |
| 8 | 1100 | 0 | 0 | 1 | 0 | 0 | 0 | 0 | 0 | 0 | 1 | 0 | 0 | 2 |
| 9 | 1200 | 0 | 0 | 1 | 0 | 0 | 1 | 0 | 0 | 0 | 0 | 0 | 0 | 2 |

The modified model appears in Figure 6.21. (See the file Locating Hubs 2.xlsx.) The typical formula in B24 is =IF(B8<=$B$4,1,0), which is then copied to the rest of the B24:M35 range.[7] You can then run SolverTable, selecting cell B4 as the single input cell, letting it vary from 800 to 1200 in increments of 100, and keeping track of where the hubs are located and the number of hubs. The SolverTable results at the bottom show the effect of the mile limit. When this limit is lowered to 800 miles, four hubs are required, but when it is increased to 1100 or 1200, only two hubs are required. By the way, the solution shown for the 1000-mile limit is different from the previous solution in Figure 6.18 (because of multiple optimal solutions), but it still requires three hubs. ▪

[7]We have warned you about using IF functions in Solver models. However, the current use affects only the *inputs* to the problem, not quantities that depend on the changing cells. Therefore, it causes no problems.

## Locating Florida Disaster Recovery Centers

In 2001, the Federal Emergency Management Agency (FEMA) required every Florida county to identify potential locations for disaster recovery centers (DRCs). Dekle et al. (2005) describe a study sponsored by Alachua County in north-central Florida to identify potential DRC sites. The authors developed a version of the set-covering model with a two-stage approach. The first stage required each resident to be within 20 miles of the closest DRC. It identified a solution with three DRC locations. The second stage then refined this solution to relax the 20-mile requirement and include evaluation criteria not included in stage 1. The final results provided significant improvements over the original FEMA location criteria, and it maintained acceptable travel distances to the nearest DRC.

## Selecting Receiver Locations for Automated Meter Reading

Gavirneni et al. (2004) developed and solved a set-covering model for Schlumberger, a utility company. The company needed to deploy its receivers on utility poles so that all wireless meters in the region can transmit their readings to at least one receiver. The authors solved a large-scale model with 116,600 meters and 20,636 utility poles. ■

The following example is similar to a set-covering model, but it also has an assignment component.

| EXAMPLE | 6.5 LOCATING AND ASSIGNING SERVICE CENTERS AT UNITED COPIERS |

United Copiers sells and services copy machines to customers in 11 cities throughout the country. The company wants to set up service centers in three of these cities. After United Copiers chooses the location of the service centers, it must assign customers in each city to one of the service centers. For example, if it decides to locate a service center in New York and then assigns its Boston customers to the New York service center, a service representative from New York will travel from Boston when services are required there. The distances (in miles) between the cities are listed in Table 6.9. The estimated annual numbers of trips to the various customers are listed in Table 6.10. What

Table 6.9   Distances for the Service Center Example

|              | Boston | Chicago | Dallas | Denver | Los Angeles | Miami | New York | Phoenix | Pittsburgh | San Francisco | Seattle |
|--------------|--------|---------|--------|--------|-------------|-------|----------|---------|------------|---------------|---------|
| Boston       | 0      | 983     | 1815   | 1991   | 3036        | 1539  | 213      | 2664    | 792        | 2385          | 2612    |
| Chicago      | 983    | 0       | 1205   | 1050   | 2112        | 1390  | 840      | 1729    | 457        | 2212          | 2052    |
| Dallas       | 1815   | 1205    | 0      | 801    | 1425        | 1332  | 1604     | 1027    | 1237       | 1765          | 2404    |
| Denver       | 1991   | 1050    | 801    | 0      | 1174        | 2041  | 1780     | 836     | 1411       | 1765          | 1373    |
| Los Angeles  | 3036   | 2112    | 1425   | 1174   | 0           | 2757  | 2825     | 398     | 2456       | 403           | 1909    |
| Miami        | 1539   | 1390    | 1332   | 2041   | 2757        | 0     | 1258     | 2359    | 1250       | 3097          | 3389    |
| New York     | 213    | 840     | 1604   | 1780   | 2825        | 1258  | 0        | 2442    | 386        | 3036          | 2900    |
| Phoenix      | 2664   | 1729    | 1027   | 836    | 398         | 2359  | 2442     | 0       | 2073       | 800           | 1482    |
| Pittsburgh   | 792    | 457     | 1237   | 1411   | 2456        | 1250  | 386      | 2073    | 0          | 2653          | 2517    |
| San Francisco| 2385   | 2212    | 1765   | 1765   | 403         | 3097  | 3036     | 800     | 2653       | 0             | 817     |
| Seattle      | 2612   | 2052    | 2404   | 1373   | 1909        | 3389  | 2900     | 1482    | 2517       | 817           | 0       |

Table 6.10   Estimated Numbers of Annual Trips to Customers

| Boston | Chicago | Dallas | Denver | Los Angeles | Miami | New York | Phoenix | Pittsburgh | San Francisco | Seattle |
|--------|---------|--------|--------|-------------|-------|----------|---------|------------|---------------|---------|
| 885 | 760 | 1124 | 708 | 1224 | 1152 | 1560 | 1222 | 856 | 1443 | 612 |

should United Copiers do to minimize the total annual distance traveled by its service representatives?

**Objective**   To develop a linear model, using binary variables, that determines the locations of service centers and then assigns customers to these service centers to minimize the total annual distance traveled.

## WHERE DO THE NUMBERS COME FROM?

The distances come directly from a map. The numbers of annual trips could be estimated in several ways. For example, the company could multiply the number of customers in each city by the estimated number of trips required per year per customer. However, this might overestimate the total number of trips because a single trip can service multiple customers. More likely, the company would estimate the numbers of trips in Table 6.10 directly from historical records. Finally, the number of service centers to use, in this case three, is probably a policy decision based on cost. However, this number is an obvious candidate for sensitivity analysis.

## Solution

*If you already knew where the service centers were located, this would just be an assignment problem of the type discussed in the previous chapter.*

The variables and constraints for this location-assignment model are listed in Table 6.11. The keys to this model are the binary decision variables and the logical constraints. For each city, a binary variable is used to indicate whether a service center is located there. Also, for each pair of cities, a binary variable is used to indicate whether a service center in the first city is assigned to the customer in the second city. Using these binary variables, the first two constraints in the table are straightforward: Three cities should include service centers, and each city should be assigned to exactly one service center. The last constraint in the table is less obvious. It states that the number of cities that can be serviced by a given city is less than or equal to a logical capacity. As you will see below, this logical capacity is either 0 or 11 (the number of cities).

Table 6.11   Variables and Constraints for the Service Center Model

| | |
|---|---|
| **Input variables** | Distances between cities, annual number of trips to each city, number of service centers to locate |
| **Decision variables (changing cells)** | Whether each city includes a service center (binary), whether a city is assigned to a particular service center (binary) |
| **Objective (target cell)** | Total distance traveled annually |
| **Other calculated variables** | Number of service center locations chosen, number of service centers assigned to each customer, total distance traveled to each customer |
| **Constraints** | Number of service center locations chosen = 3 |
| | Number of service centers assigned to each customer = 1 |
| | Number of cities serviced by a given city ≤ Logical capacity |

The spreadsheet can be developed with the following steps. (See Figure 6.22 and the file Locating Service Centers.xlsx.)[8]

**Figure 6.22**  Spreadsheet Model for the Service Center Problem

Row 1: Locating service centers and assigning service centers to customer s - an alternative way of m odeling the logical constraint

**Distances between cities**

| | Boston | Chicago | Dallas | Denver | Los Angeles | Miami | New York | Phoenix | Pittsburgh | San Francisco | Seattle |
|---|---|---|---|---|---|---|---|---|---|---|---|
| Boston | 0 | 983 | 1815 | 1991 | 3036 | 1539 | 213 | 2664 | 792 | 2385 | 2612 |
| Chicago | 983 | 0 | 1205 | 1050 | 2112 | 1390 | 840 | 1729 | 457 | 2212 | 2052 |
| Dallas | 1815 | 1205 | 0 | 801 | 1425 | 1332 | 1604 | 1027 | 1237 | 1765 | 2404 |
| Denver | 1991 | 1050 | 801 | 0 | 1174 | 2041 | 1780 | 836 | 1411 | 1765 | 1373 |
| Los Angeles | 3036 | 2112 | 1425 | 1174 | 0 | 2757 | 2825 | 398 | 2456 | 403 | 1909 |
| Miami | 1539 | 1390 | 1332 | 2041 | 2757 | 0 | 1258 | 2359 | 1250 | 3097 | 3389 |
| New York | 213 | 840 | 1604 | 1780 | 2825 | 1258 | 0 | 2442 | 386 | 3036 | 2900 |
| Phoenix | 2664 | 1729 | 1027 | 836 | 398 | 2359 | 2442 | 0 | 2073 | 800 | 1482 |
| Pittsburgh | 792 | 457 | 1237 | 1411 | 2456 | 1250 | 386 | 2073 | 0 | 2653 | 2517 |
| San Francisco | 2385 | 2212 | 1765 | 1765 | 403 | 3097 | 3036 | 800 | 2653 | 0 | 817 |
| Seattle | 2612 | 2052 | 2404 | 1373 | 1909 | 3389 | 2900 | 1482 | 2517 | 817 | 0 |

**Locations of service centers**

| | Boston | Chicago | Dallas | Denver | Los Angeles | Miami | New York | Phoenix | Pittsburgh | San Francisco | Seattle | Service centers | | Max centers |
|---|---|---|---|---|---|---|---|---|---|---|---|---|---|---|
| Include service center | 0 | 0 | 1 | 0 | 0 | 0 | 1 | 0 | 0 | 1 | 0 | 3 | <= | 3 |

**Assignments (1 if customers along side are ser viced by service center along top, 0 otherwise)**

| | Boston | Chicago | Dallas | Denver | Los Angeles | Miami | New York | Phoenix | Pittsburgh | San Francisco | Seattle | Total assignments | | Required |
|---|---|---|---|---|---|---|---|---|---|---|---|---|---|---|
| Boston | 0 | 0 | 0 | 0 | 0 | 0 | 1 | 0 | 0 | 0 | 0 | 1 | = | 1 |
| Chicago | 0 | 0 | 0 | 0 | 0 | 0 | 1 | 0 | 0 | 0 | 0 | 1 | = | 1 |
| Dallas | 0 | 0 | 1 | 0 | 0 | 0 | 0 | 0 | 0 | 0 | 0 | 1 | = | 1 |
| Denver | 0 | 0 | 1 | 0 | 0 | 0 | 0 | 0 | 0 | 0 | 0 | 1 | = | 1 |
| Los Angeles | 0 | 0 | 0 | 0 | 0 | 0 | 0 | 0 | 0 | 1 | 0 | 1 | = | 1 |
| Miami | 0 | 0 | 0 | 0 | 0 | 0 | 1 | 0 | 0 | 0 | 0 | 1 | = | 1 |
| New York | 0 | 0 | 0 | 0 | 0 | 0 | 1 | 0 | 0 | 0 | 0 | 1 | = | 1 |
| Phoenix | 0 | 0 | 0 | 0 | 0 | 0 | 0 | 0 | 0 | 1 | 0 | 1 | = | 1 |
| Pittsburgh | 0 | 0 | 0 | 0 | 0 | 0 | 1 | 0 | 0 | 0 | 0 | 1 | = | 1 |
| San Francisco | 0 | 0 | 0 | 0 | 0 | 0 | 0 | 0 | 0 | 1 | 0 | 1 | = | 1 |
| Seattle | 0 | 0 | 0 | 0 | 0 | 0 | 0 | 0 | 0 | 1 | 0 | 1 | = | 1 |
| Number serviced by | 0 | 0 | 2 | 0 | 0 | 0 | 5 | 0 | 0 | 4 | 0 | | | |
| | <= | <= | <= | <= | <= | <= | <= | <= | <= | <= | <= | | | |
| Logical capacity | 0 | 0 | 11 | 0 | 0 | 0 | 11 | 0 | 0 | 11 | 0 | | | |

**Numbers of annual trips to customers, and total distances (1000s of miles) traveled annually to customers**

| | Annual trips | Total distance |
|---|---|---|
| Boston | 885 | 189 |
| Chicago | 760 | 638 |
| Dallas | 1124 | 0 |
| Denver | 708 | 567 |
| Los Angeles | 1224 | 493 |
| Miami | 1152 | 1449 |
| New York | 1560 | 0 |
| Phoenix | 1222 | 978 |
| Pittsburgh | 856 | 330 |
| San Francisco | 1443 | 0 |
| Seattle | 612 | 500 |

These distances are 0 because the optimal solution locates service centers in these cities.

**Range names used:**

| | |
|---|---|
| Assignments | =Model!$B$23:$L$33 |
| Max_centers | =Model!$O$19 |
| Include_service_cen | =Model!$B$19:$L$19 |
| Total_assignments | =Model!$M$23:$M$33 |
| Logical_capacity | =Model!$B$36:$L$36 |
| Number_serviced_b | =Model!$B$34:$L$34 |
| Service_centers | =Model!$M$19 |
| Total_distance | =Model!$B$53 |

**Objective to minimize (1000s of miles)**

| | |
|---|---|
| Total distance | 5145 |

**1 Inputs.** Enter the given data in the blue ranges.

**2 Service center location decisions.** Enter *any* trial 0–1 values in the Include_service_center range. For example, a 1 in cell D19 means a service center is located in Dallas, whereas a 0 in cell E19 means no service center is located in Denver.

**3 Assignment decisions.** Enter *any* 0–1 trial values in the Assignments range. For example, a 1 in cell D26 means that Denver is serviced by the center in Dallas, whereas a 0 in cell D27 means that Los Angeles is not serviced by the center in Dallas. At this point, you might ask what these mean if there *is* no service center in Dallas. This is where the logical capacities are necessary, as explained shortly. For now, you can anticipate that if there is a 1 in some column of the Assignments range, the corresponding city *will* eventually include a service center.

[8]We used a slightly different model in the previous edition. It had 121 upper bound constraints for the large block of binary variables. To our surprise, this model was too large for Excel 2010's Solver because of its new limit of 100 constraints. Fortunately, the alternative shown here works fine.

**4** **Number of service centers.** Calculate the number of service centers with the formula

=SUM(Include_service_center)

in cell M19. This just sums the 0–1 range, so it equals the number of 1s.

**5** **Number of service centers assigned to each city.** Calculate the number of service centers assigned to each city with row sums in the Total_assignments range in column M. That is, enter the formula

=SUM(B23:L23)

in cell M23 and copy it down to cell M33. These row sums will eventually be constrained to equal 1 to ensure that exactly one service center is assigned to each city.

**6** **Total annual distances.** Calculate the total annual distance traveled (in 1000s of miles) to each city by entering the formula

=B40*SUMPRODUCT(B5:L5,B23:L23)/1000

in cell C40 for Boston and copying it down to cell C50 for the other cities. Note that this SUMPRODUCT includes a row of distances from Boston and a row of assignments to customers in Boston. This row of assignments will eventually include only a *single* 1—only a single service center will be assigned to customers in Boston. Therefore, this SUMPRODUCT will be the distance between Boston and the service center assigned to Boston. It is multiplied by the annual trips to Boston (cell B40) to obtain the total annual distance traveled to Boston, and it is divided by 1000 to convert to thousands of miles.

**7** **Logical capacities.** You need to ensure that only existing service locations can be assigned to customers. One way to ensure this is to calculate column sums of the binary variables in row 34. For example, the 2 in cell D34 indicates that two cities are serviced by Dallas (Dallas and Denver). Then create the logical capacities in row 36 by entering the formula

=11*B19

in cell B36 and copying it across row 36. The effect is that if a binary value in row 19 is 0, then no cities can be serviced by the corresponding city. For example, this is the case for Boston. However, if the binary value in row 19 is 1, then the logical capacity is 11, the number of cities, and this capacity constraint is essentially irrelevant.

**8** **Total annual distance traveled.** Calculate the total distance traveled annually (in 1000s of miles) in cell B53 with the formula

=SUM(C40:C50)

*Always be careful to convert to appropriate units of measurement, if necessary. A factor such as 100 or 1000 in a formula is often evidence of a measurement conversion.*

## USING SOLVER

The completed Solver dialog box is shown in Figure 6.23. You should also set the Solver tolerance to 0%. (There is no need to check the Non-Negative option because all changing cells are binary and hence non-negative.)

### Discussion of the Solution

The optimal solution in Figure 6.22 indicates that United Copiers should locate service centers in Dallas, New York, and San Francisco. Of course, each of these centers services the customers in its own city. In addition, the Dallas center services customers in Denver; the New York center services customers in Boston, Chicago, Miami, and Pittsburgh;

Figure 6.23

Solver Dialog Box
for the Service
Center Model

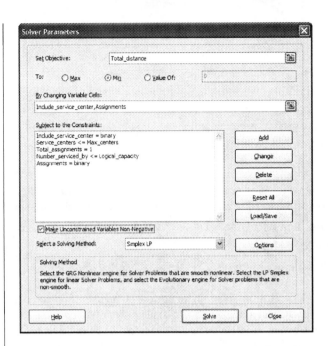

and the San Francisco center services customers in Los Angeles, Phoenix, and Seattle. The total distance traveled annually is slightly over 5.1 million miles.

### Sensitivity Analysis

A natural sensitivity analysis is to see how the service center locations and the total annual distance change as we vary the number of required service centers. This is straightforward with SolverTable. You should use cell O19 as the single input cell, vary it from 1 to 11 in increments of 1, and keep track of the binary values in row 19 and the target cell. The results are shown in Figure 6.24. As you can see, service centers are typically located in Dallas, New York, and San Francisco, but not always. In particular, if only one service center is allowed, it should be located in Dallas, but if two service centers are allowed, they should be located in New York and Phoenix. Of course, when there are more service centers, less traveling is required. At the extreme, if a service center is located in every city, no traveling is required at all.

**Figure 6.24**  Sensitivity to Number of Service Centers Allowed

| | A | B | C | D | E | F | G | H | I | J | K | L | M |
|---|---|---|---|---|---|---|---|---|---|---|---|---|---|
| 1 | Oneway analysis for Solver model in Model worksheet | | | | | | | | | | | | |
| 2 | | | | | | | | | | | | | |
| 3 | Max centers (cell $O$19) values along side, output cell(s) along top | | | | | | | | | | | | |
| 4 | | Boston | Chicago | Dallas | Denver | Los Angeles | Miami | New York | Phoenix | Pittsburgh | San Francisco | Seattle | Total_distance |
| 5 | 1 | 0 | 0 | 1 | 0 | 0 | 0 | 0 | 0 | 0 | 0 | 0 | 15202 |
| 6 | 2 | 0 | 0 | 0 | 0 | 0 | 0 | 1 | 1 | 0 | 0 | 0 | 6901 |
| 7 | 3 | 0 | 0 | 1 | 0 | 0 | 0 | 1 | 0 | 0 | 1 | 0 | 5145 |
| 8 | 4 | 0 | 0 | 1 | 0 | 0 | 1 | 1 | 0 | 0 | 1 | 0 | 3695 |
| 9 | 5 | 0 | 0 | 1 | 0 | 1 | 1 | 1 | 0 | 0 | 1 | 0 | 2711 |
| 10 | 6 | 0 | 1 | 1 | 0 | 1 | 1 | 1 | 0 | 0 | 1 | 0 | 2072 |
| 11 | 7 | 0 | 1 | 1 | 1 | 1 | 1 | 1 | 0 | 0 | 1 | 0 | 1505 |
| 12 | 8 | 0 | 1 | 1 | 1 | 1 | 1 | 1 | 0 | 0 | 1 | 1 | 1005 |
| 13 | 9 | 0 | 1 | 1 | 1 | 1 | 1 | 1 | 1 | 0 | 1 | 1 | 519 |
| 14 | 10 | 0 | 1 | 1 | 1 | 1 | 1 | 1 | 1 | 1 | 1 | 1 | 189 |
| 15 | 11 | 1 | 1 | 1 | 1 | 1 | 1 | 1 | 1 | 1 | 1 | 1 | 0 |

The final example in this section is structurally similar to the service center location model, but it arises in a slightly different business context.[9]

## 6.6 MANUFACTURING AND DISTRIBUTING FERTILIZER AT GREEN GRASS

*Like the previous example, this example is basically a fixed-cost location-assignment model. However, one difference here is that not all customers need to be assigned.*

The Green Grass Company manufactures and distributes a fertilizer product. The company sells its product to high-volume customers in various U.S. cities where it has manufacturing plants, but it can decide to operate only some of these plants in any given month. The fixed monthly cost for operating any plant is $60,000, the plant capacity for any operating plant is 2500 pounds per month, and the production cost at any operating plant is $10.25 per pound. After the product is manufactured, it is shipped to customers at a rate of $0.02 per pound per mile. The cities and the distances between them are listed in Table 6.12. The customers submit order sizes and price bids to Green Grass, as listed in Table 6.13. For example, the customer in Boston requires an order of 1430 pounds this month and is willing to pay $75,740 for it. Green Grass can decide to fill this order or not. If not, you can assume that the customer takes its business to another company. For the current month, Green Grass must decide which plants to operate and which customers to service from which operating plants to maximize its monthly profit.

Table 6.12    Distances Between Cities for the Green Grass Example

|  | Boston | Chicago | Dallas | Denver | Los Angeles | Miami | New York | Phoenix |
|---|---|---|---|---|---|---|---|---|
| Boston | 0 | 983 | 1815 | 1991 | 3036 | 1539 | 213 | 2664 |
| Chicago | 983 | 0 | 1205 | 1050 | 2112 | 1390 | 840 | 1729 |
| Dallas | 1815 | 1205 | 0 | 801 | 1425 | 1332 | 1604 | 1027 |
| Denver | 1991 | 1050 | 801 | 0 | 1174 | 2065 | 1780 | 836 |
| Los Angeles | 3036 | 2112 | 1425 | 1174 | 0 | 2757 | 2825 | 398 |
| Miami | 1539 | 1390 | 1332 | 2065 | 2757 | 0 | 1258 | 2359 |
| New York | 213 | 840 | 1604 | 1780 | 2825 | 1258 | 0 | 2442 |
| Phoenix | 2664 | 1729 | 1027 | 836 | 398 | 2359 | 2442 | 0 |

Table 6.13    Orders and Price Bids for the Green Grass Example

|  | Quantity | Price |
|---|---|---|
| Boston | 1430 | $75,740 |
| Chicago | 870 | $44,370 |
| Dallas | 770 | $46,320 |
| Denver | 1140 | $87,780 |
| Los Angeles | 700 | $43,850 |
| Miami | 830 | $21,000 |
| New York | 1230 | $74,850 |
| Phoenix | 1070 | $83,980 |

**Objective**    To develop a binary model to help Green Grass decide which manufacturing plants to operate and which customer orders to fill from which operating plants.

### WHERE DO THE NUMBERS COME FROM?

The distances in Table 6.12 are well known, and the customers can supply the data in Table 6.13. Cost accountants can supply the fixed cost of operating a plant, the variable production cost per pound, and the unit shipping cost per mile.

[9]This example is based on a real problem Winston was asked to solve during a consulting experience with a major U.S. manufacturing company.

## Solution

The variables and constraints for the Green Grass model are listed in Table 6.14. As in the previous example, there are two sets of binary variables. The first set indicates which plants are open for operation. The second set indicates which customers are supplied by which plants. The first constraint in the table ensures that no customer is supplied by more than one plant. However, it allows the possibility that the customer is not supplied by *any* Green Grass plant. The second constraint ensures that no plant produces and ships more than a logical capacity. This logical capacity is 0 if the plant is not opened at all, and it is the 2500-pound limit if the plant is opened. With these changing cells and constraints, the company must decide which plants to open and which customers to supply from which open plants to maximize profit.

**Table 6.14  Variables and Constraints for the Green Grass Model**

| | |
|---|---|
| **Input variables** | Fixed cost of operating a plant, production cost per pound, shipping cost per pound per mile, plant capacities, distance matrix, customer order sizes, and price bids |
| **Decision variables (changing cells)** | Which plants to open (binary), which customers to supply from which open plants (binary) |
| **Objective (target cell)** | Monthly profit |
| **Other calculated variables** | Pounds shipped out of each plant, logical capacity of each plant, number of plants shipping to each customer, revenue minus production and shipping cost for each plant/customer pair, total fixed plant cost |
| **Constraints** | Plants supplying each customer $\leq 1$ <br> Pounds shipped out of each plant $\leq$ Logical plant capacity |

### DEVELOPING THE SPREADSHEET MODEL

The completed spreadsheet model appears in Figure 6.25. (See the file Fixed Cost Transportation.xlsx.) It can be developed with the following steps:

**1** **Inputs.** Enter the inputs in the blue ranges.

**2** **Plant opening decisions.** Enter *any* set of 0s and 1s in the Open_plant range. These changing cells indicate which plants to open.

**3** **Assignment decisions.** Enter *any* set of 0s and 1s in the Assignments range. Each changing cell in this range indicates whether a particular plant supplies a particular customer.

**4** **Plants supplying customers.** Each customer can be supplied by at most one plant. To see how many plants are supplying each customer, create row sums of the Assignments range. That is, enter the formula

=SUM(B26:I26)

in cell J26 and copy it down to cell J33. Each such sum is just the number of 1s in that row of the Assignments range.

**5** **Amounts produced at plants.** We assume that if a plant is assigned to supply any customer, its production for that customer equals the customer's order requirement. Then to calculate the total produced (and shipped out) for each plant, enter the formula

=SUMPRODUCT(B26:B33,$L$11:$L$18)

in cell B34 for the first plant and copy it across row 34 for the other plants.

## Figure 6.25   Green Grass Production/Shipping Model

| | A | B | C | D | E | F | G | H | I | J | K | L | M |
|---|---|---|---|---|---|---|---|---|---|---|---|---|---|
| 1 | Fixed cost logistics model with customer bids for orders | | | | | | | | | | Range names used: | | |
| 2 | | | | | | | | | | | Assignments | =Model!$B$26:$I$33 | |
| 3 | Inputs | | | | | | | | | | Logical_capacity | =Model!$B$36:$I$36 | |
| 4 | Production cost per pound | $10.25 | | | | | | | | | Number_serviced_by | =Model!$J$26:$J$33 | |
| 5 | Shipping cost per pound per mile | $0.02 | | | | | | | | | Open_plant | =Model!$B$22:$I$22 | |
| 6 | Monthly plant fixed cost | $60,000 | | | | | | | | | Pounds_shipped_out_of | =Model!$B$34:$I$34 | |
| 7 | Plant capacity (pounds) | 2500 | | | | | | | | | Total_monthly_profit | =Model!$B$51 | |
| 8 | | | | | | | | | | | | | |
| 9 | Distance matrix | | | | | | | | | | Quantities required and prices bid by customers | | |
| 10 | | Boston | Chicago | Dallas | Denver | LA | Miami | NY | Phoenix | | | Quantity | Price |
| 11 | Boston | 0 | 983 | 1815 | 1991 | 3036 | 1539 | 213 | 2664 | | Boston | 1430 | $75,740 |
| 12 | Chicago | 983 | 0 | 1205 | 1050 | 2112 | 1390 | 840 | 1729 | | Chicago | 870 | $44,370 |
| 13 | Dallas | 1815 | 1205 | 0 | 801 | 1425 | 1332 | 1604 | 1027 | | Dallas | 770 | $46,320 |
| 14 | Denver | 1991 | 1050 | 801 | 0 | 1174 | 2065 | 1780 | 836 | | Denver | 1140 | $87,780 |
| 15 | LA | 3036 | 2112 | 1425 | 1174 | 0 | 2757 | 2825 | 398 | | LA | 700 | $43,850 |
| 16 | Miami | 1539 | 1390 | 1332 | 2065 | 2757 | 0 | 1258 | 2359 | | Miami | 830 | $21,000 |
| 17 | NY | 213 | 840 | 1604 | 1780 | 2825 | 1258 | 0 | 2442 | | NY | 1230 | $74,850 |
| 18 | Phoenix | 2664 | 1729 | 1027 | 836 | 398 | 2359 | 2442 | 0 | | Phoenix | 1070 | $83,980 |
| 19 | | | | | | | | | | | | | |
| 20 | Which plants to open | | | | | | | | | | | | |
| 21 | | Boston | Chicago | Dallas | Denver | LA | Miami | NY | Phoenix | | | | |
| 22 | Open plant | 1 | 0 | 0 | 1 | 0 | 0 | 1 | 1 | | | | |
| 23 | | | | | | | | | | | | | |
| 24 | Which customers (along side) to ship to from which plants (along top) | | | | | | | | | | | | |
| 25 | | Boston | Chicago | Dallas | Denver | LA | Miami | NY | Phoenix | Number supplied by | | Allowed | |
| 26 | Boston | 1 | 0 | 0 | 0 | 0 | 0 | 0 | 0 | 1 | <= | 1 | |
| 27 | Chicago | 0 | 0 | 0 | 0 | 0 | 0 | 1 | 0 | 1 | <= | 1 | |
| 28 | Dallas | 0 | 0 | 0 | 1 | 0 | 0 | 0 | 0 | 1 | <= | 1 | |
| 29 | Denver | 0 | 0 | 0 | 1 | 0 | 0 | 0 | 0 | 1 | <= | 1 | |
| 30 | LA | 0 | 0 | 0 | 0 | 0 | 0 | 0 | 1 | 1 | <= | 1 | |
| 31 | Miami | 0 | 0 | 0 | 0 | 0 | 0 | 0 | 0 | 0 | <= | 1 | |
| 32 | NY | 0 | 0 | 0 | 0 | 0 | 0 | 1 | 0 | 1 | <= | 1 | |
| 33 | Phoenix | 0 | 0 | 0 | 0 | 0 | 0 | 0 | 1 | 1 | <= | 1 | |
| 34 | Pounds shipped out of | 1430 | 0 | 0 | 1910 | 0 | 0 | 2100 | 1770 | | | | |
| 35 | | <= | <= | <= | <= | <= | <= | <= | <= | | | | |
| 36 | Logical capacity | 2500 | 0 | 0 | 2500 | 0 | 0 | 2500 | 2500 | | | | |
| 37 | | | | | | | | | | | | | |
| 38 | Monetary outputs | | | | | | | | | | | | |
| 39 | Matrix of revenue minus sum of production and shipping cost for each customer (along side) and plant (along top) pair | | | | | | | | | | | | |
| 40 | | Boston | Chicago | Dallas | Denver | LA | Miami | NY | Phoenix | | | | |
| 41 | Boston | $61,083 | $0 | $0 | $0 | $0 | $0 | $0 | $0 | | | | |
| 42 | Chicago | $0 | $0 | $0 | $0 | $0 | $0 | $20,837 | $0 | | | | |
| 43 | Dallas | $0 | $0 | $0 | $26,092 | $0 | $0 | $0 | $0 | | | | |
| 44 | Denver | $0 | $0 | $0 | $76,095 | $0 | $0 | $0 | $0 | | | | |
| 45 | LA | $0 | $0 | $0 | $0 | $0 | $0 | $0 | $31,103 | | | | |
| 46 | Miami | $0 | $0 | $0 | $0 | $0 | $0 | $0 | $0 | | | | |
| 47 | NY | $0 | $0 | $0 | $0 | $0 | $0 | $62,243 | $0 | | | | |
| 48 | Phoenix | $0 | $0 | $0 | $0 | $0 | $0 | $0 | $73,013 | | | | |
| 49 | | | | | | | | | | | | | |
| 50 | Monthly fixed cost | $240,000 | | | | | | | | | | | |
| 51 | Total monthly profit | $110,464 | | | | | | | | | | | |

⑥ **Logical plant capacities.** If a plant is not open, its capacity is 0. If it is open, its capacity is 2500. To calculate these effective plant capacities, enter the formula

=$B$7*B22

in cell B36 and copy it across row 36. The binary value in this formula reduces effective capacity to 0 or keeps it at 2500. (Note that the logic used here is very similar to the logic in the Great Threads fixed-cost model in Example 6.2. The only difference is that there is now a natural capacity, 2500, in case the plant is opened. In the Great Threads example, you had to calculate a suitable upper limit on production.)

⑦ **Revenues and variable costs.** It is useful to calculate a matrix of revenues and costs for all pairs of cities. To calculate these, enter the formula

=B26*($M11-$L11*($B$4+$B$5*B11))

in cell B41 and copy it to the range B41:I48. The first term in this formula is the binary assignment variable. If it is 0, no revenues or costs are incurred on this route because the route isn't used. However, if this binary value is 1, the formula subtracts costs from revenue. (Be careful to check the measurement units in these types of calculations. The production cost is pounds multiplied by cost per pound. The shipping cost is pounds multiplied by miles multiplied by cost per pound per mile.)

**8** **Fixed costs.** Each 1 in the Open_plant range adds a fixed cost. To calculate the total fixed cost, enter the formula

=B6*SUM(Open_plant)

in cell B50. This is the number of open plants multiplied by the fixed cost per plant.

**9** **Monthly profit.** Calculate the monthly profit in cell B51 with the formula

=SUM(B41:I48)-B50

### Using Solver

The Solver dialog box is shown in Figure 6.26. As usual, you should select the Simplex LP method, but you do not need to check the Non-Negative option because all changing cells are constrained to be binary, hence nonnegative. The last constraint ensures that each plant produces nothing if it isn't open, and no more than its capacity if it is open. The second constraint ensures that each customer's demand is satisfied by at most one plant. This allows the possibility that a customer's demand is not satisfied by Green Grass at all.

**Figure 6.26**

**Solver Dialog Box for the Green Grass Model**

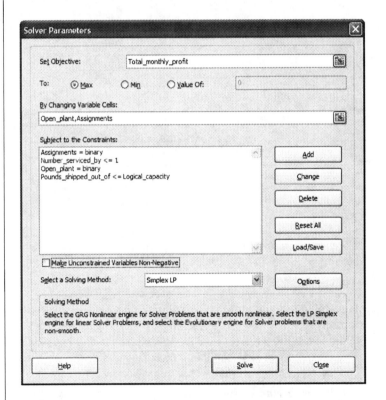

### Discussion of the Solution

The optimal solution in Figure 6.25 indicates that the company should open four plants: Boston (to supply the Boston customer), Denver (to supply the Denver and Dallas customers), New York (to supply the New York and Chicago customers), and Phoenix (to supply the Phoenix and Los Angeles customers). In addition, the model indicates that Green Grass should not supply the Miami customer at all. You can see the main reason for this if you calculate the ratio of order size to price bid for each customer. Miami's ratio is well below the others. Therefore, it is evidently not profitable to supply the Miami customer.

## Sensitivity Analysis

One possible sensitivity analysis is to see how much larger Miami's price bid needs to be before Green Grass supplies it. We tried this, varying Miami's price bid and keeping track of the row sum in cell J31 that indicates whether Miami is supplied. The results (after some trial and error to find an interesting price bid range) appear in Figure 6.27. When the Miami price bid increases to some value between $31,000 and $32,000, it becomes profitable to supply Miami. (You can check, by rerunning Solver, that Miami is then supplied by New York.)

Figure 6.27

Sensitivity to
Miami's Price Bid

| | A | B | C | D | E | F | G |
|---|---|---|---|---|---|---|---|
| 1 | Oneway analysis for Solver model in Model worksheet | | | | | | |
| 2 | | | | | | | |
| 3 | Miami bid price (cell $M$16) values along side, output cell(s) along top | | | | | | |
| 4 | | Number_serviced_by_Miami | | | | | |
| 5 | $28,000 | 0 | | | | | |
| 6 | $29,000 | 0 | | | | | |
| 7 | $30,000 | 0 | | | | | |
| 8 | $31,000 | 0 | | | | | |
| 9 | $32,000 | 1 | | | | | |
| 10 | $33,000 | 1 | | | | | |
| 11 | $34,000 | 1 | | | | | |
| 12 | $35,000 | 1 | | | | | |

Another possible sensitivity analysis is on the common plant capacity, currently 2500 pounds. The optimal solution in Figure 6.25 indicates that capacity is not currently a constraining factor. Four of the plants are open, and all are operating well under capacity. Therefore, an *increase* in the common capacity has absolutely no effect, and a slight *decrease* (down to 2100, the highest plant production) also has no effect. However, any decrease below 2100 should have an effect. This is explored in Figure 6.28, where the common plant capacity is varied and the optimal total fixed cost and profit are outputs. As you can see, if the capacity is below 2100, the total profit decreases. However, the total fixed cost remains constant, at least for this range of capacities. This implies that all of

Figure 6.28

Sensitivity to
Common Plant
Capacity

| | A | B | C | D | E | F |
|---|---|---|---|---|---|---|
| 1 | Oneway analysis for Solver model in Model worksheet | | | | | |
| 2 | | | | | | |
| 3 | Plant capacity (cell $B$7) values along side, output cell(s) along top | | | | | |
| 4 | | Monthly fixed cost | Total_monthly_profit | | | |
| 5 | 1500 | $240,000 | $32,433 | | | |
| 6 | 1750 | $240,000 | $32,433 | | | |
| 7 | 2000 | $240,000 | $89,628 | | | |
| 8 | 2250 | $240,000 | $110,464 | | | |
| 9 | 2500 | $240,000 | $110,464 | | | |

these solutions keep four plants open. How does the optimal solution change? Although the results in Figure 6.28 do not provide the answer, you can rerun Solver with any of these capacities to find out. It turns out that the *same* four plants stay open but supply fewer customers. For example, when the common capacity is 1500 or 1750, the four plants supply *only* the customers in their respective cities.

If you run these sensitivity analyses with SolverTable, you will immediately notice the longer computing times. These are *difficult* problems, even for Solver, and you won't get the immediate solutions you are accustomed to. Each problem has $2^{72}$ possible binary solutions (because there are 72 binary changing cells), which is an enormous number of potential solutions for Solver to sort through with its branch and bound algorithm. Although a binary model of this type and size is still well within Solver's capabilities, this example should convince you that not all management science optimization models are easy to solve. ▪

## MODELING ISSUES

1. We have assumed that all possible plant locations are in the same cities as the customers. This is not necessary. There could be any number of customers at one set of locations and any other number of plant locations at another set of locations. As long as the distances from each plant to each customer are known, the model changes hardly at all.

2. We have assumed that the inputs in the range B4:B7 (see Figure 6.25) are constant, the same for each plant or plant–customer pair. This is also not necessary. If these inputs differ across plants or plant–customer pairs, more input values must be estimated by the cost accountants, but modifications to the model itself are minimal.

3. We currently assume that the plants in the various locations are already built, and it is just a matter of which to open each month. Suppose instead that the company is expanding and must decide where (or whether) to build *new* plants. Then there is a one-time fixed cost of building each new plant, in addition to the fixed cost of opening an existing plant in the example. Unfortunately, combining these costs is not a trivial matter. The fixed cost of building must be amortized over some period of time so that it can be combined correctly with the *monthly* revenues and costs in the current model. ▪

## PROBLEMS

### Skill-Building Problems

**24.** In the original Western set-covering model in Figure 6.18, we used the number of hubs as the objective to minimize. Suppose instead that there is a fixed cost of locating a hub in any city, where these fixed costs can possibly vary across cities. Make up some reasonable fixed costs, modify the model appropriately, and use Solver to find the solution that minimizes the sum of fixed costs.

**25.** In the original Western set-covering model in Figure 6.18, we assumed that each city must be covered by at least one hub. Suppose that for added flexibility in flight routing, Western requires that each city

must be covered by at least two hubs. How do the model and optimal solution change?

**26.** Set-covering models such as the original Western model in Figure 6.18 often have multiple optimal solutions. See how many alternative optimal solutions you can find. Of course, each must use three hubs because this is optimal. (*Hint:* Use various initial values in the changing cells and then run Solver repeatedly.)[10]

**27.** How hard is it to expand a set-covering model to accommodate new cities? Answer this by modifying the model in Figure 6.21. (See the file Locating Hubs 2.xlsx.) Add several cities that must be served: Memphis,

[10]One of our colleagues at Indiana University, Vic Cabot, now deceased, worked for years trying to develop a general algorithm (other than trial and error) for finding *all* alternative optimal solutions to optimization models. It turns out that this is a very difficult problem—and one that Vic never totally solved.

Dallas, Tucson, Philadelphia, Cleveland, and Buffalo. You can look up the distances from these cities to each other and to the other cities in a reference book (or on the Web), or you can make up approximate distances.

   a. Modify the model appropriately, assuming that these new cities must be covered *and* are candidates for hub locations.

   b. Modify the model appropriately, assuming that these new cities must be covered but are *not* candidates for hub locations.

28. In the United Copiers service center model, we assumed that the potential locations of service centers are the same as existing customer locations. Change the model so that the customer locations are the ones given, but the only potential service center locations are in Memphis, Houston, Cleveland, Buffalo, Minneapolis, St. Louis, and Kansas City. You can look up the distances from these cities to the customer cities in a reference book (or on the Web), or you can make up approximate distances. Use Solver to find the optimal solution.

29. In the United Copiers service center model, we used total distance traveled as the objective to minimize. Suppose in addition that there is an annual fixed cost of locating a service center in any city, where this fixed cost can vary across cities. There is also a cost per mile of traveling. Modify the current model to make total annual cost the objective to minimize. You can make up reasonable fixed costs and unit traveling costs.

30. In the Green Grass shipping model, we assumed that certain inputs (see the range B4:B7 in Figure 6.25) are the same for all plants or plant–customer combinations. Change this so that the unit production cost, the monthly fixed cost, and the monthly capacity can vary by plant, and the unit shipping cost can vary by plant–customer combination. (You can make up data that vary around the values in the B4:B7 range.) Use Solver to find the new optimal solution.

31. In the optimal solution to the Green Grass shipping model, the Miami customer's order is not satisfied. Suppose that Green Grass decides, as a matter of policy, to satisfy *each* customer's order (at the customer's bid price). How much profit will the company lose from this policy decision?

32. In the Green Grass shipping model, use SolverTable to perform a sensitivity analysis on the fixed cost of opening a plant, letting it vary over some reasonable range that extends below and above the current value of $60,000. Keep track of enough outputs so that you can see the effect on the plants that are opened and the customers whose orders are satisfied, as well as on the total profit. Summarize your findings in words.

### Skill-Extending Problems

33. In the United Copiers service center model, we assumed that a customer is serviced totally by a single service center. Suppose a customer can be serviced partly by multiple service centers. For example, the customer in Denver could get half of its service from Dallas and the other half from San Francisco. In this case, you can assume that half of Denver's annual trips would be made from Dallas reps and half by San Francisco reps. Modify the model appropriately and then solve it with Solver. How do you interpret the optimal solution? (*Hint:* Allow the changing cells in the Assignments range to be fractional values between 0 and 1.)

34. In the Green Grass shipping model, we assumed that the plants are already built, so that in each month, the only decision is whether to open particular plants (at a monthly fixed cost). Consider instead a general location-shipping model of this type where the plants are not yet built. The company must first decide where to build plants, then how much to produce at the plants, and finally which customers to service from them. The problem is that the building costs are one-time costs, whereas other costs are monthly. How can you reconcile these two types of costs? What should you use as an objective to minimize? Illustrate your procedure on the Green Grass example, where the plant opening fixed costs are ignored—we assume that all plants that are built will remain open—but building costs (which you can make up) are given.

35. In the Green Grass shipping model, we currently assume that if a customer's order is satisfied, it must be satisfied from a *single* plant. Suppose instead that it can be satisfied from more than one plant. For example, if the company decides to satisfy Dallas's order, it could ship part of this order from Denver and part from Phoenix (or some other combination of open plants). Continue to assume, however, that the company must satisfy either *all* or *none* of each customer's order. Modify the model appropriately and use Solver to solve it. Does the solution change?

## 6.6 CUTTING STOCK MODELS

The final model we discuss in this chapter has found many real-world applications, especially in manufacturing. The model is relevant in situations where a product is produced in a standard size, which must then be cut into one of several patterns to satisfy customer orders. In contrast to the other models in this chapter, this cutting stock model does not have *binary* variables, but it does have *integer* variables. The problem is relatively easy to model, but it can be very time-consuming for Solver to solve. We warned you earlier that IP models are inherently more difficult to solve than general LP problems. The model in the following example illustrates that this is definitely the case.

---

| EXAMPLE | **6.7 CUTTING PAPER ROLLS AT RHEEM PAPER** |
|---|---|

The Rheem Paper Company produces rolls of paper of various types for its customers. One type is produced in standard rolls that are 60 inches wide and (when unwound) 200 yards long. Customers for this type of paper order rolls that are all 200 yards long, but can have any of the widths 12, 15, 20, 24, 30, or 40 inches. In a given week, Rheem waits for all orders and then decides how to cut its 60-inch rolls to satisfy the orders. For example, if there are five orders for 15-inch widths and two orders for 40-inch widths, Rheem could satisfy the order by producing three rolls, cutting each of the first two into a 40-inch and a 15-inch cut (with 5 inches left over) and cutting the third into four 15-inch cuts (with one of these left over). Each week, Rheem must decide how to cut its rolls in the most economical way to meet its orders. Specifically, it wants to cut as few rolls as possible.

**Objective** To find a way of cutting paper rolls in various widths so as to satisfy all customer orders and minimize the total number of rolls cut.

### Where Do the Numbers Come From?

The company knows the various widths its customers need, and it knows the orders for the various widths in the current week.

### Solution

Given the width of the rolls (60 inches) and the available widths (12, 15, 20, 24, 30, and 40), the first thing to do in this model is to "preprocess" the patterns that might be used. For example, one reasonable pattern is to cut a roll into four 15-inch cuts. In fact, this is perfect—there is no waste. Another pattern is to cut a roll into a 12-inch, a 15-inch, and a 24-inch cut, with 9 inches left over and unusable. The only patterns we consider (the feasible patterns) are the ones with no leftover paper that could be used for customer orders. For example, the pattern of a 12-inch cut and a 30-inch cut is not worth considering because another 12-inch (or 15-inch) cut could be obtained from the remainder. There is no model for determining all feasible patterns. You simply need to go through all the possibilities in a systematic way. After all possible patterns have been listed, the problem is then to decide how many rolls to cut into each pattern.

With this in mind, Table 6.15 lists the variables and constraints required for this model.

---

Table 6.15  Table of Variables and Constraints for the Cutting Stock Model

| | |
|---|---|
| **Input variables** | Width of roll, number of rolls of possible widths required by customers, list of patterns roll can be cut into (must be obtained manually) |
| **Decision variables (changing cells)** | Number of rolls cut for each pattern (integer) |
| **Objective (target cell)** | Number of rolls cut total |
| **Other output cells** | Number of each width obtained |
| **Constraints** | Number of each width obtained ≥ Number of each width required |

---

The spreadsheet model appears in Figure 6.29. (See the file Cutting Stock.xlsx.) To develop it, follow these steps:

**1 Inputs.** Enter the roll width, the available widths, and the number of orders for each width in the blue ranges. The orders in the Required range (row 42) will change from week to week, but the same model can handle any values in this range.

**2 Patterns.** Enter the feasible patterns in columns B through G, starting in row 10. The numbers in each row indicate how many of each width is in the pattern. For example, the first pattern has five 12-inch cuts with no waste. You can calculate the waste in column H by entering the formula

=$B$3-SUMPRODUCT(B$9:G$9,B10:G10)

and copying down. This waste column is useful as you try to list all feasible patterns. Specifically, the waste must be nonnegative, and it must be no greater than 12, the smallest

Figure 6.29   **Cutting Stock Model**

| | A | B | C | D | E | F | G | H | I | J | K |
|---|---|---|---|---|---|---|---|---|---|---|---|
| 1 | Cutting stock model | | | | | | | | Range names used: | | |
| 2 | | | | | | | | | Obtained | =Model!$B$40:$G$40 | |
| 3 | Width of roll | 60 | inches | | | | | | Required | =Model!$B$42:$G$42 | |
| 4 | | | | | | | | | Rolls_cut | =Model!$K$10:$K$35 | |
| 5 | Widths available | 12 | 15 | 20 | 24 | 30 | 40 | | Total_rolls_cut | =Model!$B$45 | |
| 6 | | | | | | | | | | | |
| 7 | Feasible ways of cutting up a roll | | | | | | | | | | |
| 8 | | | | | Width | | | | | Decisions | |
| 9 | Pattern | 12 | 15 | 20 | 24 | 30 | 40 | Waste | | Pattern | Rolls cut |
| 10 | 1 | 5 | 0 | 0 | 0 | 0 | 0 | 0 | | 1 | 0 |
| 11 | 2 | 3 | 1 | 0 | 0 | 0 | 0 | 9 | | 2 | 0 |
| 12 | 3 | 3 | 0 | 1 | 0 | 0 | 0 | 4 | | 3 | 0 |
| 13 | 4 | 3 | 0 | 0 | 1 | 0 | 0 | 0 | | 4 | 12 |
| 14 | 5 | 2 | 2 | 0 | 0 | 0 | 0 | 6 | | 5 | 0 |
| 15 | 6 | 2 | 1 | 1 | 0 | 0 | 0 | 1 | | 6 | 1 |
| 16 | 7 | 2 | 0 | 0 | 0 | 1 | 0 | 6 | | 7 | 0 |
| 17 | 8 | 1 | 3 | 0 | 0 | 0 | 0 | 3 | | 8 | 0 |
| 18 | 9 | 1 | 1 | 0 | 1 | 0 | 0 | 9 | | 9 | 0 |
| 19 | 10 | 1 | 1 | 0 | 0 | 1 | 0 | 3 | | 10 | 1 |
| 20 | 11 | 1 | 0 | 2 | 0 | 0 | 0 | 8 | | 11 | 0 |
| 21 | 12 | 1 | 0 | 1 | 1 | 0 | 0 | 4 | | 12 | 0 |
| 22 | 13 | 1 | 0 | 0 | 2 | 0 | 0 | 0 | | 13 | 9 |
| 23 | 14 | 1 | 0 | 0 | 0 | 0 | 1 | 8 | | 14 | 0 |
| 24 | 15 | 0 | 4 | 0 | 0 | 0 | 0 | 0 | | 15 | 1 |
| 25 | 16 | 0 | 2 | 1 | 0 | 0 | 0 | 10 | | 16 | 1 |
| 26 | 17 | 0 | 2 | 0 | 1 | 0 | 0 | 6 | | 17 | 0 |
| 27 | 18 | 0 | 2 | 0 | 0 | 1 | 0 | 0 | | 18 | 4 |
| 28 | 19 | 0 | 1 | 2 | 0 | 0 | 0 | 5 | | 19 | 2 |
| 29 | 20 | 0 | 1 | 1 | 1 | 0 | 0 | 1 | | 20 | 2 |
| 30 | 21 | 0 | 1 | 0 | 0 | 0 | 1 | 5 | | 21 | 0 |
| 31 | 22 | 0 | 0 | 3 | 0 | 0 | 0 | 0 | | 22 | 2 |
| 32 | 23 | 0 | 0 | 1 | 0 | 1 | 0 | 10 | | 23 | 1 |
| 33 | 24 | 0 | 0 | 1 | 0 | 0 | 1 | 0 | | 24 | 7 |
| 34 | 25 | 0 | 0 | 0 | 1 | 1 | 0 | 6 | | 25 | 0 |
| 35 | 26 | 0 | 0 | 0 | 0 | 2 | 0 | 0 | | 26 | 4 |
| 36 | | | | | | | | | | | |
| 37 | Constraint on satisfying orders | | | | | | | | | | |
| 38 | | | | | Width | | | | | | |
| 39 | | 12 | 15 | 20 | 24 | 30 | 40 | | | | |
| 40 | Obtained | 48 | 20 | 22 | 32 | 14 | 7 | | | | |
| 41 | | >= | >= | >= | >= | >= | >= | | | | |
| 42 | Required | 48 | 19 | 22 | 32 | 14 | 7 | | | | |
| 43 | | | | | | | | | | | |
| 44 | Objective to minimize | | | | | | | | | | |
| 45 | Total rolls cut | 47 | | | | | | | | | |

available width. (If the waste were 12 or greater, it would be possible to get another usable cut from the pattern.) For this particular roll width and this particular set of available widths, there are 26 feasible patterns. (You have to be careful when listing them. It is easy to miss some.)

**③ Decision variables.** Enter *any* values into the Rolls_cut range. These are the decision variables in this model. They indicate how many rolls to cut into the various patterns.

**④ Widths obtained.** Calculate the number of each width obtained by entering the formula

=SUMPRODUCT(Rolls_cut,B10:B35)

in cell B40 and copying it to the rest of the Obtained range. For example, the value in cell B40 is the number of rolls of width 12 inches obtained from *all* possible patterns.

**⑤ Rolls cut.** Calculate the number of rolls cut in cell B45 with the formula

=SUM(Rolls_cut)

### USING SOLVER

Fill out the Solver dialog box as indicated in Figure 6.30. The objective is to minimize the number of rolls produced, subject to meeting customer orders. Also, the number cut according to each pattern must be an integer (but not binary). As usual, you should check the Non-Negative option and choose the Simplex LP method.

**Discussion of the Solution**

The solution indicates that Rheem can meet its customer orders this week with 47 rolls, cut as specified in rows 10 through 35. For example, 12 of the 47 rolls should be cut according to pattern 4, each with three 12-inch rolls and one 24-inch roll. (There is at least one other optimal solution with objective value 47 that you might find.) Note that there are two

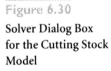

Figure 6.30

**Solver Dialog Box for the Cutting Stock Model**

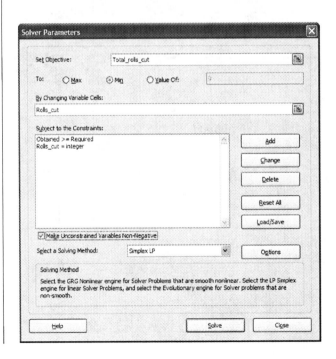

sources of waste in this solution. First, there is the unusable waste from all leftover rolls with width less than 12 inches. For example, there are two 1-inch rolls left over from the two rolls cut into pattern 20. Second, there is some waste from the usable rolls that are not needed in this week's orders. Fortunately, it is minimal—only one 15-inch roll is left over. Actually, if Rheem solves this model on a weekly basis, the model could easily incorporate the inventory of usable leftover rolls from *previous* weeks.

### Solver Tolerance Setting

Until now, we have suggested setting the Solver tolerance to 0%. This guarantees *the* optimal solution. However, this example illustrates why the default tolerance setting is 5% (or at least not 0%). If you set the tolerance to 0% and click on Solve, you will see that Solver quickly gets to a solution that requires 47 rolls, but then it runs and runs and runs. (We got tired of waiting, so we pressed the Ctrl+Break key combination to stop it prematurely.) After some experimenting, we found that with the tolerance set at 2% or above, the solution is obtained almost instantaneously, but with the tolerance set at 1% or 0%, it runs seemingly forever. This behavior is not at all uncommon in IP models. Solver often finds a very good or even optimal solution very quickly, but then it takes a long time to verify that it is optimal (or to find something slightly better). The moral is clear. If you set the tolerance to a low value and find that the Solver is taking forever without getting anywhere, press Ctrl+Break to get out. By that time, you probably already have a very good or even optimal solution. ▪

### MODELING ISSUES

We did not perform any sensitivity analysis on this model because there is no obvious sensitivity analysis to perform. The only inputs are the roll width, the set of available widths, and the order amounts. Although it would make sense to perform sensitivity analysis on the order amounts, it would make more sense (in a realistic setting) to wait for next week's orders and simply solve the problem again. Note that the model is *not* set up to perform sensitivity analysis (with SolverTable) on the roll width or the set of available widths. If these change, the entire table of patterns must be recreated manually. For example, if the roll width changes to 64 inches, patterns 2, 9, 11, 14, 16, and 23 are no longer in the list (why not?), and several new patterns enter the list (what are they?). ▪

## PROBLEMS

### Skill-Building Problems

**36.** In the cutting stock example, we minimized the total number of rolls cut. Do you get the same solution if you minimize the total inches of waste? For example, given the solution in Figure 6.29, this waste includes 2 inches from pattern 6, 12 inches from the extra 12-inch roll produced (in cell B40), and a couple of others. Solve the problem with this objective.

**37.** Woodco sells 3-foot, 5-foot, and 9-foot pieces of lumber. Woodco's customers demand 25 3-foot boards, 20 5-foot boards, and 15 9-foot boards. Woodco meets its demands by cutting up 17-foot boards. How can it satisfy its customers' demands with the least amount of waste? Assume that all boards are the same width and thickness.

### Skill-Extending Problem

**38.** The Mayfree Appliance Company requires sheet metal for its appliances. The company can purchase long coils of sheet metal in two different widths: 65 inches and 40 inches. The company must purchase the coils by linear foot of length: $1.20 per foot for a 64-inch coil and $1.00 per foot for a 40-inch coil. (This implies that a square foot, say, of the wider coil is less expensive.) Up to 4000 feet of the 65-inch coil is available, and up to 6000 feet of the 40-inch coil is available. There are manufacturing requirements for six different widths: 50, 45, 40, 35, 20, and 10 inches. Mayfree's requirements are expressed as lengths of the various widths. The company requires 1000 feet of 50-inch width, 2500 feet of 45-inch width, 3000 feet of 40-inch width, 2300 feet of 35-inch width, 1300 feet of 20-inch width, and 2000 feet of 10-inch width. Determine how much of each width coil Mayfree should purchase and how it should cut the coils into various widths to meet its requirements at minimal cost. (*Hint:* First, list all patterns that can be cut from a 65-inch coil, and do the same for a 40-inch coil. Then have a changing cell for each pattern that designates the number of linear feet to be cut in this pattern.)

## 6.7 CONCLUSION

Three important points emerge from this chapter.

▪ A wide variety of important problems can be modeled as IP problems with binary variables. These can generally be identified as problems where at least some of the activities (such as making a particular investment, opening a particular plant, or supplying a customer from a particular plant) must be done or not done; there is no in-between. Regular LP models cannot handle these problems; IP models with binary variables often can.

▪ Some IP models are simply LP models with integer constraints on the variables. For example, you might constrain the number of refrigerators produced to be an integer. These problems can often be solved by solving the associated LP model and then rounding the solution to integer values. Although there is no guarantee that the rounded solution is optimal, it is often close enough. In contrast, most of the problems discussed in this chapter introduce binary decision variables that specify whether an activity is done or not. If you ignore the binary constraints and only constrain these variables to be *between* 0 and 1, it is generally impossible to find the optimal solution by rounding.

▪ The solution approach required for IP problems, especially those with 0–1 variables, is inherently more difficult than the simplex method for LP problems. The relatively small examples in this chapter might give the impression that a spreadsheet Solver can handle IP models just as easily as it handles LP models, but this is definitely not the case. In fact, even with the most sophisticated IP computer codes on the most powerful computers, there are IP problems—from real applications—that defy solution. Analysts typically employ heuristic methods on these really difficult problems.

## Summary of Key Management Science Terms

| Term | Explanation | Page |
|---|---|---|
| Binary variables | Variables constrained to have values 1 or 0; usually used to indicate whether an activity is undertaken or not . Also called *0–1 variables* | 208 |
| IP models | Optimization models where some or all of the decision variables are constrained to have integer values | 208 |
| Branch and bound algorithm | A general algorithm for searching through all integer solutions in an IP model | 210 |
| Complete enumeration | An exhaustive method of checking the objective value of *every* feasible integer solution | 210 |
| Implicit enumeration | A clever way of checking that no feasible integer solution can possibly be better than the optimal solution, without *explicitly* looking at each feasible integer solution | 210 |
| Incumbent solution | The best feasible solution found so far | 210 |

*(continued)*

| Term | Explanation | Page |
|------|-------------|------|
| LP relaxation | The same linear model, but without the integer constraints | 211 |
| Fixed-cost models | Difficult-to-solve models where certain costs are fixed at some positive level if an activity is undertaken at any level, and are 0 otherwise | 220 |
| Either–or constraints | Constraints where one of two mutually exclusive conditions must be satisfied | 228 |
| Set-covering models | Models where members of one set (such as ambulances) must be located so that they cover members of another set (such as city districts) | 233 |
| Location models | Models where items (such as branch offices) must be located to provide required services at minimal cost | 233 |

## Summary of Key Excel Terms

| Term | Explanation | Excel | Page |
|------|-------------|-------|------|
| Solver Tolerance setting | Setting that specifies whether Solver will stop at a near-optimal integer solution or will continue to optimality | Specify under Solver Options (default 5% doesn't guarantee optimality; 0% does) | 211 |

## PROBLEMS

### Skill-Building Problems

**39.** Four projects are available for investment. The projects require the cash flows and yield the net present values (in millions) shown in the file P06_39.xlsx. If $6 million is available now for investment, find the investment plan that maximizes NPV.

**40.** You are given a group of possible investment projects for your company's capital. For each project, you are given the NPV the project would add to the firm, as well as the cash outflow required by each project during each year. Given the information in the file P06_40.xlsx, determine the investments that maximize the firm's NPV. The firm has $30 million available during each of the next five years. All numbers are in millions of dollars.

**41.** You are moving from New Jersey to Indiana and have rented a truck that can haul up to 1100 cubic feet of furniture. The volume and value of each item you are considering moving on the truck are given in the file P06_41.xlsx. Which items should you bring to Indiana?

**42.** NASA must determine how many of three types of objects to bring on board the space shuttle. The weight and benefit of each of the items are given in the file P06_42.xlsx. If the space shuttle can carry up to 2600 pounds of items 1 through 3, how many of each item should be taken on the space shuttle, assuming that at least one of each is necessary?

**43.** Coach Night is trying to choose the starting lineup for the basketball team. The team consists of seven players who have been rated on a scale of 1 (poor) to 3 (excellent) according to their ball handling, shooting, rebounding, and defensive abilities. The positions that each player is allowed to play and the players' abilities are listed in the file P06_43.xlsx. The five-player starting lineup must satisfy the following restrictions:

- At least four members must be able to play guard (G), at least two members must be able to play forward (F), and at least one member must be able to play center (C).
- The average ballhandling, shooting, and rebounding level of the starting lineup must each be at least 1.8.
- Either player 2 or player 3 (or both) must start.

Given these constraints, Coach Night wants to maximize the total defensive ability of the starting team. Use Solver to determine his starting team.

**44.** To graduate from Southeastern University with a major in operations research (OR), a student must complete at least two math courses, at least two OR courses, and at least two computer courses. Some courses can be used to fulfill more than one requirement: Calculus can fulfill the math requirement; Operations Research can fulfill the math and OR requirements; Data Structures can fulfill the computer and math requirements; Business Statistics can fulfill the math and OR requirements; Computer Simulation can fulfill the OR and computer requirements; Introduction to Computer Programming can fulfill the computer requirement; and Forecasting can fulfill the OR and math requirements. Some courses are prerequisites for others: Calculus is a prerequisite for Business Statistics; Introduction to Computer Programming is a prerequisite for Computer Simulation and for Data Structures; and Business Statistics is a prerequisite for Forecasting. Determine how to minimize the number of courses needed to satisfy the major requirements. (*Hint:* Because Calculus is a prerequisite for Business Statistics, for example, you will need a constraint that ensures that the changing cell for Calculus is greater than or equal to the changing cell for Business Statistics.)

**45.** Based on Bean et al. (1987). Boris Milkem's firm owns six assets. The expected selling price (in millions of dollars) for each asset is given in the file P06_45.xlsx. For example, if asset 1 is sold in year 2, the firm receives $20 million. To maintain a regular cash flow, Milkem must sell at least $20 million of assets during year 1, at least $30 million worth during year 2, and at least $35 million worth during year 3. Determine how Milkem can maximize his total revenue from assets sold during the next three years.

**46.** The Cubs are trying to determine which of the following free-agent pitchers should be signed: Rick Sutcliffe (RS), Bruce Sutter (BS), Dennis Eckersley (DE), Steve Trout (ST), or Tim Stoddard (TS). (Feel free to substitute your own set of players for these "old" guys.) The cost of signing each pitcher and the predicted number of victories each pitcher will add to the Cubs are listed in the file P06_46.xlsx. The Cubs want to sign the pitchers who will add the most victories to the team. Determine who the Cubs should sign based on the following restrictions:
- At most, $25 million can be spent.
- At most, two right-handed pitchers can be signed.
- The Cubs cannot sign both BS and RS.

**47.** Based on Sonderman and Abrahamson (1985). In treating a brain tumor with radiation, physicians want the maximum amount of radiation possible to bombard the tissue containing the tumors. The constraint is, however, that there is a maximum amount of radiation that normal tissue can handle without suffering tissue damage. Physicians must therefore decide how to aim the radiation to maximize the radiation that hits the tumor tissue subject to the constraint of not damaging the normal tissue. As a simple example of this situation, suppose six types of radiation beams (beams differ in where they are aimed and their intensity) can be aimed at a tumor. The region containing the tumor has been divided into six regions: three regions contain tumors and three contain normal tissue. The amount of radiation delivered to each region by each type of beam is shown in the file P06_47.xlsx. If each region of normal tissue can handle at most 60 units of radiation, which beams should be used to maximize the total amount of radiation received by the tumors?

**48.** Because of excessive pollution on the Momiss River, the state of Momiss is going to build some pollution control stations. Three sites are under consideration. Momiss is interested in controlling the pollution levels of two pollutants. The state legislature requires that at least 80,000 tons of pollutant 1 and at least 60,000 tons of pollutant 2 be removed from the river. The relevant data for this problem are shown in the file P06_48.xlsx. The last two rows indicate the number of tons of pollutants removed per ton treated.
- **a.** Determine how to minimize the cost of meeting the state legislature's goals.
- **b.** Use SolverTable to analyze how a change in the requirement for pollutant 1 changes the optimal solution. Do the same for pollutant 2.

**49.** A manufacturer can sell product 1 at a profit of $20 per unit and product 2 at a profit of $40 per unit. Three units of raw material are needed to manufacture one unit of product 1, and six units of raw material are needed to manufacture one unit of product 2. A total of 15,000 units of raw material are available. If any product 1 is produced, a setup cost of $20,000 is incurred; if any product 2 is produced, a setup cost of $35,000 is incurred.
- **a.** Determine how to maximize the manufacturer's profit.
- **b.** If either of the products is *not* produced in the optimal solution, use SolverTable to see how much this product's unit profit must be before it will be produced, and then use SolverTable again to see how much this product's fixed cost must be decreased before it will be produced.

**50.** A company is considering opening warehouses in four cities: New York, Los Angeles, Chicago, and Atlanta. Each warehouse can ship 10,000 units per week. The weekly fixed cost of keeping each warehouse open is $40,000 for New York, $50,000 for Los Angeles, $30,000 for Chicago, and $25,000 for Atlanta. Region 1 of the country requires 8000 units per week, region 2 requires 7000 units per week, and region 3 requires 4000 units per week. The costs (including production and shipping costs) of sending one unit from a warehouse to a region are shown in the file P06_50.xlsx. The company wants to meet weekly demands at minimum cost, subject to the preceding information and the following restrictions:
- If the New York warehouse is opened, then the Los Angeles warehouse must be opened.
- At most two warehouses can be opened.
- Either the Atlanta or the Los Angeles warehouse must be opened.

**51.** Glueco produces three types of glue on two different production lines. Each line can be used by up to 20 workers at a time. Workers are paid $500 per week on production line 1 and $900 per week on production line 2. For a week of production, it costs $5000 to set up production line 1 and $4000 to set up production line 2. During a week on a production line, each worker produces the number of units of glue shown in the file P06_51.xlsx. Each week, at least 800 units of glue 1, at least 750 units of glue 2, and at least 100 units of glue 3 must be produced. Determine how to minimize the total cost of meeting weekly demands. Make sure the number of workers assigned to each line is an integer.

52. Fruit Computer produces two types of computers: Pear computers and Apricot computers. The relevant data are given in the file P06_52.xlsx. The equipment cost is a fixed cost that is incurred if any of this type of computer is produced. A total of 2000 chips and 1500 hours of labor are available.
    a. Determine how Fruit can maximize its net profit.
    b. Use SolverTable to analyze the effect on the optimal solution of a change in the unit margin of Pear computers. Do the same for the unit margin of Apricot computers.

53. A product can be produced on four different machines. Each machine has a fixed setup cost, variable production cost per unit processed, and a production capacity, given in the file P06_53.xlsx. A total of 2000 units of the product must be produced. Determine how to minimize the total cost.

54. Consider the Pigskin example (Example 3.3) from Chapter 3. Find Pigskin's optimal production policy if, in addition to the given production and holding costs, there is a fixed cost of $50,000 during any month in which there is positive production. Assume now that storage capacity is 20,000 footballs.

55. McPherson Publishers is considering publishing five textbooks. The maximum number of copies of each textbook that can be sold, the variable cost of producing each textbook, the selling price of each textbook, and the fixed cost of a production run for each book are given in the file P06_55.xlsx. For example, producing 2000 copies of book 1 brings in a revenue of (2000)(50) = $100,000 but costs 80,000 + 25(2000) = $130,000.
    a. Determine how McPherson can maximize its profit if it can produce at most 10,000 books.
    b. Use SolverTable to analyze the effect on the optimal solution of a change in the demand for book 1. Repeat for the demands for the other books.

56. Comquat owns four production plants at which computer workstations are produced. Comquat can sell up to 20,000 computers per year at a price of $3500 per computer. For each plant, the production capacity, the production cost per computer, and the fixed cost of operating a plant for a year are given in the file P06_56.xlsx. Determine how Comquat can maximize its yearly profit from computer production.

57. Eastinghouse sells air conditioners. The annual demand for air conditioners in each region of the country is as follows: East, 100,000; South, 150,000; Midwest, 110,000; and West, 90,000. Eastinghouse is considering building its air conditioners in four different cities: New York, Atlanta, Chicago, and Los Angeles. The cost of producing an air conditioner in a city and shipping it to a region of the country is given in the file P06_57.xlsx. Any factory can produce up to 150,000 air conditioners per year. The annual fixed cost of operating a factory in each city is given in the same file. At least 50,000 units of the Midwest demand for air conditioners must come from New York, and at least 50,000 units of the Midwest demand must come from Atlanta. Determine how Eastinghouse can minimize the annual cost of meeting demand for air conditioners.

58. During the next five periods, the demands listed in the file P06_58.xlsx must be met on time. At the beginning of period 1, the inventory level is 0. During each period when production occurs, a setup cost of $2500 and a per-unit production cost of $20 are incurred. At the end of each period, a per-unit holding cost of $10 is incurred. Determine the cost-minimizing production schedule.

59. At a machine tool plant, five jobs must be completed each day. The time it takes to do each job depends on the machine used to do the job. If a machine is used at all, a setup time is required. The relevant times (in minutes) are given in the file P06_59.xlsx.
    a. Determine how to minimize the sum of the setup and machine operation times needed to complete all jobs.
    b. Use SolverTable to see how a change in the setup time for machine 4 changes the optimal solution.
    c. Use SolverTable to see how a change in the required time for machine 1 to complete job 3 changes the optimal solution.

60. Ford has four automobile plants. Each is capable of producing the Focus, Mustang, or Crown Victoria, but it can produce only one of these cars. The fixed cost of operating each plant for a year and the variable cost of producing a car of each type at each plant are given in the file P06_60.xlsx. Ford faces the following restrictions:
    ■ Each plant can produce only one type of car.
    ■ The total production of each type of car must be at a single plant. For example, if any Mustangs are made at plant 1, then all Mustangs must be made there.
    ■ Each year, Ford must produce five million of each type of car.
        a. Determine how to minimize the annual cost of producing these cars.
        b. Use SolverTable to see how a change in the demand for Mustangs changes the optimal solution.
        c. Use SolverTable to see how the optimal solution is affected by a change in the variable cost of producing a Focus at plant 4.

**61.** Heinsco produces tomato sauce at five different plants. The tomato sauce is then shipped to one of three warehouses, where it is stored until it is shipped to one of the company's four customers. The following inputs for the problem are given in the file P06_61.xlsx:

- The plant capacities (in tons)
- The cost per ton of producing tomato sauce at each plant and shipping it to each warehouse
- The cost of shipping a ton of sauce from each warehouse to each customer
- The customer requirements (in tons) of sauce
- The fixed annual cost of operating each plant and warehouse

Heinsco must decide which plants and warehouses to open, and which routes from plants to warehouses and from warehouses to customers to use. All customer demand must be met. A given customer's demand can be met from more than one warehouse, and a given plant can ship to more than one warehouse.

a. Determine the minimum-cost method for meeting customer demands.

b. Use SolverTable to see how a change in the capacity of plant 1 affects the total cost.

c. Use SolverTable to see how a change in the customer 2 demand affects the total cost.

d. Suppose that each customer's demand must be met from a *single* warehouse. Solve the problem with this restriction.

**62.** Eight jobs need to be completed. Each job can be completed on any of six machines, and each machine can complete any number of jobs. If a machine is assigned to at least one job, the setup time listed in the file P06_62.xlsx is required. (All times are in hours.) The time required for each machine to complete each job (excluding the setup time) is also listed in the same file. How should the jobs be assigned to machines to minimize the sum of setup times and job completion times?

**63.** Based on Walker (1974). The Smalltown Fire Department currently has seven conventional ladder companies and seven alarm boxes. The two closest ladder companies to each alarm box are listed in the file P06_63.xlsx. The town council wants to maximize the number of conventional ladder companies that can be replaced with "tower" ladder companies. Unfortunately, political considerations dictate that a conventional company can be replaced only if, after replacement, at least one of the two closest companies to each alarm box is still a conventional company. Determine how to maximize the number of conventional companies that can be replaced by tower companies.

**64.** State University must purchase 1100 computers from three vendors. Vendor 1 charges $500 per computer plus a total delivery charge of $5000. Vendor 2 charges $350 per computer plus a total delivery charge of $4000. Vendor 3 charges $250 per computer plus a total delivery charge of $6000. Vendor 1 will sell the university at most 500 computers, vendor 2, at most 900, and vendor 3, at most 400. The minimum order from any vendor is 200 computers. Determine how to minimize the cost of purchasing the needed computers.

**65.** At Blair General Hospital, six types of surgical operations are performed. The types of operations each surgeon is qualified to perform (indicated by an X) are listed in the file P06_65.xlsx. Suppose that surgeons 1 and 2 dislike each other and cannot be on duty at the same time. Determine the minimum number of surgeons required so that the hospital can perform all types of surgery.

**66.** Eastinghouse ships 12,000 capacitors per month to its customers. The capacitors can be produced at three different plants. The production capacity, fixed monthly cost of operation, and variable cost of producing a capacitor at each plant are given in the file P06_66.xlsx. The fixed cost for a plant is incurred only if the plant is used to make any capacitors. If a plant is used at all, at least 3000 capacitors per month must be produced at the plant. Determine how to minimize the company's monthly costs of meeting its customers' demands.

**67.** Based on Liggett (1973). A court decision has stated that the enrollment of each high school in Metropolis must be at least 20% black. The numbers of black students and white students in each of the city's five school districts are listed in the file P06_67.xlsx. The distance (in miles) that a student in each district must travel to each high school is shown in the same file. School board policy requires that all students in a given district must attend the same school. Assuming that each school must have an enrollment of at least 150 students, determine how to minimize the total distance that Metropolis students must travel to high school.

**68.** Based on Westerberg, Bjorklund, and Hultman (1977). Newcor's steel mill has received an order for 150 tons of steel. The steel must be 5% carbon and 5% molybdenum by weight. The steel is manufactured by combining three types of metal: steel ingots, scrap steel, and alloys. Four individual steel ingots are available. At most, one of each can be purchased. The weight (in tons), cost per ton, and the carbon and molybdenum content of each ingot are given in the file P06_68.xlsx. Three types of alloys can be purchased. The cost per ton and chemical makeup of each alloy are given in the same file. Steel scrap can be purchased at a cost of $100 per ton. Steel scrap contains 3% carbon and 9% molybdenum. Determine how Newcor can minimize the cost of filling its order.

**69.** Based on Boykin (1985). Chemco annually produces 359 million pounds of the chemical maleic anhydride.

A total of four reactors are available to produce maleic anhydride. Each reactor can be run on one of three settings. The cost (in thousands of dollars) and pounds produced (in millions) annually for each reactor and each setting are given in the file P06_69.xlsx. A reactor can be run on only one setting for the entire year. Determine how Chemco can minimize the cost of meeting its annual demand for maleic anhydride.

70. Based on Zangwill (1992). Hallco runs a day shift and a night shift. Regardless of the number of units produced, the only production cost during a shift is a setup cost. It costs $8000 to run the day shift and $4500 to run the night shift. Demand for the next two days is as follows: day 1, 2000; night 1, 3000; day 2, 2000; night 2, 3000. It costs $1 per unit to hold a unit in inventory for a shift.
    a. Determine a production schedule that minimizes the sum of setup and inventory costs. All demand must be met on time. (*Note:* Not all shifts have to be run.)
    b. After listening to a seminar on the virtues of the Japanese theory of production, Hallco has cut the setup cost of its day shift to $1000 per shift and the setup cost of its night shift to $3500 per shift. Now determine a production schedule that minimizes the sum of setup and inventory costs. All demand must be met on time. Show that the decrease in setup costs has actually raised the average inventory level. Is this reasonable?

71. Based on Fitzsimmons and Allen (1983). The State of Texas frequently audits companies doing business in Texas. Because these companies often have headquarters located outside the state, auditors must be sent to out-of-state locations. Each year, auditors must make 500 trips to cities in the Northeast, 400 trips to cities in the Midwest, 300 trips to cities in the West, and 400 trips to cities in the South. Texas is considering basing auditors in Chicago, New York, Atlanta, and Los Angeles. The annual cost of basing auditors in any city is $100,000. The cost of sending an auditor from any of these cities to a given region of the country is given in the file P06_71.xlsx. Determine how to minimize the annual cost of conducting out-of-state audits.

## Skill-Extending Problems

72. Suppose you own 11 bronze coins worth a total of $150, 11 silver coins worth a total of $160, and 11 gold coins worth a total of $170. Develop a linear integer model to find a combination of coins worth exactly $110.

73. Cousin Bruzie of radio station WABC schedules radio commercials in 60-second blocks. This hour, the station has sold time for commercials of 15, 16, 20, 25, 30, 35, 40, and 50 seconds. Determine the minimum number of 60-second blocks of commercials that must be scheduled to fit in all the current hour's commercials.

74. Based on Bean et al. (1988). Simon's Mall has 10,000 square feet of space to rent and wants to determine the types of stores that should occupy the mall. The minimum number and maximum number of each type of store (along with the square footage of each type) are given in the file P06_74.xlsx. The annual profit made by each type of store depends on how many stores of that type are in the mall. This dependence is given in the same file. For example, if two department stores are in the mall, each department store will earn $210,000 profit per year. Each store pays 5% of its annual profit as rent to Simon's. Determine how Simon can maximize its rental income from the mall.

75. Indiana University's Business School has two rooms that seat 50 students, one room that seats 100 students, and one room that seats 150 students. Classes are held five hours a day. At present, the four types of requests for rooms are listed in the file P06_75.xlsx. The business school must decide how many requests of each type to assign to each type of room. Suppose that classes that cannot be assigned to a business school room are assigned to another campus building. Determine how to assign classes to minimize the number of hours students spend each week outside the business building.

76. Based on Efroymson and Ray (1966). Stonecutters is a new bakery chain that sells bread to customers throughout the state of Indiana. Stonecutters is considering building bakeries in three locations: Evansville, Indianapolis, and South Bend. Each bakery can bake up to 900,000 loaves of bread each year. The cost of building a bakery at each site is $5 million in Evansville, $4 million in Indianapolis, and $4.5 million in South Bend. To simplify the problem, we assume that Stonecutters has only three customers. Their demands each year are 700,000 loaves (customer 1); 400,000 loaves (customer 2); and 300,000 loaves (customer 3). The total cost of baking and shipping a loaf of bread to a customer is given in the file P06_76.xlsx. Assume that future shipping and production costs are discounted at a rate of 12% per year. Assume that once built, a bakery lasts forever. How would you minimize the company's total cost of meeting demand, present and future?

77. On Monday morning, you have $3000 in cash on hand. For the next seven days, the following cash requirements must be met: Monday, $5000; Tuesday, $6000; Wednesday, $9000; Thursday, $2000; Friday, $7000; Saturday, $2000; Sunday, $3000. At the beginning of each day, you must decide how much money (if any) to withdraw from the bank. It costs $10 to make a withdrawal of any size. You believe that the

opportunity cost of having $1 of cash on hand for a year is $0.20. Assume that opportunity costs are incurred on each day's ending balance. Determine how much money you should withdraw from the bank during each of the next seven days.

78. Based on Eaton et al. (1985). Gotham City has been divided into eight districts. The time (in minutes) it takes an ambulance to travel from one district to another is shown in the file P06_78.xlsx. The population of each district (in thousands) is as follows: district 1, 40; district 2, 30; district 3, 35; district 4, 20; district 5, 15; district 6, 50; district 7, 45; district 8, 60. Suppose Gotham City has $n$ ambulance locations. Determine the locations of ambulances that maximize the number of people who live within two minutes of an ambulance. Do this separately for $n = 1$; $n = 2$; $n = 3$; $n = 4$. (*Hint:* Set it up so that SolverTable can solve all four problems simultaneously.)

79. Arthur Ross, Inc., must complete many corporate tax returns during the period February 15 to April 15. This year, the company must begin and complete the five jobs shown in the file P06_79.xlsx during this eight-week period. Arthur Ross employs four full-time accountants who normally work 40 hours per week. If necessary, however, they can work up to 20 hours of overtime per week for which they are paid $100 per hour. Determine how Arthur Ross can minimize the overtime cost incurred in completing all jobs by April 15.

80. Based on Muckstadt and Wilson (1968). PSI believes it will need the amounts of generating capacity (in millions of kwh) shown in the file P06_80.xlsx during the next five years. The company has a choice of building (and then operating) power plants with the capacities (in millions of kwh) and costs (in millions of dollars) shown in the same file. Determine how to minimize the total cost of meeting PSI's generating capacity requirements for the next five years.

81. Newsome Construction is considering erecting three office buildings. The time (in years) required to complete each of them and the number of workers required to be on the job at all times are shown in the file P06_81.xlsx. After a building is completed, it brings in the following amount of rent per year: building 1, $50,000; building 2, $30,000; building 3, $40,000. Newsome faces the following constraints:
- During each year, 60 workers are available.
- At most, one building can be started during any year.
- Building 2 must be completed by the end of year 4.

Determine the maximum total rent that can be earned by Newsome by the end of year 4.

82. Four trucks are available to deliver milk to five grocery stores. The capacity and daily operating cost of each truck are shown in the file P06_82.xlsx. The demand of each grocery store can be supplied by only one truck, but a truck can deliver to more than one grocery. The daily demands of each grocery are as follows: grocery 1, 100 gallons; grocery 2, 200 gallons; grocery 3, 300 gallons; grocery 4, 500 gallons; grocery 5, 800 gallons. Determine how to minimize the daily cost of meeting the demands of the five groceries.

83. A county is going to build two hospitals. There are nine cities in which the hospitals can be built. The number of hospital visits per year made by people in each city and the $x$-$y$ coordinates of each city are listed in the file P06_83.xlsx. The county's goal is to minimize the total distance that patients must travel to hospitals. Where should it locate the hospitals? (*Hint:* You will need to determine the distance between each pair of cities. An easy way to do this is with lookup tables.)

84. It is currently the beginning of 2010. Gotham City is trying to sell municipal bonds to support improvements in recreational facilities and highways. The face values of the bonds and the due dates at which principal comes due are listed in the file P06_84.xlsx. (The due dates are the *beginnings* of the years listed.) The Gold and Silver Company (GS) wants to underwrite Gotham City's bonds. A proposal to Gotham for underwriting this issue consists of the following: (1) an interest rate of 3%, 4%, 5%, 6%, or 7% for each bond, where coupons are paid annually; and (2) an upfront premium paid by GS to Gotham City. GS has determined the set of fair prices for the bonds listed in the same file. For example, if GS underwrites bond 2 maturing in 2013 at 5%, it would charge Gotham City $444,000 for that bond. GS is allowed to use at most three different interest rates. GS requires a profit of at least $46,000, where its profit is equal to the sale price of the bonds minus the face value of the bonds minus the premium it pays to Gotham City. To maximize the chance that GS will get Gotham City's business, GS wants to minimize the total cost of the bond issue to Gotham City, which is equal to the total interest on the bonds minus the premium paid by GS. For example, if the year 2012 bond (bond 1) is issued at a 4% rate, then Gotham City must pay two years of coupon interest: $2(0.04)($700,000) = $56,000$. What assignment of interest rates to each bond and upfront premium ensure that GS will make the desired profit (assuming it gets the contract) and minimize the cost to Gotham City?

85. Based on Spencer et al. (1990). When you lease 800 phone numbers from AT&T for telemarketing, AT&T uses an optimization model to tell you where you should locate calling centers to minimize your operating costs over a 10-year horizon. To illustrate the model, suppose you are considering seven calling center locations: Boston, New York, Charlotte, Dallas, Chicago, Los Angeles, and Omaha. You know the average cost incurred if a telemarketing call is made

from any of these cities to any region of the country. You also know the hourly wage that you must pay workers in each city. This information is listed in the file P06_85.xlsx. Assume that an average call requires four minutes of labor. You make calls 250 days per year, and the average number of calls made per day to each region of the country is listed in the same file. The cost of building a calling center in each possible location is also listed in this file. Each calling center can make up to 5000 calls per day. Given this information, how can you minimize the discounted cost (at 10% per year) of running the telemarketing operation for 10 years? Assume all wage and calling costs are paid at the *ends* of the respective years.

86. State University is scheduling 24 sections of a large computer skills course in the Fall semester. There are eight time slots for these sections, four on Monday/Wednesday (MW) and four on Tuesday/Thursday (TR). In each time slot, three sections are scheduled. These are shown in the file P06_86.xlsx. The sections will be taught by six instructors. Instructors 1 to 3 must teach at least three sections and no more than four sections each. Instructors 4 to 6 must teach at least four sections and no more than five sections each. The instructors have submitted their top four preferences for time slots, as shown in the file. Four points are awarded for satisfying an instructor's first preference, three for second preference, two for third preference, and one for fourth preference. These points appear in the file. For example, instructor 1's preferences are, in decreasing order, MW 9-10, MW 11-noon, MW 1-2, and TR 11-noon. Find an assignment of instructors to sections that maximizes the points from satisfying preferences. Of course, no instructor can teach more than one section in the same time slot.

87. Hoosier Power needs to determine a capacity expansion plan to meet Bloomington's power needs for the next 20 years. The current capacity is 5000 kwh. The demand for the current year is 4000 kwh, and demand is expected to increase by 1000 kwh in each succeeding year. At the beginning of each year, Hoosier Power must determine the amount of capacity to add, given the following inputs:
- Any year in which capacity is added, a fixed cost of $120,000 is incurred plus a cost of $120 per kwh of capacity.
- At most 10,000 kwh of capacity can be added in a single year.
- It costs $25 per year to maintain a unit of capacity.
- It costs $12 per year to produce a kwh.
- If production does not meet demand, a shortage cost of $80 per kwh short is incurred.

Develop a linear integer model to help Hoosier Power minimize its costs for the next 20 years.

88. Based on Angel et al. (2003). A fertilizer company is trying to determine the cheapest fertilizer mix that provides desired amounts of nutrients. The mix is made by combining the following fertilizers: SSA, SPO, GUR, TSP, KCI, FERT, and SPF. The mix cannot contain both GUR and TSP. The percentage of potassium (K), sulfur (S), calcium (Ca), sodium (Na) and phosphorus (P) in each fertilizer is listed in the file P06_88.xlsx. For example, a pound of SSA is 16% K and 26% Na. The mix must contain at least 600 pounds of K, 550 pounds of S, 750 pounds of Ca, 900 pounds of Na, and 750 pounds of P. The mix cannot contain both GUR and TSP, because if both are present in the mix, the affect of other fertilizers is nullified. The cost per pound (in cents) of each fertilizer is listed in the same file. Develop a linear integer model to find the minimum-cost fertilizer mixture that meets the stated chemical requirements.

89. Sam is in his final year of college and is trying to schedule his courses for the year. He has narrowed his search to 16 courses, each of which is offered in at least one time slot (out of a possible five time slots) in each semester. The file P06_89.xlsx lists the courses and when they are offered. For example, course C1 is offered in time slots T4 and T5 during semester S1 and in time slot T3 in semester S2. The course also lists the values Sam attaches to the various course/time slot/semester combinations (on a 1 to 10 scale). Assuming that Sam must take exactly five courses each semester, find the combination that maximizes the total value of the courses he takes. Of course, he can't take the same course more than once, and he can't take more than one course at the same time.

90. A medical supply company has customers in eight cities. It is trying to decide how many salespeople it needs to service these customers. Each salesperson needs to be located in one of the eight cities and needs to be assigned to a subset of the customers. For example, the company might base a salesperson in New York and have this person service customers in New York, Boston, and Philadelphia. Each salesperson receives an annual salary of $50,000 and can work as many as 230 days per year. This includes days working with customers and days traveling to and from customers. The file P06_90.xlsx contains data on the annual travel costs (for example, $15,900 for a salesperson based in New York traveling for customers in Orlando), the annual number of days of work required for the customers, and the annual number of days traveling to and from customers. Find an assignment that minimizes the total cost of salaries and traveling. The solution should indicate the number of salespeople to employ, where they should be based, and which cities they should serve. Assume that customers in a given city must be serviced by a single salesperson.

**91.** You are scheduling company interviews at the annual university career fair. Five interview rooms are available. Interviews are conducted from 9 AM to 5 PM. Each company wants all of its interviews conducted in a single room. The time preferences for the companies are listed in the file P06_91.xlsx. Develop a linear integer model to determine whether five rooms are sufficient to complete the interviews.

**92.** The file P06_92.xlsx lists the distances between 21 U.S. cities. You want to locate liver transplant centers in a subset of these 21 cities.
  **a.** Suppose you plan to build four liver transplant centers and your goal is to minimize the maximum distance a person in any of these cities has to travel to a center. In which cities should the centers be located?
  **b.** How many centers are needed, and in which cities should they be located, so that residents of all cities are within 800 miles of a transplant center? (The model must be linear.)
  **c.** You know that a transplant center is sometimes filled to capacity. With this in mind, you would like everyone to be relatively close to two transplant centers. How many centers are needed, and in which cities should the centers be located, to ensure that residents of all cities are within 800 miles of *two* transplant centers? (Again, the model must be linear.)
  **d.** The same file also lists the number of people (in millions) living in each city's metropolitan area. Where should you locate three transplant centers to maximize the number of people within 800 miles of a transplant center?

**93.** This problem is based on Motorola's online method for choosing suppliers. Suppose Motorola solicits bids from five suppliers for eight products. The list price for each product and the quantity of each product that Motorola needs to purchase during the next year are listed in the file P06_93.xlsx. Each supplier has submitted the percentage discount it will offer on each product. These percentages are also listed in the file. For example, supplier 1 offers a 7% discount on product 1 and a 30% discount on product 2. The following considerations also apply:

  - There is an administrative cost of $5000 associated with setting up a supplier's account. For example, if Motorola uses three suppliers, it incurs an administrative cost of $15,000.
  - To ensure reliability, no supplier can supply more than 80% of Motorola's demand for any product.
  - A supplier must supply an integer amount of each product it supplies.

Develop a linear integer model to help Motorola minimize the sum of its purchase and administrative costs.

**94.** Specialty Software is considering 10 projects. The years each project will be developed, the number of programmers needed each year for each project, and the revenue (exclusive of labor costs) from each project are listed in the file P06_94.xlsx. For example, project 1, if undertaken, will require 37 programmers in each of the first four years. The company currently employs 100 programmers. At the beginning of each year, it can hire as many as 80 programmers. If any are hired in a given year, a training program must be run at a cost of $5 million, regardless of the number hired. Programmers are paid a salary of $50,000 per year.
  **a.** How can Specialty Software maximize the net profit from these projects? (*Hint:* First use IF functions to create a matrix of programmers required each year for each project.)
  **b.** Assuming that 10% of all programmers quit at the end of each year, how does the solution change? (Don't worry about noninteger numbers of workers.)

**95.** You are moving away from Bloomington and need to load a truck. The items that will go on the truck must all be packed in boxes. The size (in cubic feet) of each item and each available box are listed in the file P06_95.xlsx. For example, the first item requires 87 cubic feet, and the first box can hold 126 cubic feet of stuff. Develop a linear integer model to find the minimum amount of cubic feet needed to pack all items in boxes.

**96.** Based on McBride and Zufryden (1988). A company is trying to determine which of five possible products to include in its product line. The fixed cost of producing each product and the unit profit for each product are listed in the file P06_96.xlsx. There are five customer segments. The number of customers in each segment and the utility each customer segment associates with each product are also listed in this file. If a consumer believes that all available products have a negative utility, this customer will buy nothing. Otherwise, each customer will buy the available product that has the largest utility. For example, if products 1, 2, and 3 are available, customer segment 4 will purchase product 3. Determine which products the company should produce to maximize its profit, assuming that it will produce exactly enough to meet customer demand. (*Hint:* Use a binary changing cell for each product and a binary changing cell for each customer segment-product combination. To ensure that a customer buys only the product with the largest utility, include the following constraint for each combination of product and customer segment:

$$U_{cj}x_j \geq U_{ci}x_i - M(1 - y_{cj}) \text{ for each } i, j, c$$

Here, $U_{cj}$ is the utility for customer segment $c$ buying product $j$, $x_j$ is a binary for product $j$ being offered, $y_{cj}$

is a binary for customer segment $c$ buying product $j$, and $M$ is a large number ($M$ equal to the largest product utility will work). This constraint ensures that the $y_{cj}$ binary can equal 1 only if the binary $x_j$ equals 1, that is, customer segment $c$ can buy product $j$ only if it is included in the product line. Note that if $y_{cj}$ is 0, then this inequality is automatically satisfied.)

## Modeling Problems

**97.** Suppose that you want to divide a state containing 12 cities into five congressional districts. How might you use IP to assign cities to districts?

**98.** An insurance company has hired you to determine the number of sales divisions into which the country should be divided. Each division will need a president, a vice president, and a divisional staff. The time needed to call on a client will depend on the distance of the salesperson from the client. Discuss how you would determine the optimal number of sales divisions and the allocation of the company's sales force to the various divisions.

**99.** Ten different types of brownies are sold. You are thinking of developing a new brownie for sale. Brownies are rated on the basis of five qualities: price, chocolate flavor, chewiness, sweetness, and ease of preparation. You want to group the 10 brownies on the market into three clusters. Each cluster should contain brownies that are relatively similar.
  **a.** Why would this be useful to you?
  **b.** How would you do it?

**100.** Telco, a national telemarketing firm, usually picks a number of sites around the country from which it makes its calls. As a service, AD&D's telecommunication marketing department wants to help Telco choose the number and location of its sites. How can IP be used to approach this problem?

This case deals with strategic planning issues for a large company. The main issue is planning the company's production capacity for the coming year. At issue is the overall level of capacity and the type of capacity—for example, the degree of *flexibility* in the manufacturing system. The main tool used to aid the company's planning process is a mixed integer linear programming (MILP) model. A *mixed* integer program has both integer and continuous variables.

## Problem Statement

The Giant Motor Company (GMC) produces three lines of cars for the domestic (U.S.) market: Lyras, Libras, and Hydras. The Lyra is a relatively inexpensive subcompact car that appeals mainly to first-time car owners and to households using it as a second car for commuting. The Libra is a sporty compact car that is sleeker, faster, and roomier than the Lyra. Without any options, the Libra costs slightly more than the Lyra; additional options increase the price. The Hydra is the luxury car of the GMC line. It is significantly more expensive than the Lyra and Libra, and it has the highest profit margin of the three cars.

## Retooling Options for Capacity Expansion

Currently GMC has three manufacturing plants in the United States. Each plant is dedicated to producing a single line of cars. In its planning for the coming year, GMC is considering the retooling of its Lyra and/or Libra plants. Retooling either plant would

represent a major expense for the company. The retooled plants would have significantly increased production capacities. Although having greater *fixed* costs, the retooled plants would be more efficient and have lower *marginal* production costs—that is, higher *marginal* profit contributions. In addition, the retooled plants would be *flexible*—they would have the capability of producing more than one line of cars.

The characteristics of the current plants and the retooled plants are given in Table 6.16. The retooled Lyra and Libra plants are prefaced by the word *new*. The fixed costs and capacities in Table 6.16 are given on an annual basis. A dash in the profit margin section indicates that the plant cannot manufacture that line of car. For example, the new Lyra plant would be capable of producing both Lyras and Libras but not Hydras. The new Libra plant would be capable of producing any of the three lines of cars. Note, however, that the new Libra plant has a slightly lower profit margin for producing Hydras than the Hydra plant. The flexible new Libra plant is capable of producing the luxury Hydra model but is not as efficient as the current Hydra plant that is dedicated to Hydra production.

The fixed costs are annual costs incurred by GMC, independent of the number of cars produced by the plant. For the current plant configurations, the fixed costs include property taxes, insurance, payments on the loan that was taken out to construct the plant, and so on. If a plant is retooled, the fixed costs will include the previous fixed costs plus the additional cost of the renovation. The additional

Table 6.16 Plant Characteristics

|  | Lyra | Libra | Hydra | New Lyra | New Libra |
|---|---|---|---|---|---|
| Capacity (in 1000s) | 1000 | 800 | 900 | 1600 | 1800 |
| Fixed cost (in $millions) | 2000 | 2000 | 2600 | 3400 | 3700 |
| **Profit Margin by Car Line (in $1000s)** | | | | | |
| Lyra | 2 | — | — | 2.5 | 2.3 |
| Libra | — | 3 | — | 3.0 | 3.5 |
| Hydra | — | — | 5 | — | 4.8 |

renovation cost will be an annual cost representing the cost of the renovation amortized over a long period.

## Demand for GMC Cars

Short-term demand forecasts have been very reliable in the past and are expected to be reliable in the future. The demand for GMC cars for the coming year is given in Table 6.17.

Table 6.17   Demand for GMC Cars

|        | Demand (in 1000s) |
|--------|-------------------|
| Lyra   | 1400              |
| Libra  | 1100              |
| Hydra  | 800               |

A quick comparison of plant capacities and demands in Table 6.16 and Table 6.17 indicates that GMC is faced with insufficient capacity. Partially offsetting the lack of capacity is the phenomenon of **demand diversion.** If a potential car buyer walks into a GMC dealer showroom wanting to buy a Lyra but the dealer is out of stock, frequently the salesperson can convince the customer to purchase the better Libra car, which is in stock. Unsatisfied demand for the Lyra is said to be *diverted* to the Libra. Only rarely in this situation can the salesperson convince the customer to switch to the luxury Hydra model.

From past experience, GMC estimates that 30% of unsatisfied demand for Lyras is diverted to

demand for Libras and 5% to demand for Hydras. Similarly, 10% of unsatisfied demand for Libras is diverted to demand for Hydras. For example, if the demand for Lyras is 1,400,000 cars, then the unsatisfied demand will be 400,000 if no capacity is added. Out of this unsatisfied demand, 120,000 (= 400,000 × 0.3) will materialize as demand for Libras, and 20,000 (= 400,000 × 0.05) will materialize as demand for Hydras. Similarly, if the demand for Libras is 1,220,000 cars (1,100,000 original demand plus 120,000 demand diverted from Lyras), then the unsatisfied demand for Lyras would be 420,000 if no capacity is added. Out of this unsatisfied demand, 42,000 (= 420,000 × 0.1) will materialize as demand for Hydras. All other unsatisfied demand is lost to competitors. The pattern of demand diversion is summarized in Table 6.18.

Table 6.18   Demand Diversion Matrix

|       | Lyra | Libra | Hydra |
|-------|------|-------|-------|
| Lyra  | NA   | 0.3   | 0.05  |
| Libra | 0    | NA    | 0.10  |
| Hydra | 0    | 0.0   | NA    |

## Question

GMC wants to decide whether to retool the Lyra and Libra plants. In addition, GMC wants to determine its production plan at each plant in the coming year. Based on the previous data, formulate a MILP model for solving GMC's production planning–capacity expansion problem for the coming year. ▨

During 2001, many European markets for mobile phones reached saturation. Because of this, mobile phone operators started to shift their focus from growth and market share to cutting costs. One way to do this is to reduce spending on international calls. These calls are routed through network operating companies called carriers. The carriers charge per call-minute for each destination, and they often use a discount on total business volume to price their services. A mobile phone operator must decide how to allocate destinations to carriers.

V-Mobile, a mobile phone operator in Denmark, must make such a decision for a $T$-month planning horizon when it has $C$ carriers to choose from, $D$ destinations for its customers' calls, and there are $I$ price intervals for a typical carrier. (These intervals define a carrier's discount structure.) The inputs include the following:

- The price per call-minute for destination $d$ from carrier $c$ in price interval $i$ in month $t$
- The (forecasted) number of call-minutes for destination $d$ in month $t$
- The lower and upper limits for carrier $c$ in price interval $i$
- The lower and upper limits on capacity (number of call-minutes) for carrier $c$ in month $t$

- The penalty per call-minute (to discourage poor-quality options) for carrier $c$ to destination $d$ in month $t$

V-Mobile wants to find a least-cost way of routing its call-minutes through the various carriers. Of course, it hopes to take advantage of price discounts offered by the carriers.

The file Carrier Selection.xlsx provides inputs for one version of V-Mobile's problem. This version has $T = 2$, $C = 3$, $D = 5$, and $I = 3$. The decision variables (changing cells) should include the following:

- The number of call-minutes routed through carrier $c$ to destination $d$ in price interval $i$ in month $t$
- A binary variable for each carrier $c$ and price interval $i$ combination that equals 1 if the total call-minutes for this carrier (over all destinations and months) falls in price interval $i$, and equals 0 otherwise.

Develop an optimization model that helps V-Mobile allocate its international calls in a cost-efficient manner. Then write a brief memo stating (1) how V-Mobile should implement your results for this particular version of the problem, and (2) how the model would need to be modified for other potential problem parameters. ▪

---

[11] This case is based on van de Klundert et al. (2005).

# Evolutionary Solver: An Alternative Optimization Procedure

© Soleg1974 | Dreamstime.com

## DEVELOPING AN OPERATING-PLAN MODEL AT SANTA FE RAILWAY

Like many other companies, Santa Fe Railway faces increasing demands for customer service, cost pressures, and changing market conditions. This is particularly true in its intermodal business area, in which traffic moves on some combination of ship or truck and train. The company averaged almost 8% growth per year in intermodal traffic handled during the period from 1989 to 1996. This increased growth and changing patterns of customer traffic created difficult problems for Santa Fe, as described in Gorman (1998). The company needed to use its trains and rail lines efficiently from a cost standpoint, but it also had to provide customers with high-quality service. In addition, the company had to be flexible to change its operating plan quickly in response to changing customer traffic patterns.

Historically, Santa Fe's service design was rather myopic. The service designers tried their best to make incremental refinements to current operations, but their thinking was based too much on historical procedures and could not adapt sufficiently to changing customer needs. They eventually decided to create an operating-plan model capable of building an operating plan for the intermodal business unit from scratch, one that could best adapt to the current and expected traffic patterns and would not be constrained by traditional patterns or historical schedules. As inputs, this model required customer service requirements, engineering capabilities, and physical plant constraints. The outputs included a weekly train timetable, traffic-to-train assignments, yard and railway line schedules, and equipment and locomotive flows. The objective was to simultaneously allocate physical rail network resources to trains and allocate scarce train space to traffic flows to minimize operating costs while meeting customer requirements.

The operating-plan problem was decomposed into two problems: the train timetable problem and the traffic assignment problem. The former prescribes which trains will travel on which lines at which times. Given this information, the latter problem prescribes which customer loads are assigned to which trains. Each problem is huge, and much ingenuity was required to model and solve these problems. For the timetable problem, the original model represented each hour of the week for every possible train as a binary decision variable, where 1 indicates a train and 0 indicates no train. This model was impossibly large, so the service design team reduced its size by specifying a menu of allowable train routes (about 200) from which the model could choose. Even this reduced problem was much too large for traditional integer programming algorithms to solve, so the analysts did what is becoming more common in large optimization models: they turned to newer, emerging types of algorithms. In particular, they tried the genetic "survival of the fittest" algorithms discussed in this chapter, where they mixed schedules from a given population of schedules to carry over the best characteristics of these schedules to the next generation of schedules. Unfortunately, genetic algorithms alone were painfully slow at producing useful populations of train schedules for this large problem. Therefore, the authors combined genetic algorithms with another type of algorithm, called *tabu search,* to speed up the process. (Tabu search uses information from previous iterations to search in a promising direction. However, a *tabu list* prohibits the algorithm from undoing recent changes to the schedule or revisiting recent solutions.) This method of combining algorithms worked and enabled Santa Fe to solve the timetable problem reasonably quickly. The company was then able to solve the traffic assignment problem by a clever priority-based, shortest-path heuristic.

Santa Fe Intermodal used its operating-plan model to study many major changes in rail operations: to predict train volumes based on long-term forecasts, to quantify the impact of containerization of intermodal business on train operations, and to develop a cost basis in contract negotiations for large amounts of incremental business. The model has shown the potential to improve global service by 4% while reducing costs by 6% over the previous operating plan. As R. Mark Schmidt, an analyst at Santa Fe, stated, "Obviously, as with any major deviation from traditional processes, the acceptance of the operating-plan model has been a gradual one. Recent successes of the model are building confidences and as a result, the model is being interwoven into the intermodal service design process at Santa Fe." ■

## 8.1 INTRODUCTION

In Chapters 3 through 7, we used Excel's Solver to solve many interesting and important problems. Unfortunately, there are many optimization problems where Solver's Simplex LP and GRG Nonlinear algorithms are unable to find optimal solutions. However, genetic algorithms often perform well on optimization problems where Solver's other algorithms perform poorly. The purpose of this chapter is to illustrate some interesting models that cannot be solved by the Solver algorithms discussed in previous chapters, at least not easily or without tricks, but can be solved with genetic algorithms in a reasonably straightforward manner. In short, the methods in this chapter enable you to solve a much wider range of optimization models.

Fortunately, Solver for Excel 2010 includes the Evolutionary algorithm, which was previously available only in Premium Solver (included with previous versions of the book). Therefore, Premium Solver is no longer necessary. In fact, we were told by Frontline Systems, the developer of Solver, that Solver for Excel 2010 is essentially the old Premium Solver. The following summarizes the three algorithms included with Solver for Excel 2010. To avoid confusion, from here on we will refer to the three Solver algorithms available with Excel 2010 as Simplex LP Solver, GRG Nonlinear Solver, and Evolutionary Solver.

- Simplex LP Solver is used to solve linear models, including models where some or all of the changing cells are restricted to be binary and/or integer.
- GRG Nonlinear Solver is used to solve nonlinear models when the objective cell and constraints are "smooth" functions of the changing cells.
- Evolutionary Solver uses genetic algorithms to find good (close to optimal) solutions to more difficult problems, including those where the objective cell and/or constraints are "nonsmooth" functions of the changing cells.

Several times in previous chapters, we stated that the first two Solvers cannot handle models with IF, MAX, MIN, and several other Excel functions. The problem is that such models often contain nonsmooth functions in the objective cell and/or the constraint cells. (Technically, a nonsmooth function has discontinuities or points where its derivatives do not exist.) It is sometimes possible to make these models linear so that the Simplex LP Solver can be used, but nonobvious tricks are usually necessary to do so. Fortunately, this is *not* necessary with Evolutionary Solver, as illustrated in this chapter. Evolutionary Solver uses a type of algorithm called a genetic algorithm, which is much more flexible.

Before discussing genetic algorithms and Evolutionary Solver, we review the strengths and weaknesses of the Solvers used in previous chapters.

Recall that an optimization model is linear if the objective cell is a linear function of the changing cells, the left and right sides of all constraints are linear functions of the changing cells, and all changing cells are allowed to contain fractional values—that is, there are no integer constraints. For such models, Simplex LP Solver is guaranteed to find an optimal solution (if an optimal solution exists). We have discussed many linear models in Chapters 3 through 5. Simplex LP Solver is an excellent method to use for any optimization problem that can be set up as a linear model, provided that the model does not exceed Solver's size restrictions—up to 200 changing cells and 100 constraints (not counting simple upper or lower bounds on changing cells). Most larger linear models are difficult to handle in a spreadsheet format. These larger models are often solved using a modeling language such as LINGO, GAMS, or AMPL. With a modeling language, a user can generate, say, 10,000 supply constraints for a transportation model with one line of computer code. This makes it easy to compactly represent and solve large models. (We should also mention that Frontline Systems has developed commercial large-scale Solvers that are capable of solving very large spreadsheet models.)

In Chapter 6, we considered linear models where some or all of the changing cells are constrained to be integers. In theory, Simplex LP Solver should be able to find optimal solutions to these problems, but in practice it can take hours, days, or even weeks to find optimal solutions to difficult, integer-constrained models. This is not necessarily a weakness of Solver—integer-constrained models are inherently difficult for *any* optimization software package—but there are algorithms other than the algorithm used by Solver that work better for some integer models.

In the previous chapter, we discussed nonlinear models and saw that GRG Nonlinear Solver is capable of solving many of these. However, nonlinear models present two problems. First, as discussed in section 7.2 of Chapter 7, GRG Nonlinear Solver can get stuck at a local maximum or a local minimum and never find the global maximum or minimum. The function shown in Figure 7.1 illustrates this situation. In this example, GRG Nonlinear Solver fails to find the global optimal solution for certain starting solutions. Fortunately, as discussed in Chapter 7, GRG Nonlinear Solver for Excel 2010 has a Multistart option that increases the chances of finding the global optimal solution in problems like this one.

Second, if a spreadsheet model uses IF, ABS, MAX, or MIN functions that depend on any of the model's changing cells, the model is typically nonsmooth, and GRG Nonlinear Solver can have difficulty finding an optimal solution. One possibility that could be caused by an IF function is illustrated in Figure 8.1. The context here is ordering a product with a quantity discount, so that the order quantity is on the horizontal axis and the total cost (ordering cost plus inventory holding cost) is on the vertical axis. The IF function specifies that if the order quantity is less than $A$, one function specifies the total cost. If the order quantity is between $A$ and $B$, another function specifies the total cost. Finally, if the order quantity is greater than $B$, a third function specifies the total cost. The resulting graph is not only nonlinear, but it has *discontinuities* at $A$ and $B$, where the total cost jumps from one value to another. The overall cost-minimizing order quantity is to the right of $B$. If you select an initial solution to the right of $B$, GRG Nonlinear Solver will locate the correct optimal solution. However, if you start at a point to the left of $B$, GRG Nonlinear Solver will almost certainly not find the optimal solution.

**Figure 8.1**

**A Cost Function with Discontinuities**

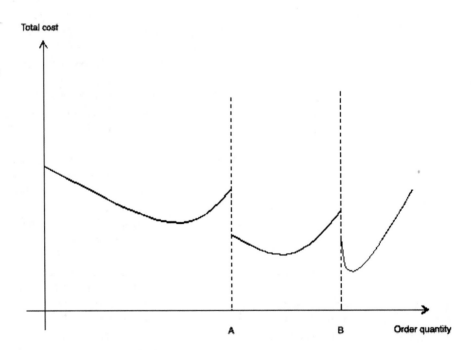

The point of this discussion is that although Simplex LP Solver and GRG Nonlinear Solver can handle many models with no difficulty, they are not well suited to finding optimal solutions for certain types of models. We now discuss a completely different solution method that is sometimes more successful at solving these difficult problems.

# 8.2 INTRODUCTION TO GENETIC ALGORITHMS

*In GA terms, a chromosome is a binary (0-1) representation of a potential solution.*

In the early 1970s, John Holland of the University of Michigan realized that many features espoused in the theory of natural evolution, such as survival of the fittest and mutation, could be used to help solve difficult optimization problems.[1] Because his methods were based on behavior observed in nature, Holland coined the term *genetic algorithm* to describe his algorithm. Simply stated, a **genetic algorithm** (GA) provides a method of intelligently searching an optimization model's feasible region for an optimal solution. Biological terminology is used to describe the algorithm. The objective function is called a *fitness function*, and a specification of values for all changing cells is called a *chromosome*. For most problems, a GA codes changing cells in binary notation. For example, 1001 represents

$$1(2^3) + 0(2^2) + 0(2^1) + 1(2^0) = 8 + 1 = 9$$

The following is a rough outline of how a GA might work. (There are various implementations of GAs, and the details vary from one implementation to another.) Suppose a company must decide how many units of each of two products to order. Because of quantity discounts, the function that represents total cost has discontinuities of the type observed in Figure 8.1. Actually, the total cost is even more complex than in Figure 8.1 because there are two products, not just one. However, the only requirement of the algorithm is that total cost $TC(Q_1, Q_2)$ can be calculated for any combination of the order quantities $Q_1$ and $Q_2$. Suppose $Q_1$ and $Q_2$ must each be between 0 and 500. (In this discussion, we assume that the model has no constraints other than lower bounds and upper bounds on each changing cell. Later we discuss how a GA can handle other types of constraints.) Then the GA uses the following steps:

1. **Generate a population.** The GA randomly samples values of the changing cells between the lower and upper bounds to generate a set of (usually at least 50) chromosomes. The initial set of chromosomes is called the **population.** For example, two members of the population might be

   - **Chromosome 1:** $Q_1 = 100$ and $Q_2 = 400$ (or in binary, $Q_1 = 001100100$ and $Q_2 = 110010000$)
   - **Chromosome 2:** $Q_1 = 300$ and $Q_2 = 200$ (or in binary, $Q_1 = 100101100$ and $Q_2 = 011001000$)

   The initial population is constructed by randomly choosing points from the problem's feasible region. (Note that nine binary digits are sufficient to represent any order quantity from 0 to 500.)

2. **Create a new generation.** Create a new generation of chromosomes in the hope of finding an improvement. In the new generation, chromosomes with a smaller fitness function (in a minimization problem) have a greater chance of surviving to the next generation. Suppose in our example that chromosome 1 has a fitness value (total cost) of \$2560, and chromosome 2 has a fitness value of \$3240. Then chromosome 1 should have a larger chance of surviving to the next generation. *Crossover* and *mutation* are also used to generate chromosomes for the next generation.

   a. Crossover (fairly common) splices together two chromosomes at a prespecified point. For example, if chromosomes 1 and 2 are combined by crossover and the crossover point is between the fourth and fifth digits from the right, the resulting chromosomes (in binary) are

      - **New chromosome 1:** $Q_1 = 100100100$ and $Q_2 = 011000000$ (or $Q_1 = 292$ and $Q_2 = 192$)

[1]Goldberg (1989), Davis (1991), and Holland (1992) are good references on genetic algorithms.

- **New chromosome 2:** $Q_1 = 001101100$ and $Q_2 = 110011000$ (or $Q_1 = 108$ and $Q_2 = 408$)

Note that the two original $Q_1$s are used to create the two new $Q_1$s and similarly for the $Q_2$s. For example, $Q_1$ for the new chromosome 1 splices together the left digits 10010 from $Q_1$ of the original chromosome 2 and the right digits 0100 from $Q_1$ of the original chromosome 1.

b. Mutation (very rare) randomly selects a digit and changes it from 0 to 1 or vice versa. For example, if we mutate the left digit of $Q_1$ in chromosome 2, the new $Q_1$ in chromosome 2 becomes $Q_1 = 000101100$ (or $Q_1 = 44$). As this example indicates, mutation can provide a dramatic effect, leading to a completely different location in the feasible region. Therefore, an occasional mutation is useful for getting the algorithm "unstuck."

3. **Stopping condition.** At each generation, the best value of the fitness function in the generation is recorded, and the algorithm repeats step 2. If no improvement in the best fitness value is observed after many consecutive generations, the GA terminates.

To handle a constraint such as $Q_1 + Q_2 \leq 700$, the GA adds (in a minimization problem), $M(Q_1 + Q_2 - 700)$ to the fitness function, where $M$ is a suitably large number such as 1,000,000. Now any chromosome that violates the constraint has a high value of the fitness function because the "penalty" $M(Q_1 + Q_2 - 700)$ greatly increases the value of the new fitness function. This causes the GA to avoid chromosomes that violate the constraint.

### Strengths and Weaknesses of GAs

*GAs have a particular advantage on non-smooth problems—those with discontinuities, for example. However, they are much less efficient than traditional algorithms such as the simplex method on "nice" problems.*

If you let a GA run long enough, it is *guaranteed* to find the solution to any optimization problem. The problem is that the sun could explode before the GA finds the optimal solution. In general, you never know how long to run a GA. For the problems discussed in this chapter, an optimal solution is usually found within five minutes or less, although timing depends on the problem, and some experimentation is invariably necessary. Therefore, you usually let Evolutionary Solver run for a few minutes and report the best solution found. Unfortunately, you do not know if the best solution you have found is optimal, but it is usually a *good* solution—that is, very close to being optimal.

As a rule, GAs do very well in problems with few constraints (excluding bounds on changing cells). In addition, the complexity of the objective cell does not bother a GA. For example, a GA can easily handle MIN, MAX, IF, and ABS functions in spreadsheet models. This is the key advantage of GAs. On the other hand, GAs do not usually perform very well on problems that have many constraints. For example, Simplex LP Solver has no difficulty with the multiple-constraint linear models in Chapters 3 through 5, but GAs perform much more slowly on them.

## 8.3 INTRODUCTION TO EVOLUTIONARY SOLVER

GAs have been available for several years and have been implemented in several software packages. However, they have been available as Excel add-ins only recently. In this chapter, we use Evolutionary Solver developed by Frontline Systems and available as part of Solver for Excel 2010. To get started with Evolutionary Solver, we examine a simple nonlinear function of a single variable.

## 8.1 MAXIMIZING A NONLINEAR FUNCTION WITH LOCAL MAXIMA

To see how Evolutionary Solver works, we consider a simple function that is difficult for GRG Nonlinear Solver. This example, analyzed in Chapter 7, is a function of a single variable $x$: $f(x) = (x - 1)(x - 2)(x - 3)(x - 4)(x - 5)$ for $1 \le x \le 5$. The objective is to maximize $f(x)$ over this range. However, the graph of this function shown in Figure 8.2 indicates that there are two local maxima: one at around $x = 3.5$ and the other at $x = 5$. The global maximum, the one we want, is near $x = 1.5$. Can Evolutionary Solver find this global maximum?

**Figure 8.2**

**Function with Local Maxima**

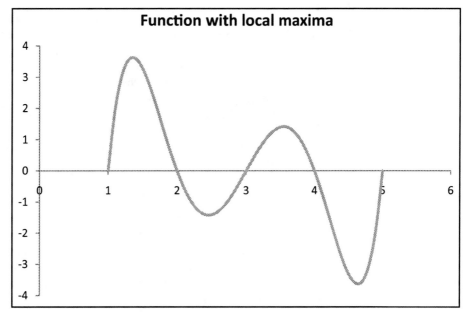

**Objective**   To illustrate how Evolutionary Solver works and to see how it can successfully find a global maximum for a function with several local maxima.

### Solution

The model is particularly simple. (See Figure 8.3 and the file Local Maxima.xlsx.) To set it up, enter any value in cell B5 (the only changing cell), enter the formula =B5-1 in cell B6, copy this down to cell B10, and enter the formula =PRODUCT(B6:B10) in cell B11. The objective is to maximize the value in cell B11 while constraining the value in cell B5 to be between 1 and 5.

**Figure 8.3**

**Model for Evaluating the Function**

| | A | B | C | D |
|---|---|---|---|---|
| 1 | Function with local maxima | | | |
| 2 | | | | |
| 3 | The function is: y=(x-1)(x-2)(x-3)(x-4)(x-5) | | | |
| 4 | | | | |
| 5 | x | 1.355567 | | |
| 6 | x-1 | 0.355567 | | |
| 7 | x-2 | -0.64443 | | |
| 8 | x-3 | -1.64443 | | |
| 9 | x-4 | -2.64443 | | |
| 10 | x-5 | -3.64443 | | |
| 11 | Product | 3.631432 | | |

If GRG Nonlinear Solver is used, the solution depends on the starting value in cell B6. If this starting point is near 5, the Solver solution is 5, corresponding to the local maximum at $x = 5$. If the starting point is near 3.5, then the Solver solution is 3.54, corresponding to the local maximum at $x = 3.54$. Only if the starting point is sufficiently small does Solver correctly find the global maximum at $x = 1.356$. This is disturbing. If you didn't have a graph of the function to lead you in the right direction, how would you know where to start? The Multistart option discussed in the previous chapter is perfect for this type of problem with multiple local maxima, but you can also use Evolutionary Solver, as discussed next.

## USING EVOLUTIONARY SOLVER

Evolutionary Solver uses GAs to obtain "good" solutions. It begins with a population containing, say, 100 sets of values—chromosomes—for the changing cells. For example, one chromosome might be 3.778. (This would be coded in binary form by the algorithm.) This chromosome represents the value of $x$ in this example, but it generally represents a set of values in the changing cells. Chromosomes that yield large objective values have more chance of surviving to the next generation of chromosomes. Chromosomes that yield small objective values have little chance of surviving to the next generation. Occasionally, Evolutionary Solver drastically changes—mutates—the value of a changing cell. You usually stop Evolutionary Solver after a specified time period (such as one minute) or when there has been no improvement in the objective cell value for a given amount of time. Here is some general information about Evolutionary Solver:

*Evolutionary Solver doesn't handle constraints well. It is usually better to penalize constraint violations and include the penalties in the objective.*

- Evolutionary Solver usually finds a good solution, but there is no guarantee that it will find the *best* solution.

- Evolutionary Solver is not very efficient at handling constraints. The best way to handle constraints is to penalize a violation of a constraint. This is done by including a numeric **penalty** as part of the objective. Penalties are not used in this example, but they will be illustrated in a later example.

- A good starting solution—the values you place in the changing cells—usually helps Evolutionary Solver in its search for an optimal solution. However, the starting solution is not absolutely critical to success.

- Evolutionary Solver places more of a burden on you to specify certain parameters of the algorithm. These parameters are specified in the Options dialog box, as will be illustrated shortly. Unfortunately, these parameters are not very intuitive to most users, and some experimentation is necessary to find the best settings of these parameters for any given model. Nevertheless, if you use the default settings or the settings we suggest, they should work reasonably well.

*Evolutionary Solver uses random numbers in its search; therefore, two different runs can lead to different solutions.*

- Much of the solution process is driven by random numbers that direct the search. Therefore, two people can get different solutions to the same problem. In fact, running Evolutionary Solver a second time can possibly yield a different solution. You can set a random seed parameter to ensure the same solution on two successive runs.

- After Evolutionary Solver has found a good solution, you can use GRG Nonlinear Solver to try to find a slightly better solution. If there is no improvement, you can probably infer that the solution found by Evolutionary Solver is optimal or close to optimal.

In general, use the following steps to implement Evolutionary Solver:

**1** **Open Solver.** Open Solver in the usual way, from the Data ribbon.

**2** **Specify the objective cell, changing cells, and constraints.** Do this in the usual way. The only difference is that you should put lower and upper bounds on all changing cells—in addition to any other constraints that might be in the model.

**3 Select Evolutionary Solver.** Click on the drop-down list of available algorithms to select Evolutionary Solver (see Figure 8.4). This is the option used throughout this chapter, but you can also experiment with GRG Nonlinear Solver, especially after Evolutionary Solver finds a good solution.

Figure 8.4

Selecting
Evolutionary Solver

**4 Solver Options.** Click on the Options button and then the All Methods tab to see the dialog box in Figure 8.5. The bottom section of this dialog box, relevant for all Solver algorithms, allows you to change some limits to higher values. The main reason for doing so is to keep Evolutionary Solver from repeatedly beeping at you as it reaches these limits.

Figure 8.5

Solver's All Methods
Options

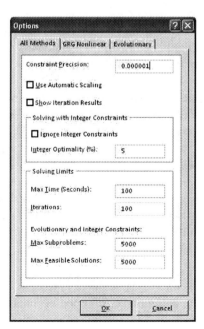

Figure 8.6

Solver's
Evolutionary
Options

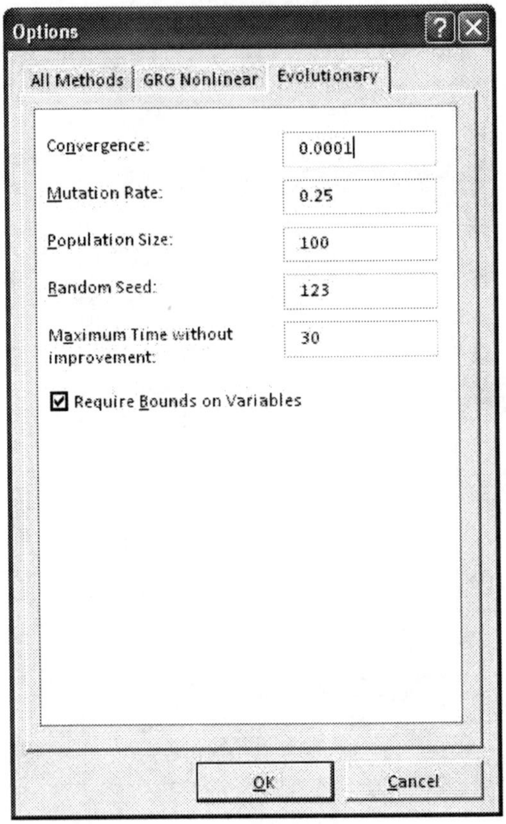

Next, click on the Evolutionary tab to see the dialog box in Figure 8.6. These are the settings that control Evolutionary Solver. The following information about them is available in online help.

▨ *Convergence* measures the rate of change of the objective. You can leave this at its default value.

▨ *Mutation rate* governs the frequency at which mutations are introduced into the population of solutions. Mutations shouldn't be introduced too often, but by introducing them every now and then, the GA gets a chance to explore a completely different area of the feasible region. You can leave this setting at its default value (0.075), but we have sometimes had success by increasing it to 0.25.

▨ *Population size* is the number of candidate solutions (chromosomes) at any point in time, and the default value of 100 should work well, although we sometimes increase it to 150. Note that the initial population is chosen randomly, but it includes at least one instance of the starting solution you specify in the changing cells.

▨ Evolutionary Solver uses a random mechanism to perform its search, but you can make it go through exactly the same calculations on two separate runs if you use the same *random seed* (any integer) on each run. You can leave this box blank, in which case Evolutionary Solver bases the seed on the system clock.

*Some experimentation with Evolutionary Solver's settings may be necessary. No single group of settings works best on every problem.*

▨ You *should* check the Require Bounds on Variables option. This forces you to enter explicit upper and lower bounds on all changing cells, which aids Evolutionary Solver in its search process.

▨ *Maximum Time without Improvement* (measured in seconds) indicates the stopping rule for the algorithm. If it doesn't find a "meaningful" improvement in this amount of time, it will stop and report the best solution so far.

**⑤ Solve.** Go back to the main Solver dialog box and click on Solve. You can watch the progress of the solution process in the status bar of your screen. In particular, watch the *incumbent,* which is the current best value of the objective cell. Typically, this value decreases (for a minimization problem) rapidly at first, and then very slowly. If you sense that it is going nowhere after a minute or two (and you are tired of waiting), you can press the Esc key a few times to stop the process. (Don't be impatient. Evolutionary Solver tends to keep running for awhile even after you press Esc.) From there, you can either let the process continue or accept the best solution to this point. Don't be surprised if the solution process takes *much* longer than you have experienced for Solver models in previous chapters. GAs are not guaranteed to be fast, but they make up for it by being more flexible.

For this particular model, Evolutionary Solver gets to the solution shown earlier in Figure 8.2 almost instantaneously. Then it runs for 30 seconds (the time specified in the dialog box in Figure 8.6) without being able to find a better solution, at which time it quits. Note that this solution is indeed the global optimal solution (refer to Figure 8.2), and Evolutionary Solver finds it almost immediately, even when starting at a solution, such as 3.5 or 4.9, that is close to a local but not global maximum. This is because Evolutionary Solver looks all over the feasible region for potentially good solutions. Therefore, Evolutionary Solver is not as likely to get stuck at a local optimum as GRG Nonlinear Solver. ▩

### Limits on Changing Cells: Required?

In the Evolutionary Solver Options dialog box in Figure 8.6, we suggest checking the Required Bounds on Variables box, which forces you to include constraints with lower and upper bounds on the changing cells. Is it possible to leave this box unchecked and ignore bounds on the changing cells? Evidently, the answer is yes, but it is not a good idea—the GA will not work as well. Therefore, always check this box and always include bounds on the changing cells in your list of constraints.

## PROBLEMS

*Solutions for problems whose numbers appear within a colored box can be found in the Student Solutions Files. Refer to this book's preface for purchase information.*

### Skill-Building Problems

**1.** Modify the function in Example 8.1 so that it becomes $f(x) = (x - 1)(x - 2)(x - 3)(x - 4)(x - 5)(x - 6)(x - 7)$ for $1 \le x \le 7$. Plot a lot of points from 1 to 7 to see what the graph of this function looks like. Then use GRG Nonlinear Solver to find its maximum. Try the following starting points (and don't use the Multistart option): 1, 3, 5, 6, and 6.9. Report what you find. Then

try Evolutionary Solver. Does it find the correct solution?

**2.** Modify the function in Example 8.1 so that it becomes $f(x) = x \sin(x)$ for $0 \le x \le 30$. (Here, $\sin(x)$ is the sine function from trigonometry. You can evaluate it with Excel's SIN function.) Plot a lot of points from 0 to 30 to see what the graph of this function looks like. Then use GRG Nonlinear Solver to find its maximum. Try the following starting points (and don't use the Multistart option): 1, 6, 15, 20, and 27. Report what you find. Then try Evolutionary Solver. Does it find the correct solution?

## 8.4 NONLINEAR PRICING MODELS

We examined several pricing models in the previous chapter. We now examine one more such model, where customers of a certain product place less and less value on each succeeding item of the product. You will see that if the company selling the product sets a constant price per item, it earns considerably less profit than if it uses a more imaginative pricing scheme, called a **two-part tariff.** In this pricing scheme, each customer pays a fixed amount each time she buys *any* amount of the product. In addition, she pays a variable amount per item purchased.

| EXAMPLE | 8.2 PRICING MENTHOS CANDY |
| --- | --- |

*Piecewise linear objectives, implemented with IF logic, are good candidates for Evolutionary Solver.*

Suppose you sell Menthos candy. Most people value the first pack of Menthos they purchase more than the second pack. They also value the second pack more than the third pack, and so on. How can you take advantage of this when pricing Menthos? If you charge a single price for each pack of Menthos, only a few people are going to buy more than one or two packs. Alternatively, however, you can try the two-part tariff approach, where you charge an "entry fee" to anyone who buys Menthos, plus a reduced price per pack purchased. For example, if a reasonable *single* price per pack is $1.10, then a reasonable two-part tariff might be an entry fee of $1.50 and a price of $0.50 per pack. This gives some customers an incentive to purchase many packs of Menthos. Because the total cost of purchasing $n$ packs of Menthos is no longer a linear function of $n$—it is now *piecewise linear*—the two-part tariff is a nonlinear pricing strategy.

As usual with pricing models, the key input is customer sensitivity to price. Rather than having a single demand function, however, we now assume that each customer has a unique sensitivity to price. To keep the example fairly small, we assume that four typical customers from the four market segments for the product have been asked what they would pay for each successive pack of Menthos, with the results listed in Figure 8.7. For example, customer 1 is willing to pay $1.24 for the first pack of Menthos, $1.03 for the second pack, and only $0.35 for the tenth pack. These four customers are considered representative of the four market segments. If it costs $0.40 to produce a pack of Menthos, determine a profit-maximizing single price and a profit-maximizing two-part tariff. Assume that the four market segments have 10,000, 5000, 7500, and 15,000 customers, respectively, and that the customers within a market segment all respond identically to price.

**Figure 8.7**

Price Sensitivity of Four Representative Customers

| | A | B | C | D | E |
| --- | --- | --- | --- | --- | --- |
| 1 | Pricing Menthos - single price model | | | | |
| 2 | | | | | |
| 3 | Price sensitivity of four types of customers | | | | |
| 4 | | Price willing to pay (or marginal value of packs) | | | |
| 5 | Pack # | Customer 1 | Customer 2 | Customer 3 | Customer 4 |
| 6 | 1 | 1.24 | 0.92 | 1.27 | 1.49 |
| 7 | 2 | 1.03 | 0.85 | 1.11 | 1.24 |
| 8 | 3 | 0.89 | 0.69 | 0.96 | 1.10 |
| 9 | 4 | 0.80 | 0.58 | 0.85 | 0.97 |
| 10 | 5 | 0.77 | 0.50 | 0.73 | 0.81 |
| 11 | 6 | 0.66 | 0.43 | 0.63 | 0.71 |
| 12 | 7 | 0.59 | 0.36 | 0.51 | 0.63 |
| 13 | 8 | 0.51 | 0.32 | 0.45 | 0.53 |
| 14 | 9 | 0.42 | 0.26 | 0.39 | 0.42 |
| 15 | 10 | 0.35 | 0.22 | 0.32 | 0.35 |

**Objective** To use Evolutionary Solver to find the best pricing strategies for customers who value each succeeding unit of a product less than the previous unit.

WHERE DO THE NUMBERS COME FROM?

The price sensitivity data listed in Figure 8.7 would be the most difficult to find. However, a well-studied technique in marketing research called *conjoint analysis* can be used to estimate such data. See Green et al. (2001) for a nontechnical discussion of conjoint analysis.

## Solution

You should first set up the single-price model. Then, with very little modification, you can develop the two-part tariff model. The approach for each model is as follows.

For any pricing scheme, you need to calculate the customer's cost if he purchases $n$ packs. Then you can compare this cost to the corresponding value in the appropriate column in Figure 8.7. As an example, suppose you charge a single price of $0.80 per pack. If a customer of type 2 purchases three packs, the **surplus value** to this customer is the total value to him of the three packs, $0.92 + $0.85 + $0.69 = $2.46, minus the cost of the packs, $2.40. Because the value is greater than the cost, a purchase of three packs is attractive to this customer. We assume that a customer of a given type will purchase the quantity $n$ that provides the *largest* surplus value. In simple terms, each customer buys the quantity that provides the largest difference between value and cost. However, if a customer's surplus value is always negative, this customer won't purchase any packs.

By knowing how many packs each customer segment will purchase at each price, you can then maximize the company's profit by setting the price accordingly.

### DEVELOPING THE SINGLE-PRICE MODEL

The single-price model appears in Figure 8.8. (See the Single Price.xlsx file.) It can be formed with the following steps:

## Figure 8.8 Single-Price Model

| | A | B | C | D | E | F | G | H | I | J | K |
|---|---|---|---|---|---|---|---|---|---|---|---|
| 1 | Pricing Menthos - single price model | | | | | | | | | | |
| 2 | | | | | | | | | | | |
| 3 | Price sensitivity of four types of customers | | | | | | Total value of purchases | | | | |
| 4 | | Price willing to pay (or marginal value of packs) | | | | | | Total value from this many packs | | | |
| 5 | Pack # | Customer 1 | Customer 2 | Customer 3 | Customer 4 | | # of packs | Customer 1 | Customer 2 | Customer 3 | Customer 4 |
| 6 | 1 | 1.24 | 0.92 | 1.27 | 1.49 | | 1 | 1.24 | 0.92 | 1.27 | 1.49 |
| 7 | 2 | 1.03 | 0.85 | 1.11 | 1.24 | | 2 | 2.27 | 1.77 | 2.38 | 2.73 |
| 8 | 3 | 0.89 | 0.69 | 0.96 | 1.10 | | 3 | 3.16 | 2.46 | 3.34 | 3.83 |
| 9 | 4 | 0.80 | 0.58 | 0.85 | 0.97 | | 4 | 3.96 | 3.04 | 4.19 | 4.80 |
| 10 | 5 | 0.77 | 0.50 | 0.73 | 0.81 | | 5 | 4.73 | 3.54 | 4.92 | 5.61 |
| 11 | 6 | 0.66 | 0.43 | 0.63 | 0.71 | | 6 | 5.39 | 3.97 | 5.55 | 6.32 |
| 12 | 7 | 0.59 | 0.36 | 0.51 | 0.63 | | 7 | 5.98 | 4.33 | 6.06 | 6.95 |
| 13 | 8 | 0.51 | 0.32 | 0.45 | 0.53 | | 8 | 6.49 | 4.65 | 6.51 | 7.48 |
| 14 | 9 | 0.42 | 0.26 | 0.39 | 0.42 | | 9 | 6.91 | 4.91 | 6.90 | 7.90 |
| 15 | 10 | 0.35 | 0.22 | 0.32 | 0.35 | | 10 | 7.26 | 5.13 | 7.22 | 8.25 |
| 16 | | | | | | | | | | | |
| 17 | Unit cost | $0.40 | | Total cost of packs | | | Surplus (value minus cost) from purchasing | | | | |
| 18 | | | | # of packs | Cost | | # of packs | Customer 1 | Customer 2 | Customer 3 | Customer 4 |
| 19 | Unit price | $0.80 | | 1 | 0.80 | | 1 | 0.44 | 0.12 | 0.47 | 0.69 |
| 20 | | | | 2 | 1.60 | | 2 | 0.67 | 0.17 | 0.78 | 1.13 |
| 21 | | | | 3 | 2.40 | | 3 | 0.76 | 0.06 | 0.94 | 1.43 |
| 22 | | | | 4 | 3.20 | | 4 | 0.76 | -0.16 | 0.99 | 1.60 |
| 23 | | | | 5 | 4.00 | | 5 | 0.73 | -0.46 | 0.92 | 1.61 |
| 24 | | | | 6 | 4.80 | | 6 | 0.59 | -0.83 | 0.75 | 1.52 |
| 25 | | | | 7 | 5.60 | | 7 | 0.38 | -1.27 | 0.46 | 1.35 |
| 26 | | | | 8 | 6.40 | | 8 | 0.09 | -1.75 | 0.11 | 1.08 |
| 27 | | | | 9 | 7.20 | | 9 | -0.29 | -2.29 | -0.30 | 0.70 |
| 28 | | | | 10 | 8.00 | | 10 | -0.74 | -2.87 | -0.78 | 0.25 |
| 29 | | | | | | | | | | | |
| 30 | Customer behavior | | | | | | Range names used: | | | | |
| 31 | | Customer 1 | Customer 2 | Customer 3 | Customer 4 | | Profit | =Model!$B$37 | | | |
| 32 | Max surplus | 0.76 | 0.17 | 0.99 | 1.61 | | Unit_cost | =Model!$B$17 | | | |
| 33 | # purchased | 4 | 2 | 4 | 5 | | Unit_price | =Model!$B$19 | | | |
| 34 | Market size (1000s) | 10 | 5 | 7.5 | 15 | | | | | | |
| 35 | | | | | | | | | | | |
| 36 | Total purchased (1000s) | 155 | | | | | | | | | |
| 37 | Profit ($1000s) | 62.000 | | | | | | | | | |

**1** **Inputs.** Enter the inputs in the blue ranges. Note that the large blue range is the price sensitivity table from Figure 8.7.

**2** **Price.** The *only* decision variable in this model is the single price charged for every pack of Menthos sold. Enter any value in this Unit_price cell.

**3** **Total value table.** The values in the shaded price sensitivity range are *marginal* values, the most each customer would pay for the next pack of Menthos. In the range H6:K15, calculate the *total* value of *n* packs for each customer (for *n* from 1 to 10). First, enter the formula

=B6

in cell H6 and copy it across row 6. Then enter the formula

=H6+B7

in cell H7 and copy it to the range H7:K15.

**4** **Total cost column.** Using the single-price scheme, each customer must pay *np* for *n* packs if the price is *p*. Calculate these amounts in the range E19:E28 by entering the formula

=Unit_price*D19

in cell E19 and copying down.

**5** **Surplus table.** This is the key to the model. You need to calculate the surplus for any customer from buying *n* packs as the total value of *n* packs minus the total cost of *n* packs, and you assume that the customer buys the number of packs with the largest surplus. This makes sense economically. If a customer places more value on *n* packs than it costs to buy *n* packs, then presumably the customer will consider purchasing *n* packs. But a customer will not purchase *n* packs if they cost more than she values them. To calculate these surplus values, enter the formula

=H6-$E19

in cell H19 and copy it to the range H19:K28.

**6** **Maximum surplus.** Calculate the maximum surplus for each customer by entering the formula

=MAX(H19:H28)

in cell B32 and copying it across row 32.

**7** **Packs purchased.** For each customer, you need to find the number of packs that corresponds to the maximum surplus. This can be done best with Excel's MATCH function. Specifically, enter the formula

=IF(B32<0,0,MATCH(B32,H19:H28,0))

in cell B33 and copy it across row 33. This formula says that if the maximum surplus is negative, the customer will not purchase any packs at all. Otherwise, it matches the maximum surplus to the entries in the range H19:H28 and returns the index of the cell where the match occurs. In this example, the match for customer 1 occurs in the fourth cell of the range H19:H28, so the MATCH function returns 4. (Note that the last argument of the MATCH function is 0 if you want an *exact* match, as you do here.) Then calculate the total number of packs purchased by *all* customers with the formula

=SUMPRODUCT(B34:E34,B33:E33)

in cell B36.

*The MATCH function, with the syntax MATCH*(Value,Range,Type), *returns the position (as an integer) of the first match to* Value *in the given* Range. *For example, if* Value *is 6 and the values in the given* Range *are 8, 7, 6, 5, 6, 5, 8, the MATCH function returns 3. The* Type *argument is usually set to 0, which returns an exact match. Other options for the* Type *parameter can be found in Excel's online help.*

**⑧ Profit.** Calculate the profit in cell B37 with the formula

=(Unit_price-Unit_cost)*B36

### USING EVOLUTIONARY SOLVER

First, note that GRG Nonlinear Solver has trouble with this model because of the MAX, IF, and MATCH functions. However, these functions present no difficulties to Evolutionary Solver. It should be set up as shown in Figure 8.9, using the same values for the Evolutionary options as in the previous example. Note that an upper limit of $1.50 has been used for the unit price. This suffices because the most any customer will pay for *any* pack of Menthos is $1.49.

**Figure 8.9**

**Solver Dialog Box for the Single-Price Model**

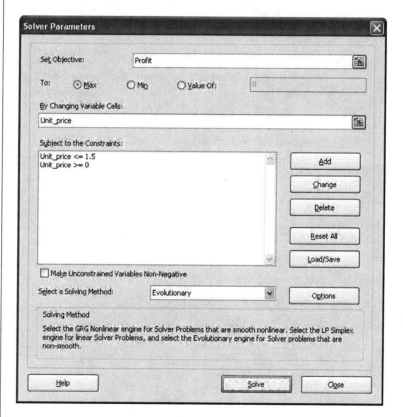

### Discussion of the Solution

Again, Evolutionary Solver converges to the solution in Figure 8.8 quickly and then tries for a long time—unsuccessfully—to find a better solution. You can be fairly certain that this solution is optimal, but this is not guaranteed. The single price of $0.80 produces a profit of $62,000. It strikes the best balance for these four market segments. A lower price would needlessly sacrifice revenue, whereas a higher price would cause at least one market segment to buy fewer packs.

## DEVELOPING THE TWO-PART TARIFF MODEL

The two-part tariff model is so similar that you can make a copy of the Single Price.xlsx file and then make the following modifications. (See Figure 8.10 and the Two-Part Tariff.xlsx file.) The steps that are the same as before are omitted.

**1** **Decision variables.** Now there are two decision variables—the fixed entry fee and the variable cost per pack. Enter any values for these in cells B20 and B21.

**2** **Total cost column.** The total cost of purchasing *n* packs is now the fixed entry fee plus the variable cost times *n*. Calculate this in the range E19:E28 by entering the formula

=Fixed_price+Variable_price*D19

in cell E19 and copying it to the rest of the range.

**3** **Revenues.** Calculate the amount paid by the customers in row 34 by entering the formula

=IF(B33>0,Fixed_price+Variable_price*B33,0)

in cell B34 and copying it across. Note that the entry fee is evidently too high for customer 2, so she does not purchase any packs, and there is no corresponding revenue.

**4** **Profit.** Calculate the profit in the Profit cell with the formula

=SUMPRODUCT(B34:E34,B35:E35)-Unit_cost*B37

The Evolutionary Solver setup is almost the same as before. However, you should now select both the Fixed_price and Variable_price cells as changing cells, and you should put upper limits on each of them, as shown in Figure 8.11. (We used $10 as an upper limit on Fixed_price and $1.50 for Variable_price, reasoning that these would almost certainly be large enough.)

**Figure 8.10** Two-Part Tariff Model

| | A | B | C | D | E | F | G | H | I | J | K |
|---|---|---|---|---|---|---|---|---|---|---|---|
| 1 | Pricing Menthos - two-part tariff model | | | | | | | | | | |
| 2 | | | | | | | | | | | |
| 3 | Price sensitivity of four typical customers | | | | | | Total value of purchases | | | | |
| 4 | | Price willing to pay (or marginal value of packs) | | | | | | Total value from this many packs | | | |
| 5 | Pack # | Customer 1 | Customer 2 | Customer 3 | Customer 4 | | # of packs | Customer 1 | Customer 2 | Customer 3 | Customer 4 |
| 6 | 1 | 1.24 | 0.92 | 1.27 | 1.49 | | 1 | 1.24 | 0.92 | 1.27 | 1.49 |
| 7 | 2 | 1.03 | 0.85 | 1.11 | 1.24 | | 2 | 2.27 | 1.77 | 2.38 | 2.73 |
| 8 | 3 | 0.89 | 0.69 | 0.96 | 1.10 | | 3 | 3.16 | 2.46 | 3.34 | 3.83 |
| 9 | 4 | 0.80 | 0.58 | 0.85 | 0.97 | | 4 | 3.96 | 3.04 | 4.19 | 4.80 |
| 10 | 5 | 0.77 | 0.50 | 0.73 | 0.81 | | 5 | 4.73 | 3.54 | 4.92 | 5.61 |
| 11 | 6 | 0.66 | 0.43 | 0.63 | 0.71 | | 6 | 5.39 | 3.97 | 5.55 | 6.32 |
| 12 | 7 | 0.59 | 0.36 | 0.51 | 0.63 | | 7 | 5.98 | 4.33 | 6.06 | 6.95 |
| 13 | 8 | 0.51 | 0.32 | 0.45 | 0.53 | | 8 | 6.49 | 4.65 | 6.51 | 7.48 |
| 14 | 9 | 0.42 | 0.26 | 0.39 | 0.42 | | 9 | 6.91 | 4.91 | 6.90 | 7.90 |
| 15 | 10 | 0.35 | 0.22 | 0.32 | 0.35 | | 10 | 7.26 | 5.13 | 7.22 | 8.25 |
| 16 | | | | | | | | | | | |
| 17 | Unit cost | $0.40 | | Total cost of packs | | | Surplus (value minus cost) from purchasing | | | | |
| 18 | | | | # of packs | Cost | | # of packs | Customer 1 | Customer 2 | Customer 3 | Customer 4 |
| 19 | Price parameters | | | 1 | 3.70 | | 1 | -2.46 | -2.78 | -2.43 | -2.21 |
| 20 | Fixed price | $3.30 | | 2 | 4.10 | | 2 | -1.83 | -2.33 | -1.72 | -1.37 |
| 21 | Variable price | $0.40 | | 3 | 4.50 | | 3 | -1.34 | -2.04 | -1.16 | -0.67 |
| 22 | | | | 4 | 4.90 | | 4 | -0.94 | -1.86 | -0.71 | -0.10 |
| 23 | | | | 5 | 5.31 | | 5 | -0.58 | -1.77 | -0.39 | 0.30 |
| 24 | | | | 6 | 5.71 | | 6 | -0.32 | -1.74 | -0.16 | 0.61 |
| 25 | | | | 7 | 6.11 | | 7 | -0.13 | -1.78 | -0.05 | 0.84 |
| 26 | | | | 8 | 6.51 | | 8 | -0.02 | -1.86 | 0.00 | 0.97 |
| 27 | | | | 9 | 6.91 | | 9 | 0.00 | -2.00 | -0.01 | 0.99 |
| 28 | | | | 10 | 7.31 | | 10 | -0.05 | -2.18 | -0.09 | 0.94 |
| 29 | | | | | | | | | | | |
| 30 | Customer behavior | | | | | | Range names used: | | | | |
| 31 | | Customer 1 | Customer 2 | Customer 3 | Customer 4 | | Fixed_price | =Model!$B$20 | | | |
| 32 | Max surplus | 0.00 | -1.74 | 0.00 | 0.99 | | Profit | =Model!$B$38 | | | |
| 33 | # purchased | 9 | 0 | 8 | 9 | | Unit_cost | =Model!$B$17 | | | |
| 34 | Amount paid | 6.910 | 0.000 | 6.509 | 6.910 | | Variable_price | =Model!$B$21 | | | |
| 35 | Market size (1000s) | 10 | 5 | 7.5 | 15 | | | | | | |
| 36 | | | | | | | | | | | |
| 37 | Total purchased (1000s) | 285 | | | | | | | | | |
| 38 | Profit ($1000s) | 107.567 | | | | | | | | | |

Figure 8.11

Solver Dialog Box
for Two-Part Tariff
Model

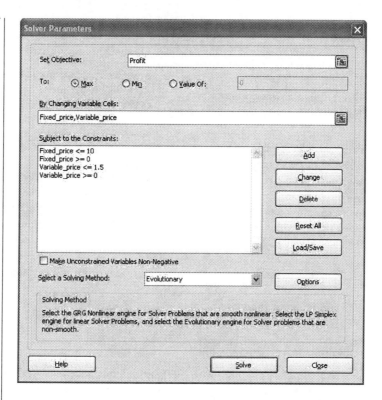

## Discussion of the Solution

The solution in Figure 8.10 was found after about a minute. The solution indicates that the company should charge all customers $3.30 plus $0.40 for each pack purchased. This pricing scheme is too high for the second market segment, which doesn't buy any packs, but it entices segments 1, 3, and 4 to purchase many more packs than they purchased with the single price of $0.80. (Check the price sensitivity columns for these segments. Can you see why they are willing to purchase so many packs with this particular two-part tariff?) More important, it yields a profit of $107,567, about 73% more than the profit from the single-price policy. The moral is clear—clever pricing schemes can make companies significantly larger profits than the simple pricing schemes that are typically used. ▪

## Other Forms of Nonlinear Pricing

There are many other forms of nonlinear pricing, such as the following:

▪ Sell only single-item packs or packs with six items.

▪ Charge one price for the first $n$ packs and another price for the rest.

With Evolutionary Solver, it is easy to experiment with these types of nonlinear pricing schemes and determine the profit earned by each of them. For example, if you allow Menthos to be sold only in a one-pack or a six-pack, it turns out that you can earn a profit of $97,175 by charging $5.39 for a six-pack and virtually any price for a one-pack. Then you will sell three customer segments a six-pack and make $5.39 − $2.40 = $2.99 per customer. Similarly, the best form of the "charge one price for first $n$ packs and another price for remaining packs" scheme (where $n$ is also a decision variable) is to sell up to four packs at $1.28 and $0.40 for each additional pack. See the book by Dolan and Simon (1996) for further discussion and applications of pricing models.

## Skill-Building Problems

**3.** In Example 8.2, determine the best pricing policy if quantity discounts with a single-price breakpoint are used.

**4.** In Example 8.2, determine the optimal pricing policy if Menthos are sold in only a one-pack or a six-pack.

**5.** Based on Schrage (1997). The file P08_05.xlsx lists the size of the four main markets for Excel, Word, and the bundle of Excel and Word. (We assume that Microsoft is willing to sell Excel or Word separately, and it is willing to sell a package with Excel and Word

only.) It also shows how much members of each group are willing to pay for each product combination. How can Microsoft maximize the revenue earned from these products? You should consider the following options:

- No bundling, where Word and Excel are sold separately
- Pure bundling, where purchasers can buy only Word and Excel together
- Mixed bundling, where purchasers can buy Word or Excel separately, or they can buy them as a bundle

# 8.5 COMBINATORIAL MODELS

Consider the following situations:

- Xerox must determine where to place maintenance facilities. The more maintenance facilities selected, the more copiers the company will sell due to better availability of maintenance. How can the company locate maintenance facilities to maximize total profit?

- A gasoline company is loading three different products on a tanker truck with five compartments. Each compartment can handle at most one product. How should the company load the truck to come as close as possible to meeting its delivery requirements?

- Fox has 30 different ads of different lengths that must be assigned to 10 different two-minute commercial breaks. How should the company assign ads to maximize its total ad revenue?

- John Deere must schedule its production of lawn mowers over the next four weeks. The company wants to meet its forecasted demands, keep production hours fairly constant from week to week, and avoid model changeovers as much as possible. How should the company schedule its production?

*Combinatorial problems have only a finite number of feasible solutions. However, they can still be very difficult because this finite number is often enormous.*

Each of these problems is a **combinatorial** optimization problem that requires a company to choose the best of many different combinations available. Although combinatorial optimization problems can often be handled as Solver models with 0–1 changing cells, it is often difficult to develop the constraints in a way that keeps the model linear. (You saw examples of the tricks required in Chapter 6.) With Evolutionary Solver, however, it doesn't matter whether the constraints or the objective are linear. The SUMIF and COUNTIF functions are often useful in such problems. The two examples in this section illustrate typical combinatorial optimization problems.

## Loading Products on a Truck

The following example might appear simple when you first read it, but it is not. The number of possible solutions is enormous, and it can take a Solver, even Evolutionary Solver, a long time to find an optimal (or nearly optimal) solution.

EXAMPLE | 8.3 LOADING A GAS STORAGE TRUCK

A gas truck contains five compartments with the capacities listed in Table 8.1. Three products must be shipped on the truck, and there can be only one product per compartment. The demand for each product, the shortage cost per gallon, and the maximum allowable shortage for each product are listed in Table 8.2. How should the truck be loaded to minimize the shortage costs?

Table 8.1 Truck Capacities

| Compartment | Capacity (Gallons) |
|-------------|--------------------|
| 1 | 2700 |
| 2 | 2800 |
| 3 | 1100 |
| 4 | 1800 |
| 5 | 3400 |

Table 8.2 Demand and Shortage Data

| Product | Demand | Max Shortage Allowed | Cost per Gallon Short |
|---------|--------|----------------------|-----------------------|
| 1 | 2900 | 900 | $10 |
| 2 | 4000 | 900 | $8 |
| 3 | 4900 | 900 | $6 |

**Objective** To use Evolutionary Solver to find the combination of products to load in compartments that minimizes the total shortage cost.

WHERE DO THE NUMBERS COME FROM?

The data would be based on the truck dimensions and presumably on contracts the company has with its customers.

Solution

The objective in this problem is to minimize the total shortage cost. The decision variables indicate the type of product stored in each compartment and the amount of that product to load in the compartment. The constraints must ensure that no compartment is overfilled and that the maximum allowable shortage is not exceeded.

DEVELOPING THE SPREADSHEET MODEL

The completed model appears in Figure 8.12. (See the file Loading Truck.xlsx.) It can be developed as follows:

**1** **Inputs.** Enter the inputs from Tables 8.1 and 8.2 into the shaded ranges.

**2** **Decision variables.** Enter any integer values (from 1 to 3) in the Product range and any values (integer or noninteger) in the Amount range. These two ranges represent the changing cells.

**Figure 8.12** Truck Loading Model

| | A | B | C | D | E | F | G | H | I |
|---|---|---|---|---|---|---|---|---|---|
| 1 | Storing gas products in compartments | | | | | | | | |
| 2 | | | | | | | | | |
| 3 | Unit shortage costs and penalty cost for violating shortage constraints | | | | | | Range names used | | |
| 4 | Product | Cost/gallon | | | | | Amount | =Model!$C$13:$C$17 | |
| 5 | 1 | $10.00 | | | | | Capacity | =Model!$E$13:$E$17 | |
| 6 | 2 | $8.00 | | | | | Product | =Model!$B$13:$B$17 | |
| 7 | 3 | $6.00 | | | | | Total_cost | =Model!$B$28 | |
| 8 | | | | | | | | | |
| 9 | Shortage penalty | $100 | | | | | | | |
| 10 | | | | | | | | | |
| 11 | Storing decisions | | | | | | | | |
| 12 | Compartment | Product | Amount | | Capacity | | | | |
| 13 | 1 | 2 | 2700.0 | <= | 2700 | | | | |
| 14 | 2 | 1 | 2800.0 | <= | 2800 | | | | |
| 15 | 3 | 2 | 1100.0 | <= | 1100 | | | | |
| 16 | 4 | 3 | 1677.8 | <= | 1800 | | | | |
| 17 | 5 | 3 | 3400.0 | <= | 3400 | | | | |
| 18 | | | | | | | | | |
| 19 | Shortages | | | | | | | | |
| 20 | Product | Amount Stored | Demand | Shortage | Max Shortage | Shortage Violation | | | |
| 21 | 1 | 2800.0 | 2900 | 100.0 | 900 | 0.0 | | | |
| 22 | 2 | 3800.0 | 4000 | 200.0 | 900 | 0.0 | | | |
| 23 | 3 | 5077.8 | 4900 | 0.0 | 900 | 0.0 | | | |
| 24 | | | | | | | | | |
| 25 | Costs and penalties | | | | | | | | |
| 26 | Shortage cost | $2,600.00 | | | | | | | |
| 27 | Penalty cost | $0.00 | | | | | | | |
| 28 | Total cost | $2,600.00 | | | | | | | |

③ **Amounts stored total.** To calculate the gallons of each product stored on the truck from the values in the changing cells, you can use the SUMIF function. Specifically, enter the formula

=SUMIF(Product,A21,Amount)

in cell B21. This formula sums the values in the Amount range for all rows where the product index, 1, in cell A21 matches the index in the Product range. Therefore, it calculates the total amount of product 1 stored on the truck. Copy this formula down for the other two products.

④ **Shortages.** To calculate the shortages, enter the formula

=IF(B21<C21,C21-B21,0)

in cell D21 and copy it down. Note that shortages were discussed in previous chapters, but they always required some tricks to keep the models linear. Now you can use straightforward IF functions, which present no difficulty for Evolutionary Solver.

⑤ **Shortage violations.** You could *constrain* the shortages to be less than the maximum allowable shortages, but because the Evolutionary Solver works best with as few constraints as possible, there is a better approach. (This approach is used in the following example as well.) You can calculate the amount by which each maximum storage constraint is violated (if at all) and then add these violations, multiplied by a suitably large penalty, to the cost objective. Because the objective is to minimize total cost, Evolutionary Solver tries to stay away from solutions where this penalty is positive. Therefore, it favors solutions where the maximum storage constraints are satisfied. To implement this strategy, calculate the maximum storage violations in column F by entering the formula

=IF(D21>E21,D21-E21,0)

in cell F21 and copying it down. The solution shown in Figure 8.12 does not have any violations, but the values in column F would be positive if any shortages in column D were greater than 900.

**6** **Costs.** Calculate the total shortage cost in cell B26 with the formula

=SUMPRODUCT(B5:B7,D21:D23)

Then calculate the penalty cost from maximum shortage violations in B27 with the formula

=B9*SUM(F21:F23)

Note that a penalty of $100 per unit shortage above the maximum allowed was chosen. Any large dollar value would suffice here. Finally, calculate the total cost in cell B28 by summing the values in cells B26 and B27.

### USING EVOLUTIONARY SOLVER

The Solver setup for this model is straightforward, as shown in Figure 8.13. Unlike some previous models, there are now natural lower limits and upper limits for the changing cells. The Product range must be between 1 and 3 (and they must be integers) because there are only three products. The Amount range must be between 0 and the given capacities of the compartments.

### Discussion of the Solution

The solution in Figure 8.12 shows that product 1 should be stored in compartment 2, product 2 should be stored in compartments 1 and 3, and product 3 should be stored in compartments 4 and 5, the only compartments that end up with excess capacity. The demands for products 1 and 2 are not quite met, and the total shortage cost is $2600, but the shortages are well below the maximum shortages allowed. Therefore, there is no penalty cost for violating the maximum shortage constraints.

**Figure 8.13**

**Solver Dialog Box for the Truck Loading Model**

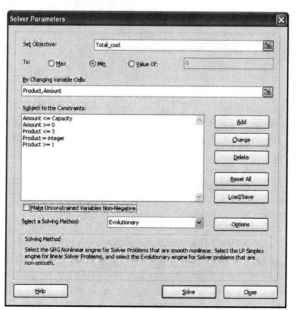

This model is not easy for Evolutionary Solver, in spite of its rather small size, and its success depends a lot on the starting solution. For example, we tried one solution with all 3s in the Product range and all 1000s in the Amount range. It got to a solution with objective value $3200 fairly quickly, but then it spun its wheels for a long time and never improved. In contrast, when we entered a random combination of 1, 2, and 3 in the Product range and all 0s in the Amount range, the optimal solution was found very quickly.

### Sensitivity Analysis with SolverTable

Nothing prevents you from using SolverTable on an Evolutionary Solver model—except time. You fill in the SolverTable dialog box exactly as before. The only difference is that Evolutionary Solver can take a lot of time to solve *one* problem, let alone a whole series of problems. Also, to provide some assurance that it does not stop prematurely at a suboptimal solution for at least one of the problems, you need to experiment with the Evolutionary Solver settings in the Options dialog boxes, because the appropriate settings are not always obvious.

We tried a sensitivity analysis on the capacity of compartment 3 for this example, allowing it to vary from 300 to 1100 in multiples of 200, and we obtained the results in Figure 8.14. We are not really sure whether these results are optimal. (The equal objective values for capacities of 700 and 900 are somewhat suspicious.) However, we ran this same SolverTable several times, with different Solver option settings and different starting solutions, and we usually obtained *worse* results than in Figure 8.14 on at least one problem. This is not the fault of SolverTable or even the fault of Evolutionary Solver. This storage problem, like many combinatorial problems, is difficult, and unless Evolutionary Solver is allowed to run for a very long time, it can easily get stuck at a suboptimal solution fairly far from the optimal solution. For this reason, we do not mention SolverTable again in this chapter, but there is nothing to prevent you from trying it. You just need to be patient.

**Figure 8.14** SolverTable Results for the Truck Loading Model

| | A | B | C | D | E | F | G | H | I | J | K | L |
|---|---|---|---|---|---|---|---|---|---|---|---|---|
| 30 | Sensitivity of solution to capacity of compartment 3 | | | | | | | | | | | |
| 31 | | | | | | | | | | | | |
| 32 | | $B$13 | $C$13 | $B$14 | $C$14 | $B$15 | $C$15 | $B$16 | $C$16 | $B$17 | $C$17 | $B$28 |
| 33 | 300 | 3 | 2700.0 | 1 | 2800.0 | 2 | 300.0 | 3 | 1800.0 | 2 | 3392.5 | $5,860.33 |
| 34 | 500 | 3 | 2700.0 | 1 | 2800.0 | 2 | 500.0 | 3 | 1800.0 | 2 | 3400.0 | $4,200.00 |
| 35 | 700 | 3 | 2700.0 | 1 | 2800.0 | 2 | 669.5 | 3 | 1800.0 | 2 | 3400.0 | $3,400.00 |
| 36 | 900 | 3 | 2700.0 | 1 | 2800.0 | 2 | 669.5 | 3 | 1800.0 | 2 | 3400.0 | $3,400.00 |
| 37 | 1100 | 2 | 2700.0 | 1 | 2800.0 | 2 | 1100.0 | 3 | 1800.0 | 3 | 3399.1 | $2,600.00 |

## Finding a Good Production Schedule

Determining a monthly production schedule at a manufacturing facility such as a John Deere manufacturing plant is very difficult. Many conflicting objectives must be balanced. The following example illustrates how these competing objectives can be modeled.[2]

EXAMPLE | 8.4 SCHEDULING PRODUCTION OF LAWN MOWERS AT EASYRIDE

EasyRide, a lawn mower manufacturer, needs to set its weekly production schedule for the next four weeks. The company produces seven models of lawn mowers. At the beginning of each month, the company has reasonably accurate forecasts for the demand of each model for the month. It also has forecasts for the portion of this demand from customers who will drive to the plant to pick up their lawn mowers. The company has four competing objectives regarding its production schedule.

■ Avoid costly model changeovers during each week as much as possible.

[2]This example is based on a model actually developed by John Deere, as described to the authors by John Deere managers.

- Come as close as possible to producing the mowers demanded by customers during week 1 (assuming the "pickup" customers, those who drive to the plant to pick up their mowers, typically arrive during week 1).

- Keep weekly production hours as constant as possible across weeks at each of the three machining centers that the models go through.

- Come as close as possible to producing as many mowers of each model as its monthly forecasts require.

**Objective** To use Evolutionary Solver to find a production schedule that achieves the company's goals as fully as possible.

## WHERE DO THE NUMBERS COME FROM?

As in other production scheduling models we have discussed, the most crucial inputs are the demand forecasts. The company presumably has a method for forecasting demands, probably based on historical data and orders already on the books.

## Solution

It is typically not possible to satisfy all of EasyRide's objectives. Therefore, think of the objectives as targets. If any solution falls short of the target, it is penalized—the farther from the target, the larger the penalty. This is an especially useful technique when using Evolutionary Solver, which thrives on messy objective functions but does less well with a lot of constraints. Therefore, instead of using constraints, the deviations from targets are penalized, and the objective to minimize is the total of the penalties.

The data for the problem appear in Figure 8.15 (see the file Lawnmower Production.xlsx). Rows 5 and 6 indicate the forecasts of customer pickups and monthly totals, and rows 10 through 12 indicate the number of hours required at each machine center to produce a mower of each model. The unit penalty costs in rows 15 to 18 are not really "givens." They must be estimated by EasyRide to reflect trade-offs among the competing objectives. They imply the following:

- A changeover penalty of 200 is incurred for each model produced at any *positive* level during a week. For example, if 3 models are produced the first week, 4 the second, 3 the third, and 5 the fourth, the total changeover penalty is (3 + 4 + 3 + 5) (200) = 3000.

Figure 8.15

Inputs for the Lawn Mower Production Model

| | A | B | C | D | E | F | G | H |
|---|---|---|---|---|---|---|---|---|
| 1 | Lawnmower production model | | | | | | | |
| 2 | | | | | | | | |
| 3 | Forecasts of demand | | | | | | | |
| 4 | | Model 1 | Model 2 | Model 3 | Model 4 | Model 5 | Model 6 | Model 7 |
| 5 | Pickups | 30 | 20 | 15 | 30 | 23 | 12 | 12 |
| 6 | Total | 110 | 90 | 100 | 115 | 80 | 60 | 80 |
| 7 | | | | | | | | |
| 8 | Hours per mower required in the machine centers | | | | | | | |
| 9 | | Model 1 | Model 2 | Model 3 | Model 4 | Model 5 | Model 6 | Model 7 |
| 10 | Center 1 | 3 | 2 | 2 | 2 | 2 | 4 | 2 |
| 11 | Center 2 | 1 | 2 | 1 | 3 | 3 | 3 | 4 |
| 12 | Center 3 | 2 | 3 | 0 | 4 | 3 | 3 | 2 |
| 13 | | | | | | | | |
| 14 | Unit penalty "costs" | | | | Range names used: | | | |
| 15 | Model changeover | 200 | | | Production | =Sheet1!$B$22:$H$25 | | |
| 16 | Satisfy pickups | 50 | | | Total_penalty | =Sheet1!$B$46 | | |
| 17 | Smooth production | 1 | | | | | | |
| 18 | Meet forecasts | 10 | | | | | | |

The IF logic required
to implement penal-
ties of these types
makes the model
nonsmooth. Therefore,
such models are
perfect candidates for
Evolutionary Solver.

- A pickup shortage penalty of 50 is incurred for each unit of pickup demand not satisfied during week 1. For example, if 20 units of model 1 are produced during week 1, the pickup penalty for this model is (10)(50) = 500 because 20 is 10 short of the required 30.

- A smoothing production penalty of 1 is incurred during each week at each machine center per hour of deviation from the required weekly average at that center. Here, the required weekly average is based on the production levels needed to meet monthly forecasts. Their implementation will be explained shortly.

- A meeting monthly forecasts penalty of 10 is incurred per unit of each model produced above *or* below the monthly forecast. For example, if the total monthly production of model 1 is 105 or 115 (a deviation of 5 below or 5 above the monthly forecast), the penalty in either case is (5)(10) = 50.

Again, these unit penalties are not givens, and they must be chosen carefully by EasyRide, perhaps on the basis of a sensitivity analysis. Clearly, if one unit penalty is too large, its corresponding objective tends to dominate the solution. In the same way, if a unit penalty is too small, its corresponding objective is practically ignored. We have tried to choose unit penalties that produce a reasonable solution, but you might want to experiment with others.

## DEVELOPING THE SPREADSHEET MODEL

The completed model appears in Figure 8.16. It can be developed with the following steps:

**1 Production schedule.** The decision variables are the weekly production levels of each model. Enter *any* values for these in the Production range. (Refer to Figure 8.15 for range names used.)

**Figure 8.16**   Lawn Mower Production Model

| | A | B | C | D | E | F | G | H | I | J | K |
|---|---|---|---|---|---|---|---|---|---|---|---|
| 20 | **Weekly production levels** | | | | | | | | | | |
| 21 | | Model 1 | Model 2 | Model 3 | Model 4 | Model 5 | Model 6 | Model 7 | Models | | |
| 22 | Week 1 | 31 | 21 | 19 | 30 | 29 | 14 | 14 | 7 | | |
| 23 | Week 2 | 0 | 69 | 81 | 42 | 0 | 0 | 0 | 3 | | |
| 24 | Week 3 | 79 | 0 | 0 | 0 | 51 | 0 | 32 | 3 | | |
| 25 | Week 4 | 0 | 0 | 0 | 43 | 0 | 46 | 34 | 3 | | |
| 26 | Mowers produced | 110 | 90 | 100 | 115 | 80 | 60 | 80 | | | |
| 27 | Deviations from forecasts | 0 | 0 | 0 | 0 | 0 | 0 | 0 | | | |
| 28 | Shortages for pickups | 0 | 0 | 0 | 0 | 0 | 0 | 0 | | | |
| 29 | | | | | | | | | | | |
| 30 | **Average hours need per week to meet monthly forecasts** | | | | | | | | | | |
| 31 | Center 1 | 375 | | | | | | | | | |
| 32 | Center 2 | 368.75 | | | | | | | | | |
| 33 | Center 3 | 382.5 | | | | | | | | | |
| 34 | | | | | | | | | | | |
| 35 | **Hours used each week in each center** | | | | | | **Deviations from hourly targets** | | | | |
| 36 | | Week 1 | Week 2 | Week 3 | Week 4 | | | Week 1 | Week 2 | Week 3 | Week 4 |
| 37 | Center 1 | 375 | 384 | 403 | 338 | | Center 1 | 0.00 | 9.00 | 28.00 | 37.00 |
| 38 | Center 2 | 367 | 345 | 360 | 403 | | Center 2 | 1.75 | 23.75 | 8.75 | 34.25 |
| 39 | Center 3 | 402 | 375 | 375 | 378 | | Center 3 | 19.50 | 7.50 | 7.50 | 4.50 |
| 40 | | | | | | | | | | | |
| 41 | **Penalty costs** | | | | | | | | | | |
| 42 | Model changeover | 3200 | | | | | | | | | |
| 43 | Satisfy pickups | 0 | | | | | | | | | |
| 44 | Smooth production | 182 | | | | | | | | | |
| 45 | Meet forecasts | 0 | | | | | | | | | |
| 46 | Total penalty | 3382 | | | | | | | | | |
| 47 | | | | | | | | | | | |
| 48 | | | | | | | | | | | |
| 49 | | | | | | | | | | | |
| 50 | | | | | | | | | | | |

Production Hours across Weeks

**2** **Models produced.** To calculate the number of different models produced each week (which are needed for the model changeover objective), enter the formula

=COUNTIF(B22:H22,">0")

in cell I22 and copy it down.

**3** **Deviations from forecasts.** To calculate the total monthy production levels for each model and see how much they deviate from the monthly forecasts, enter the formulas

=SUM(B22:B25)

and

=ABS(B6-B26)

in cells B26 and B27 for model 1, and copy these across for the other models. (Recall that ABS is Excel's absolute value function.)

**4** **Pickup shortages.** To see how much week 1 production of each model is short (if any) of the pickup demand, enter the formula

=IF(B22<B5,B5-B22,0)

in cell B28 and copy it across.

**5** **Hourly smoothing.** This is the trickiest objective. The production hours at each machine center should remain as constant as possible across weeks. Although there are undoubtedly other ways to implement this, we suggest the following approach. First, calculate the weekly average hours required at each machine center *if* the company produces exactly enough in the month to meet monthly forecasts. To do this, enter the formula

=SUMPRODUCT($B$6:$H$6,B10:H10)/4

in cell B31 for center 1 and copy it down for the other two centers. (Note that division by 4 is used to obtain a weekly average.) These weekly averages become the targets. Next, calculate the *actual* hours used at each center each week in the range B37:E39. Unfortunately, there is no way to enter a *single* formula and then copy it to the rest of the range. However, you can try the following. Enter the formula

=SUMPRODUCT($B$22:$H$22,$B10:$H10)

in cell B37 and copy it down to cell B39. Then copy the range B37:B39 to the range C37:E39. The resulting formulas for weeks 2 to 4 in columns C to E will not be quite correct, but you can modify them easily. Specifically, change each 22 in the column C formulas to 23, to 24 in column D, and to 25 in column E. The point is that when copying is not possible, sometimes copying a formula and then modifying it is easier than entering new formulas from scratch. Finally, calculate the deviations from targets in the range H37:K39 by entering the formula

=ABS(B37-$B31)

in cell H37 and copying it to the rest of the range. (Here, copying *is* possible.)

**6** **Penalties.** Calculate the various penalties in the range B42:B45 with the formulas

=B15*SUM(I22:I25)

=B16*SUM(B28:H28)

=B17*SUM(H37:K39)

and

=B18*SUM(B27:H27)

Then calculate the total penalty as their sum in cell B46.

### USING EVOLUTIONARY SOLVER

The Solver setup for this model appears in Figure 8.17. The objective is to minimize the total of penalties, the changing cells are the production levels, and there are no constraints other than lower and upper bounds and integer constraints on the production levels. As for the upper bounds, 150 is fairly arbitrary. The largest monthly forecast for any model is 115, but the company might want production to exceed this forecast. Therefore, you can build in some "padding" with the upper limit of 150.

Figure 8.17

Solver Setup for the
Lawn Mower
Production Model

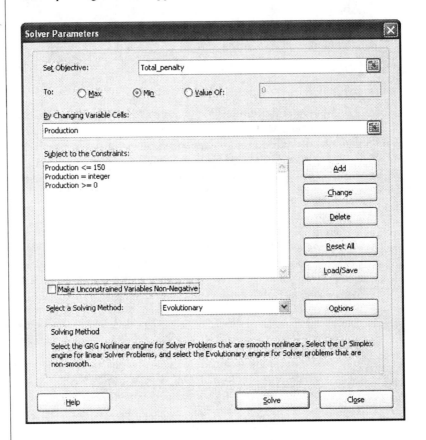

After some experimenting, you will see that this is a difficult problem even for Evolutionary Solver. Depending on the starting solution, it can take some time to find as good a solution as the one in Figure 8.16. Therefore, it helps to enter large values in the Solver Options dialog boxes for Max Time, Max Subproblems, Max Feasible Solutions, and Maximum Time without Improvement (this latter setting under the Evolutionary tab). Otherwise, Evolutionary Solver might quit prematurely at a solution far from optimal. Another possible strategy is to drop the integer constraint by checking the box in Figure 8.18. This will find a "good" noninteger solution relatively quickly. Then you can run the Solver again, starting from this noninteger solution, with the box unchecked to find a good integer solution.

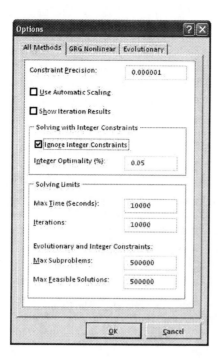

Figure 8.18

Option to Ignore
Integer Constraints

## Discussion of the Solution

The solution in Figure 8.16 represents the best compromise we could find. It produces all seven models during week 1 to keep the pickup shortages low. In fact, it has no pickup shortages. After that, it produces only three separate models each week to keep the changeover penalties low. This solution produces exactly to the monthly forecasts. Finally, all of this is done in a way to keep the production hours as constant as possible across weeks. Even so, the chart in Figure 8.16, based on the data in the range B37:E39, shows that the production hours still vary to some extent across weeks at each machine center. Of course, if you change the unit penalties to reflect different priorities on the objectives and then rerun Evolutionary Solver, you could get a much different solution. For example, if EasyRide decides that pickup shortages are not such an important concern, it could reduce the unit shortage penalty from 50 to, say, 25 or even 5. Then the production schedule might change so that all seven models are *not* produced in week 1. ▪

# PROBLEMS

### Skill-Building Problems

6. In the truck-loading problem in Example 8.3, we assumed that any product could be loaded into any compartment. Suppose the following are *not* allowed: product 1 in compartment 2, product 2 in compartment 1, and product 3 in compartment 4. Modify the model appropriately, and then use Evolutionary Solver to find the new optimal solution. (*Hint*: Add a penalty to the objective for violating these new constraints.)

7. In the lawn mower production problem in Example 8.4, the model changeover cost dominates in the optimal

objective value. Is this because we assumed such a large unit penalty cost, 200, for each model changeover? Explore this question by changing this unit penalty cost to lower values such as 100 and 50 (or even smaller). What happens to the optimal solution?

8. In the lawn mower production problem in Example 8.4, experiment with the penalty cost for unsatisfied pick-ups in week 1. If this cost is sufficiently small, does the company ever produce fewer than seven models in week 1 and allow some week 1 pickups to be unsatisfied?

Suppose a company wants to see how its revenue from sales is related to its sales force effort. If $R$ is revenue and $E$ is sales force effort, marketing researchers have found that the relationship between $R$ and $E$ is often well described by a function of the following form:

$$R = a + \frac{(b-a)E^c}{d + E^c} \tag{8.1}$$

for suitable constants $a$, $b$, $c$, and $d$. This function can exhibit diminishing returns, where each extra unit of $E$ contributes less and less to $R$, or it can represent an S-shaped curve, as in Figure 8.19. An S-shaped curve starts out flat, gets steep, and then flattens out. This shape is appropriate if sales effort needs to exceed some critical value to generate significant sales. The following example illustrates how Evolutionary Solver can be used to estimate this type of curve.[3]

**Figure 8.19**

S-Shaped Sales
Response Curve

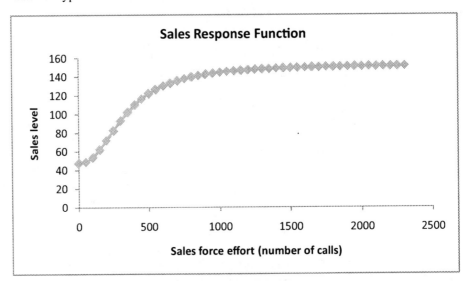

| EXAMPLE | 8.5 ESTIMATING THE SALES RESPONSE FUNCTION AT LYNTEX LABS |

Lyntex Labs wants to estimate the sales response function that relates its revenue from sales of a certain drug to the number of sales calls made. Company experts estimate the revenue that would be obtained in the following five scenarios:

⬛ No sales effort is assigned to the drug.

⬛ Sales effort assigned to the drug is cut in half.

⬛ Sales force effort stays at the current level.

⬛ Sales force effort is increased by 50%.

⬛ Sales force effort saturates the market.

The resulting estimates appear in Table 8.3. Note that the current sales effort is 350,000 sales calls. Also, all sales revenue estimates are expressed relative to an index of 100, where

---

[3]The model in this section has smooth functions, and it can be solved successfully with GRG Nonlinear Solver *if* the initial solution is not too far from the optimal solution. Alternatively, GRG Nonlinear Solver with the Multistart option works great. However, we illustrate Evolutionary Solver as an alternative.

100 represents the current level of sales revenue. For example, the experts estimate that if sales effort is cut in half, sales revenue from the drug will decrease to 68% of the current level. Lyntex assumes that its sales revenue function is of the form in Equation (8.1). It wants to find the constants $a$, $b$, $c$, and $d$ that provide the best fit to the values in Table 8.3.

**Table 8.3  Estimated Sales Revenues**

| Sales Calls (1000s) | Sales Revenue |
|---|---|
| 0 | 47 |
| 175 | 68 |
| 350 | 100 |
| 525 | 126 |
| 3500 | 152 |

**Objective**   To use Evolutionary Solver to estimate the assumed S-shaped relationship between revenue and sales force effort, as measured by the number of sales calls.

WHERE DO THE NUMBERS COME FROM?

The required data in Table 8.3 could be historical data, based on various levels of sales force effort the company has used in the past, or, as suggested in the problem statement, they could be educated guesses by people in the marketing department.

Solution

The model development is basically the same as for Example 7.5 from the previous chapter. (See Figure 8.20 and the file Sales Response.xlsx.) The objective is again to find the model parameters that minimize the sum of squared errors between the actual revenues and the revenues predicted from the sales response function.

**Figure 8.20  Sales Response Function Estimation**

| | A | B | C | D | E | F | G | H |
|---|---|---|---|---|---|---|---|---|
| 1 | Estimating the sales response function at Lyntex Labs | | | | | | | |
| 2 | | | | | | | | |
| 3 | Assumed sales response function: | | | | | | Range names used: | |
| 4 | Estimate sales level when x sales calls (in 1000s) are made is a+(b-a)xᶜ/(d+xᶜ) | | | | | | a | =Estimation!$B$7 |
| 5 | | | | | | | b | =Estimation!$C$7 |
| 6 | Model parameters | | a | b | c | d | c_ | =Estimation!$D$7 |
| 7 | | | 47.480 | 152.914 | 2.264 | 534155 | d | =Estimation!$E$7 |
| 8 | | | | | | | Sum_of_squared_errors | =Estimation!$B$17 |
| 9 | Estimates from management | | | | | | | |
| 10 | | | Sales calls (1000s) | Sales level | Sales estimate | Error | | |
| 11 | | | 0 | 47 | 47.480 | -0.480 | | |
| 12 | | | 175 | 68 | 66.747 | 1.253 | | |
| 13 | | | 350 | 100 | 102.070 | -2.070 | | |
| 14 | | | 525 | 126 | 124.327 | 1.673 | | |
| 15 | | | 3500 | 152 | 152.381 | -0.381 | | |
| 16 | | | | | | | | |
| 17 | Sum of squared errors | | 9.028 | | | | | |

DEVELOPING THE SPREADSHEET MODEL

To develop the spreadsheet model, use the following steps:

1 **Inputs.**  Enter the data in the blue region from Table 8.3.

2 **Decision variables.**  The only decision variables are the constants $a$, $b$, $c$, and $d$ of the sales response function. Enter any values for these. [Note that we tried to give the

corresponding cells range names of a, b, c, and d. However, Excel doesn't allow the range name c. (It also doesn't allow the range name r.) Instead, it changes this name to c_].

**3** **Predicted sales revenues.** In column D, calculate the sales revenue levels (remember that these are relative to 100) predicted from Equation (8.1). To do so, enter the formula

=a+((b-a)*B11^c_)/(d+B11^c_)

in cell D11 and copy it down to cell D15.

**4** **Prediction errors.** For a good fit, the predictions in column D should match the experts' estimates in column C as closely as possible. As usual, a good way to do this is to minimize the sum of squared differences between the two columns. First, calculate the errors in column E by entering the formula

=C11-D11

in cell E11 and copying down. Then calculate the sum of squared errors in cell B17 with the formula

=SUMSQ(E11:E15)

### USING EVOLUTIONARY SOLVER

No IF, ABS, MAX, or MIN functions are used in this model, so you might try GRG Nonlinear Solver, just as in the previous chapter. However, there might be *local* minima in this model that are not *globally* optimal. Alternatively, you could try the Multistart option. However, Evolutionary Solver is also a good choice because it searches the entire feasible region and is less likely to get stuck at a local minimum. The only problem is to find a decent starting solution and reasonable lower and upper limits for the changing cells. It is difficult to tell, just by looking at Equation (8.1), what reasonable values for a, b, c, and d might be. Must they be positive? How large can they be? The answers are certainly not obvious.

*Even though this model is smooth, its nonlinearity makes it difficult. The standard nonlinear Solver can get stuck at the wrong solution, depending on the starting solution.*

Therefore, some analysis of Equation (8.1) is useful before turning to Evolutionary Solver. First, note that when $E = 0$, estimated sales $R$ equals $a$. Therefore, $a$ should be positive. Second, the fraction in Equation (8.1) approaches $b - a$ as $E$ gets large, so $b$ is the limiting value of $R$ as $E$ gets large. Third, $E^c$ should increase when $E$ increases, so that $R$ will increase with $E$. This occurs only if $c$ is positive. Finally, to keep the denominator positive for all values of $E$, $d$ must be positive.

If this quick analysis is not convincing, another strategy is to graph Equation (8.1) and then *watch* how the graph changes as you manually change a, b, c, and d (see Figure 8.21).

**Figure 8.21    Graph of Sales Response Function**

| | A | B | C | D | E | F | G | H | I | J | K | L | M |
|---|---|---|---|---|---|---|---|---|---|---|---|---|---|
| 1 | Graphing the sales response function | | | | | | | | | | | | |
| 2 | | | | | | | | | | | | | |
| 3 | Model parameters | a | b | c | d | | | | | | | | |
| 4 | | 40.000 | 150.000 | 2.500 | 500000 | | | | | | | | |
| 5 | | | | | | | | | | | | | |
| 6 | Points on the graph | E | Actual R | Predicted R | | | | | | | | | |
| 7 | | 0 | 47 | 40.000 | | | | | | | | | |
| 8 | | 175 | 68 | 89.235 | | | | | | | | | |
| 9 | | 350 | 100 | 130.299 | | | | | | | | | |
| 10 | | 525 | 126 | 141.930 | | | | | | | | | |
| 11 | | 3500 | 152 | 149.924 | | | | | | | | | |
| 12 | | | | | | | | | | | | | |
| 13 | | | | | | | | | | | | | |
| 14 | | | | | | | | | | | | | |
| 15 | | | | | | | | | | | | | |
| 16 | | | | | | | | | | | | | |

Sales Level versus Sales Calls

This chart is a scatter chart (where the dots are connected with lines) that plots the actual sales (the experts' estimates) in column C and the predicted values from the sales response function in column D. By changing the constants in row 4 and seeing when the fit between the two curves is fairly good, you can quickly see that *a* should be around 47, *b* should be somewhere between 150 and 160, the exponent *c* should be somewhere 1.5 and 5, and the constant *d* should be a large positive number. These are fairly wide ranges, but the only goal at this point is to find reasonable lower and upper limits for Evolutionary Solver.

Using this (somewhat inexact) information, you should fill in the Solver dialog box as shown in Figure 8.22.

**Figure 8.22**

**Solver Dialog Box for Sales Response Estimation**

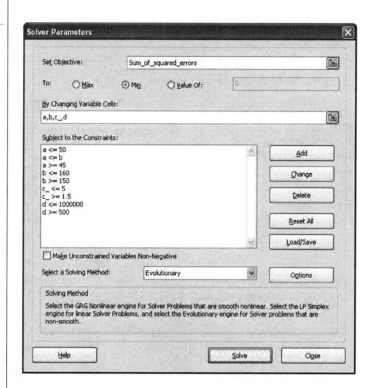

### Discussion of the Solution

The best solution found by Evolutionary Solver appears earlier in Figure 8.20. Unfortunately, there is nothing very intuitive about these particular values of *a*, *b*, *c*, and *d*. However, if you substitute them into row 4 of Figure 8.21, you will see that they provide a very good fit. In other words, the sales response function with these parameters should provide very useful predictions of sales levels.

It is interesting to compare Evolutionary Solver with GRG Nonlinear Solver (without using the Multistart option) for this smooth model. For example, we started each of them at a fairly poor solution: $a=40$, $b=100$, $c=1$, and $d=5000$. (The sum of squared errors for this solution is almost 18,000.) Evolutionary Solver found the solution in Figure 8.20 almost immediately. GRG Nonlinear Solver also found a solution almost immediately, but it was the *wrong* solution. Its objective was about 190, well above the minimum value in Figure 8.20. Again, this is because Evolutionary Solver does a more thorough job of searching the entire feasible region and not getting stuck at a local minimum. (To be fair, GRG Nonlinear Solver with the Multistart option also found the solution quickly, even after starting from the poor solution.) ▩

## PROBLEMS

### Skill-Building Problems

9. You are given the following information concerning how a change in sales force effort impacts sales:
   - A 50% cut in sales force effort reduces sales to 48% of its current value.
   - Sales force effort of 0 reduces sales to 15% of its current value.
   - A 50% increase in sales force effort increases sales by 20%.
   - A saturation of sales effort (a 10-fold increase) increases sales by 35%.

   Fit an S-shaped curve as described by Equation (8.1) to these data.

10. The file P08_10.xlsx contains per capita data on annual advertising and annual unit sales in different regions of the country. Determine an S-shaped curve as described by Equation (8.1) that can be used to determine how advertising influences sales.

11. The adoption level of a new product often can be modeled as an S-shaped curve called the Pearl (or logistic) curve. The equation of this curve is

$$Y = \frac{L}{1 + ae^{-bt}}$$

where $Y$ is the adoption level, $L$ is an (unknown) upper limit on adoptions, and $a$ and $b$ are parameters to be estimated. The file P08_11.xlsx lists information on U.S. cell phones since 1990 (which corresponds to year 1). For this problem, define $Y$ as the number of cell phones per capita. As $t$ increases, $Y$ approaches the limit $L$. Therefore, you can use this curve to estimate the upper limit on U.S. cell phones per person. Use Evolutionary Solver to estimate the eventual number of cell phones per person in the United States.

### Skill-Extending Problem

12. Sales of a product over time often follow an S-shaped curve. Two functions that yield S-shaped curves are the Pearl (or logistic) curve

$$Y = \frac{L}{1 + ae^{-bt}}$$

and the Gompertz curve

$$Y = Le^{-be^{-kt}}$$

Here, $Y$ is annual sales, $t$ is time (in years), $L$ is the upper limit on sales, and $a$, $b$, and $k$ are parameters to be estimated. (Actually, $L$ must also be estimated.) The file P08_12.xlsx contains data for sales of a new device. Use Evolutionary Solver to fit a Pearl and a Gompertz curve to these data. Let $t = 0$ correspond to year 1. Which curve provides the better fit? (*Hint:* You need to use reasonable bounds for the parameters for each curve. For example, $L \geq 14.5$ is reasonable.)

## 8.7 PORTFOLIO OPTIMIZATION

In the previous chapter, we discussed one approach to portfolio optimization. The objective in that chapter was to minimize the portfolio variance subject to keeping the mean portfolio return above some required level. This resulted in a nonlinear model (because of the squares and product terms in the portfolio variance formula), but this nonlinear objective was sufficiently smooth to permit using GRG Nonlinear Solver. Now we look at another possible objective. This objective is *not* smooth, so Evolutionary Solver is necessary.

EXAMPLE **8.6 BEATING THE S&P INDEX AT E.T. BARNEY**

E. T. Barney, an investment company, wants to form a portfolio consisting of a number of well-known stocks. The objective is to find the appropriate portfolio that, based on historical data, has the largest probability of beating the S&P 500 market index. How should the company proceed?[4]

**Objective** To use Evolutionary Solver to find the portfolio that has the highest chance of beating the S&P 500 Index.

[4]We have not seen this particular objective discussed in finance books or articles, but it is clear from discussions with investors that the goal of "beating the market" is important. For an excellent discussion of investment models in general, read the book by Luenberger (1997).

The historical returns from the stocks and the market index are widely available on the Web. In fact, you can download more recent data if you like.

## Solution

The file Beating S&P 500.xlsx contains monthly returns for a period of more than eight years for 29 large companies. See the blue area in Figure 8.23. (Note that there are many hidden rows and columns in this figure.) We decided to base the optimization on the earliest four years of data. Then we can see how the portfolio based on this data performs on the most recent four-plus years of data.

Figure 8.23   Portfolio Optimization Model

| | A | B | C | D | E | F | G | H | I | AB | AC | AD | AE | AF | AG |
|---|---|---|---|---|---|---|---|---|---|---|---|---|---|---|---|
| 1 | Maximizing the probability of beating the S&P 500 | | | | | | | | | | | | | | |
| 2 | | | | | | | | | | | | | | | |
| 3 | Weights on stocks for portfolio | | | | | | | | | | | | | | |
| 4 | | MMM | AA | MO | AXP | AIG | BA | CAT | C | VZ | WMT | DIS | | | |
| 5 | | 0.226844 | 0.247194 | 0 | 0.220331 | 0 | 0 | 0 | 0 | 0 | 0 | 0 | | | |
| 6 | | | | | | | | | | | | | | | |
| 7 | Constraint on weights | | | | | Percent of months beating S&P 500 | | | | | | | | | |
| 8 | | Sum weights | | Required | | Old Pct | 70.83% | | | | | | | | |
| 9 | | 1 | = | 1 | | Recent Pct | 48.21% | | | | | | | | |
| 10 | | | | | | | | | | | | | | | |
| 11 | Historical data on returns | | | | | | | | | | | | | | |
| 12 | Month | MMM | AA | MO | AXP | AIG | BA | CAT | C | VZ | WMT | DIS | S&P 500 | Portfolio Return | Beat S&P? |
| 13 | Feb-99 | -0.0387 | -0.0261 | -0.1650 | 0.0548 | 0.1068 | 0.0311 | 0.0520 | 0.0481 | -0.0396 | 0.0015 | 0.0662 | -0.0323 | -0.0100 | Yes |
| 14 | Mar-99 | -0.0448 | 0.0169 | -0.0908 | 0.0870 | 0.0591 | -0.0458 | 0.0081 | 0.0873 | -0.1031 | 0.0715 | -0.1156 | 0.0388 | 0.0384 | No |
| 15 | Apr-99 | 0.2582 | 0.5114 | -0.0041 | 0.1100 | -0.0299 | 0.1952 | 0.4085 | 0.1752 | 0.1233 | -0.0021 | 0.0202 | 0.0379 | 0.2067 | Yes |
| 16 | May-99 | -0.0305 | -0.1136 | 0.1003 | -0.0738 | -0.0230 | 0.0385 | -0.1477 | -0.1149 | -0.0501 | -0.0732 | -0.0828 | -0.0250 | -0.0574 | No |
| 17 | Jun-99 | 0.0139 | 0.1251 | 0.0533 | 0.0769 | 0.0263 | 0.0460 | 0.0933 | 0.0752 | 0.1939 | 0.1332 | 0.0579 | 0.0544 | 0.0406 | No |
| 18 | Jul-99 | 0.0115 | -0.0323 | -0.0734 | 0.0124 | -0.0097 | 0.0313 | -0.0175 | -0.0591 | -0.0148 | -0.1244 | -0.1053 | -0.0320 | 0.0052 | Yes |
| 19 | Aug-99 | 0.0807 | 0.0816 | 0.0049 | 0.0438 | -0.0022 | 0.0015 | -0.0339 | -0.0028 | -0.0422 | 0.0490 | 0.0067 | -0.0063 | 0.0758 | Yes |
| 20 | Sep-99 | 0.0166 | -0.0384 | -0.0750 | -0.0182 | -0.0616 | -0.0591 | -0.0321 | -0.0096 | 0.0979 | 0.0744 | -0.0628 | -0.0286 | -0.0273 | Yes |
| 21 | Oct-99 | -0.0104 | -0.0211 | -0.2286 | 0.1425 | 0.1841 | 0.0804 | 0.0150 | 0.2362 | -0.0294 | 0.1838 | 0.0212 | 0.0625 | 0.0540 | No |
| 112 | May-07 | 0.0687 | 0.1689 | 0.0316 | 0.0711 | 0.0371 | 0.0857 | 0.0820 | 0.0265 | 0.1402 | -0.0021 | 0.0132 | 0.0325 | 0.0735 | Yes |
| 113 | Jun-07 | -0.0133 | -0.0182 | -0.0037 | -0.0585 | -0.0319 | -0.0441 | -0.0036 | -0.0587 | -0.0543 | 0.0108 | -0.0367 | -0.0178 | -0.0285 | No |
| 114 | Jul-07 | 0.0246 | -0.0575 | -0.0523 | -0.0408 | -0.0835 | 0.0757 | 0.0106 | -0.0921 | 0.0454 | -0.0449 | -0.0334 | -0.0320 | -0.0152 | Yes |
| 115 | Aug-07 | 0.0288 | -0.0394 | 0.0443 | 0.0014 | 0.0283 | -0.0619 | -0.0385 | 0.0185 | -0.0174 | -0.0457 | 0.0182 | 0.0129 | 0.0126 | No |
| 116 | Sep-07 | 0.0285 | 0.0709 | 0.0130 | 0.0128 | 0.0281 | 0.0857 | 0.0351 | -0.0045 | 0.0573 | 0.0005 | 0.0235 | 0.0358 | 0.0476 | Yes |

## DEVELOPING THE SPREADSHEET MODEL

You can create the model with the following steps:

**1 Enter weights.** As in the previous chapter, the portfolio is based on the fractions (called weights) of each dollar invested in the various stocks. Enter *any* values for the weights in the Weights range. These weights will eventually be constrained to be between 0 and 1. Then calculate the sum of the weights in cell B9 with the SUM function.

**2 Portfolio returns.** For the historical period, the period of the data, calculate the portfolio returns by weighting the actual returns by the weights. To do this, enter the formula

=SUMPRODUCT(Weights,B13:AD13)

in cell AF13 and copy it down.

**3 Beats S&P 500?** The returns from the S&P 500 market index appear in column AE. (These are given. As with the stock returns, they can be found on the Web.) For each month, see whether the portfolio beats the S&P 500 by entering the formula

=IF(AF13>AE13,"Yes","No")

in cell AG13 and copying down.

**4** **Objective.** Calculate the fraction of months during the earliest four years where the portfolio beats the S&P 500. Do this in cell G8 with the formula

=COUNTIF(AG13:AG60,"Yes")/48

This is the objective to maximize. Note that it contains the COUNTIF function. This is the feature that necessitates Evolutionary Solver. For comparison, calculate the similar fraction for the most recent four-plus years in cell G9 with the formula

=COUNTIF(AG61:AG116,"Yes")/56

## USING EVOLUTIONARY SOLVER

The Solver setup appears in Figure 8.24. You should constrain the sum of the weights to be 1 so that all of the money is invested, and you should constrain the weights to be between 0 and 1 so that the investment in each stock is a positive fraction of the total investment. (You can allow negative weights if you want to permit short selling.)

Figure 8.24

**Solver Dialog Box for the Portfolio Optimization Model**

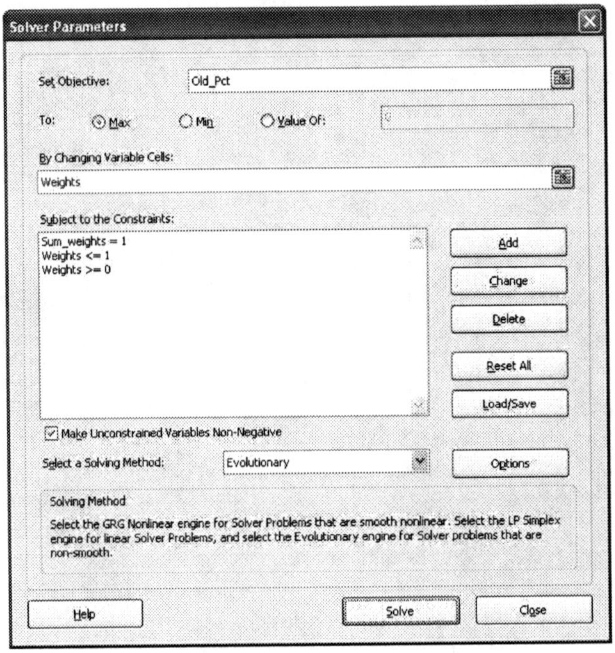

## Discussion of the Solution

There are several things to note about the optimal solution found in Figure 8.23. First, this portfolio puts most of the weight on four companies: 3M (22.7%), Alcoa (24.7%), American Express (22.0%), and Procter & Gamble (21.3%). The rest of the weight is divided among four other companies, and the rest of the companies are not in the portfolio at all. Second, this solution represents the portfolio that beats the S&P 500 most frequently *in the optimization period*—that is, the earliest four years. Whenever an optimization is based on a historical period, there is no guarantee that this solution will work as well in a later time period. The calculation in cell G9 shows how well the portfolio does in the most recent four-plus years of the data set. Clearly, it does not do as well. The portfolio beats the S&P 500 about 71% of the time during the earliest four years, but only about 48% of the time during the most recent four-plus years. Any time historical data is used to forecast what might happen in the future, the implicit assumption is that historical patterns will repeat themselves. As many forecasters have discovered to their dismay, this assumption is not always correct.

Finally, this is the best solution we found after experimenting with several random number seeds and several starting solutions for the weights. Some of these converged to a solution with an objective *less than* 75%, which is clearly suboptimal. This is due to the randomness component built into GAs. Different runs can have varying levels of success depending on the luck of the draw. ▪

Is this method of portfolio optimization any better or worse than the variance-minimizing method discussed in the previous chapter? The answer probably depends on the investor's attitude toward risk. There is no guarantee that the probability-maximizing model in this chapter will achieve any particular expected return, although if it beats the market index consistently, it seems that it should provide a decent return. Also, there is no guarantee that this portfolio will provide an acceptable risk—measured by a small variance. Nevertheless, this model might have an intuitive appeal to many investors. If you can beat the S&P 500 consistently, you must be doing a good job.

## PROBLEMS

### Skill-Building Problems

**13.** Visit http://biz.yahoo.com/r/. Under Research Tools, click on Historical Quotes, and then download the monthly returns on at least four stocks for the preceding 60 months. Use this data to determine the portfolio that maximizes the chance of beating the S&P 500 for these years. (Note that the ticker symbol for the S&P 500 is ^GSPC. Also, this Web site gives closing prices, which you will need to convert to returns.)

**14.** Continuing the previous problem, determine the portfolio that minimizes the chance that you will lose money during any month, subject to a lower bound constraint on your expected monthly return. (The lower bound will depend on your data. It must not be above the largest average return of your stocks. For example, if you require the mean portfolio return to be greater than 1% and all stocks average *less than* 1%, the constraint can't possibly be satisfied.)

## 8.8 CLUSTER ANALYSIS

Marketers often want to group objects into clusters of similar objects. For example, identifying similar customers can help a company identify market segments. Identifying a cluster of similar products can help a company identify its main competitors. Here are two actual examples of how the United States is divided into clusters.[5]

▪ Claritas divides each block of the United States into one of 62 clusters. These include Blue Blood Estates, New Homesteaders, Middle America, God's Country, and so on. For example, Blue Blood Estates consists primarily of America's richest suburbs. (Over 1 in 10 residents of Blue Blood Estates is a millionaire.) This is valuable information for marketers. For example, Blue Blood Estates residents consume imported beer at a rate nearly three times the national average.

▪ SRI clusters families based on their financial status and demographics. For example, the cluster Bank Traditionalists consists of upper-middle-class families of larger than average size with school-age children. This cluster is a natural prospecting ground for life insurance salespeople.

The following example illustrates how Evolutionary Solver can be used to cluster cities. The same method could be use to cluster people, products, or other entities.[6]

---

[5] The book by Johnson and Wichern (2002) has an excellent, although somewhat mathematically advanced, discussion of cluster analysis and the topic of the next section, discriminant analysis.

[6] This example is for illustration only. There are many software packages other than Excel that are much more powerful for data mining tasks such as cluster analysis or discriminant analysis, the subject of the next example.

EXAMPLE     **8.7 CLUSTERING LARGE CITIES IN THE UNITED STATES**

The file City Clusters.xlsx contains demographic data on 49 of the largest cities in the United States. Some of the data appear in the shaded region of Figure 8.25. For example, Atlanta is 67% African American, 2% Hispanic, and 1% Asian. It has a median age of 31, a 5% unemployment rate, and a per-capita income of $22,000. The goal in this example is to group these 49 cities into four clusters of cities that are demographically similar. (You could then experiment with the number of clusters. For this discussion, the number is fixed at four.) The basic idea is to choose a city to anchor, or center, each cluster. Each city is then assigned to the nearest cluster center, where *nearest* is defined in terms of the six demographic variables. The objective is to minimize the sum of the distances from each city to its cluster center.

Figure 8.25   Demographic Data for Selected Cities

| | A | B | C | D | E | F | G | H | I | J | K | L | M | N |
|---|---|---|---|---|---|---|---|---|---|---|---|---|---|---|
| 13 | City data | | | | | | | | | | | | | |
| | | | | | | | | | Standardized | | | | | |
| 14 | Index | City | PctAfrAmer | PctHispanic | PctAsian | MedianAge | UnempRate | PCIncome | PctAfrAmer | PctHispanic | PctAsian | MedianAge | UnempRate | PCIncome |
| 15 | 1 | Albuquerque | 3 | 35 | 2 | 32 | 5 | 18 | -1.179 | 1.239 | -0.363 | 0.061 | -0.751 | -0.875 |
| 16 | 2 | Atlanta | 67 | 2 | 1 | 31 | 5 | 22 | 2.355 | -0.764 | -0.452 | -0.440 | -0.751 | 0.324 |
| 17 | 3 | Austin | 12 | 23 | 3 | 29 | 3 | 19 | -0.682 | 0.510 | -0.273 | -1.442 | -1.495 | -0.575 |
| 18 | 4 | Baltimore | 59 | 1 | 1 | 33 | 11 | 22 | 1.913 | -0.825 | -0.452 | 0.562 | 1.480 | 0.324 |
| 19 | 5 | Boston | 26 | 11 | 5 | 30 | 5 | 24 | 0.091 | -0.218 | -0.093 | -0.941 | -0.751 | 0.924 |
| 20 | 6 | Charlotte | 32 | 1 | 2 | 32 | 3 | 20 | 0.423 | -0.825 | -0.363 | 0.061 | -1.495 | -0.275 |
| 21 | 7 | Chicago | 39 | 20 | 4 | 31 | 9 | 24 | 0.809 | 0.328 | -0.183 | -0.440 | 0.736 | 0.924 |
| 22 | 8 | Cincinnati38 | 1 | 1 | 31 | 8 | 21 | 0.75 | 4 | -0.825 | -0.452 | -0.440 | 0.364 | 0.024 |
| 23 | 9 | Cleveland | 47 | 5 | 1 | 32 | 13 | 22 | 1.251 | -0.582 | -0.452 | 0.061 | 2.224 | 0.324 |
| 24 | 10 | Columbus | 23 | 1 | 2 | 29 | 3 | 13 | -0.074 | -0.825 | -0.363 | -1.442 | -1.495 | -2.375 |
| 25 | 11 | Dallas | 30 | 21 | 2 | 30 | 9 | 22 | 0.312 | 0.389 | -0.363 | -0.941 | 0.736 | 0.324 |
| 26 | 12 | Denver | 13 | 23 | 2 | 34 | 7 | 23 | -0.627 | 0.510 | -0.363 | 1.063 | -0.008 | 0.624 |
| 27 | 13 | Detroit | 76 | 3 | 1 | 31 | 9 | 21 | 2.852 | -0.704 | -0.452 | -0.440 | 0.736 | 0.024 |
| 28 | 14 | El Paso | 3 | 69 | 1 | 29 | 11 | 13 | -1.179 | 3.303 | -0.452 | -1.442 | 1.480 | -2.375 |
| 29 | 15 | Fort Worth | 22 | 20 | 2 | 30 | 9 | 20 | -0.130 | 0.328 | -0.363 | -0.941 | 0.736 | -0.275 |
| 30 | 16 | Fresno | 9 | 30 | 13 | 28 | 13 | 16 | -0.847 | 0.935 | 0.624 | -1.942 | 2.224 | -1.475 |

**Objective**   To use Evolutionary Solver to find four cities to be used as cluster centers and to assign all other cities to one of these cluster centers.

### WHERE DO THE NUMBERS COME FROM?

This basic demographic data on cities is widely available. Note that the data used here is several years old.

### Solution

The first problem is that if you use raw units, percentage African American and Hispanic will drive everything because these values are more spread out than the other demographic attributes. You can see this by calculating means and standard deviations of the characteristics. (See Figure 8.26, which also includes correlations between the attributes.) To remedy this problem, each demographic attribute should be standardized by subtracting the attribute's mean and dividing the difference by the attribute's standard deviation. For example, the average city has 24.35% African Americans with a standard deviation of 18.11%. On a standardized basis, Atlanta is larger by $(67 - 24.35)/18.11 = 2.355$ standard deviations on the African-American attribute than a typical city. Working with standardized values for each attribute ensures that the analysis is unit-free. To create the standardized values shown in Figure 8.25, enter the formula

=(C15-AVERAGE(C$15:C$63))/STDEV(C$15:C$63)

in cell I15 and copy it across to column N and down to row 63.

## Figure 8.26　Summary Data for Demographic Attributes

| | A | B | C | D | E | F | G |
|---|---|---|---|---|---|---|---|
| 7 | | PctAfrAmer | PctHispanic | PctAsian | MedianAge | UnempRate | PCIncome |
| 8 | *One Variable Summary* | Data Set #1 | Data Set #1 | Data Set #1 | Data Set #1 | Data Set #1 | Data Set #1 |
| 9 | Mean | 24.35 | 14.59 | 6.04 | 31.878 | 7.020 | 20.918 |
| 10 | Std. Dev. | 18.11 | 16.47 | 11.14 | 1.996 | 2.689 | 3.334 |
| 11 | | | | | | | |
| 12 | | PctAfrAmer | PctHispanic | PctAsian | MedianAge | UnempRate | PCIncome |
| 13 | *Correlation Table* | Data Set #1 | Data Set #1 | Data Set #1 | Data Set #1 | Data Set #1 | Data Set #1 |
| 14 | PctAfrAmer | 1.000 | | | | | |
| 15 | PctHispanic | -0.404 | 1.000 | | | | |
| 16 | PctAsian | -0.317 | 0.000 | 1.000 | | | |
| 17 | MedianAge | 0.010 | -0.221 | 0.373 | 1.000 | | |
| 18 | UnempRate | 0.308 | 0.341 | -0.001 | -0.007 | 1.000 | |
| 19 | PCIncome | 0.126 | -0.298 | 0.374 | 0.480 | 0.014 | 1.000 |

## DEVELOPING THE SPREADSHEET MODEL

Now that all of the attributes have been standardized, you can develop the spreadsheet model as follows. It is shown in two parts in Figures 8.27 and 8.28.

## Figure 8.27　Decision Variables and Objective Cell

| | A | B | C | D | E | F | G | H | I | J | K | L |
|---|---|---|---|---|---|---|---|---|---|---|---|---|
| 1 | Clustering cities | | | | | | | | | | | |
| 2 | | | | | | | | | | | | |
| 3 | Cluster centers and standardized values | | | | | | | | | Range names used | | |
| 4 | | Column offset: | 9 | 10 | 11 | 12 | 13 | 14 | | City_index | =Model!$B$6:$B$9 | |
| 5 | Cluster center | City index | PctAfrAmer | PctHispanic | PctAsian | MedianAge | UnempRate | PCIncome | | Cluster_center | =Model!$A$6:$A$9 | |
| 6 | San Francisco | 43 | -0.737 | -0.036 | 2.060 | 2.065 | -0.380 | 3.024 | | LookupTable | =Model!$A$15:$N$63 | |
| 7 | Philadelphia | 35 | 0.864 | -0.522 | -0.273 | 0.562 | 0.736 | 0.624 | | Sum_Distances | =Model!$B$11 | |
| 8 | Omaha | 34 | -0.627 | -0.704 | -0.452 | 0.061 | -0.751 | -0.275 | | | | |
| 9 | Long Beach | 23 | -0.571 | 0.571 | 0.714 | -0.941 | 0.364 | 0.024 | | | | |
| 10 | | | | | | | | | | | | |
| 11 | Sum Distances | 77.578 | | | | | | | | | | |

## Figure 8.28　Other Calculations for Cluster Analysis

| | P | Q | R | S | T | U | V |
|---|---|---|---|---|---|---|---|
| 13 | Distances to centers | | | | | Assigned to | |
| 14 | To 1 | To 2 | To 3 | To 4 | Minimum | Index | Center |
| 15 | 5.200 | 3.463 | 2.109 | 2.243 | 2.109 | 3 | Omaha |
| 16 | 5.487 | 2.371 | 3.083 | 3.646 | 2.371 | 2 | Philadelphia |
| 17 | 5.678 | 3.727 | 2.100 | 2.249 | 2.100 | 3 | Omaha |
| 18 | 5.193 | 1.367 | 3.472 | 3.616 | 1.367 | 2 | Philadelphia |
| 19 | 4.352 | 2.299 | 1.823 | 1.941 | 1.823 | 3 | Omaha |
| 20 | 4.897 | 2.517 | 1.295 | 2.941 | 1.295 | 3 | Omaha |
| 21 | 4.414 | 1.352 | 2.665 | 1.992 | 1.352 | 2 | Philadelphia |
| 22 | 4.998 | 1.280 | 1.873 | 2.306 | 1.280 | 2 | Philadelphia |
| 23 | 5.352 | 1.655 | 3.571 | 3.250 | 1.655 | 2 | Philadelphia |
| 24 | 7.044 | 4.356 | 2.747 | 3.581 | 2.747 | 3 | Omaha |
| 25 | 4.971 | 1.868 | 2.379 | 1.484 | 1.484 | 4 | Long Beach |
| 26 | 3.616 | 2.025 | 1.962 | 2.383 | 1.962 | 3 | Omaha |
| 27 | 6.013 | 2.320 | 3.828 | 3.885 | 2.320 | 2 | Philadelphia |
| 28 | 7.909 | 5.692 | 5.292 | 4.055 | 4.055 | 4 | Long Beach |
| 29 | 5.247 | 2.188 | 2.130 | 1.281 | 1.281 | 4 | Long Beach |
| 30 | 6.789 | 4.330 | 4.266 | 2.632 | 2.632 | 4 | Long Beach |
| 31 | 4.427 | 6.942 | 6.901 | 6.508 | 4.427 | 1 | San Francisco |

**① Lookup table.** One key to the model is to have an index (1 to 49) for the cities so that you can refer to them by index and then look up their characteristics with a VLOOKUP function. Therefore, name the range A15:N63 as LookupTable.

**② Decision variables.** The only changing cells appear in the City_index range of Figure 8.27. They are the indexes of the four cities chosen as cluster centers. Enter any four integers from 1 to 49 in these cells.

**③ Corresponding cities and standardized attributes.** You can find the names and standardized attributes of the cluster centers with VLOOKUP functions. First, enter the function

=VLOOKUP(B6,LookupTable,2)

in cell A6 and copy it to the range A6:A9. Then enter the formula

=VLOOKUP($B6,LookupTable,C$4)

in C6 and copy it to the range C6:H9. Note, for example, that the standardized PctAfrAmer is the ninth column of the lookup table. This explains the column offset entries in row 4.

**④ Distances to centers.** The next step is to see how far each city is from each of the cluster centers. Let $z_i$ be standardized attribute $i$ for a typical city, and let $c_i$ be standardized attribute $i$ for a typical cluster center. You can measure the distance from this city to this cluster center with the usual Euclidean distance formula

$$\text{Distance} = \sqrt{\sum_i (z_i - c_i)^2}$$

where the sum is over all six attributes. These distances appear in columns P through S of Figure 8.28. For example, the value in cell P15 is the distance from Albuquerque to the first cluster center (San Francisco), the value in Q15 is the distance from Albuquerque to the second cluster center (Philadelphia), and so on. These calculations can be performed in several equivalent ways. Probably the quickest way is to enter the formula

=SQRT(SUMXMY2($I15:$N15,$C$6:$H$6))

in cell P15 and copy it to the range P15:S63. (The function SUMXMY2 calculates the differences between the elements of the two range arguments and then sums the squares of these differences—exactly what is required.) The copied versions in columns Q, R, and S then have to be modified slightly. Each 6 in the second range argument needs to be changed to 7 in column Q, to 8 in column R, and to 9 in column S.

**⑤ Assignments to cluster centers.** Each city is assigned to the cluster center that has the smallest distance. Therefore, find the minimum distances in column T by entering the formula

=MIN(P15:S15)

in cell T15 and copying it down. Then you can identify the cluster index (1 through 4) and city name of the cluster center that yields the minimum with the MATCH function. Specifically, enter the formula

=MATCH(T15,P15:S15,0)

in cell U15 and copy it down. For example, the 4.447 minimum distance for Albuquerque corresponds to the second distance, so Albuquerque is assigned to the second cluster center. Finally, to get the *name* of the second cluster center, you can use the INDEX function. Enter the formula

=INDEX(Cluster_center,U15,1)

in cell V15 and copy it down. This formula returns the name in the second row and first (only) column of the Cluster_center range (in Figure 8.27).

### Excel Function: *INDEX*

*The function INDEX, using the syntax INDEX(Range,Row,Column), is usually used to return the value in a given row and column of a specified range. For example, INDEX(A5:C10,3, 2) returns the value in the third row and second column of the range A5:C10, that is, the value in cell B7. If the given range is a single row, the row argument can be omitted. If the given range is a single column, the column argument can be omitted.*

**6** **Sum of distances.** The objective is to minimize the sum of distances from all cities to the cluster centers to which they are assigned. Calculate this objective in cell B11 (in Figure 8.27) with the formula

=SUM(T15:T63)

### USING EVOLUTIONARY SOLVER

The Solver dialog box should be set up as shown in Figure 8.29. Because the changing cells represent *indexes* of cluster centers, they must be integer-constrained, and suitable lower and upper limits are 1 and 49 (the number of cities). This problem is considerably more difficult to solve, so you should allow Evolutionary Solver plenty of time to search through a lot of potential solutions.

**Figure 8.29**

**Solver Dialog Box for Cluster Model**

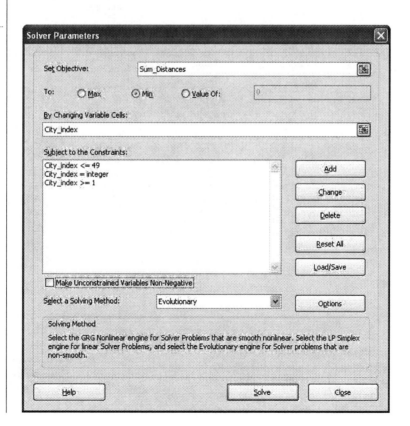

## Discussion of the Solution

In cluster analysis, the number of clusters is typically unknown ahead of time. Some experimentation with the number of clusters is usually required.

The solution in Figure 8.27, which uses San Francisco, Philadelphia, Omaha, and Long Beach, is the best we found. You might find a slightly different solution, depending on your Solver settings and how long you let Solver run, but you should obtain a similar value in the objective cell. If you look closely at the cities assigned to each cluster center, this solution begins to make intuitive sense (see Figure 8.30). The San Francisco cluster consists of rich, older, highly Asian cities. The Philadelphia cluster consists of highly African-American cities with high unemployment rates. The Omaha cluster consists of average income cities with few minorities. The Long Beach cluster consists of highly Hispanic cities with high unemployment rates.

Why four clusters? You could easily try three clusters or five clusters. Note that when the number of clusters increases, the sum of distances will certainly decrease. In fact, you could obtain an objective value of 0 by using 49 clusters, one for each city, but this would hardly provide much information. Therefore, to choose the "optimal" number of clusters, the typical approach is to stop adding clusters when the sum of distances fails to decrease by a substantial amount.

Figure 8.30

Clusters in the Solver Solution

|    | W | X | Y | Z | AA |
|----|---|---|---|---|----|
| 13 | **Clusters** | | | | |
| 14 | Center: | San Francisco | Philadelphia | Omaha | Long Beach |
| 15 | | Honolulu | Atlanta | Albuquerque | Dallas |
| 16 | | San Francisco | Baltimore | Austin | El Paso |
| 17 | | Seattle | Chicago | Boston | Fort Worth |
| 18 | | | Cincinnati | Charlotte | Fresno |
| 19 | | | Cleveland | Columbus | Houston |
| 20 | | | Detroit | Denver | Long Beach |
| 21 | | | Memphis | Indianapolis | Los Angeles |
| 22 | | | Miami | Jacksonville | Sacramento |
| 23 | | | New Orleans | Kansas City | San Antonio |
| 24 | | | NY | Las Vegas | San Diego |
| 25 | | | Oakland | Milwaukee | San Jose |
| 26 | | | Philadelphia | Minneapolis | |
| 27 | | | Pittsburgh | Nashville | |
| 28 | | | St. Louis | Oklahoma City | |
| 29 | | | | Omaha | |
| 30 | | | | Phoenix | |
| 31 | | | | Portland | |
| 32 | | | | Toledo | |
| 33 | | | | Tucson | |
| 34 | | | | Tulsa | |
| 35 | | | | Virginia Beach | |

## PROBLEM

### Skill-Building Problem

15. The file P08_15.xlsx contains the following information about the top 25 MBA programs (according to the 1997 Business Week Guide): percentage of applicants accepted, percentage of accepted applicants who enroll, mean GMAT score of enrollees, mean undergraduate GPA of enrollees, annual cost of school (for state schools, this is the cost for out-of-state students), percentage of students who are minorities, percentage of students who are non-U.S. residents, and mean starting salary of graduates (in thousands of dollars). Use these data to divide the top 25 schools into four clusters. Then interpret your clusters.

# 8.9 DISCRIMINANT ANALYSIS

*In classification examples such as these, you typically create an optimization model on a "training" data set and then apply it to a new data set to predict group membership.*

Discriminant analysis is a statistical tool used by analysts in marketing and other fields of business. Although somewhat similar to cluster analysis, it is also quite different. In cluster analysis, there are no predefined clusters. You look at the information on the different members of the population (cities, products, or whatever) to see which members should be clustered together because of similar characteristics. You do not even know the *number* of clusters to use. In discriminant analysis, however, the clusters (usually called groups) are predefined. For example, there might be two groups: users of a particular product and nonusers. You collect data on a sample (often called a *training sample*) of users and nonusers—their income, their ages, and other possibly relevant data—and use this data to classify the customers as users or nonusers. The analysis is successful if a large percentage of the customers in the training sample are classified correctly. Of course, the group membership of each customer in the training sample is already known. Therefore, the real purpose is to see whether a large percentage of customers outside of the training sample can be classified correctly on the basis of their income, age, and other relevant variables.

Discriminant analysis has been used in many situations, including the following:

- Based on gender, age, income, and residential location, classify a consumer as a user or nonuser of a new breakfast cereal.

- Based on income, type of residence, credit card debt, and other information, classify a consumer as a good or bad credit risk.

- Based on financial ratios, classify a company as a likely or unlikely candidate for bankruptcy.

In general, discriminant analysis can be used to classify members of two or more groups. We focus only on two-group discriminant analysis. In this case, the approach is to find a weighted combination of the data for each member, called a *discriminant score,* and then to classify the member into group 1 or group 2 depending on which side of a cutoff score the member's discriminant score falls. The problem is to find the appropriate weights for the discriminant scores and the appropriate cutoff score that maximize the percentage of correct classifications in the training sample. The following example illustrates the procedure.

---

**EXAMPLE** 

## 8.8 CLASSIFYING SUBSCRIBERS AND NONSUBSCRIBERS TO THE WALL STREET JOURNAL

The file WSJ Subscribers.xlsx contains the annual income and size of investment portfolio (both in thousands of dollars) for 84 people. It also indicates whether or not each of these people subscribes to the *Wall Street Journal*. Using income and size of investment portfolio, determine a classification rule that maximizes the number of people correctly classified as subscribers or nonsubscribers.

**Objective** To use Evolutionary Solver to find a function of income and investment that does the best job of classifying subscribers and nonsubscribers.

### WHERE DO THE NUMBERS COME FROM?

In a general discriminant analysis, you collect as much relevant financial and demographic data as possible about the people (or companies) to be classified.

## Solution

The model is actually simpler than the cluster analysis model. Using appropriate weights, you create a discriminant score for each of the 84 customers. Then based on a cutoff score, you classify each customer as a subscriber or nonsubscriber, and you tally the number of correct classifications.

### DEVELOPING THE SPREADSHEET MODEL

The model appears (with several data rows not shown) in Figure 8.31 and can be developed as follows:

Figure 8.31    Discriminant Analysis Model

| | A | B | C | D | E | F | G | H | I | J | K |
|---|---|---|---|---|---|---|---|---|---|---|---|
| 1 | Discriminant analysis | | | | | | | | | | |
| 2 | | | | | | | | | | | |
| 3 | Weights for discriminant function | | | | | Range names used: | | | | | |
| 4 | | Income | InvestAmt | | | Cutoff | =Model!$B$8 | | | | |
| 5 | | -0.094 | 0.950 | | | Pct_correct | =Model!$I$17 | | | | |
| 6 | | | | | | Weights | =Model!$B$5:$C$5 | | | | |
| 7 | Cutoff value for classification | | | | | | | | | | |
| 8 | | 33.545 | | | | | | | | | |
| 9 | | | | | | | | | | | |
| 10 | Customer data | | | | | | | | Classification matrix | | |
| 11 | Person | Income | InvestAmt | WSJSubscriber | Score | Classified as | | (Actual along side, predicted along top) | | | |
| 12 | 1 | 59.7 | 14.9 | No | 8.6 | No | | | | Yes | No |
| 13 | 2 | 60.9 | 25.8 | No | 18.8 | No | | Yes | | 23 | 4 |
| 14 | 3 | 67.6 | 37.6 | Yes | 29.4 | No | | No | | 2 | 55 |
| 15 | 4 | 86.6 | 37.0 | No | 27.0 | No | | | | | |
| 16 | 5 | 90.4 | 21.4 | No | 11.8 | No | | Percent correct classifications | | | |
| 17 | 6 | 67.2 | 26.4 | No | 18.8 | No | | | | 92.86% | |
| 18 | 7 | 85.1 | 59.8 | Yes | 48.8 | Yes | | | | | |
| 19 | 8 | 89.9 | 46.2 | No | 35.5 | Yes | | | | | |
| 20 | 9 | 100.3 | 55.5 | Yes | 43.3 | Yes | | | | | |
| 21 | 10 | 57.6 | 22.2 | No | 15.7 | No | | | | | |

**①  Customer data.** Enter the customer data in the blue range. This includes the data on the variables used for classification (income and investment amount), as well as an indication of which group each customer is in. These 84 customers represent the training sample, so group membership (subscriber or nonsubscriber) for each of them is known.

**②  Decision variables.** The decision variables are the weights used to form discriminant scores and the cutoff value for classification. Enter any values for these in the Weights and Cutoff ranges.

**③  Discriminant scores.** Each discriminant score is a weighted combination of the person's income and investment amount. To calculate these in column E, enter the formula

=SUMPRODUCT(Weights,B12:C12)

in cell E12 and copy it down.

**④  Classifications.** A person is classified as a nonsubscriber if the person's discriminant score is *below* the cutoff value; otherwise, the person is classified as a subscriber. Therefore, enter the formula

=IF(E12<Cutoff, "No","Yes")

in cell F12 and copy it down. (It could be done the opposite way, where people *above* the cutoff are classified as subscribers, but the results would be equivalent.)

**⑤ Tallies.** It is customary to tally the classifications in a classification matrix, as shown in the range H12:J14. The easiest way to find these tallies is to use the COUNTIFS function (new in Excel 2007). Specifically, enter the formula

=COUNTIFS($D$12:$D$95,$H13,$F$12:$F$95,I$12)

in cell I13 and copy it to the range I13:J14. Then calculate the percent correctly classified in cell I17 with the formula

=(I13+J14)/SUM(I13:J14)

This is the objective to minimize.

**Excel Function: *COUNTIFS***
*The function COUNTIFS, new to Excel 2007, enables you to count the number of values that satisfy multiple criteria. The arguments come in pairs. The first member of each pair is a range, and the second is a criterion. In the example above, there are two pairs. The first requires a match between the values in column D and one of the values in the H13:H14 range. The second requires a match between column F and one of the values in the I12:J12 range. For example, the value in cell I13 means that 23 of the data rows have Yes in column D and in column F.*

## USING EVOLUTIONARY SOLVER

First, note that Evolutionary Solver is required because of the IF and COUNTIFS functions used to make and tally the classifications. The completed Solver dialog box appears in Figure 8.32 and is straightforward except for the lower and upper limits on the changing cells. There are no natural weights or cutoff values to use. However, the weights can always be constrained to be between –1 and 1. (The reasoning is that if you solve the problem with weights equal to, say, –15 and 15, you can divide them *and* the resulting cutoff score by 15 and obtain exactly the same classifications.) To obtain lower and upper limits on the cutoff value, we first calculated the maximum sum of income and investment amount for any customer, which is slightly less than 160. This means that the largest discriminant score, using weights of 1, is no larger than 160, and the smallest discriminant score, using weights of –1, is no less than –160. Therefore, there is no need to consider cutoff values below –160 or above 160.

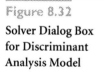

**Figure 8.32**

**Solver Dialog Box for Discriminant Analysis Model**

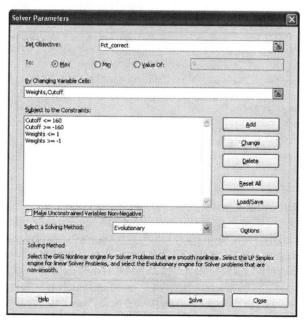

### Discussion of the Solution

The solution shown in Figure 8.31 is certainly not unique. Many other sets of weights and cutoff values can obtain a 92.86% correct classification rate, and you will probably obtain a different solution from ours. Note that only six of the 84 people are misclassified—four subscribers are misclassified as nonsubscribers and two nonsubscribers are misclassified as subscribers. Also, you can see from the weights that the classification is based primarily on the investment amount, with very little weight placed on income. Because of the *positive* weight on the investment amount, people with large investment amounts tend to be classified as subscribers. Therefore, a subscriber such as person 3 is misclassified because his investment amount is abnormally small relative to other subscribers. On the other hand, a nonsubscriber such as person 8 is misclassified because his investment amount is abnormally large relative to other nonsubscribers.

In a real application, you would use this analysis for people other than the 84 in the training sample. That is, you would calculate a discriminant score for each such person and then classify each as a nonsubscriber if her discriminant score is less than the cutoff value. However, the percentage correctly classified would typically be less—maybe considerably less—than the 92.86% rate achieved in the training sample. The reason is that the optimization procedure takes advantage of all the data for these particular 84 people to derive the weights and the cutoff score. Unfortunately, there is no reason to believe that these will work as well for *another* group of people. ∗

## PROBLEMS

### Skill-Building Problems

**16.** For data in the file P08_16.xlsx, develop a rule to predict whether a person is likely to purchase your lasagna product. What variables appear to be the most useful?

**17.** For the data in the file P08_17.xlsx, develop a classification rule to classify students as likely admits, likely rejects, or borderline.

**18.** The file P08_18.xlsx contains information on the following items about 24 companies: EBITASS (earnings before income and taxes, divided by total assets), ROTC (return on total capital), and Group (1 for most admired companies and 2 for least admired companies). Use these data to develop a rule that can be used to classify a company as a most admired or least

admired company. Which variable appears to be most important for this classification?

**19.** The term *churn* is common in marketing. It means that a customer switches loyalty to another company. The file P08_19.xlsx contains data on over 3000 customers of a cell phone provider. Columns B through N provide information about the account and usage of each customer, and column O indicates whether the customer churned during the given period of time. Use these data to develop a rule for predicting whether a customer will churn. Can you make any (qualitative) sense out of the discriminant function? Does this problem appear to be much harder for Evolutionary Solver because of the large size of the data set?

## 8.10 THE TRAVELING SALESPERSON PROBLEM

One of the most studied management science problems (at least by academics) is called the traveling salesperson problem. Although easy to state, the problem is very difficult to solve. A salesperson must travel from his home base to a number of other cities, visiting each city exactly once, and finally return to his home base. The goal is to find the route that has the shortest total distance. Note that a potential solution is simple to describe. If we index the home base as 0 and the cities to be visited as 1 through $n$, then any solution is a permutation of the numbers 1 through $n$. For example, if $n = 8$, a potential solution is 2, 5, 7, 1, 3, 8, 4, 6. The salesperson goes from 0 to 2, from 2 to 5, and so on, finishing by going from 6 back to 0. Because there are $n!$ permutations of the numbers 1 through $n$, you might think that checking each of them and choosing the best is easy. However, $n!$ grows extremely fast as $n$ increases. For example, 8! is "only" 43,020, but 16! is close to 21 *trillion*. This explosion in the number of permutations is what makes the problem so difficult. Nevertheless, it is easy to model the problem in such a way that Evolutionary Solver can be used to find good, and possibly even optimal, solutions. The following example illustrates the method.

EXAMPLE | 8.9 MINIMIZING A SALESPERSON'S DISTANCE TRAVELED

Willie Lowman is a salesman who lives in Boston. He needs to visit each of the cities listed in Figure 8.33 (see the file Traveling Salesperson.xlsx) and then return to Boston. What route should Willie use to minimize the total distance traveled?

Figure 8.33    Distance Matrix

| | A | B | C | D | E | F | G | H | I | J | K | L |
|---|---|---|---|---|---|---|---|---|---|---|---|---|
| 1 | Traveling salesperson problem | | | | | | | | | | | |
| 2 | | | | | | | | | | | | |
| 3 | Distance matrix | | | | | | | | | | | |
| 4 | | Boston | Chicago | Dallas | Denver | Los Angeles | Miami | New York | Phoenix | Pittsburgh | San Francisco | Seattle |
| 5 | Boston | 0 | 983 | 1815 | 1991 | 3036 | 1539 | 213 | 2664 | 792 | 2385 | 2612 |
| 6 | Chicago | 983 | 0 | 1205 | 1050 | 2112 | 1390 | 840 | 1729 | 457 | 2212 | 2052 |
| 7 | Dallas | 1815 | 1205 | 0 | 801 | 1425 | 1332 | 1604 | 1027 | 1237 | 1034 | 2404 |
| 8 | Denver | 1991 | 1050 | 801 | 0 | 1174 | 2057 | 1780 | 836 | 1411 | 1765 | 1373 |
| 9 | Los Angeles | 3036 | 2112 | 1425 | 1174 | 0 | 2757 | 2825 | 398 | 2456 | 403 | 1919 |
| 10 | Miami | 1539 | 1390 | 1332 | 2057 | 2757 | 0 | 1258 | 2359 | 1250 | 3097 | 3389 |
| 11 | New York | 213 | 840 | 1604 | 1780 | 2825 | 1258 | 0 | 2442 | 386 | 3036 | 2900 |
| 12 | Phoenix | 2664 | 1729 | 1027 | 836 | 398 | 2359 | 2442 | 0 | 2073 | 800 | 1482 |
| 13 | Pittsburgh | 792 | 457 | 1237 | 1411 | 2456 | 1250 | 386 | 2073 | 0 | 2653 | 2517 |
| 14 | San Francisco | 2385 | 2212 | 1765 | 1034 | 403 | 3097 | 3036 | 800 | 2653 | 0 | 817 |
| 15 | Seattle | 2612 | 2052 | 2404 | 1373 | 1919 | 3389 | 2900 | 1482 | 2517 | 817 | 0 |

**Objective**    To use Evolutionary Solver, with a special kind of constraint, to find the shortest route that starts and ends in Boston and visits each of the other 10 cities exactly once.

WHERE DO THE NUMBERS COME FROM?

The numbers in this example could be found from a map. In general, the required data are the distances from each city to each other city, where distance can be interpreted as a cost. For example, if Willie is flying from city to city, the costs of the various flights is the more relevant "distance" measure, and these costs are not necessarily proportional to the actual distances.

Solution

This problem is surprisingly easy to model in a spreadsheet. You simply need a way to specify that any potential solution is a permutation of the numbers 1 through 10. Fortunately, Evolutionary Solver has a special type of constraint developed specifically for this kind of problem that is called an **alldifferent** constraint. You constrain the indexes of the cities visited to be between 1 and 10, and you also constrain them to be all different. Of course, the only way this can occur is if they are a permutation of the numbers 1 through 10. With this in mind, the model is straightforward.

The completed model appears in Figure 8.34 and can be developed with the following steps:

Figure 8.34  **Traveling Salesperson Model**

| | A | B | C | D | E | F | G | H | I | J | K | L |
|---|---|---|---|---|---|---|---|---|---|---|---|---|
| 1 | Traveling salesperson problem | | | | | | | | | | | |
| 2 | | | | | | | | | | | | |
| 3 | Distance matrix | | | | | | | | | | | |
| 4 | | Boston | Chicago | Dallas | Denver | Los Angeles | Miami | New York | Phoenix | Pittsburgh | San Francisco | Seattle |
| 5 | Boston | 0 | 983 | 1815 | 1991 | 3036 | 1539 | 213 | 2664 | 792 | 2385 | 2612 |
| 6 | Chicago | 983 | 0 | 1205 | 1050 | 2112 | 1390 | 840 | 1729 | 457 | 2212 | 2052 |
| 7 | Dallas | 1815 | 1205 | 0 | 801 | 1425 | 1332 | 1604 | 1027 | 1237 | 1034 | 2404 |
| 8 | Denver | 1991 | 1050 | 801 | 0 | 1174 | 2057 | 1780 | 836 | 1411 | 1765 | 1373 |
| 9 | Los Angeles | 3036 | 2112 | 1425 | 1174 | 0 | 2757 | 2825 | 398 | 2456 | 403 | 1919 |
| 10 | Miami | 1539 | 1390 | 1332 | 2057 | 2757 | 0 | 1258 | 2359 | 1250 | 3097 | 3389 |
| 11 | New York | 213 | 840 | 1604 | 1780 | 2825 | 1258 | 0 | 2442 | 386 | 3036 | 2900 |
| 12 | Phoenix | 2664 | 1729 | 1027 | 836 | 398 | 2359 | 2442 | 0 | 2073 | 800 | 1482 |
| 13 | Pittsburgh | 792 | 457 | 1237 | 1411 | 2456 | 1250 | 386 | 2073 | 0 | 2653 | 2517 |
| 14 | San Francisco | 2385 | 2212 | 1765 | 1034 | 403 | 3097 | 3036 | 800 | 2653 | 0 | 817 |
| 15 | Seattle | 2612 | 2052 | 2404 | 1373 | 1919 | 3389 | 2900 | 1482 | 2517 | 817 | 0 |
| 16 | | | | | | | | | | | | |
| 17 | Indexes of cities | | | Route to travel | | | Range names used: | | | | | |
| 18 | City | Index | | Index | Distance | | Distance_matrix | =Model!$B$5:$L$15 | | | | |
| 19 | Boston | 0 | | 0 | | | Route | =Model!$D$20:$D$29 | | | | |
| 20 | Chicago | 1 | | 6 | 213 | | Total_distance | =Model!$B$32 | | | | |
| 21 | Dallas | 2 | | 8 | 386 | | | | | | | |
| 22 | Denver | 3 | | 1 | 457 | | | | | | | |
| 23 | Los Angeles | 4 | | 3 | 1050 | | | | | | | |
| 24 | Miami | 5 | | 10 | 1373 | | | | | | | |
| 25 | New York | 6 | | 9 | 817 | | | | | | | |
| 26 | Phoenix | 7 | | 4 | 403 | | | | | | | |
| 27 | Pittsburgh | 8 | | 7 | 398 | | | | | | | |
| 28 | San Francisco | 9 | | 2 | 1027 | | | | | | | |
| 29 | Seattle | 10 | | 5 | 1332 | | | | | | | |
| 30 | | | | 0 | 1539 | | | | | | | |
| 31 | | | | | | | | | | | | |
| 32 | Total distance | 8995 | | | | | | | | | | |

**①** **Distance matrix.** Enter the distance matrix in the blue range.

**②** **Index cities.** The cities need to be referenced by numerical indexes rather than names, so enter appropriate indexes in the range B19:B29. These indexes are based on alphabetical order, but any order could be used. Still, it is convenient to index the home city, Boston, as 0.

**③** **Specify route.** Enter any route in the Route range. Note that 0 is entered in cells B19 and B30 because the route must start and end in Boston. However, the numbers in between can be any permutation of the numbers 1 through 10. This Route range becomes the changing cell range.

**④** **Calculate distances.** To calculate the distances on the various legs of the trip, you can use the INDEX function to perform a lookup in the distance matrix. Specifically, enter the formula

*In models such as this, where a solution is a list of indexes, the INDEX and/or VLOOKUP functions are very handy.*

=INDEX(Distance_matrix,D19+1,D20+1)

in cell E20 and copy it down to cell E30. This formula looks up the appropriate distance in the distance matrix. (The +1s are necessary because the cities are indexed from 0 to 10, not from 1 to 11.) Then calculate the total distance in cell B32 with the SUM function.

The Solver dialog box should be set up as shown in Figure 8.35. The objective is to minimize the total distance traveled, subject to the constraints that all indexes on the route (other than Boston's) are between 1 and 10, and they must be all different. Specifying this "AllDifferent" constraint is similar to specifying an integer or binary constraint. When you choose Evolutionary Solver, a "dif" option is available when you add a constraint. (See Figure 8.36.) It is useful in exactly this type of model, where the numbers in a permutation must all be different.

**Figure 8.35**

Solver Dialog Box with the AllDifferent Constraint

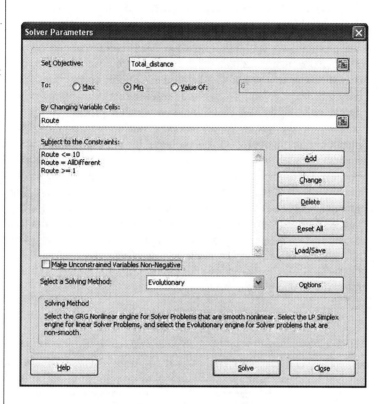

**Figure 8.36**

Specifying an AllDifferent Constraint

## Discussion of the Solution

The optimal solution appears in Figure 8.34. Willie should go from Boston to New York to Pittsburgh to Chicago to Denver to Seattle to San Francisco to Los Angeles to Phoenix to Dallas to Miami and finally to Boston. Essentially, Willie should travel around the country in a counter clockwise manner. The distance of this route is 8995 miles. Is this solution unique? It definitely is not. Willie could travel in a clockwise direction instead: Boston to Miami to Dallas and so on. Because the distance matrix is symmetric, this clockwise route is bound to have the same total distance as the counterclockwise route.

### Other Uses for the AllDifferent Constraint

We introduced the alldifferent constraint in the context of the traveling salesperson problem, but it has applications in many other problems. Specifically, it can be used in any model where the solution is defined by a permutation of integers from 1 to $n$. You are asked to explore some possibilities in the problems. ▨

---

### ADDITIONAL APPLICATIONS

### Sequence-Dependent Scheduling at Baxter International

Two of the problems discussed in this chapter, cluster analysis and the traveling salesperson problem, do not appear to have much in common. However, Moss et al. (2000) describe how they used both of these methodologies to sequence products through production at Baxter International, a large manufacturer of medical supplies. The problem is to reduce setup costs and setup time. Each product in its intravenous (IV) class of products requires a set of components to be present on the production line, and some of these components are common to various products. When production of one product follows the production of another product, components for the previous product not used by the new product have to be repackaged and stored, and components required by the new product but not used by the previous product have to be set up. Therefore, it makes sense to schedule products that use common components next to one another. The authors attacked this problem with cluster analysis (find clusters of products that are similar in terms of the components they require) and the traveling salesperson problem (find a permutation of the products to schedule through production). They estimate that their study saved Baxter about $165,000 annually by reducing setup times. ■

---

## PROBLEMS

### Skill-Building Problems

**20.** An important problem in operations management is the job sequencing problem. Actually, there are many versions of this problem, but they all basically attempt to find the proper sequencing of jobs on a machine. Here is one version of the problem. There are 10 jobs to perform on a single machine. Each job has a given batch size (items to produce), and each item in the batch takes a certain time to perform. Also, each job (the whole batch) has a given due date. These data are listed in the file P08_20.xlsx. The "lateness" of any job is 0 if the job is finished on or before its due date, but it is the finish time minus the due date otherwise. The objective is to sequence the jobs to minimize the total lateness. Use Evolutionary Solver to find an optimal sequence of jobs.

**21.** The traveling salesperson problem is notoriously difficult when the number of cities is even of moderate size. The file P08_21.xlsx contains two sheets, one with a distance matrix for a 30-city problem and the other with a distance matrix for a 45-city problem. See whether Evolutionary Solver can successfully solve these problems. How will you know if it is successful?

### Skill-Extending Problems

**22.** Repeat Problem 20, but now assume there is a setup time for changing from any job to another job, and this setup time can depend on the jobs. For example, the setup time when changing from job 2 to job 4 can be different from the setup time when changing from job 3 to job 4. The data from Problem 20, plus the setup times, are listed in the file P08_22.xlsx. Use Evolutionary Solver to find an optimal sequence of jobs.

**23.** You are operating a Web site to match up sellers and buyers of a product. 35 sellers and 35 buyers have input their reservation prices, as listed in the file P08_23.xlsx. For example, buyer 1 is willing to pay up to $8 for an item, and seller 1 is willing to accept $9 or more for an item. This means that buyer 1 and seller 1 cannot be matched. Suppose the goal is to pair buyers with sellers to maximize the sum of buyers' and sellers' surplus. For example, if buyer 31 and seller 31 are matched, a deal can be made by splitting the difference with a price of $57. Then buyer 31 earns a surplus of 60 − 57 = $3, and seller 31 earns a surplus of 57 − 54 = $3. What is the maximum sum of buyers' and sellers' surplus that can be obtained?

**24.** The 30 teams in the NBA are each assigned to one of six divisions, where each division has five teams. Suppose the goal is to assign the teams to divisions so that the average distance among teams in the divisions is minimized. In other words, the goal is to make the assignments so that teams within a division are close to one another. The file P08_24.xlsx contains distances between all NBA cities. (Actually, this was before the Seattle SuperSonics switched to Oklahoma City.) Use Evolutionary Solver to find an optimal assignment of teams to divisions. Does it turn out that your assignments to divisions are the same as the NBA's? (*Hint:* Arrange the 30 teams into six contiguous blocks of five teams each. Each block will have five team indexes. With an AllDifferent constraint, you can ensure that the 30 team indexes are all different. For each block, use lookups to find all distances between pairs of teams in that block and average these. Then average these averages over the six divisions to obtain the objective value.)

## 8.11 CONCLUSION

This chapter contains cutting-edge material. The Simplex LP and GRG Nonlinear Solvers have been available for several years to solve many linear, integer, and nonlinear problems. However, they have not been able to solve the types of problems discussed in this chapter, except possibly by employing tricks or by using a lucky initial solution. With Evolutionary Solver now available to a large audience, a much wider variety of problems can be solved, and the spreadsheet models are usually straightforward—they do not require tricks. Evolutionary Solver is typically much slower than other Solver algorithms, especially for linear models with many constraints, because it uses a totally different search procedure. Because of this, we do not recommend that you try Evolutionary Solver unless your model contains functions such as IF, COUNT, COUNTIF, SUMIF, MIN, MAX, and ABS that the other Solvers cannot handle reliably. But if your model is formulated more naturally by using such functions, or if you can think of no other way of formulating it, then Evolutionary Solver can be very useful.

### Summary of Key Management Science Terms

| Term | Explanation | Page |
|------|-------------|------|
| Genetic algorithm (GA) | Optimization search procedure that mimics the theory of evolution, using crossovers, mutations, and the survival of the fittest | 271 |
| Penalties | Often used in Evolutionary Solver models to handle constraints; penalties are included in objective for violating constraints | 274 |
| Two-part tariff | One of several pricing schemes that can be used to increase revenue; includes a fixed price and a variable price | 278 |
| Surplus value (to customer) | Value to customer of purchasing product minus purchase cost; assumption is that customer purchases the amount that maximizes surplus value | 279 |
| Combinatorial problems | Optimization problems where there are a finite number of feasible solutions (combinations); often difficult because this finite number is huge | 284 |
| Cluster analysis | General method of grouping people, products, cities, and so on, so that members within a cluster are similar and members in different clusters are dissimilar | 301 |

*(continued)*

| Term | Explanation | Page |
|------|-------------|------|
| Discriminant analysis | One (of several) methods used to classify people, products, cities, and so on, into well-defined groups based on data about the members | 307 |
| Traveling salesperson problem | Famously difficult management science problem; tries to find optimal route for a salesperson who starts and ends in a given city and visits all other cities exactly once | 310 |

## Summary of Key Excel Terms

| Term | Explanation | Excel | Page |
|------|-------------|-------|------|
| Evolutionary Solver | Solver's implementation of GA (in Excel 2010 only) | Start up Solver, choose Evolutionary item | 272 |
| Evolutionary Solver settings | Various settings that control the way the GA works (see text for details) | Choose Solver Options, then Evolutionary tab | 276 |
| AllDifferent constraint | Type of constraint available in Evolutionary Solver; useful for models where potential solutions are permutations of integers 1 through $n$ | One of several options for constraint type in Add Constraint dialog box | 311 |

## PROBLEMS

### Skill-Building Problems

**25.** Fourteen jobs must be assigned to one of three identical machines. The goal is to minimize the total time needed to complete all 14 jobs. The machine capacities and times needed for the jobs are given in file P08_25.xlsx. For example, job 8 requires three units of capacity on a machine for two hours. At any given time, a machine has five units of capacity. How should the jobs be assigned to machines to achieve the earliest possible completion of all jobs?

**26.** Nine jobs need to be completed within eight weeks. The number of weeks required to complete each job is given in the file P08_26.xlsx. For example, job 2 requires three weeks. Each job requires 40 hours of labor per week. Each week, 160 hours of regular time labor are available. Up to 40 hours of overtime labor can be purchased each week at a cost of $10 per hour. Additional overtime hours cost $20 per hour.
   **a.** Determine how to minimize the overtime cost incurred in completing the jobs within eight weeks.
   **b.** The same file also lists the due date for each job. For example, job 2 should be completed within six weeks. A penalty of $500 is incurred for each day a job is late. Determine how to minimize the sum of overtime and due date penalties.

**27.** Eight students need to be assigned to four dorm rooms (two students to a room) at State University. Based on incompatibility measures, the "cost" incurred

if two students room together is shown in the file P08_27.xlsx. How should these students be assigned to rooms to minimize the total incompatibility?

**28.** The costs of producing product A, product B, or products A and B bundled together are $50, $90, and $140, respectively. The file P08_28.xlsx lists the sizes of the three market segments for these products and how much each of the segments is willing to pay for A alone, B alone, or the bundle. Under the assumptions that a market segment will buy the product combination that yields the maximum nonnegative surplus (value minus cost), and a segment will buy no product if no product has a nonnegative surplus, determine an optimal set of product prices. Should the company offer all products for sale?

**29.** Cook County needs to build two hospitals. There are nine cities where the hospitals can be built. The number of hospital visits made annually by the inhabitants of each city and the $x$ and $y$ coordinates of each city are listed in the file P08_29.xlsx. To minimize the total distance that patients must travel to hospitals, where should the hospitals be located? Solve the problem when people can travel in straight lines ("as the crow flies") between cities. Then solve it when people must travel along a horizontal/vertical grid of roads. (*Hint:* Use lookup functions to generate the distances between each pair of cities.)

**30.** The file P08_30.xlsx contains quarterly revenue for Nike for the years 1991 to 1998. It also contains quarterly "indicator" variables Q1, Q2, and Q3. Here Q1 is 1 for the first quarter of a fiscal year (July–September) and 0 otherwise. Q2 and Q3 are defined similarly for the second and third quarters of the fiscal year (October–December and January–March). The "Quarter #" variable is simply the chronological number of the quarter, 1 to 32. The goal is to build a quantitative model to explain the variation in quarterly revenue. A reasonable model is as follows:

$$\text{Predicted Sales} = ab^{Quarter\#}c^{Q1}d^{Q2}e^{Q3}$$

where $a$, $b$, $c$, $d$, and $e$ are parameters to estimate.

a. Find the values of $a$, $b$, $c$, $d$, and $e$ that best fit this model.

b. What does your model say about the trend and seasonal aspects of Nike sales? (*Hint:* The trend effect is captured by the term involving Quarter #. Seasonal effects may be interpreted relative to the quarter, Q4, that we have omitted from the analysis.)

31. Music radio WABC has commercials of the following lengths (in seconds): 15, 15, 20, 25, 30, 35, 40, 57. The commercials must be assigned to 60-second breaks. What is the fewest number of breaks that are needed to air all of the commercials?

32. A Wall Street firm is trying to package nine mortgages for sale. The sizes of the mortgages (in thousands of dollars) are listed in the file P08_32.xlsx. To be sold, each package must consist of at least $1,000,000 in mortgages. What is the largest number of packages that can be created?

33. During the next 12 months, the amounts of electric power needed (in thousands of kwh) are listed in the file P08_33.xlsx. This power can be supplied using four generators. The generating capacity (in thousands of kwh), the operating cost, the startup cost, and the shutdown cost (all costs in thousands of dollars) are also listed in the same file. At the beginning of month 1, generators 1 and 2 are in operation. At the end of each month, it is possible to either shut down an operating generator or start up a shutdown generator. Find the strategy that minimizes the cost of meeting demand for power during the next 12 months.

34. Bus 99 serves towns 1 through 10. We assume that town $k$ is $|k - j|$ miles from town $j$. The numbers of people in the towns who want to take the bus each hour are listed in the file P08_34.xlsx. Bus 99 will make two stops and anyone who wants to take the bus will walk to the closest bus stop.

a. If the goal is to minimize the total distance people walk, where should the bus stop?

b. If the bus is allowed to make three stops, how much will the total walking distance be reduced?

35. Ten data sets must be assigned for storage to one of three disk drives. Each disk drive can store 25 GB (about 25,000 MB). The sizes of the data sets (in MB) are listed in the file P08_35.xlsx. When many people access a disk drive, there is a significant reduction in the speed at which the data are retrieved. To reduce the number of people accessing a disk drive, the goal is to make the data sets on each disk drive as different as possible. To achieve this goal, penalties have been assigned for assigning similar data sets to the same disk drive. These penalties are isted in the same file. For example, if data sets 9 and 10 are assigned to the same drive, a penalty of 221 is incurred, whereas if disks 8 and 10 are assigned to the same drive, a penalty of only 35 is incurred. You can think of the penalty as the number of times two data sets are accessed at the same time. Assign the data sets to disk drives to minimize total penalties.

36. Xerox is trying to determine how many maintenance centers are needed in the mid-Atlantic states. Xerox earns $500 profit (excluding the cost of running maintenance centers) on each copier sale. The sales of copiers in each major market (Boston, New York, Philadelphia, Washington, Providence, and Atlantic City) depend on the proximity of the nearest maintenance facility. If a maintenance facility is within 100 miles of a city, sales will be high; if a maintenance facility is within 150 miles of a city, sales will be medium; otherwise, sales will be low. The predicted annual sales (that is, the meaning of low, medium, and high) are listed in the file P08_36.xlsx. It costs $200,000 per year to place a maintenance representative in a city. It is possible to locate a representative in any city except for Atlantic City and Providence. The distances between the cities are listed in the same file. Where should maintenance representatives be located?

## Skill-Extending Problems

37. You are the Democratic campaign manager for the state of Indiana. There are 15 fairly large cities in the state of Indiana. The numbers of Democrats and Republican voters in these cities (in thousands) are listed in the file P08_37.xlsx. The Democrats control the state legislature, so they can redistrict as they wish. There will be eight congressional districts. Each city must be assigned in its entirety to a single district. Each district must contain between 150,000 and 250,000 voters. Use Evolutionary Solver to assign voters to districts in a way that maximizes the number of districts that will vote Democratic. (*Hint:* The SUMIF function is useful.)

38. A steel manufacturer needs to cool 17 pieces of steel. The weight and due date for each piece are listed in the file P08_38.xlsx. Processing and cooling a batch in

the furnace takes five minutes regardless of the weight in the furnace. The furnace can handle up to 1000 pounds at a time. Jobs 6 and 7 (size 640 and 450, respectively) must be completed on time. How can the company minimize the total time the jobs are late?

**39.** Suppose you are the ad manager for Fox NFL football. Thirty bids for ads on today's game between the Packers and the Colts have been submitted. Information on these ads is given in the file P08_39.xlsx. For example, ad 1 is 23 seconds in length and will bring in $53,000 in revenues. During the game, 14 one-minute slots are available for ads. Determine how Fox can maximize the revenue earned from game ads.

**40.** Assume that a consumer's purchase decision on an electric razor is based on four attributes, each of which can be set at one of three levels (1, 2, or 3). Using conjoint analysis (a type of analysis used in marketing research), our analysts have divided the market into five segments (labeled as customers 1, 2, 3, 4, and 5) and have determined the "part-worth" that each customer gives to each level of each attribute. These are listed in the file P08_40.xlsx. Conjoint analysis usually assumes the customer buys the product yielding the highest total part-worth. Currently there is a single product in the market that sets all four attributes equal to 1. You are going to sell two types of electric razors. Design a product line that maximizes the number of market segments that will buy your product. For example, if you design a product that is level 2 of each attribute, then customer 1 will not buy the product because he values the current product at $1 + 4 + 4 + 4 = 13$ and values your product at $1 + 1 + 1 + 2 = 5$. Assume that in the case of a tie, the consumer does not purchase your product.

**41.** An important problem in manufacturing is the assembly line balancing problem. When setting up a manufacturing line, activities must be assigned to workstations. The maximum time spent at a workstation is called the cycle time. Minimizing the cycle time translates to maximizing the number of items that can be produced each hour. Here is a typical assembly line balancing problem that can be solved with the Evolutionary Solver. Manufacture of a product consists of 10 activities (A–J) that require the times (in seconds) in the file P08_41.xlsx to complete. Certain activities must be completed before others. These precedence relations are also given in the same file. For example, activity A cannot be performed on a higher numbered workstation than activity B. Use Evolutionary Solver to determine an assignment of activities to workstations that minimizes the total cycle time.

**42.** A common approach to clustering is called **multidimensional scaling** (MDS). To apply MDS, we rank each pair of objects we want to cluster from least similar (higher number) to most similar (lower number). For example, in the file P08_42.xlsx, we compared the similarity of 10 banks and found banks 5 and 10 to be most similar and banks 9 and 10 to be least similar. We now assign a location in the x-y plane to each bank. The goal is to ensure that when we rank the distances between pair of banks, the ordering of these distances matches (as closely as possible) the similarity rankings of the banks.

  **a.** Constrain each bank to have an x and y coordinate between $-1$ and $+1$ and determine the "location" of each bank. (*Hint:* Use Excel's RANK function to rank the distances from smallest to largest.)

  **b.** How does this method lead to a natural clustering of banks?

  **c.** How could you determine whether you need more than two dimensions to adequately locate the banks?

**43.** Based on Meneses et al. (2004). A string is a list of characters such as "1differ%". The length of the string is the number of characters in the string. The distance between two strings is the number of positions in which the two strings differ. For example, the distance between the strings "1differ%" and "1dizzzr%" is 3. Given a set of strings of the same length, the closest string problem is to find a string of the same length that minimizes the maximum distance between the chosen string and the given list of strings. Consider the following four strings: "median," "differ," "length," and "medium," all with six characters. Find a closest string to these strings. (*Hint:* There are many alternative solutions.)

**44.** A company has nine jobs that must be assigned to three ordered workstations. The file P08_44.xlsx lists the times required for each job, which are independent of the workstations they are assigned to. It also lists precedence relationships between the jobs. For example, job 2 is a precedent of job 5. This means that job 2 cannot be assigned to a higher-numbered workstation than job 5. Note that job 6 has two precedents, jobs 3 and 4, which means that neither of jobs 3 and 4 can be assigned to a higher-numbered workstation than job 6. The cycle time of the system is the maximum time load assigned to any workstation. Find an assignment of jobs to workstations that minimizes the cycle time without violating any of the precedence relationships.

**45.** Suppose you are the new supply manager at FedEx. You need to choose three hubs for the company. Each of 28 cities will send *all* of its outgoing packages to one of the hubs. The packages will then be sent from the hubs to their final destinations. The file P08_45.xlsx lists the distances between cities and the number of packages to be sent from each city to each other city. Each hub, regardless of its location, can handle at most 1600 packages. Where should the hubs be located (they must be located in three of the 29 cities), and which cities should be assigned to which hubs, to minimize the total distance the shipments travel?

## Modeling Problems

46. The discussion at the beginning of section 8.8 mentions Claritas. If you were in the direct-mail business, how would you use the information sold by Claritas to improve your profitability?

47. How would you use cluster analysis to help test market a consumer goods product?

48. Your company sells credit card services, and you are concerned with churn. (*Churn* occurs when your customers go to a different company.) Describe how you could use discriminant analysis to learn what distinguishes the customers who switch to another company from those who stay loyal to your company. How might you use such a model?

49. Your company provides credit to customers. Some of these customers default on their loans, with very negative implications for you. Describe how you could use discriminant analysis to learn what distinguishes the customers who default on their loans from those who pay back their loans. How might you use such a model?

The MBA program at State University has approximately 260 incoming students each fall semester. These students are divided into cohorts of approximately 65 students each, and the students in each cohort sit through exactly the same set of fall courses together. Much of the work in these courses is done in teams. To ensure that the teams are comparable, the MBA Office tries to divide the students in each cohort into 14 teams so that each team has the following qualities:

- Four or five members
- At least one member with a CPA
- At least one member with quantitative expertise
- At least one female
- At least one minority student
- At least one international student

The file MBA Teams.xlsx indicates the characteristics of the students in a particular cohort of this year's incoming class. Your job is to use the Evolutionary Solver to see if you can create teams that have all of the desired properties. It is not clear whether this will be possible—for example, there might not be enough minority students for each team—so you should create penalties for failing to meet the various goals, where the penalties can be different for different goals. ▨

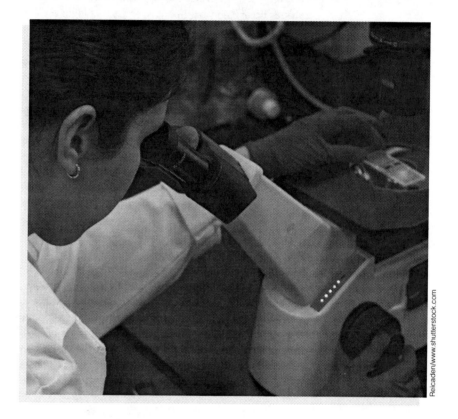

Reicaden/www.shutterstock.com

## DECIDING WHETHER TO DEVELOP NEW DRUGS AT BAYER

The formal decision-making process discussed in this chapter is often used to make difficult decisions in the face of much uncertainty, large monetary values, and long-term consequences. Stonebraker (2002) chronicles one such decision-making process he performed for Bayer Pharmaceuticals in 1999. The development of a new drug is a time-consuming and expensive process that is filled with risks along the way. A pharmaceutical company must first get the proposed drug through preclinical trials, where the drug is tested on animals. Assuming this stage is successful (and only about half are), the company can then file an application with the Food and Drug Administration (FDA) to conduct clinical trials on humans. These clinical trials have three phases. Phase 1 is designed to test the safety of the drug on a small sample of healthy patients. Phase 2 is designed to identify the optimal dose of the new drug on patients with the disease. Phase 3 is a statistically designed study to prove the efficacy and safety of the new drug on a larger sample of patients with the disease. Failure at any one of these phases means that further testing stops and the drug is never brought to market. Of course, this means that all costs up to the failure point are lost. If the drug makes it through the clinical tests (and only about 25% of all drugs do so), the company can then apply to the FDA for permission to manufacture and market its drug in the United States. Assuming that FDA approves, the company is then free to launch the drug in the marketplace.

The study involved the evaluation of a new drug for busting blood clots called BAY 57-9602, and it commenced at a time just prior to the first decision point: whether to conduct preclinical tests. This was the company's first formal use of decision making for evaluating a new drug, so to convince the company of the worth of such a study, Stonebraker did exactly what a successful management scientist should do. He formulated the problem and its objectives; he identified risks, costs, and benefits; he involved key people in the organization to help provide the data needed for the decision analysis; and, because much of the resulting data consisted of educated guesses at best, he performed a thorough sensitivity analysis on the inputs. Although we are not told in the article how everything turned out, the analysis did persuade Bayer management to proceed in January 2000 with preclinical testing of the drug.

The article provides a fascinating look at how such a study should proceed. Because there is so much uncertainty, the key is determining probabilities and probability distributions for the various inputs. First, there are uncertainties in the various phases of testing. Each of these can be modeled with a probability of success. For example, the chance of making it through preclinical testing was assessed to be about 65% for BAY 57-9602, although management preferred to use the more conservative benchmark of 50% (based on historical data on other drugs) for the decision analysis. Many of the other uncertain quantities, such as the eventual market share, are continuous random variables. Because the decision tree approach discussed in this chapter requires discrete random variables, usually with only a few possible values, Stonebraker used a popular three-point approximation for all continuous quantities. He asked experts to assess the 10th percentile, the 50th percentile, and the 90th percentile, and he assigned probabilities 0.3, 0.4, and 0.3 to these three values. [The validity of such an approximation is discussed in Keefer and Bodily (1983).]

After getting all such estimates of uncertain quantities from the company experts, the author examined the expected net present value (NPV) of all costs and benefits from developing the new drug. To see which of the various uncertain quantities affected the expected NPV most, he varied each such quantity, one at a time, from its 10th percentile to its 90th percentile, leaving the other inputs at their base 50th percentile values. This identified several quantities that the expected NPV was most sensitive to, including the peak product share, the price per treatment in the United States, and the annual growth rate. The expected NPV was not nearly as sensitive to other uncertain inputs, including the product launch date and the production process yield. Therefore, in the final decision analysis, Stonebraker treated the sensitive inputs as uncertain and the less sensitive inputs as certain at their base values. He also calculated the risk profile from developing the drug. This indicates the probability distribution of NPV, taking all sources of uncertainty into account. Although this risk profile was not exactly optimistic (90% chance of losing money using the conservative probabilities of success, 67% chance of losing money with the more optimistic product-specific probabilities of success), this risk profile compared favorably with Bayer's other potential projects. This evaluation, plus the rigor and defensibility of the study, led Bayer management to give the go-ahead on preclinical testing. ■

## 9.1 INTRODUCTION

This chapter provides a formal framework for analyzing decision problems that involve uncertainty. Our discussion includes the following:

* criteria for choosing among alternative decisions
* how probabilities are used in the decision-making process

- how early decisions affect decisions made at a later stage
- how a decision maker can quantify the value of information
- how attitudes toward risk can affect the analysis

Throughout, we employ a powerful graphical tool—a decision tree—to guide the analysis. A decision tree enables a decision maker to view all important aspects of the problem at once: the decision alternatives, the uncertain outcomes and their probabilities, the economic consequences, and the chronological order of events. We show how to implement decision trees in Excel by taking advantage of a very powerful and flexible add-in from Palisade called PrecisionTree.

Many examples of decision making under uncertainty exist in the business world, including the following:

- Companies routinely place bids for contracts to complete a certain project within a fixed time frame. Often these are sealed bids, where each company presents a bid for completing the project in a sealed envelope. Then the envelopes are opened, and the low bidder is awarded the bid amount to complete the project. Any particular company in the bidding competition must deal with the uncertainty of the other companies' bids, as well as possible uncertainty regarding their cost to complete the project if they win the bid. The trade-off is between bidding low to win the bid and bidding high to make a larger profit.

- Whenever a company contemplates introducing a new product into the market, there are a number of uncertainties that affect the decision, probably the most important being the customers' reaction to this product. If the product generates high customer demand, the company will make a large profit. But if demand is low—and, after all, the vast majority of new products do poorly—the company could fail to recoup its development costs. Because the level of customer demand is critical, the company might try to gauge this level by test marketing the product in one region of the country. If this test market is a success, the company can then be more optimistic that a full-scale national marketing of the product will also be successful. But if the test market is a failure, the company can cut its losses by abandoning the product.

- Whenever manufacturing companies make capacity expansion decisions, they face uncertain consequences. First, they must decide whether to build new plants. If they don't expand and demand for their products is higher than expected, they will lose revenue because of insufficient capacity. If they do expand and demand for their products is lower than expected, they will be stuck with expensive underutilized capacity. Of course, in today's global economy, companies also need to decide *where* to build new plants. This decision involves a whole new set of uncertainties, including exchange rates, labor availability, social stability, competition from local businesses, and others.

- Banks must continually make decisions on whether to grant loans to businesses or individuals. As we all know, many banks made many very poor decisions, especially on mortgage loans, during the years leading up to the financial crisis in 2008. They fooled themselves into thinking that housing prices would only increase, never decrease. When the bottom fell out of the housing market, banks were stuck with loans that could never be repaid.

- Utility companies must make many decisions that have significant environmental and economic consequences. For these companies it is not necessarily enough to conform to federal or state environmental regulations. Recent court decisions have found companies liable—for huge settlements—when accidents occurred, even though the companies followed all existing regulations. Therefore, when utility companies decide, say, whether to replace equipment or mitigate the effects of environmental pollution, they must take into account the possible environmental consequences (such as injuries to people) as well as economic consequences (such as lawsuits). An aspect of these situations that makes decision analysis particularly difficult is that the potential "disasters" are often extremely unlikely; hence, their probabilities are difficult to assess accurately.

- Sports teams continually make decisions under uncertainty. Sometimes these decisions involve long-run consequences, such as whether to trade for a promising but as yet untested pitcher in baseball. Other times these decisions involve short-run consequences, such as whether to go for a fourth down or kick a field goal late in a close football game. You might be surprised at the level of quantitative sophistication in professional sports these days. Management and coaches typically do *not* make important decisions by gut feel. They employ many of the tools in this chapter and in other chapters of this book.

## 9.2 ELEMENTS OF DECISION ANALYSIS

Although decision making under uncertainty occurs in a wide variety of contexts, all problems have three common elements: (1) the set of decisions (or strategies) available to the decision maker, (2) the set of possible outcomes and the probabilities of these outcomes, and (3) a value model that prescribes monetary values for the various decision-outcome combinations. Once these elements are known, the decision maker can find an optimal decision, depending on the optimality criterion chosen.

Before moving on to realistic business problems, we discuss the basic elements of any decision analysis for a very simple problem. We assume that a decision maker must choose among three decisions, labeled $D1$, $D2$, and $D3$. Each of these decisions has three possible outcomes, labeled $O1$, $O2$, and $O3$.

### 9.2.1 Payoff Tables

At the time the decision must be made, the decision maker does *not* know which outcome will occur. However, once the decision is made, the outcome will eventually be revealed, and a corresponding payoff will be received. This payoff might actually be a cost, in which case it is indicated as a negative value. The listing of payoffs for all decision–outcome pairs is called the **payoff table**.[1] For our simple decision problem, this payoff table appears in Table 9.1. For example, if the decision maker chooses decision $D2$ and outcome $O3$ then occurs, a payoff of $30 is received.

> **A payoff table** lists the payoff for each decision-outcome pair. Positive values correspond to *rewards* (or gains) and negative values correspond to *costs* (or losses).

Table 9.1    Payoff Table for Simple Decision Problem

|  |  | Outcome | | |
| --- | --- | --- | --- | --- |
|  |  | *O1* | *O2* | *O3* |
| **Decision** | *D1* | 10 | 10 | 10 |
|  | *D2* | −10 | 20 | 30 |
|  | *D3* | −30 | 30 | 80 |

[1]In situations where all monetary consequences are costs, it is customary to list these costs in a *cost table*. In this case, all monetary values are shown as *positive* costs.

This table shows that the decision maker can play it safe by choosing decision $D1$. This provides a sure $10 payoff. With decision $D2$, rewards of $20 or $30 are possible, but a loss of $10 is also possible. Decision $D3$ is even riskier; the possible loss is greater, and the maximum gain is also greater. Which decision would you choose? Would your choice change if the values in the payoff table were measured in *thousands* of dollars? The answers to these questions are what this chapter is all about. There must be a criterion for making choices, and this criterion must be evaluated so that the *best* decision can be identified. As you will see, it is customary to use one particular criterion for decisions involving moderate amounts of money.

Before proceeding, there is one very important point we need to emphasize: the distinction between good *decisions* and good *outcomes*. In any decision-making problem where there is uncertainty, the "best" decision can have less than optimal results—that is, you can be unlucky. Regardless of which decision you choose, you might get an outcome that, in hindsight, makes you wish we had made a different decision. For example, if you make decision $D3$, hoping for a large reward, you might get outcome $O1$, in which case you will wish you had chosen decision $D1$ or $D2$. Or if you choose decision $D2$, hoping to limit possible losses, you might get outcome $O3$, in which case you will wish you had chosen decision $D3$. The point is that decision makers must make rational decisions, based on the information they have when the decisions must be made, and then live with the consequences. Second-guessing these decisions, just because of bad luck with the outcomes, is not appropriate.

---

### FUNDAMENTAL INSIGHT

#### What Is a "Good" Decision?

In the context of decision making under uncertainty, a "good" decision is one that is based on the sound decision-making principles discussed in this chapter. Because the decision must usually be made before uncertainty is resolved, a good decision might have unlucky consequences. However, decision makers should not be criticized for unlucky outcomes. They should be criticized only if their analysis *at the time the decision has to be made* is faulty.

---

### 9.2.2 Possible Decision Criteria

What do we mean when we call a decision the "best" decision? We will eventually settle on one particular criterion for making decisions, but we first explore some possibilities. With respect to Table 9.1, one possibility is to choose the decision that maximizes the *worst* payoff. This criterion, called the **maximin** criterion, is appropriate for a very conservative (or pessimistic) decision maker. The worst payoffs for the three decisions are the minimums in the three rows: 10, $-10$, and $-30$. The maximin decision maker chooses the decision corresponding to the best of these: decision $D1$ with payoff 10. Such a criterion tends to avoid large losses, but it fails to even consider large rewards. Hence, it is typically *too* conservative and is seldom used.

---

The **maximin** criterion finds the worst payoff in each row of the payoff table and chooses the decision corresponding to the best of these.

---

At the other extreme, the decision maker might choose the decision that maximizes the *best* payoff. This criterion, called the **maximax** criterion, is appropriate for a risk taker (or optimist). The best payoffs for the three decisions are the maximums in the three rows: 10, 30, and 80. The maximax decision maker chooses the decision corresponding to the best of these: decision *D*3 with payoff 80. This criterion looks tempting because it focuses on large gains, but its very serious downside is that it ignores possible losses. Because this type of decision making could eventually bankrupt a company, the maximax criterion is also seldom used.

> The **maximax** criterion finds the best payoff in each row of the payoff table and chooses the decision corresponding to the best of these.

### 9.2.3 Expected Monetary Value (EMV)

We have introduced the maximin and maximax criteria because (1) they are occasionally used to make decisions, and (2) they illustrate that there are several "reasonable" criteria for making decisions. In fact, there are other possible criteria that we will not discuss (although a couple are explored in the problems). Instead, we now focus on a criterion that is generally regarded as the preferred criterion in most decision problems. It is called the **expected monetary value**, or **EMV**, criterion. To motivate the EMV criterion, we first note that the maximin and maximax criteria make no reference to how *likely* the various outcomes are. However, decision makers typically have at least some idea of these likelihoods, and they ought to use this information in the decision-making process. After all, if outcome *O*1 in our problem is extremely unlikely, then the pessimist who uses maximin is being overly conservative. Similarly, if outcome *O*3 is quite unlikely, then the optimist who uses maximax is taking an unnecessary risk.

The EMV approach assesses probabilities for each outcome of each decision and then calculates the *expected* payoff from each decision based on these probabilities. This expected payoff, or EMV, is a weighted average of the payoffs in any given row of the payoff table, weighted by the probabilities of the outcomes. You calculate the EMV for each decision, then choose the decision with the largest EMV. (Note that the terms *expected payoff* and *mean payoff* are equivalent. We will use them interchangeably.)

> The **expected monetary value**, or **EMV**, for any decision is a weighted average of the possible payoffs for this decision, weighted by the probabilities of the outcomes. Using the EMV criterion, you choose the decision with the largest EMV. This is sometimes called "playing the averages."

Where do the probabilities come from? This is a difficult question to answer in general because it depends on each specific situation. In some cases the current decision problem is similar to those a decision maker has faced many times in the past. Then the probabilities can be estimated from the knowledge of previous outcomes. If a certain type of outcome occurred, say, in about 30% of previous situations, an estimate of its current probability might be 0.30.

However, there are many decision problems that have no parallels in the past. In such cases, a decision maker must use whatever information is available, plus some intuition, to assess the probabilities. For example, if the problem involves a new product decision, and one possible outcome is that a competitor will introduce a similar product in the coming year, the decision maker will have to rely on any knowledge of the market and the competitor's situation to assess the probability of this outcome. It is important to note that this assessment can be very subjective. Two decision makers could easily assess the probability of the *same* outcome as 0.30 and 0.45, depending on their information and feelings, and neither could be considered "wrong." This is the nature of assessing probabilities subjectively in real business situations. Still, it is important for the decision maker to consult all relevant sources (historical data, expert opinions, government forecasts, and so on) when assessing these probabilities. As you will see, they are crucial to the decision-making process.

With this general framework in mind, let's assume that a decision maker assesses the probabilities of the three outcomes in Table 9.1 as 0.3, 0.5, and 0.2 if decision $D2$ is made, and as 0.5, 0.2, 0.3 if decision $D3$ is made.[2] Then the EMV for each decision is the sum of products of payoffs and probabilities:

$$\text{EMV for } D1\text{: } 10 \text{ (a sure thing)}$$

$$\text{EMV for } D2\text{: } -10(0.3) + 20(0.5) + 30(0.2) = 13$$

$$\text{EMV for } D3\text{: } -30(0.5) + 30(0.2) + 80(0.3) = 15$$

These calculations lead to the optimal decision: Choose decision $D3$ because it has the largest EMV.

It is important to understand what the EMV of a decision represents—and what it doesn't represent. For example, the EMV of 15 for decision $D3$ does *not* mean that you expect to gain $15 from this decision. The payoff table indicates that the result from $D3$ will be a loss of $30, a gain of $30, or a gain of $80; it will *never* be a gain of $15. The EMV is only a weighted average of the possible payoffs. As such, it can be interpreted in one of two ways. First, imagine that this situation can occur many times, not just once. If decision $D3$ is used each time, then *on average*, you will make a gain of about $15. About 50% of the time you will lose $30, about 20% of the time you will gain $30, and about 30% of the time you will gain $80. These average to $15. For this reason, using the EMV criterion is sometimes referred to as "playing the averages."

But what if the current situation is a one-shot deal that will *not* occur many times in the future? Then the second interpretation of EMV is still relevant. It states that the EMV is a "sensible" criterion for making decisions under uncertainty. This is actually a point that has been debated in intellectual circles for years—what is the best criterion for making decisions? However, researchers have generally concluded that EMV makes sense, even for one-shot deals, as long as the monetary values are not too large. For situations where the monetary values are extremely large, we will introduce an alternative criterion in the last section of this chapter. Until then, however, we will use EMV.

This is the gist of decision-making uncertainty. You develop a payoff table, assess probabilities of outcomes, calculate EMVs, and choose the decision with the largest EMV. However, before proceeding to examples, it is useful to introduce a few other concepts: *sensitivity analysis*, *decision trees*, and *risk profiles*.

---

[2]In a change from the previous edition of this book, we allow these probabilities to depend on the decision that is made, which is often the case in real decision problems.

Some of the quantities in a decision analysis, particularly the probabilities, are often intelligent guesses at best. Therefore, it is important, especially in real-world business problems, to accompany any decision analysis with a sensitivity analysis. Here we systematically vary inputs to the problem to see how (or if) the outputs—the EMVs and the best decision—change. For our simple decision problem, this is easy to do in a spreadsheet. The spreadsheet model is shown in Figure 9.1. (See the file Simple Decision Problem.xlsx.)

**Figure 9.1**

Spreadsheet Model
of a Simple Decision
Problem

|   | A | B | C | D | E | F |
|---|---|---|---|---|---|---|
| 1 | Simple decision problem under uncertainty | | | | | |
| 2 |   |   |   |   |   |   |
| 3 |   |   | Outcome |   |   |   |
| 4 |   |   | O1 | O2 | O3 | EMV |
| 5 | Decision | D1 | 10 | 10 | 10 | 10 |
| 6 |   | D2 | -10 | 20 | 30 | 13 |
| 7 |   | D3 | -30 | 30 | 80 | 15 |
| 8 |   |   |   |   |   |   |
| 9 | Probabilities |   |   |   |   |   |
| 10 |   | D2 | 0.3 | 0.5 | 0.2 |   |
| 11 |   | D3 | 0.5 | 0.2 | 0.3 |   |

*Usually, the most important information from a sensitivity analysis is whether the optimal decision continues to be optimal as one or more inputs change.*

After entering the payoff table and probabilities, calculate the EMVs in column F as a sum of products, using the formula

=SUMPRODUCT(C6:E6,C10:E10)

in cell F6 and copying it down. (A link to the sure 10 for *D*1 is entered in cell F5.) Then it is easy to change any of the inputs and see whether the optimal decision continues to be *D*3. For example, you can check that if the probabilities for *D*3 change only slightly to 0.6, 0.2, and 0.2, the EMV for *D*3 changes to 4. Now *D*3 is the worst decision and *D*2 is the best, so it appears that the optimal decision is quite sensitive to the assessed probabilities. As another example, if the probabilities remain the same but the last payoff for *D*2 changes from 30 to 45, then its EMV changes to 16, and *D*2 becomes the best decision.

Given a simple spreadsheet model, it is easy to make a number of ad hoc changes to inputs, as we have done here, to answer specific sensitivity questions. However, it is often useful to conduct a more systematic sensitivity analysis, as we will do this later in the chapter. The important thing to realize at this stage is that a sensitivity analysis is not an afterthought to the overall analysis; it is a key component of the analysis.

## 9.2.5 Decision Trees

The decision problem we have been analyzing is very basic. You make a decision, you then observe an outcome, you receive a payoff, and that is the end of it. Many decision problems are of this basic form, but many are more complex. In these more complex problems, you make a decision, you observe an outcome, you make a second decision, you observe a second outcome, and so on. A graphical tool called a **decision tree** has been developed to represent decision problems. Decision trees can be used for any decision problems, but they are particularly useful for the more complex types. They clearly show the sequence of events (decisions and outcomes), as well as probabilities and monetary values. The decision tree for the simple problem appears in Figure 9.2. This tree is based on one we drew and calculated by hand. We urge you to try this on your own, at least once. However, later in the chapter we will introduce an Excel add-in that automates the procedure.

Figure 9.2

Decision Tree for
Simple Decision
Problem

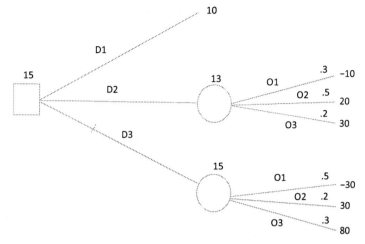

To explain this decision tree, we introduce a number of decision tree conventions that have become standard.

---

### Decision Tree Conventions

1. Decision trees are composed of *nodes* (circles, squares, and triangles) and *branches* (lines).

2. The nodes represent points in time. A *decision node* (a square) represents a time when the decision maker makes a decision. A *probability node* (a circle) represents a time when the result of an uncertain outcome becomes known. An *end node* (a triangle) indicates that the problem is completed— all decisions have been made, all uncertainty has been resolved, and all payoffs and costs have been incurred. (When people draw decision trees by hand, they often omit the actual triangles, as we have done in Figure 9.2. However, we still refer to the right-hand tips of the branches as the end nodes.)

3. Time proceeds *from left to right*. This means that any branches leading into a node (from the left) have already occurred. Any branches leading out of a node (to the right) have not yet occurred.

4. Branches leading out of a decision node represent the possible decisions; the decision maker can choose the preferred branch. Branches leading out of probability nodes represent the possible outcomes of uncertain events; the decision maker has no control over which of these will occur.

5. Probabilities are listed on probability branches. These probabilities are *conditional* on the events that have already been observed (those to the left). Also, the probabilities on branches leading out of any probability node must sum to 1.

6. Monetary values are shown to the right of the end nodes. (As we discuss shortly, some monetary values are also placed under the branches where they occur in time.)

7. EMVs are calculated through a "folding-back" process, discussed next. They are shown above the various nodes. It is then customary to mark the optimal decision branch(es) in some way. We have marked ours with a small notch.

The decision tree in Figure 9.2 follows these conventions. The decision node comes first (to the left) because the decision maker must make a decision *before* observing the uncertain outcome. The probability nodes then follow the decision branches, and the probabilities appear above their branches. (Actually, there is no need for a probability node after the $D1$ branch because its monetary value is a sure 10.) The ultimate payoffs appear next to the end nodes, to the right of the probability branches. The EMVs above the probability nodes are for the various decisions. For example, the EMV for the $D2$ branch is 13. The maximum of the EMVs is for the D2 branch written above the decision node. Because it corresponds to $D3$, we put a notch on the $D3$ branch to indicate that this decision is optimal.

This decision tree is almost a direct translation of the spreadsheet model in Figure 9.1. Indeed, the decision tree is overkill for such a simple problem; the spreadsheet model provides all of the required information. However, decision trees are very useful in business problems. First, they provide a graphical view of the whole problem. This can be useful in its own right for the insights it provides, especially in more complex problems. Second, the decision tree provides a framework for doing all of the EMV calculations. Specifically, it allows you to use the following **folding-back procedure** to find the EMVs and the optimal decision.

---

*Folding-Back Procedure*

Starting from the right of the decision tree and working back to the left:

**1.** At each probability node, calculate an EMV—a sum of products of monetary values and probabilities.

**2.** At each decision node, take a maximum of EMVs to identify the optimal decision.

---

This is exactly what we did in Figure 9.2. At each probability node, we calculated EMVs in the usual way (sums of products) and wrote them above the nodes. Then at the decision node, we took the maximum of the three EMVs and wrote it above this node. Although this procedure entails more work for more complex decision trees, the same two steps—taking EMVs at probability nodes and taking maximums at decision nodes—are the only arithmetic operations required. In addition, the PrecisionTree add-in in the next section does the folding-back calculations for you.

### 9.2.6 Risk Profiles

In our small example each decision leads to three possible monetary payoffs with various probabilities. In more complex problems, the number of outcomes could be larger, maybe considerably larger. It is then useful to represent the probability distribution of the monetary values for any decision graphically. Specifically, we show a "spike" chart, where the spikes are located at the possible monetary values, and the heights of the spikes correspond to the probabilities. In decision-making contexts, this type of chart is called a **risk profile**. By looking at the risk profile for a particular decision, you can see the risks and rewards involved. By comparing risk profiles for different decisions, you can gain more insight into their relative strengths and weaknesses.

---

The **risk profile** for a decision is a "spike" chart that represents the probability distribution of monetary outcomes for this decision.

---

The risk profile for decision $D3$ appears in Figure 9.3. It shows that a loss of $30 has probability 0.5, a gain of $30 has probability 0.2, and a gain of $80 has probability 0.3. The risk profile for decision $D2$ is similar, except that its spikes are above the values $-10$, 20, and 30, and the risk profile for decision $D1$ is a single spike of height 1 over the value 10. (The finished version of the Simple Decision Problem.xlsx file provides instructions for constructing such a chart with Excel tools.)

**Figure 9.3**

**Risk Profile for Decision $D3$**

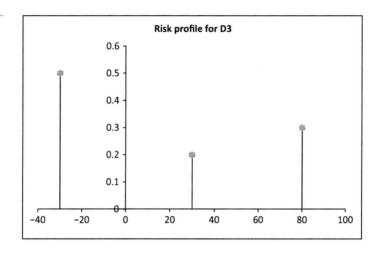

Risk profile for D3

*A risk profile shows the complete probability distribution of monetary outcomes, but you typically use only its mean, the EMV, for making decisions.*

Note that the EMV for any decision is a summary measure of the complete risk profile—it is the *mean* of the corresponding probability distribution. Therefore, when you use the EMV criterion for making decisions, you are not using *all* of the information in the risk profiles; you are comparing only their means. Nevertheless, risk profiles can be useful as extra information for making decisions. For example, a manager who sees too much risk in the risk profile of the EMV-maximizing decision might choose to override this decision and instead choose a somewhat less risky alternative.

We now apply all of these concepts to the following example.

EXAMPLE **9.1 BIDDING FOR A GOVERNMENT CONTRACT AT SCITOOLS**

SciTools Incorporated, a company that specializes in scientific instruments, has been invited to make a bid on a government contract. The contract calls for a specific number of these instruments to be delivered during the coming year. The bids must be sealed, so that no company knows what the others are bidding, and the low bid wins the contract. SciTools estimates that it will cost $5000 to prepare a bid and $95,000 to supply the instruments if it wins the contract. On the basis of past contracts of this type, SciTools believes that the possible low bids from the competition, if there is any competition, and the associated probabilities are those shown in Table 9.2. In addition, SciTools believes there is a 30% chance that there will be *no* competing bids. What should SciTools bid to maximize its EMV?

**Objective**   To develop a decision model that finds the EMV for various bidding strategies and indicates the best bidding strategy.

Table 9.2   Data for Bidding Example

| Low Bid | Probability |
| --- | --- |
| Less than $115,000 | 0.2 |
| Between $115,000 and $120,000 | 0.4 |
| Between $120,000 and $125,000 | 0.3 |
| Greater than $125,000 | 0.1 |

## WHERE DO THE NUMBERS COME FROM?

The company has probably done a thorough cost analysis to estimate its cost to prepare a bid and its cost to manufacture the instruments if it wins the contract. (Actually, even if there is uncertainty in the manufacturing cost, the only value required for the decision problem is the *mean* manufacturing cost.) The company's estimates of whether, or how, the competition will bid are probably based on previous bidding experience and some subjectivity. This is discussed in more detail next.

## Solution

Let's examine the three elements of SciTools's problem. First, SciTools has two basic strategies: submit a bid or do not submit a bid. If SciTools submits a bid, then it must decide how much to bid. Based on the cost to SciTools to prepare the bid and supply the instruments, there is clearly no point in bidding less than $100,000—SciTools wouldn't make a profit even if it won the bid. (Actually, this isn't totally true. Looking ahead to future contracts, SciTools might make a low bid just to "get in the game" and gain experience. However, we won't consider such a possibility here.) Although any bid amount over $100,000 might be considered, the data in Table 9.2 suggest that SciTools might limit its choices to $115,000, $120,000, and $125,000.[3]

The next element of the problem involves the uncertain outcomes and their probabilities. We have assumed that SciTools knows exactly how much it will cost to prepare a bid and how much it will cost to supply the instruments if it wins the bid. (In reality, these are probably only estimates of the actual costs, and a follow-up study could perform a sensitivity analysis on these quantities.) Therefore, the only source of uncertainty is the behavior of the competitors—will they bid, and if so, how much? From SciTools's standpoint, this is difficult information to obtain. The behavior of the competitors depends on (1) how many competitors are likely to bid and (2) how the competitors assess *their* costs of supplying the instruments. Nevertheless, we assume that SciTools has been involved in similar bidding contests in the past and can reasonably predict competitor behavior from past competitor behavior. The result of such prediction is the assessed probability distribution in Table 9.2 and the 30% estimate of the probability of no competing bids.

The last element of the problem is the value model that transforms decisions and outcomes into monetary values for SciTools. The value model is straightforward in this example. If SciTools decides not to bid, its monetary value is $0—no gain, no loss. If it makes a bid and is underbid by a competitor, it loses $5000, the cost of preparing the bid. If it bids $B$ dollars and wins the contract, it makes a profit of $B$ minus $100,000— that is, $B$ dollars for winning the bid, minus $5000 for preparing the bid and $95,000 for supplying the instruments. For example, if it bids $115,000 and the lowest competing bid, if any, is greater than $115,000, then SciTools wins the bid and makes a profit of $15,000.

[3]The problem with a bid such as $117,000 is that the data in Table 9.2 make it impossible to calculate the probability of SciTools winning the contract if it bids this amount. Other than this, however, there is nothing that rules out such "in-between" bids.

## Developing the Payoff Table

The corresponding payoff table, along with probabilities of outcomes, appears in Table 9.3. At the bottom of the table, the probabilities of the various outcomes are listed. For example, the probability that the competitors' low bid is less than $115,000 is 0.7 (the probability of at least one competing bid) multiplied by 0.2 (the probability that the lowest competing bid is less than $115,000).

**Table 9.3  Payoff Table for SciTools Bidding Example**

|  |  | No bid | <115 | >115, <120 | >120, <125 | >125 |
|---|---|---|---|---|---|---|
|  |  | | Competitors' Low Bid ($1000s) | | | |
| **SciTools' Bid** | **No** | 0 | 0 | 0 | 0 | 0 |
| **($1000s)** | **bid** | | | | | |
|  | **115** | 15 | −5 | 15 | 15 | 15 |
|  | **120** | 20 | −5 | −5 | 20 | 20 |
|  | **125** | 25 | −5 | −5 | −5 | 25 |
| **Probability** | | 0.3 | 0.7(0.2) = 0.14 | 0.7(0.4) = 0.28 | 0.7(0.3) = 0.21 | 0.7(0.1) = 0.07 |

It is sometimes possible to simplify a payoff table to better understand the essence of the problem. In the present example, if SciTools bids, the only necessary information about the competitors' bid(s) is whether SciTools has the lowest bid. That is, SciTools really only cares whether it wins the contract. Therefore, an alternative way of presenting the payoff table is shown in Table 9.4. (See the file SciTools Bidding Decision 1.xlsx for these and other calculations. However, we urge you to work this problem on a piece of paper with a calculator, just for practice with the concepts.)

**Table 9.4  Alternative Payoff Table for SciTools Bidding Example**

|  |  | Monetary Value | | Probability That SciTools Wins |
|---|---|---|---|---|
|  |  | SciTools Wins | SciTools Loses |  |
| | **No Bid** | NA | 0 | 0.00 |
| **SciTools' Bid ($1000s)** | **115** | 15 | −5 | 0.86 |
| | **120** | 20 | −5 | 0.58 |
| | **125** | 25 | −5 | 0.37 |

The Monetary Value columns of this table indicate the payoffs to SciTools, depending on whether it wins or loses the bid. The rightmost column shows the probability that SciTools wins the bid for each possible decision. For example, if SciTools bids $120,000, then it wins the bid if there are no competing bids (probability 0.3) *or* if there are competing bids and the lowest of these is greater than $120,000 [probability 0.7(0.3 + 0.1) = 0.28]. In this case the total probability that SciTools wins the bid is 0.3 + 0.28 = 0.58.

## Developing the Risk Profiles

Table 9.4 contains all the required information to obtain a risk profile for each of SciTools's decisions. Again, each risk profile indicates all possible monetary values and their corresponding probabilities in a spike chart. For example, if SciTools bids $120,000, there are two monetary values possible, a profit of $20,000 and a loss of $5000, and their probabilities are 0.58 and 0.42, respectively. The corresponding risk profile, shown in Figure 9.4, is a spike chart with two spikes, one above −$5000 with height 0.42 and one above $20,000 with height 0.58. On the other hand, if SciTools decides not to bid, there is a sure monetary value of $0—no profit, no

Figure 9.4

Risk Profile for a Bid
of $120,000

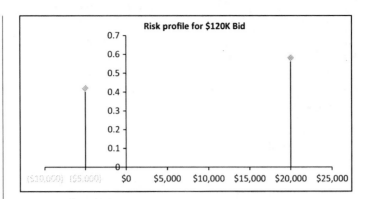

loss. Therefore, the risk profile for the "no bid" decision, not shown here, has a single spike
above $0 with height 1.

### Calculating EMVs

The EMVs for SciTools's problem are listed in Table 9.5. As always, each EMV (other than
the EMV of $0 for not bidding) is a sum of products of monetary outcomes and probabili-
ties. These EMVs indicate that if SciTools uses the EMV criterion for making its decision,
it should bid $115,000. The EMV from this bid, $12,200, is the largest of the EMVs.

**Table 9.5    EMVs for SciTools Bidding Example**

| Alternative | EMV Calculation | EMV |
|---|---|---|
| No bid | 0(1) | $0 |
| Bid $115,000 | 15,000(0.86) + (−5000)(0.14) | $12,200 |
| Bid $120,000 | 20,000(0.58) + (−5000)(0.42) | $9500 |
| Bid $125,000 | 25,000(0.37) + (−5000)(0.63) | $6100 |

As discussed previously, it is important to understand what an EMV implies and what
it does not imply. If SciTools bids $115,000, its EMV is $12,200. However, SciTools will
definitely *not* earn a profit of $12,200. It will earn $15,000 or it will lose $5000. The EMV
of $12,200 represents only a weighted average of these two possible values. Nevertheless,
it is the value that is used as the decision criterion. In words, if SciTools is truly an EMV
maximizer, it considers this gamble equivalent to a sure return of $12,200.

### Developing the Decision Tree

The corresponding decision tree for this problem is shown in Figure 9.5. This is a direct
translation of the payoff table and EMV calculations. The company first makes a bidding

Figure 9.5

Decision Tree for
SciTools Bidding
Example

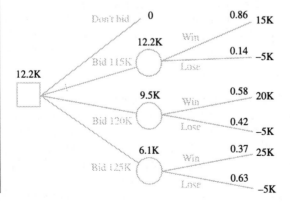

decision, then observes what the competition bids, if anything, and finally receives a payoff. The folding-back process is equivalent to the calculations shown in Table 9.5.

There are often equivalent ways to structure a decision tree. One alternative for this example appears in Figure 9.6. This tree shows exactly how the problem unfolds. The company first decides whether to bid at all. If the company does not make a bid, the profit is a sure $0. Otherwise, the company then decides how much to bid. Note that if the company decides to bid, it incurs a sure cost of $5000, so this cost is placed under the Bid branch. It is a common procedure to place the monetary values on the branches where they occur in time, and we typically do so. Once the company decides how much to bid, it then observes whether there is any competition. If there isn't any, the company wins the bid for sure and makes a corresponding profit. Otherwise, if there is competition, the company eventually discovers whether it wins or loses the bid, with the corresponding probabilities and payoffs. Note that these payoffs are placed below the branches where they occur in time. Also, the *cumulative* payoffs are placed at the ends of the branches. Each cumulative payoff is the sum of all payoffs on branches that lead to that end node.

**Figure 9.6**

**Equivalent Decision Tree for SciTools Bidding Example**

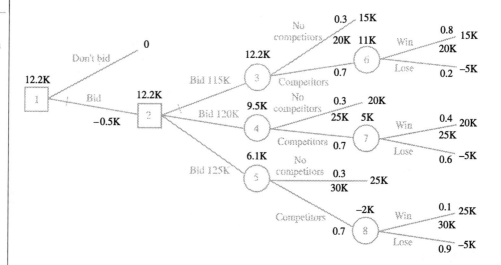

## Folding Back the Decision Tree

The folding-back procedure is somewhat more complex than it was for the smaller tree in Figure 9.5. To illustrate, the nodes in Figure 9.6 have been numbered for reference. The EMVs above a selected few of these nodes are calculated as follows:

- Node 7: EMV = $20000(0.40) + (-5000)(0.60) = \$5000$ (uses monetary values from end nodes)
- Node 4: EMV = $20000(0.30) + (5000)(0.70) = \$9500$ (uses monetary value from an end node and the EMV from node 7)
- Node 2: EMV = $\max(12200, 9500, 6100) = \$12{,}200$ (uses EMVs from nodes 3, 4, and 5)
- Node 1: EMV = $\max(0, 12200) = \$12{,}200$ (uses monetary value from an end node and EMV from node 2)

The results are the same, regardless of whether you use the table of EMVs in Table 9.5, the decision tree in Figure 9.5, or the decision tree in Figure 9.6, because they all calculate the same EMVs in equivalent ways. In each case, the bottom line is that the company should bid $115,000, with a resulting EMV of $12,200. Of course, this decision is not *guaranteed* to produce a good outcome for the company. For example, the competition could bid less than

$115,000, in which case SciTools would lose $5000. Alternatively, the competition could bid more than $120,000, in which case SciTools would be kicking itself for not bidding $120,000 and gaining an extra $5000 in profit. Unfortunately, in problems with uncertainty, there is virtually never a guarantee that the optimal decision will produce the best result. The only guarantee is that the EMV-maximizing decision is the most rational decision, given the information known when the decision must be made.

## Sensitivity Analysis

The next step in the SciTools decision analysis is to perform a sensitivity analysis. You will eventually see that PrecisionTree, an Excel add-in that helps automate the decision-making process, has some powerful sensitivity analysis tools. However, it is also possible to use Excel data tables. One example is shown in Figure 9.7. (See the finished version of the file SciTools Bidding Decision 1.xlsx.) The EMVs are calculated in column G, exactly as described previously. Then you can find the maximum of these in cell B21, and you can use the following nested IF formula in cell B22 to find the decision from column B that achieves this maximum:

```
=INDEX(B16:B19,MATCH(B21,G16:G19,0))
```

This formula checks which EMV in column G matches the maximum EMV in cell B21 and returns the corresponding decision from column B. (This combination of the INDEX and MATCH functions is often useful for finding the value that corresponds to a maximum or minimum. For an explanation of this combination, see the Excel Tutorial.xlsx file that accompanies this book.)

**Figure 9.7** Sensitivity Analysis with a Data Table

| | A | B | C | D | E | F | G |
|---|---|---|---|---|---|---|---|
| 1 | SciTools Bidding Example | | | | | | |
| 2 | | | | | | | |
| 3 | Inputs | | | | | | |
| 4 | Cost to prepare a bid | $5,000 | | Range names used: | | | |
| 5 | Cost to supply instruments | $95,000 | | BidCost | =Data!$B$4 | | |
| 6 | | | | PrNoBid | =Data!$B$7 | | |
| 7 | Probability of no competing bid | 0.3 | | ProdCost | =Data!$B$5 | | |
| 8 | Comp bid distribution (if they bid) | | | | | | |
| 9 | <$115K | 0.2 | | | | | |
| 10 | $115K to $120K | 0.4 | | | | | |
| 11 | $120K to $125K | 0.3 | | | | | |
| 12 | >$125K | 0.1 | | | | | |
| 13 | | | | | | | |
| 14 | EMV analysis | | Monetary outcomes | | Probabilities | | |
| 15 | | | SciTools wins | SciTools loses | SciTools wins | SciTools loses | EMV |
| 16 | | No bid | NA | 0 | 0 | 1 | $0 |
| 17 | SciTools' Bid | $115,000 | $15,000 | -$5,000 | 0.86 | 0.14 | $12,200 |
| 18 | | $120,000 | $20,000 | -$5,000 | 0.58 | 0.42 | $9,500 |
| 19 | | $125,000 | $25,000 | -$5,000 | 0.37 | 0.63 | $6,100 |
| 20 | | | | | | | |
| 21 | Maximum EMV | $12,200 | | | | | |
| 22 | Best decision | $115,000 | | | | | |
| 23 | | | | | | | |
| 24 | Data table for sensitivity analysis | | | | | | |
| 25 | Probability of no competing bid | Maximum EMV | Best decision | | | | |
| 26 | | $12,200 | $115,000 | | | | |
| 27 | 0.2 | $11,800 | $115,000 | | | | |
| 28 | 0.3 | $12,200 | $115,000 | | | | |
| 29 | 0.4 | $12,600 | $115,000 | | | | |
| 30 | 0.5 | $13,000 | $115,000 | | | | |
| 31 | 0.6 | $14,200 | $125,000 | | | | |
| 32 | 0.7 | $16,900 | $125,000 | | | | |

Once the formulas in cells B21 and B22 have been entered, the data table is easy. In Figure 9.7 the probability of no competing bid is allowed to vary from 0.2 to 0.7. The data table shows how the optimal EMV increases over this range. Also, its third column shows that the $115,000 bid is optimal for small values of the input, but that a $125,000 bid becomes optimal for larger values. The main point here is that if you set up a spreadsheet model that links all of the EMV calculations to the inputs, it is easy to use data tables to perform sensitivity analyses on selected inputs. ∎

# PROBLEMS

*Solutions for problems whose numbers appear within a colored box can be found in the Student Solutions Files. Refer to this book's preface for purchase information.*

## Skill-Building Problems

1. For the example in Simple Decision Problem.xlsx, are there any probabilities that make the EMV criterion equivalent to the maximin criterion? Are there any probabilities that make the EMV criterion equivalent to the maximax criterion? Explain.

2. Using a data table in Excel, perform a sensitivity analysis on the example in Simple Decision Problem.xlsx. Specifically, keep the probabilities in row 10 (for *D2*) as they are, but vary the probability in cell C11 from 0 to 1 in increments of 0.05, and keep the probabilities in cells D11 and E11 in the same ratio as they are currently (2 to 3).

3. In the SciTools example, make two changes: change all references to $115,000 to $110,000, and change all references to $125,000 to $130,000. Rework the EMV calculations and the decision tree. What is the best decision and its corresponding EMV?

4. In the SciTools example, which decision would a maximin decision maker choose? Which decision would a maximax decision maker choose? Would you defend either of these criteria for this particular example? Explain.

5. In the SciTools example, use a two-way data table to see how (or whether) the optimal decision changes as the bid cost and the company's production cost change simultaneously. Let the bid cost vary from $2000 to $8000 in increments of $1000, and let the production cost vary from $90,000 to $105,000 in increments of $2500. Explain your results.

6. In the SciTools example, the probabilities for the low bid of competitors, given that there is at least one competing bid, are currently 0.2, 0.4, 0.3, and 0.1. Let the second of these be *p*, and let the others sum to $1 - p$ but keep the same ratios to one another: 2 to 3 to 1. Use a one-way data table to see how (or whether) the optimal decision changes as *p* varies from 0.1 to 0.7 in increments of 0.05. Explain your results.

## Skill-Extending Problems

7. For the example in Simple Decision Problem.xlsx, we found that decision *D3* is the EMV-maximizing decision for the given probabilities. See whether you can find probabilities that make decision *D1* the best. If the probabilities in row 10 (for *D2*) are the same as the probabilities in row 11 (for *D3*), is it possible for *D2* to be the best decision? What if these two rows are allowed to be different? Qualitatively, how can you explain the results? That is, which types of probabilities tend to favor the various decisions? (*Hint:* To search for probabilities where *D2* is better than the other two decisions, given that rows 10 and 11 are the same, you can use Solver.)

8. A decision *d* is said to be *dominated* by another decision *D* if, for every outcome, the payoff from *D* is better than (or no worse than) the payoff from *d*.
   a. Explain why you would never choose a dominated decision using the maximin criterion, the maximax criterion, or the EMV criterion.
   b. Are any of the decisions in the example in Simple Decision Problem.xlsx dominated by any others? What about in the SciTools example?

9. Besides the maximin, maximax, and EMV criteria, there are other possible criteria for making decisions. One possibility involves *regret*. The idea behind regret is that if you make any decision and then some outcome occurs, you look at that outcome's column in the payoff table to see how much more you could have made if you had chosen the best payoff in that column. For example, if the decision you make and the outcome you observe lead to a $50 payoff, and if the highest payoff in this outcome's column is $80, then your regret is $30. You regret looking back and seeing how much more you could have made, if only you had made a different decision. Therefore, you calculate the regret for each cell in the payoff table (as the maximum payoff in that column minus the payoff in that cell), calculate the maximum regret in each row, and choose the row with the smallest maximum regret. This is called the *minimax regret criterion.*

**a.** Apply this criterion to the example in Simple Decision Problem.xlsx. Which decision do you choose?

**b.** Repeat part **a** for the SciTools example.

**c.** In general, discuss potential strengths and weaknesses of this decision criterion.

**10.** Referring to the previous problem, another possible criterion is called *expected regret*. Here you calculate the regret for each cell, take a weighted average of these regrets in each row, weighted by the probabilities of the outcomes, and choose the decision with the smallest expected regret.

**a.** Apply this criterion to the SciTools example. Which decision do you choose?

**b.** The expected regret criterion is actually *equivalent* to the EMV criterion, in that they always lead to the same decisions. Argue why this is true.

In the SciTools example, you might argue that there is a *continuum* of possible low competitor bids (given that there is at least one competing bid), not just four possibilities. In fact, assume the low competitor bid in this case is normally distributed with mean $118,000 and standard deviation $4500. Also, assume that SciTools will still either not bid or bid $115,000, $120,000, or $125,000. Use Excel's NORMDIST function to find the EMV for each alternative. Which is the best decision now? Why can't this be represented in a decision tree?

## 9.3 THE PRECISIONTREE ADD-IN

Decision trees present a challenge for Excel. We must somehow take advantage of Excel's calculating capabilities (to calculate EMVs, for example) and its graphical capabilities (to depict the decision tree). Fortunately, there is a powerful add-in, **PrecisionTree**, developed by Palisade Corporation, that makes the process relatively straightforward. This add-in not only enables you to draw and label a decision tree, but it performs the folding-back procedure automatically and then allows you to perform sensitivity analysis on key input parameters.

The first thing you must do to use PrecisionTree is to "add it in." We assume you have already installed the Palisade DecisionTools suite. Then to run PrecisionTree, you have two options:

※ If Excel is not currently running, you can launch Excel *and* PrecisionTree by clicking on the Windows Start button and selecting the PrecisionTree item from the Palisade Decision Tools group in the list of Programs.

※ If Excel is currently running, the first procedure will launch PrecisionTree on top of Excel.

You will know that PrecisionTree is ready for use when you see its tab and the associated ribbon (shown in Figure 9.8). If you want to unload PrecisionTree *without* closing Excel, you can do so from its Utilities dropdown list in the Tools group.

**Figure 9.8  PrecisionTree Ribbon**

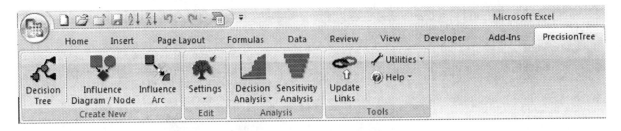

### The Decision Tree Model

PrecisionTree is quite easy to use—at least its most basic items are. We will lead you through the steps for the SciTools example. Figure 9.9 shows the results of this procedure, just so that you can see what you are working toward. (See the file SciTools Bidding Decision 2.xlsx.)

However, we recommend that you work through the steps on your own, starting with a blank spreadsheet.

**Figure 9.9  Completed Tree from PrecisionTree**

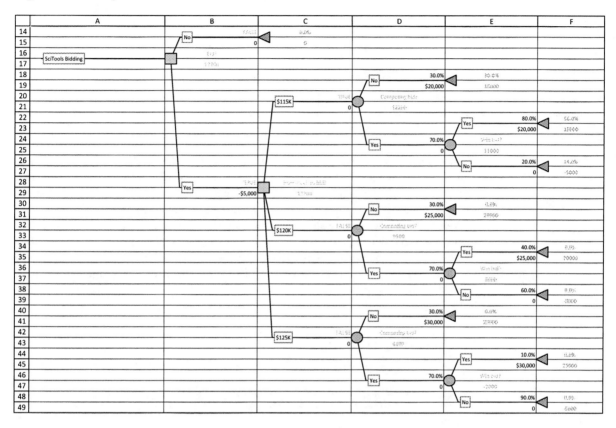

## BUILDING THE DECISION TREE

**①  Inputs.** Enter the inputs shown in columns A and B of Figure 9.10. (We have listed the possible bids in column D so that they can be linked through formulas in the tree.)

**Figure 9.10  Inputs for SciTools Bidding Example**

| | A | B | C | D | E |
|---|---|---|---|---|---|
| 1 | SciTools Bidding Decision | | | | |
| 2 | | | | | |
| 3 | Inputs | | | Range names used: | |
| 4 | Cost to prepare a bid | $5,000 | | BidCost | =Model!$B$4 |
| 5 | Cost to supply instruments | $95,000 | | PrNoBid | =Model!$B$7 |
| 6 | | | | ProductionCost | =Model!$B$5 |
| 7 | Probability of no competing bid | 0.3 | | | |
| 8 | Comp bid distribution (if they bid) | | | SciTools's possible bids | |
| 9 | <$115K | 0.2 | | $115,000 | |
| 10 | $115K to $120K | 0.4 | | $120,000 | |
| 11 | $120K to $125K | 0.3 | | $125,000 | |
| 12 | >$125K | 0.1 | | | |

②  **New tree.** Click on the Decision Tree button on the PrecisionTree ribbon, and then select cell A14 below the input section to start a new tree. You will immediately see a dialog box where, among other things, you can name the tree. Enter a descriptive name for the tree, such as SciTools Bidding, and click on OK. You should now see the beginnings of a tree, as shown in Figure 9.11.

**Figure 9.11**   Beginnings of a New Tree

| | A | B | C |
|---|---|---|---|
| 14 | SciTools Bidding | 100.0% | |
| 15 | | 0 | |

③  **Decision nodes and branches.** From here on, keep the tree in Figure 9.9 in mind. This is the finished product you eventually want. To obtain decision nodes and branches, select the (only) triangle end node to open the dialog box in Figure 9.12. Click on the green square to indicate that you want a decision node, and fill in the dialog box as shown. Then click on the Branches (2) tab and supply labels for the branches under Name, as shown in Figure 9.13. By default, you get two branches, which is what you want in this case. However, if you wanted more than two branches, you would click on Add to get additional branches. The tree expands as shown in Figure 9.14. Under the "Yes" branch, enter the following link to the bid cost cell:

=–BidCost

(Note that it is negative to reflect a *cost*.)

**Figure 9.12**

Dialog Box for Adding a New Decision Node and Branches

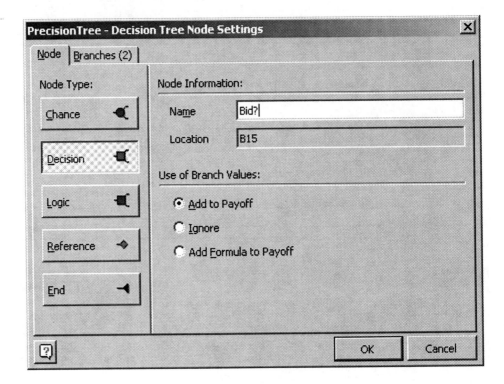

Figure 9.13    Dialog Box for Adding or Labeling Branches

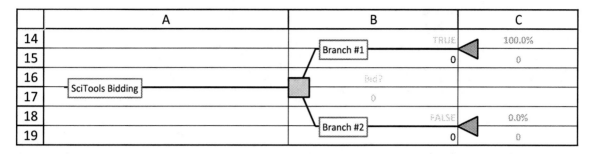

Figure 9.14    Decision Tree with Decision Branches Labeled

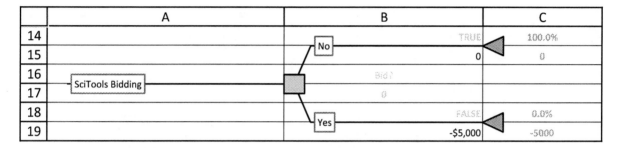

**PrecisionTree Tip:  *Allowable Entries***

*On your computer screen, you will note the color-coding PrecisionTree uses. If you investigate any colored (nonblack) cells, you will see strange formulas that PrecisionTree uses for its own purposes. You should not modify these formulas. You should enter your own probabilities and monetary values only in the cells with black font.*

④ **More decision branches.** The top branch is completed; if SciTools does not bid, there is nothing left to do. So click on the bottom end node (the triangle), following SciTools's decision to bid, and proceed as in the previous step to add and label the decision node and three decision branches for the amount to bid. (Again, refer to Figure 9.9.) The tree to this point should appear as in Figure 9.15. Note that there are no monetary values below these decision branches because no *immediate* payoffs or costs are associated with the bid amount decision.

Figure 9.15    Tree with All Decision Nodes and Branches

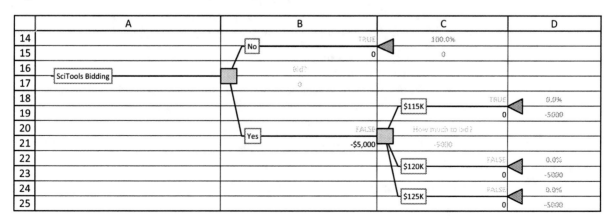

**5** **Probability nodes and branches.** Using the same procedure (and using Figure 9.9 as a guide), create probability nodes extending from the "bid $115,000" decision. You should have the skeleton in Figure 9.16.

**Figure 9.16** Decision Tree with One Set of Probability Nodes and Branches

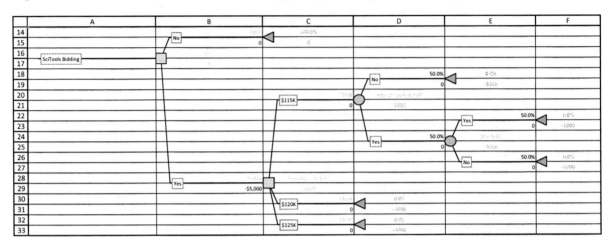

**6** **Copying probability nodes and branches.** You could now repeat the same procedure from the previous step to build probability nodes and branches following the other bid amount decisions, but because they are structurally equivalent, you can save a lot of work by using PrecisionTree's copy and paste feature. Right-click on the leftmost probability node and click on Copy SubTree. Then right-click on either end node below it and click on Paste SubTree. Do this again with the other end node. Decision trees can get very "bushy," but this copy and paste feature can make them much less tedious to construct.

**7** **Enter probabilities on probability branches.** You should now have the decision tree shown in Figure 9.17. It is structurally the same as the completed tree in Figure 9.9, but the probabilities and monetary values on the probability branches are incorrect. Note that each probability branch has a value above and below the branch. The value above is the probability (the default values make the branches equally likely), and the value below is the monetary value (the default values are 0). You can enter any values or formulas in these cells (remember, the cells with black font only), exactly as you do in typical Excel worksheets. As usual, it is a good practice to enter cell references, not numbers, whenever possible. In addition, range names can be used instead of cell addresses.

PrecisionTree Tip: *Sum of Probabilities*
*PrecisionTree does not enforce the rule that probabilities on branches leading out of a node must sum to 1. You must enforce this rule with appropriate formulas.*

PrecisionTree Tip: *Entering Monetary Values, Probabilities*
*A good practice is to calculate all of the monetary values and probabilities that will be needed in the decision tree in some other area of the spreadsheet. Then the values needed next to the tree branches can be created with simple linking formulas.*

We will get you started with the probability branches following the decision to bid $115,000. First, enter the probability of no competing bid in cell D18 with the formula

=PrNoBid

and enter its complement in cell D24 with the formula

=1-D18

Figure 9.17   Structure of Completed Tree

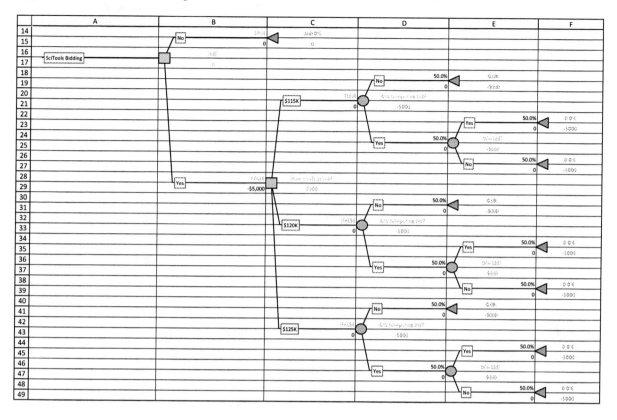

Next, enter the probability that SciTools wins the bid in cell E22 with the formula

=SUM(B10:B12)

and enter its complement in cell E26 with the formula

=1-E22

(Remember that SciTools wins the bid only if the competition bids higher, and in this part of the tree, SciTools is bidding $115,000.) For the monetary values, enter the formula

=D9-ProductionCost

in the two cells, D19 and E23, where SciTools wins the contract. Note that the cost of the bid was already subtracted in cell B29, so it should *not* be subtracted again. This would be double-counting, which you should always avoid in decision trees.

**8** **Enter the other formulas on probability branches.** Using the previous step and Figure 9.9 as a guide, enter formulas for the probabilities and monetary values on the other probability branches, those following the decision to bid $120,000 or $125,000.

PrecisionTree Tip:  *Copying Subtrees*
*Before taking advantage of PrecisionTree's subtree copying capability , it is generally a good idea to fill the subtree as much as possible (with labels, probabilities, and monetary values). In this way, the copies will require less work. Note that formulas on the subtree are copied in the usual Excel way (in terms of relative and absolute references), so that the formulas on the copies often have to be adjusted slightly. In this example, you could have sped up the process slightly by completing step 7 before copying. Then step 8 would entail only a few formula adjustments on the copied subtrees.*

### Interpreting the Decision Tree

*To find the optimal decision strategy in any PrecisionTree tree, follow the TRUE labels.*

You are finished! The completed tree in Figure 9.9 shows the best strategy and its associated EMV, as we discussed previously. In fact, a comparison of the decision tree in Figure 9.6 that was created manually and the tree from PrecisionTree in Figure 9.9 indicates virtually identical results. The best decision strategy is now indicated by the TRUE and FALSE labels above the decision branches (rather than the notches we entered by hand). Each TRUE corresponds to the optimal decision out of a decision node, whereas each FALSE corresponds to a suboptimal decision. Therefore, you simply follow the TRUE labels. In this case, the company should bid, and its bid amount should be $115,000.

Note that you do *not* have to perform the folding-back procedure manually. PrecisionTree does this for you. Essentially, the tree is completed as soon as you finish entering the relevant inputs. In addition, if you change any of the inputs, the tree reacts automatically. For example, try changing the bid cost in cell B4 from $5000 to some large value such as $20,000. You will see that the tree calculations update automatically, and the best decision is then *not* to bid, with an associated EMV of $0.

### PrecisionTree Tip: *Values at End Nodes*

*You will notice that there are two values following each triangle end node. The bottom value is the sum of all monetary values on branches leading to this end node. The top value is the probability of getting to this end node when the optimal strategy is used. This explains why many of these probabilities are 0; the optimal strategy will never lead to these end nodes.*

### Policy Suggestion and Risk Profile for Optimal Strategy

*The Policy Suggestion shows only the subtree corresponding to the optimal decision strategy.*

Once the decision tree is completed, PrecisionTree has several tools you can use to gain more information about the decision analysis. First, you can see a subtree (called a Policy Suggestion) for the *optimal* decision. To do so, choose Policy Suggestion from the Decision Analysis dropdown list and fill in the resulting dialog box as shown in Figure 9.18. (You can experiment with other options.) The Policy Suggestion option shows only the part of the tree that corresponds to the best decision, as shown in Figure 9.19.

**Figure 9.18**

**Dialog Box for Information about Optimal Decision**

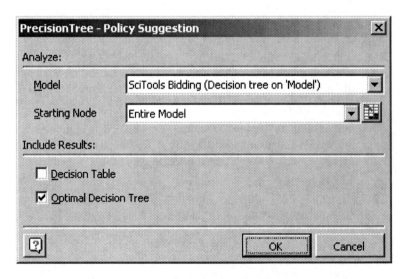

You can also obtain a graphical risk profile of the optimal decision by selecting Risk Profile from the Decision Analysis dropdown list and filling in the resulting dialog box as shown in Figure 9.20. (Again, you can experiment with the other options.) As the risk profile in Figure 9.21 indicates, there are only two possible monetary outcomes if SciTools bids $115,000. It either wins $15,000 or loses $5000, and the former is much more likely.

**Figure 9.19** Subtree for Optimal Decision

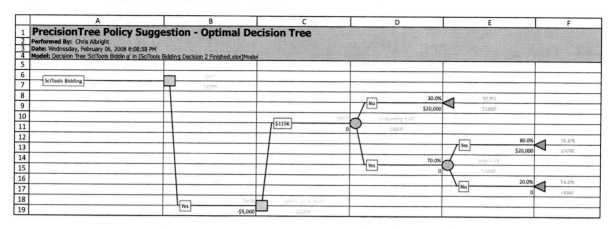

**Figure 9.20**

Risk Profile Dialog Box

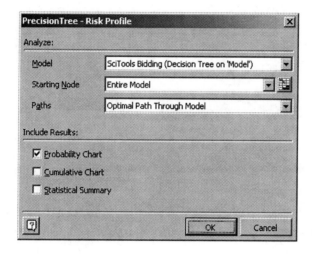

**Figure 9.21**

Risk Profile of Optimal Decision

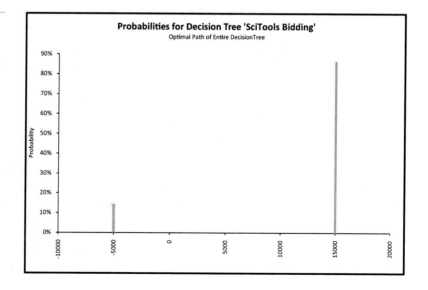

(The associated probabilities are 0.86 and 0.14, respectively.) This graphical information is even more useful when there are a larger number of possible monetary outcomes. You can see what they are and how likely they are.

### Sensitivity Analysis

We have already stressed the importance of a follow-up sensitivity analysis to any decision problem, and PrecisionTree makes this relatively easy to perform. Of course, you can enter any values in the input cells and watch how the tree changes, but you can obtain more systematic information by clicking on PrecisionTree's Sensitivity Analysis button. This brings up the dialog box in Figure 9.22. Although it has a lot of options, it is easy to use once you understand the ideas behind it. Here are the main options and how to use them.

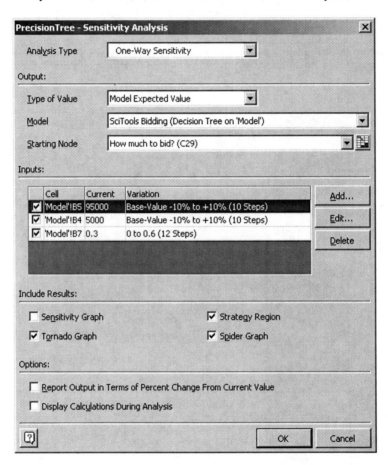

■ The Analysis Type dropdown list allows you to vary one input (One-Way Sensitivity) or two inputs (Two-Way Sensitivity) simultaneously.

■ The Starting Node dropdown list lets you choose any node in the tree, and the sensitivity analysis is then performed for the EMV *from that node to the right.* In other words, it assumes you have gotten to that node and are now interested in what will happen from then on. The node selected in the figure, C29, is the leftmost node, so by selecting it, the sensitivity analysis is on the EMV of the entire tree. This is the most common setting.

■ You add inputs to vary in the Inputs section. You can add as many as you like, and all of the checked inputs are included in any particular sensitivity analysis. When you add an input to this section, you can specify the range over which you want it to vary. For example, you can vary it by plus or minus 10% in 10 steps from a selected base value, as we did for the production cost in cell B5, or you can vary it from 0 to 0.6 in 12 steps, as we did for the probability of no competing bids in cell B7.

▦ The Include Results checkboxes allow you to select up to four types of charts, depending on the type of sensitivity analysis. (The bottom two options are disabled for a two-way sensitivity analysis.) You can experiment with these options, but we will illustrate our favorites shortly.

When you click on OK, PrecisionTree varies each of the checked inputs in the middle section, one at a time if you select the One-Way option, and presents the results in new worksheets. By default, these new worksheets are placed in a new workbook. If you would rather have them in the same workbook as the model, click on the PrecisionTree Utilities dropdown arrow, select Application Settings, and select Active Workbook from the Replace Reports In option. (This is a global setting. It will take effect for all future PrecisionTree analyses.)

### Strategy Region Chart

*In strategy region charts, the primary interest is in where (or whether) lines cross. This is where decisions change.*

Figure 9.23 illustrates **a strategy region chart** from a one-way analysis. This chart shows how the EMV varies with the production cost for *both* of the original decisions (bid or don't bid). This type of chart is useful for seeing whether the optimal decision *changes* over the range of the input variable. It does so only if the two lines cross. In this particular graph it is clear that the "Bid" decision dominates the "No bid" decision over the selected production cost range.

**Figure 9.23**

EMV Versus
Production Cost for
Each of Two
Decisions

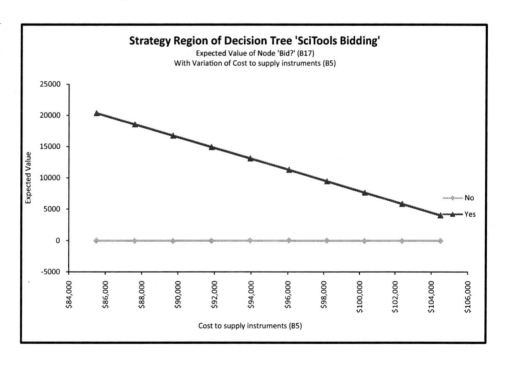

### Tornado Chart

*Tornado charts and spider charts indicate which inputs the selected EMV is most sensitive to.*

A **tornado chart** shows how sensitive the EMV of the *optimal* decision is to each of the selected inputs over the specified ranges. (See Figure 9.24.) The length of each bar shows the change in the EMV in either direction, so inputs with longer bars have a greater effect on the selected EMV. (If you checked the next-to-bottom checkbox in Figure 9.22, the lengths of the bars would indicate *percentage* changes from the base value.) The bars are always arranged from longest on top to shortest on the bottom—hence the name *tornado* chart. Here it is apparent that production cost has the largest effect on EMV, and bid cost has the smallest effect.

Figure 9.24

Tornado Chart for
SciTools Example

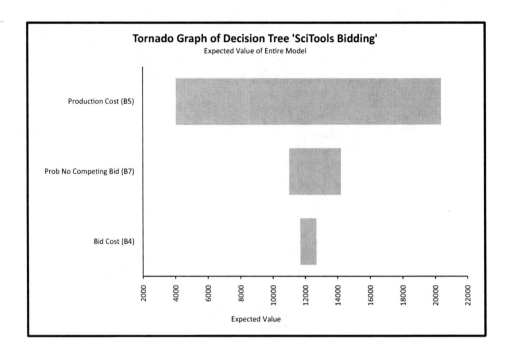

## Spider Chart

Finally, a **spider chart** shows how much the optimal EMV varies in magnitude for various percentage changes in the input variables. (See Figure 9.25.) The steeper the slope of the line, the more the EMV is affected by a particular input. It is again apparent that the production cost has a relatively large effect, whereas the other two inputs have relatively small effects.

Figure 9.25

Spider Chart for
SciTools Example

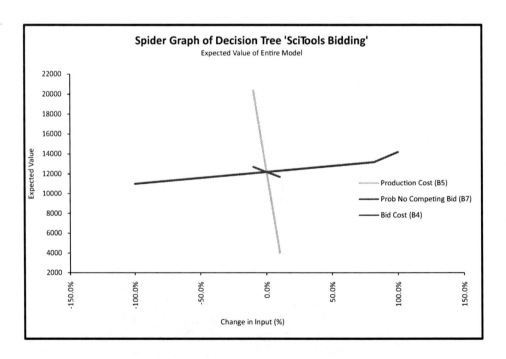

## Another Sensitivity Chart

Each time you click on the Sensitivity Analysis button, you can run a different sensitivity analysis. For example, you might want to choose cell C29 as the cell to analyze. This is the optimal EMV for the problem, *given* that the company has decided to place a bid. One interesting chart from this analysis is the strategy region chart in Figure 9.26. It indicates how the EMV varies with the probability of no competing bid for *each* of the three bid amount decisions. The $115,000 bid is best for most of the range, but when the probability of no competing bid is sufficiently large (about 0.55), the $120,000 bid becomes best (by a small margin.)

Figure 9.26

Strategy Region
Chart for Another
EMV Cell

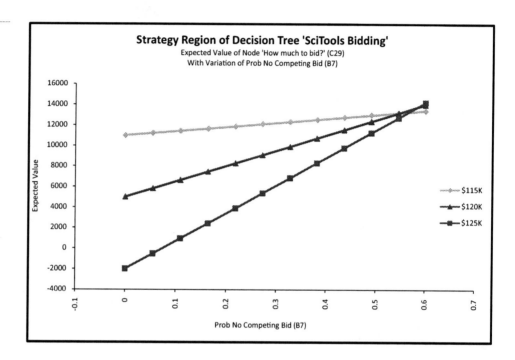

A one-way sensitivity
analysis varies only one
input at a time. A two-
way analysis varies two
inputs simultaneously.

## Two-Way Sensitivity Chart

Another interesting option is to run a two-way analysis. This shows how the selected EMV varies as each *pair* of inputs varies simultaneously. We analyzed the EMV in cell C29 with this option, using the same inputs as before. A typical result is shown in Figure 9.27. For each of the possible values of production cost and the probability of no competitor bid, this chart indicates which bid amount is optimal. (By choosing cell C29, we are assuming SciTools will bid; the only question is how much.) As you can see, the optimal bid amount remains $115,000 unless the production cost *and* the probability of no competing bid are both large. Then it becomes optimal to bid $120,000 or $125,000. This makes sense intuitively. As the probability of no competing bid increases and a larger production cost must be recovered, it seems reasonable that SciTools should increase its bid.

We reiterate that a sensitivity analysis is always an important component of any real-world decision analysis. If you had to construct decision trees by hand—with paper and pencil—a sensitivity analysis would be very tedious, to say the least. You would have to recalculate everything each time through. Therefore, one of the most valuable features of the PrecisionTree add-in is that it enables you to perform sensitivity analyses in a matter of seconds.

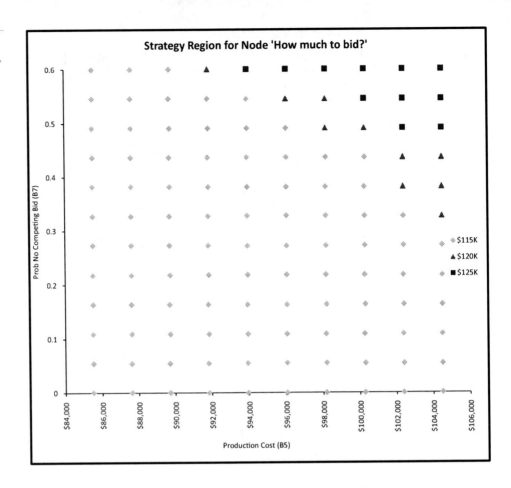

**Figure 9.27**

Two-Way Sensitivity Analysis

## PROBLEMS

### Skill-Building Problems

**12.** In a tree built with PrecisionTree, there are two blue values at each end node, the top one of which is a probability. Why are so many of these probabilities 0 in the finished tree in Figure 9.9? What do the remaining (positive) probabilities represent?

**13.** In the SciTools example, there are two equivalent decision tree structures, shown in Figures 9.5 and 9.6. Use PrecisionTree to create the first of these, and verify that it yields the same EMVs and the same optimal decision as the tree developed in this section.

**14.** For the completed decision tree in Figure 9.9, the monetary values in black are those you enter. The monetary values in color are calculated automatically by PrecisionTree. For this particular example, explain exactly how these latter values are calculated (remember the folding-back process) and what they represent. These include the blue values at the end

nodes, the red values at the probability nodes, and the green values at the decision nodes.

**15.** For the SciTools example, once you build the tree as in Figure 9.9 and then run a one-way sensitivity analysis with the dialog box filled in as in Figure 9.22, you obtain three strategy charts. (Try it.) Explain exactly what each of these charts represents. (For this problem, you can ignore the tornado and spider charts.)

**16.** The tornado chart in Figure 9.24 and the spider chart in Figure 9.25 show basically the same information in slightly different forms. Explain in words exactly what information they provide. (If necessary, consult PrecisionTree's online help.)

**17.** Explain in words what information a two-way sensitivity chart, such as the one in Figure 9.27, provides. Demonstrate how you could provide this same information without PrecisionTree's sensitivity tools, using only data tables. (You can still use the tree built with PrecisionTree.)

# 9.4 BAYES' RULE

The examples to this point have required a single decision. We now examine multistage problems, where a decision maker must make at least two decisions that are separated in time, such as when a company must first decide whether to buy information that will help it make a second decision. In multistage decision problems there are typically alternating sets of decision nodes and probability nodes. The decision maker makes a decision, some uncertainty is resolved, the decision maker makes another decision, more uncertainty is resolved, and so on. Before analyzing such problems, we must discuss one important probability issue.

In a multistage decision tree, all probability branches at the *right* of the tree are conditional on outcomes that have occurred earlier, to their left. Therefore, the probabilities on these branches are of the form $P(A|B)$, read "A given B," where A is an event corresponding to a current probability branch, and B is an event that occurs *before* event A in time. However, when gathering data for the problem, it is sometimes more natural to *assess* conditional probabilities in the opposite order, that is, $P(B|A)$. Whenever this is the case, **Bayes' rule** must be used to obtain the probabilities needed on the tree. Essentially, Bayes' rule is a mechanism for revising probabilities as new information becomes available.

To develop Bayes' rule, let $A_1$ through $A_n$ be any outcomes. Without any further information, we believe the probabilities of the As are $P(A_1)$ through $P(A_n)$. These are called **prior probabilities**. We then have the possibility of gaining some information. There are several information outcomes we might observe, a typical one of which is labeled B. We assume the probabilities of B, given that any of the As will occur, are known. These probabilities, labeled $P(B|A_1)$ through $P(B|A_n)$, are often called *likelihoods*. Because an information outcome might influence our thinking about the probabilities of the As, we need to find the conditional probability $P(A_i|B)$ for each outcome $A_i$. This is called the **posterior probability** of $A_i$. This is where Bayes' rule enters the picture. It states that we can calculate posterior probabilities from the following formula.

---

*Bayes' Rule*

$$P(A_i|B) = \frac{P(B|A_i)P(A_i)}{P(B|A_1)P(A_1) + \cdots + P(B|A_n)P(A_n)} \qquad (9.1)$$

---

In words, Bayes' rule says that the posterior is the likelihood times the prior, divided by a sum of likelihoods times priors. As a side benefit, the denominator in Bayes' rule is also useful in multistage decision trees. It is the probability $P(B)$ of the information outcome.

---

*Denominator of Bayes' Rule (Law of Total Probability)*

$$P(B) = P(B|A_1)P(A_1) + \cdots + P(B|A_1)P(A_n) \qquad (9.2)$$

---

This formula is important in its own right. For B to occur, it must occur along with one of the As. Formula 9.2) simply decomposes the probability of B into all of these possibilities. It is sometimes called the **law of total probability**.

In the case where there are only two As, labeled as A and Not A, Bayes' rule takes the following form:

$$P(A|B) = \frac{P(B|A)P(A)}{P(B|A)P(A) + P(B|\text{Not }A)P(\text{Not }A_n)} \qquad (9.3)$$

We illustrate the mechanics of Bayes' rule in the following example. [See Feinstein (1990) for a real application of this example.]

## EXAMPLE 9.2 DRUG TESTING COLLEGE ATHLETES

If an athlete is tested for a certain type of drug use (steroids, say), the test result will be either positive or negative. However, these tests are never perfect. Some drug-free athletes test positive, and some drug users test negative. The former are called *false positives*; the latter are called *false negatives*. Let's assume that 5% of all athletes use drugs, 3% of all tests on drug-free athletes yield false positives, and 7% of all tests on drug users yield false negatives. Suppose a typical athlete is tested. If this athlete tests positive, can you be sure that he is a drug user? If he tests negative, can you be sure he does not use drugs?

**Objective** To use Bayes' rule to revise the probability of being a drug user, given the positive or negative results of the test.

### WHERE DO THE NUMBERS COME FROM?

The estimate that 5% of all athletes are drug users is probably based on a well-known national average. The error rates from the tests are undoubtedly known from extensive experience with the tests. (However, we are not claiming that the numbers used here match reality.)

### Solution

Let $D$ and $ND$ denote that a randomly chosen athlete is or is not a drug user, and let $T+$ and $T-$ indicate a positive or negative test result. (The outcomes $D$ and $ND$ correspond to $A$ and Not $A$ in Equation (9.3), and either $T+$ or $T-$ corresponds to $B$.) The following probabilities are given. First, because 5% of all athletes are drug users, you know that $P(D) = 0.05$ and $P(ND) = 0.95$. These are the prior probabilities. They represent the chance that an athlete is or is not a drug user *prior* to the results of a drug test.

Second, from the information on the accuracy of the drug test, you know the conditional probabilities $P(T+|ND) = 0.03$ and $P(T-|D) = 0.07$. In addition, a drug-free athlete tests either positive or negative, and the same is true for a drug user. Therefore, you also know the probabilities $P(T-|ND) = 0.97$ and $P(T+|D) = 0.93$. These four conditional probabilities of test results given drug user status are the likelihoods of the test results.

Given these priors and likelihoods, you need to calculate posterior probabilities such as $P(D|T+)$, the probability that an athlete who tests positive is a drug user, and $P(ND|T-)$, the probability that an athlete who tests negative is drug free. They are called posterior probabilities because they are assessed *after* the drug test results.

Using Bayes' rule for two outcomes, Equation (9.3), you can calculate

$P(D|T+)$

$$= \frac{P(T+|D)P(D)}{P(T+|D)P(D) + P(T+|ND)P(ND)} = \frac{(0.93)(0.05)}{(0.93)(0.05) + (0.03)(0.95)} = 0.620$$

and

$P(ND|T-)$

$$= \frac{P(T-|ND)P(D)}{P(T-|D)P(D) + P(T-|ND)P(ND)} = \frac{(0.97)(0.95)}{(0.07)(0.05) + (0.97)(0.95)} = 0.996$$

In words, if the athlete tests positive, there is still a 38% chance that he is *not* a drug user, but if he tests negative, you are virtually sure he is not a drug user. The denominators of these two formulas are the probabilities of the test results. They can be calculated from Equation (9.2):

$$P(T+) = 0.93(0.05) + 0.03(0.95) = 0.075$$

and

$$P(T-) = 0.07(0.05) + 0.97(0.95) = 0.925$$

The first Bayes' rule result might surprise you. After all, the test is reasonably accurate, so if you observe a positive test result, you should be pretty sure that the athlete is a drug user, right? The reason the first posterior probability is "only" 0.620 is that very few athletes in the population are drug users—only 5%. Therefore, you need a lot of evidence to be convinced that a particular athlete is a drug user, and a positive test result from a somewhat inaccurate test is not enough evidence to be totally convincing. On the other hand, a negative test result simply adds confirmation to what you already suspected—that a typical athlete is *not* a drug user. This is why $P(ND|T-)$ is so close to 1.

## A More Intuitive Calculation

If you have trouble understanding or implementing Bayes' rule, you are not alone. At least one study has shown that even trained medical specialists have trouble with this type of calculation (in the context of tests for cancer). Most of us do not think intuitively about conditional probabilities. However, there is an equivalent and more intuitive way to obtain the same result.

*This alternative procedure, using counts instead of probabilities, is equivalent to Bayes' rule and is probably more intuitive.*

Imagine that there are 100,000 athletes. Because 5% of all athletes are drug users, we assume that 5000 of these athletes use drugs and the other 95,000 do not. Now we administer the test to all of them. We expect 3%, or 2850, of the nonusers to test positive (because the false-positive rate is 3%), and we expect 93%, or 4650, of the drug users to test positive (because the false-negative rate is 7%). Therefore, we observe a total of 2850 + 4650 = 7500 positives. If one of these 7500 athletes is chosen at random, what is the probability that a drug user is chosen? It is clearly

$$P(D|T+) = 4650/7500 = 0.620$$

This is the same result we got using Bayes' rule! So if you have trouble with Bayes' rule using probabilities, you can use this alternative method of using *counts*. (By the way, the 100,000 value is irrelevant. We could have used 10,000, 50,000, 1,000,000, or any other convenient value.)

## Spreadsheet Implementation of Bayes' Rule

It is fairly easy to implement Bayes' rule in a spreadsheet, as illustrated in Figure 9.28 for the drug example. (See the file Bayes Rule.xlsx.[4])

---

[4]The Bayes2 sheet in this file illustrates how Bayes' rule can be used when there are more than two possible test results and/or drug user categories.

Figure 9.28

Bayes' Rule for
Drug-Testing
Example

| | A | B | C | D | E | F |
|---|---|---|---|---|---|---|
| 1 | Illustration of Bayes' rule using drug example | | | | | |
| 2 | | | | | | |
| 3 | Prior probabilities of drug user status | | | | | |
| 4 | | User | Non-user | | | |
| 5 | | 0.05 | 0.95 | 1 | | |
| 6 | | | | | | |
| 7 | Likelihoods of test results, given drug user status | | | | | |
| 8 | | User | Non-user | | | |
| 9 | Test positive | 0.93 | 0.03 | | | |
| 10 | Test negative | 0.07 | 0.97 | | | |
| 11 | | 1 | 1 | | | |
| 12 | | | | | | |
| 13 | Unconditional probabilities of test results (denominators of Bayes' rule) | | | | | |
| 14 | Test positive | 0.075 | | | | |
| 15 | Test negative | 0.925 | | | | |
| 16 | | 1 | | | | |
| 17 | | | | | | |
| 18 | Posterior probabilities of drug user status (Bayes' rule) | | | | | |
| 19 | | User | Non-user | | | |
| 20 | Test positive | 0.620 | 0.380 | 1 | | |
| 21 | Test negative | 0.004 | 0.996 | 1 | | |

The given priors and likelihoods are listed in the ranges B5:C5 and B9:C10. You first use Equation (9.2) to calculate the denominators for Bayes' rule, the unconditional probabilities of the two possible test results, in the range B14:B15. Because each of these is a sum of products of priors and likelihoods, the formula in cell B14 is

=SUMPRODUCT($B$5:$C$5,B9:C9)

and this is copied to cell B15. Then you use Equation (9.1) to calculate the posterior probabilities in the range B20:C21. Because each of these is a product of a prior and a likelihood, divided by a denominator, the formula in cell B20 is

=B$5*B9/$B14

and this is copied to the rest of the B20:C21 range. The various 1s in the margins of Figure 9.28 are row sums or column sums that must equal 1. They are shown only as checks of the logic.

As we have noted, a positive drug test still leaves a 38% chance that the athlete is *not* a drug user. Is this a valid argument for not requiring drug testing of athletes? We explore this question in a continuation of the drug-testing example in the next section. ▨

# PROBLEMS

## Skill-Building Problems

18. For each of the following, use a one-way data table to see how the posterior probability of being a drug user, given a positive test, varies as the indicated input varies. Write a brief explanation of your results.
   a. Let the input be the prior probability of being a drug user, varied from 0.01 to 0.10 in increments of 0.01.
   b. Let the input be the probability of a false positive from the test, varied from 0 to 0.10 in increments of 0.01.
   c. Let the input be the probability of a false negative from the test, varied from 0 to 0.10 in increments of 0.01.

19. In the drug testing, assume there are three possible test results: positive, negative, and inconclusive. For a drug user, the probabilities of these outcomes are 0.65, 0.06, and 0.29. For a nonuser, they are 0.03, 0.72, and 0.25. Use Bayes' rule to find a table of all posterior probabilities. (The prior probability of

being a drug user is still 0.05.) Then answer the following.

   **a.** What is the posterior probability that the athlete is a drug user, (1) given that her test results are positive, (2) given that her test results are negative, and (3) given that her drug results are inconclusive?

   **b.** What is the probability of observing a positive test result, a negative test result, or an inconclusive test result?

**20.** Referring to the previous problem, find the same probabilities through the counting argument explained in this section. Start with 100,000 athletes and divide them into the various categories.

**21.** Suppose you are a heterosexual white male and are going to be tested to see if you are HIV positive. Assume that if you are HIV positive, your test will always come back positive. Assume that if you are not HIV positive, there is still a 0.001 chance that your test will indicate that you are HIV positive. In reality, 1 of 10,000 heterosexual white males is HIV positive. Your doctor calls and says that you have tested HIV positive. He is sorry but there is a 99.9% $(1 - 0.001)$ chance that you have HIV. Is he correct? What is the actual probability that you are HIV positive?

## Skill-Extending Problems

**22.** The terms *prior* and *posterior* are relative. Assume that the drug test has been performed, and the outcome

is positive, which leads to the posterior probabilities in row 20 of Figure 9.28. Now assume there is a *second* test, independent of the first, that can be used as a follow-up. Assume that its false-positive and false-negative rates are 0.02 and 0.06.

   **a.** Use the posterior probabilities from row 20 as *prior* probabilities in a second Bayes' rule calculation. (Now *prior* means prior to the second test.) If the athlete also tests positive in this second test, what is the posterior probability that he is a drug user?

   **b.** We assumed that the two tests are independent. Why might this not be realistic? If they are not independent, what kind of additional information would you need about the likelihoods of the test results?

**23.** In the OJ Simpson trial it was accepted that OJ had battered his wife. OJ's lawyer tried to negate the impact of this information by stating that in a one-year period, only 1 out of 2500 battered women are murdered, so the fact that OJ battered his wife does not give much evidence that he was the murderer. The prosecution (foolishly!) let this go unchallenged. Here are the relevant statistics: In a typical year 6.25 million women are battered, 2500 are battered and murdered, and 2250 of the women who were battered and murdered were killed by the batterer. How should the prosecution have refuted the defense's argument?

# 9.5 MULTISTAGE DECISION PROBLEMS

In this section we investigate multistage decision problems. In many such problems the first-stage decision is whether to purchase information that will help make a better second-stage decision. In this case the information, if obtained, typically changes the probabilities of later outcomes. To revise the probabilities once the information is obtained, you often need to apply Bayes' rule, as discussed in the previous section. In addition, you typically want to learn how much the information is worth. After all, information usually comes at a price, so you want to know whether the information is worth its price. This leads to an investigation of the value of information, an important theme of this section.

We begin with a continuation of the drug-testing example from the previous section. If drug tests are not completely reliable, should they be used? As you will see, it all depends on the "costs."[5]

### EXAMPLE 9.3 DRUG TESTING COLLEGE ATHLETES

The administrators at State University are trying to decide whether to institute mandatory drug testing for athletes. They have the same information about priors and likelihoods as in Example 9.2, but they now want to use a decision tree approach to see whether the benefits outweigh the costs.[6]

---

[5]It might also depend on whether there is a second type of test that could help confirm the findings of the first test. However, we will not consider such a test.

[6]Again, see Feinstein (1990) for an enlightening discussion of this drug-testing problem at a real university.

**Objective** To use a multistage decision framework to see whether mandatory drug testing can be justified, given a somewhat unreliable test and a set of "reasonable" monetary values.

We already discussed the source of the probabilities in Example 9.2. The monetary values we need are discussed in detail here.

## Solution

We have already discussed the uncertain outcomes and their probabilities. Now we need to discuss the decision alternatives and the monetary values, the other two elements of a decision analysis. We will assume that there are only two alternatives: perform drug testing on all athletes or don't perform any drug testing. In the former case we assume that if an athlete tests positive, this athlete is barred from athletics.

### Assessing the Monetary Values

The "monetary" values are more difficult to assess. They include

- the benefit $B$ from correctly identifying a drug user and barring this person from athletics
- the cost $C1$ of the test itself for a single athlete (materials and labor)
- the cost $C2$ of falsely accusing a nonuser (and barring this person from athletics)
- the cost $C3$ of not identifying a drug user and allowing this person to participate in athletics
- the cost $C4$ of violating a nonuser's privacy by performing the test.

*Real decision problems often involve nonmonetary benefits and costs. These must be assessed, relative to one another, before rational decisions can be made.*

It is clear that only $C1$ is a direct monetary cost that is easy to measure. However, the other "costs" and the benefit $B$ are real, and they must be compared on some scale to enable administrators to make a rational decision. We will do so by comparing everything to the cost $C1$, to which we assign value 1. (This does not mean that the cost of testing an athlete is necessarily \$1; it just means that all other monetary values are expressed as multiples of $C1$.) Clearly, there is a lot of subjectivity involved in making these comparisons, so sensitivity analysis on the final decision tree is a must.

### Developing a Benefit-Cost Table

Before developing this decision tree, it is useful to form a benefit-cost table for both alternatives and all possible outcomes. Because we will eventually maximize expected net *benefit*, all benefits in this table have a positive sign and all costs have a negative sign. These net benefits are listed in Table 9.6. As before, let $D$ and $ND$ denote that a randomly chosen athlete is or is not a drug user, and let $T+$ and $T-$ indicate a positive or negative test result. The first two columns are relevant if no tests are performed; the last four are relevant when

**Table 9.6** Net Benefit for Drug-Testing Example

| | Don't Test | | Perform Test | | | |
|---|---|---|---|---|---|---|
| Ultimate decision | $D$ | $ND$ | $D$ and $T+$ | $ND$ and $T+$ | $D$ and $T-$ | $ND$ and $T-$ |
| Bar from athletics | $B$ | $-C_2$ | $B-C_1$ | $-(C_1+C_2+C_4)$ | $B-C_1$ | $-(C_1+C_2+C_4)$ |
| Don't bar from athletics | $-C_3$ | $0$ | $-(C_1+C_3)$ | $-(C_1+C_4)$ | $-(C_1+C_3)$ | $-(C_1+C_4)$ |

testing is performed. For example, if a positive test is obtained for a nonuser and this athlete is barred from athletics, there are three costs: the cost of the test ($C_1$), the cost of falsely accusing the athlete ($C_2$), and the cost of violating the athlete's privacy ($C_4$). The other entries are obtained similarly.

## DEVELOPING THE DECISION TREE MODEL

The decision model, developed with PrecisionTree and shown in Figures 9.29 and 9.30, is now fairly straightforward. (See the file Drug Testing Decision.xlsx.) You first enter all of the benefits and costs in an input section. These, together with the Bayes' rule calculations from Example 9.2, appear at the top of Figure 9.29. Then you use PrecisionTree in the usual way to build the tree in Figure 9.30 and enter the links to the values and probabilities.

**Figure 9.29**    Inputs and Bayes' Rule Calculations for Drug-Testing Example

| | A | B | C | D | E | F |
|---|---|---|---|---|---|---|
| 1 | Drug testing decision | | | | | |
| 2 | | | | | | |
| 3 | Benefits | | | Given probabilities | | |
| 4 | Identifying user | 25 | | Prior probabilities | | |
| 5 | | | | | User | Non-user |
| 6 | Costs | | | | 0.05 | 0.95 |
| 7 | Test cost | 1 | | | | |
| 8 | Barring non-user | 50 | | Conditional probabilities of test results | | |
| 9 | Not identifying user | 20 | | | User | Non-user |
| 10 | Violation of privacy | 2 | | Positive | 0.93 | 0.03 |
| 11 | | | | Negative | 0.07 | 0.97 |
| 12 | Key probabilities | | | | | |
| 13 | PrUser | 0.05 | | Bayesian revision | | |
| 14 | PrFalseNegative | 0.07 | | Unconditional probabilities of test results | | |
| 15 | PrFalsePositive | 0.03 | | Positive | 0.075 | |
| 16 | | | | Negative | 0.925 | |
| 17 | | | | | | |
| 18 | | | | Posterior probabilities | | |
| 19 | | | | | User | Non-user |
| 20 | | | | Positive | 0.620 | 0.380 |
| 21 | | | | Negative | 0.004 | 0.996 |

It is important to understand the timing (from left to right) in this decision tree. If drug testing is performed, the result of the drug test is observed first (a probability node). Each test result leads to an action (bar from sports or don't), and then the eventual benefit or cost depends on whether the athlete uses drugs (again a probability node). You might argue that the university never knows for certain whether the athlete uses drugs, but you must include this information in the tree to get the correct benefits and costs. On the other hand, if no drug testing is performed, there is no intermediate test result node or branch.

*Bayes' rule is required because it yields exactly those probabilities that are needed in the decision tree.*

Make sure you understand which probabilities are used in the tree. In the lower part, where no testing takes place, the probabilities are the prior probabilities. There is no test information in this case. In the upper part, where the test is performed, the probabilities for the user and nonuser branches are posterior probabilities, given the results of the test. The reason is that by the time we get to these nodes, the results of the test have already been observed. However, the probabilities for the test results are *unconditional* probabilities, the denominators in Bayes' rule. They are not conditional probabilities such as $P(T+|D)$ because you condition only on information to the *left* of any given branch. In other words, by the time you get to the test result branches, you do not yet know whether the athlete is a user.

### Discussion of the Solution

Now we analyze the solution. First, we discuss the benefits and costs shown in Figure 9.29. These were chosen fairly arbitrarily, but with some hope of reflecting reality. The largest

Figure 9.30    Decision Tree for Drug-Testing Example

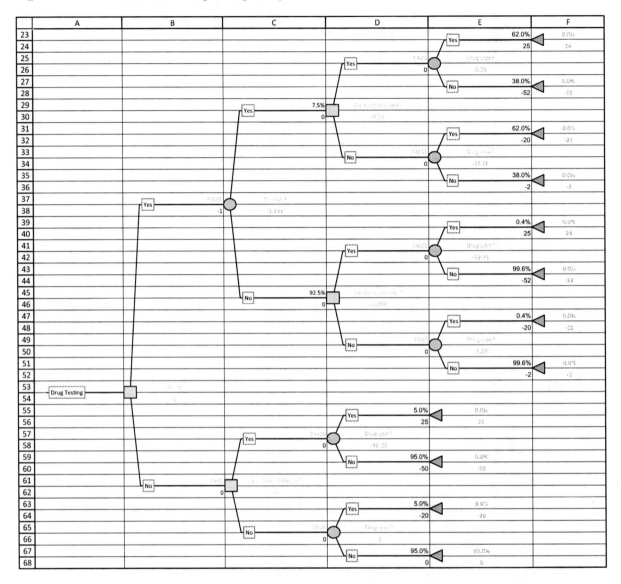

cost is falsely accusing (and then barring) a nonuser. This is 50 times as large as the cost of the test. The benefit of identifying a drug user is only half this large, and the cost of not identifying a user is 40% as large as barring a nonuser. The violation of the privacy of a nonuser is twice as large as the cost of the test. Based on these values, the decision tree implies that drug testing should *not* be performed (and no athletes should be barred). The EMVs for testing and for not testing are both negative, indicating that the costs outweigh the benefits for each, but the EMV for not testing is slightly *less* negative.[7]

### Sensitivity Analysis

What would it take to change this decision? We begin with the assumption, probably accepted by most people in our society, that the cost of falsely accusing a nonuser $(C_2)$ is the largest of the benefits and costs in the range B4:B10. In fact, because of possible legal

[7]The university in the Feinstein (1990) study came to the same conclusion.

costs, you might argue that $C_2$ is *more* than 50 times the cost of the test. But if $C_2$ increases, the scales are tipped even further in the direction of not testing. On the other hand, if the benefit $B$ from identifying a user and the cost $C_3$ for not identifying a user increase, then testing might be the preferred alternative. We tried this, keeping $C_2$ constant at 50. When $B$ and $C_3$ both had value 45, no testing was still optimal, but when they both increased to 50—the same magnitude as $C_2$—testing won out by a small margin. However, it would be difficult to argue that $B$ and $C_3$ are of the same magnitude as $C_2$.

Other than the benefits and costs, the only other input you might vary is the accuracy of the test, measured by the error probabilities in cells B14 and B15. Presumably, if the test makes fewer false positives and false negatives, testing might be a more attractive alternative. We tried this, keeping the benefits and costs the same as those in Figure 9.29 but changing the error probabilities. Even when each error probability was decreased to 0.01, however, the no-testing alternative was still optimal—by a fairly wide margin.

In summary, based on a number of reasonable assumptions and parameter settings, this example has shown that it is difficult to make a case for mandatory drug testing. ▪

### 9.5.1 The Value of Information

The drug-testing decision problem represents a typical multistage decision problem. You first decide whether to obtain some information that could be useful—the results of a drug test. If you decide not to obtain the information, you make a decision right away (bar the athlete or don't), based on prior probabilities. If you do decide to obtain the information, then you first observe the information and *then* make the final decision, based on posterior probabilities.

The questions we ask now are: How much is the information worth, and if it costs a given amount, should you purchase it? Presumably, information that will help you make your ultimate decision should be worth something, but it might not be clear how much the information is worth. In addition, even if the information is worth something, it might not be worth as much as its actual price. Fortunately, the answers to these questions are embedded in the decision tree itself.

We will find the values of two types of information: sample information and perfect information. **Sample information** is the information from the experiment itself. For example, it is the information from the (less than perfect) drug test. (It has become customary to use the term *sample* information, and we will continue the practice here, but a more precise term would be *imperfect* information.) **Perfect information**, on the other hand, is information from a perfect test—that is, a test that will indicate with certainty which ultimate outcome will occur. In the drug example, this would correspond to a test that never makes mistakes. Admittedly, perfect information is almost never available at any price, but finding its value is still useful because it provides an upper bound on the value of *any* information. For example, if perfect information is valued at $2000, then *no* information can possibly be worth more than $2000.

We will find the **expected value of sample information**, or **EVSI**, and the **expected value of perfect information**, or **EVPI**. They are defined as follows:

The **EVSI** is the most you would be willing to pay for the sample information.

*Formula for EVSI*

EVSI = EMV with (free) sample information – EMV without information    **(9.4)**

The **EVPI** is the most you would be willing to pay for perfect information.

> *Formula for EVPI*
>
> EVPI = EMV with (free) perfect information − EMV without information $\qquad$ (9.5)

We first make one important general point about the value of information. Suppose there is an ultimate decision to make. Before making this decision, you can obtain information, supposedly to help you make the ultimate decision. But suppose you make the *same* ultimate decision, regardless of the information you obtain—the same decision you would have made in the absence of information. Can you guess the value of this information? It is zero. The information cannot be worth anything if it never leads to a different decision than you would have made without the information. The moral is that if you plan to pay something for information, you are wasting your money unless this information influences your decision making.

---

## FUNDAMENTAL INSIGHT

### The Value of Information

The amount you should be willing to spend for information is the expected increase in EMV you can obtain from having the information. If the actual price of the information is less than or equal to this amount, you should purchase it; otherwise, the information is not worth its price. In addition, information that never affects your decision is worthless, and it should not be purchased at any price. Finally, the value of *any* information can never be greater than the value of perfect information that would eliminate all uncertainty.

---

We now see how Bayes' rule can be used and the value of information can be evaluated in a typical multistage decision problem.

---

**EXAMPLE**    9.4 MARKETING A NEW PRODUCT AT ACME

The Acme Company is trying to decide whether to market a new product. As in many new-product situations, there is considerable uncertainty about whether the new product will eventually succeed. Acme believes that it might be wise to introduce the product in a regional test market before introducing it nationally. Therefore, the company's first decision is whether to conduct the test market.

Acme estimates that the net cost of the test market is $100,000. We assume this is mostly fixed costs, so that the same cost is incurred regardless of the test-market results. If Acme decides to conduct the test market, it must then wait for the results. Based on the results of the test market, it can then decide whether to market the product nationally, in which case it will incur a fixed cost of $7 million. On the other hand, if the original decision is *not* to run a test market, then the final decision—whether to market the product nationally—can be made without further delay. Acme's unit margin, the difference between its selling price and its unit variable cost, is $18. We assume this is relevant only for the national market.

Acme classifies the results in either the test market or the national market as great, fair, or awful. Each of these results in the national market is accompanied by a forecast of total units sold. These sales volumes (in 1000s of units) are 600 (great), 300 (fair), and 90 (awful). In the absence of any test market information, Acme estimates that probabilities of the three national market outcomes are 0.45, 0.35, and 0.20, respectively.

In addition, Acme has the following historical data from products that were introduced into both test markets and national markets.

- Of the products that eventually did great in the national market, 64% did great in the test market, 26% did fair in the test market, and 10% did awful in the test market.

- Of the products that eventually did fair in the national market, 18% did great in the test market, 57% did fair in the test market, and 25% did awful in the test market.
- Of the products that eventually did awful in the national market, 9% did great in the test market, 48% did fair in the test market, and 43% did awful in the test market.[8]

The company wants to use a decision tree approach to find the best strategy. It also wants to find the expected value of the information provided by the test market.

**Objective** To develop a decision tree to find the best strategy for Acme, to perform a sensitivity analysis on the results, and to find EVSI and EVPI.

## Where Do the Numbers Come From?

The fixed costs of the test market and the national market are probably accurate estimates, based on planned advertising and overhead expenses. The unit margin is just the difference between the anticipated selling price and the known unit cost of the product. The sales volume estimates are clearly approximations to reality, because the sales from any new product would form a continuum of possible values. Here, the company has "discretized" the problem into three possible outcomes for the national market, and it has estimated the sales for each of these discrete outcomes. The conditional probabilities of national-market results given test-market results are probably based on results from previous products that went through test markets and then national markets.

## Solution

We begin by discussing the three basic elements of this decision problem: the possible strategies, the possible outcomes and their probabilities, and the value model. The possible strategies are clear. Acme must first decide whether to run a test market. Then it must decide whether to introduce the product nationally. However, it is important to realize that if Acme decides to run a test market, it can base the national market decision on the results of the test market. In this case its final strategy will be a **contingency plan**, where it conducts the test market, then introduces the product nationally if it receives sufficiently positive test-market results but abandons the product if it receives sufficiently negative test-market results. The optimal strategies from many multistage decision problems involve similar contingency plans.

> In a **contingency plan**, later decisions can depend on earlier decisions and information received.

## Fundamental Insight

### Making Sequential Decisions

Whenever you have a chance to make several sequential decisions and you will learn useful information between decision points, the decision you make initially depends on the decisions you plan to make in the future, and these depend on the information you will learn in the meantime. In other words, when you decide what to do initially, you should look ahead to see what your future options will be, and what your decision will be under each option. Such a contingency plan is typically superior to a *myopic* (short-sighted) plan that doesn't take into account future options in the initial decision making.

---

[8]You can question why the company ever marketed products nationally after awful test-market results, but we will assume that, for whatever reason, the company made a few such decisions—and that a few even turned out to be winners.

Regarding the uncertain outcomes and their probabilities, we note that the given prior probabilities of national-market results in the absence of test-market results will be needed in the part of the tree where Acme decides not to run a test market. However, the historical percentages we quoted are really likelihoods of test-market results, given national-market results. For example, one of these is $P$(Great test market | Great national market) = 0.64. Such probabilities are the opposite of those needed in the tree. This is because the event to the right of the given sign, "great national market," occurs in time *after* the event to the left of the given sign, "great test market." This is a sure sign that Bayes' rule is required.

The required posterior probabilities of national-market results, given test-market results, are calculated directly from Bayes' rule, Equation (9.1). For example, if NG, NF, and NA represent great, fair, and awful national-market results, respectively, and if TG, TF, and TA represent similar events for the test market, than one typical example of a posterior probability calculation is

$$P(NG|TF) = \frac{P(TF|NG)P(NG)}{P(TF|NG)P(NG) + P(TF|NF)P(NF) + P(TF|NA)P(NA)}$$

$$= \frac{0.26(0.45)}{0.26(0.45) + 0.57(0.35) + 0.48(0.20)} = \frac{0.117}{0.4125} = 0.2836$$

This is a reasonable result. In the absence of test market information, the probability of a great national market is 0.45. However, after a test market with only fair results, the probability of a great national market is revised down to 0.2836. The other posterior probabilities are calculated similarly. In addition, the denominator in this calculation, 0.4125, is the unconditional probability of a fair test market. Such test-market probabilities will be needed in the tree.

Finally, the monetary values in the tree are straightforward. There are fixed costs of test marketing or marketing nationally, which are incurred as soon as these go-ahead decisions are made. From that point, if the company markets nationally, it observes the sales volumes and multiplies them by the unit margin to obtain the selling profits.

## Implementing Bayes' Rule

The inputs and Bayes' rule calculations are shown in Figure 9.31. (See file Acme Marketing Decisions 1.xlsx.) You perform the Bayes' rule calculations exactly as in the

---

**Figure 9.31**    Inputs and Bayes' Rule Calculations for Acme Marketing Example

| | A | B | C | D | E | F | G | H | I | J | K | L | M | N |
|---|---|---|---|---|---|---|---|---|---|---|---|---|---|---|
| 1 | Acme marketing decisions | | | | | | | | | | | | | |
| 2 | | | | | | | | | | | | | | |
| 3 | Inputs | | | | | | | | | | | | | |
| 4 | Fixed costs ($1000s) | | | | | | | | | | | | | |
| 5 | Test market | 100 | | | | | | | | | | | | |
| 6 | National market | 7000 | | | | | | | | | | | | |
| 7 | | | | | | | | | | | | | | |
| 8 | Unit margin (either market) | $18 | | | | | | | | | | | | |
| 9 | | | | | | | | | | | | | | |
| 10 | Possible quantities sold (1000s of units) in national market | | | | | | | | | | | | | |
| 11 | Great | 600 | | | | | | | | | | | | |
| 12 | Fair | 300 | | | | | | | | | | | | |
| 13 | Awful | 90 | | | | | | | | | | | | |
| 14 | | | | | | Bayes' rule calculations | | | | | | | | |
| 15 | Prior probabilities of national market results | | | | | Unconditional probabilities of test mkt results (denominators of Bayes' rule) | | | | | | | | |
| 16 | | Great | Fair | Awful | | Great | 0.3690 | | | | | | | |
| 17 | | 0.45 | 0.35 | 0.20 | | Fair | 0.4125 | | | | | | | |
| 18 | | | | | | Awful | 0.2185 | | | | | | | |
| 19 | Likelihoods of test market results (along side), given national market results (along top) from historical data | | | | | | | | | | | | | |
| 20 | | Great | Fair | Awful | | Posterior probabilities of national mkt results (along top), given test mkt results (along side) | | | | | | | | |
| 21 | Great | 0.64 | 0.18 | 0.09 | | | Great | Fair | Awful | | | | | |
| 22 | Fair | 0.26 | 0.57 | 0.48 | | Great | 0.7805 | 0.1707 | 0.0488 | | | | | |
| 23 | Awful | 0.10 | 0.25 | 0.43 | | Fair | 0.2836 | 0.4836 | 0.2327 | | | | | |
| 24 | | | | | | Awful | 0.2059 | 0.4005 | 0.3936 | | | | | |

drug example. To calculate the unconditional probabilities for test-market results, the denominators for Bayes' rule from Equation (9.2), enter the formula

=SUMPRODUCT($B$17:$D$17,B21:D21)

in cell G16 and copy it down to cell G18. To calculate the posterior probabilities from Equation (9.1), enter the formula

=B$17*B21/$G16

in cell G22 and copy it to the range G22:I24.

## DEVELOPING THE DECISION TREE MODEL

The tree is now straightforward to build and label, as shown in Figure 9.32. Note that the fixed costs of test marketing and marketing nationally appear on the decision branches

Figure 9.32   Decision Tree for Acme Marketing Example

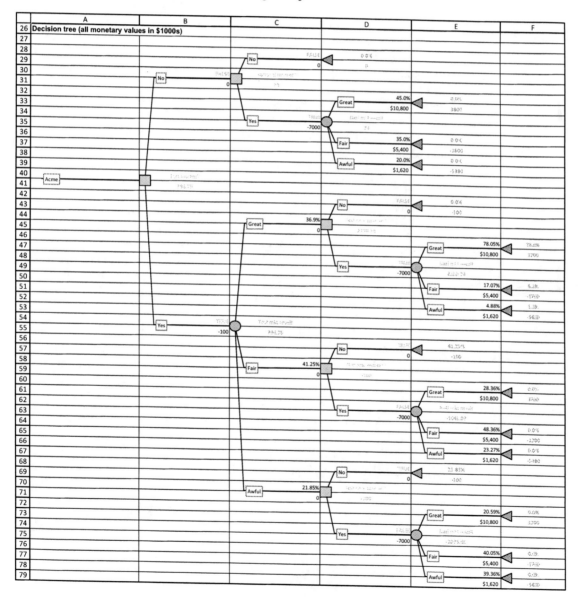

where they occur in time, so that only the selling profits need to be placed on the probability branches. For example, the formula for the selling profit in cell D33 is

$-\$B\$8*\$B\$11$

Pay particular attention to the probabilities on the branches. The top group are the prior probabilities from the range B17:D17. In the bottom group, the probabilities on the left are unconditional probabilities of test-market results from the range G16:G18, and those on the right are posterior probabilities of national-market results from the range G22:I24. Again, this corresponds to the standard decision tree convention, where all probabilities on the tree are conditioned on any events that have occurred to the left of them.

## Discussion of the Solution

To interpret this tree, note that each value just below each node name is an EMV. (These are colored red or green in Excel.) For example, the 796.76 in cell B41 is the EMV for the entire decision problem. It means that Acme's best EMV from acting optimally is $796,760. As another example, the 74 in cell D35 means that if Acme ever gets to that point—there is no test market and the product is marketed nationally—the EMV is $74,000. Actually, this is the expected selling profit minus the $7 million fixed cost, so the expected selling profit, given that no information from a test market has been obtained, is $7,074,000.

Acme's optimal strategy is apparent by following the TRUE branches from left to right. Acme should first run a test market. If the test-market result is great, the product should be marketed nationally. However, if the test-market result is fair or awful, the product should be abandoned. In these cases the prospects from a national market look bleak, so Acme should cut its losses. (And there *are* losses. In these latter two cases, Acme has already spent $100,000 on the test market and has nothing to show for it.)

Once you have done the work to build the tree, you can reap the benefits of PrecisionTree's tools. For example, its policy suggestion and risk profile outputs are given in Figures 9.33 and 9.34. The policy suggestion shows only the part of the tree corresponding to the optimal strategy. Note that there are two values at each end node. The bottom number is the combined monetary value along this sequence of branches, and the top number is the probability of this sequence of branches. This information leads directly to probability distribution in the risk profile. For this optimal strategy, the only possible

Figure 9.33

Policy Suggestion (Optimal Strategy Branches)

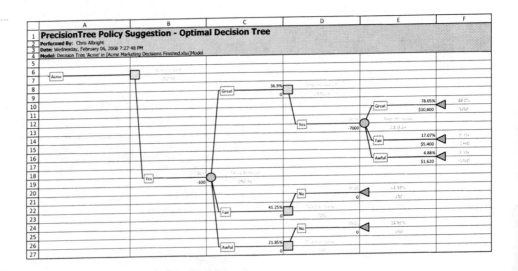

Figure 9.34

Risk Profile of
Optimal Strategy

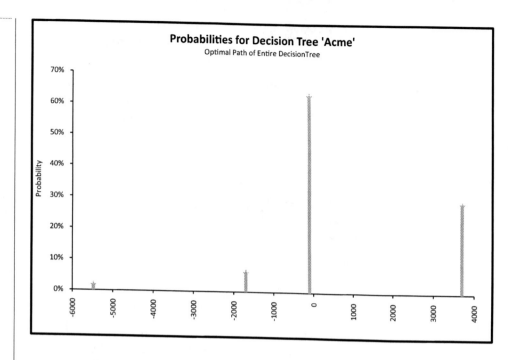

monetary outcomes are a gain of $3,700,000 and losses of $100,000, $1,700,000, and $5,480,000. Their respective probabilities are 0.288, 0.631, 0.063, and 0.018. Fortunately, the large possible losses are unlikely enough that the EMV is still positive, $796,760.

You might argue that the large potential losses and the slightly higher than 70% chance of *some* loss should persuade Acme to abandon the product right away—without a test market. However, this is what "playing the averages" with EMV is all about. Because the EMV of this optimal strategy is greater than 0, the EMV from abandoning the product right away, Acme should go ahead with this optimal strategy if the company is indeed an EMV maximizer. In section 9.6 we will see how this reasoning can change if Acme is a risk-averse decision maker—as it might be with multimillion-dollar losses looming in the future.

### Sensitivity Analysis

There are several sensitivity analyses that can performed on this model. We investigate how things change when the unit margin, currently $18, varies from $8 to $28. This could change the decision about whether to run a test market or to market nationally.

We first analyze the overall EMV in cell B41, setting up the sensitivity dialog box as in Figure 9.35. The resulting chart is shown in Figure 9.36. The chart indicates that for small unit margins, it is better *not* to run a test market. The top line, at value 0, corresponds to abandoning the product altogether, whereas the bottom line, at value −100, corresponds to running a test market and then abandoning the product regardless of the results. Similarly, for large unit margins, it is also best not to run a test market. Again, the top line is 100 above the bottom line. However, the reasoning now is different. For large unit margins, the company should market nationally *regardless* of test-market results, so there is no reason to spend money on a test market. Finally, for intermediate unit margins, as in the original model, the chart shows that it is best to run a test market. We hope you agree that this one single chart provides a lot of information and insight.

By changing the cell to analyze in Figure 9.35, we can gain additional insight. For example, if no test market is available, the EMV for deciding nationally right away, in cell C31, is

Figure 9.35

Dialog Box for
Sensitivity

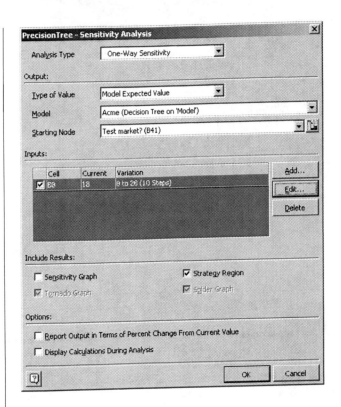

Figure 9.36

Sensitivity Analysis
on Overall Profit

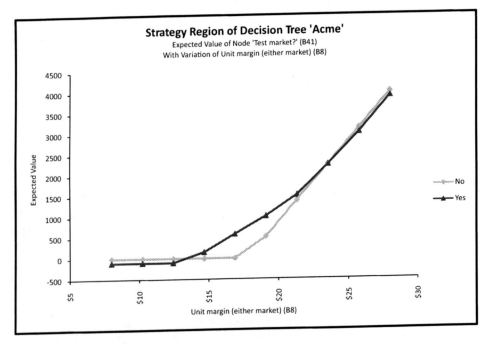

relevant. The resulting chart appears in Figure 9.37. Now it is a contest between getting zero profit from abandoning the product and getting a linearly increasing profit from marketing nationally. The breakpoint appears to be slightly below $18. If the unit margin is above this value, Acme should market nationally; otherwise, it should abandon the product.

Figure 9.37

Sensitivity Analysis
for Deciding
Nationally Right
Away

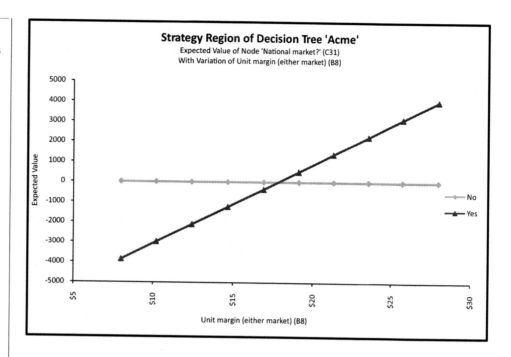

You can also choose to analyze any of the EMVs in cells D45, D59, or D71. Each of these is relevant in the case where the company has run the test market, has observed the test-market results, and is about to decide whether to market nationally. For example, if you choose D71 as the cell to analyze, you obtain the chart in Figure 9.38. It indicates that there are indeed situations—where the unit margin is about $26 or more—when the company should market nationally, even though the test market is awful. In contrast, the chart in

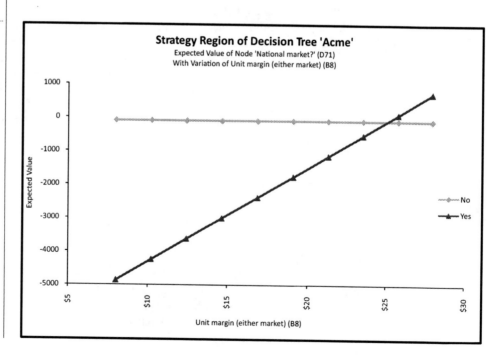

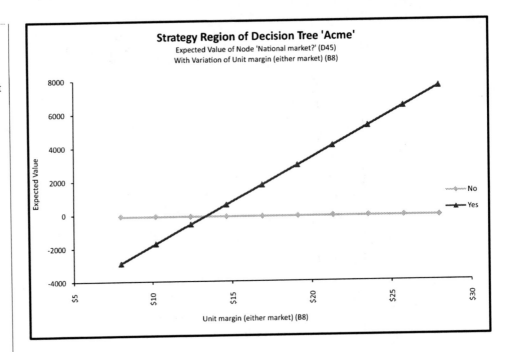

Figure 9.39, where we analyze cell D45, indicates the opposite behavior. It shows that if the unit margin is low enough—about $13.50 or less—the company should abandon the product nationally, even though the test-market results are great. These are again very useful insights.

## Expected Value of Sample Information

The role of the test market in this example is to provide information in the form of more accurate probabilities of national-market results. Information usually costs something, as it does in Acme's problem. Currently, the fixed cost of the test market is $100,000, which is evidently not too much to pay because Acme's best strategy is to run the test market. However, you might ask how much this test market is really worth. This is the expected value of sample information, or EVSI, and it is easy to obtain from the tree. From Figure 9.32, the EMV from test marketing is $796,760, $100,000 of which is the cost of the test market. Therefore, if this test market were free, the expected profit would be $896,760. On the other hand, the EMV from not running a test market is $74,000 (see cell C31 in the tree). From Equation (9.4), the difference is EVSI:

$$\text{EVSI} = \$896,760 - \$74,000 = \$822,760$$

You can check that if you put any value less than 822.76 in the test-market fixed-cost cell (cell B5), the decision to test-market will continue to be best.

Intuitively, running the test market is worth something because it changes the optimal decision. With no test-market information, the best decision is to market nationally. (See the top part of the tree in Figure 9.32.) However, with the test-market information, the ultimate decision depends on the test-market results. Specifically, Acme should market nationally only if the test-market result is great. This is what makes information worth something—its outcome affects the optimal decision.

## Expected Value of Perfect Information

It took a lot of work to find EVSI. You had to assess various conditional probabilities, use Bayes' rule, and then build a fairly complex decision tree. In general, Acme might have many sources of information it could obtain that would help it make its national decision; the test market is just one of them. The question, then, is how much such information *could* be worth. This is answered by EVPI, the expected value of perfect information. It provides an upper bound on how much *any* information could be worth, and it is relatively easy to calculate.

Imagine that Acme could purchase an envelope that has the true national-market result—great, fair, or awful—written inside. Once opened, this envelope would remove all uncertainty, and Acme could make an easy decision. (We assume that Acme can open the envelope *before* having to make the national decision.) EVPI is what this envelope is worth. To calculate it, you build the tree in Figure 9.40. The key here is that the nodes are reversed in time. You first open the envelope to discover what is inside. This corresponds to the probability node. Then you make the final decision. Given the cost parameters, it is easy to see that Acme should market nationally only if the contents of the envelope reveal that the national market will be great. Otherwise, Acme should abandon the product right away.

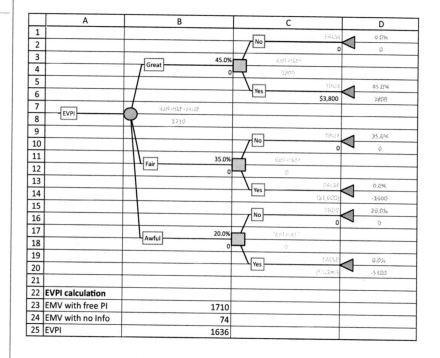

**Figure 9.40**

**Decision Tree for Evaluating EVPI**

The EVPI calculation is now straightforward. If the envelope (perfect information) is free, the tree in Figure 9.40 indicates that the EMV is $1,710,000. If there is no information, the EMV is $74,000 (cell C31 of Figure 9.32). Therefore, from Equation (9.5),

$$\text{EVPI} = \$1,710,000 - \$74,000 = \$1,636,000$$

No sample information, test market or otherwise, could possibly be worth more than this. So if some hotshot market analyst offers to provide "extremely reliable" market information to Acme for, say, $1.8 million, Acme knows this information cannot be worth its cost. ∎

### Skill-Building Problems

**24.** In deciding whether to perform mandatory drug testing, we claimed that it is difficult to justify such testing under reasonable conditions. Check this yourself in the following questions.

    **a.** Drug testing ought to be more attractive if the test is more reliable. Keeping the costs the same as in the example, use PrecisionTree's two-way sensitivity tool to see whether the optimal decision (test or not test) changes as the probability of a false positive and the probability of a false negative both change. You can let them vary through some reasonable ranges. Explain the results.

    **b.** Repeat part **a**, but first double the two monetary values that make the test more attractive: the benefit of identifying a user and the cost of not identifying a user. How do your results differ from those in part **a**?

    **c.** In this part, keep the probabilities of false positives and false negatives the same, but let the benefits and costs vary. Specifically, let the benefit of identifying a user and the cost of not identifying a user be of the form 25*a* and 20*a*, where *a* is some factor that you can vary. Similarly, let the cost of barring a nonuser and the cost of violating privacy be of the form 50*b* and 2*b*. The cost of the test is still 1. (The idea is that large values of *a* and/or small values of *b* will make the testing more attractive.) Use PrecisionTree's two-way sensitivity tool to see whether the optimal decision (test or not test) changes for a reasonable range of values of *a* and *b*. Discuss your results.

**25.** In the drug testing decision, find and interpret EVSI and EVPI. Here, "sample" information refers to the information from the imperfect drug test, whereas "perfect" information refers to completely reliable information on whether the athlete uses drugs.

**26.** Explain in general why EVSI is the same, regardless of the actual cost of the information. For example, in the Acme problem EVSI is the same regardless of whether the actual cost of the test market is $100,000, $200,000, or any other value. Then explain how EVSI, together with the actual cost of the information, leads to the decision about whether to purchase the information.

**27.** Following up on the previous problem, the *expected net gain from information* is defined as the expected amount gained by having access to the information, at its given cost, as opposed to not having access to the information. Explain how you would calculate this in general. What is its value for the Acme problem?

**28.** Prior probabilities are often educated guesses at best, so it is worth performing a sensitivity analysis on their values. However, you must make sure that they are varied so that all probabilities are nonnegative and sum to 1. For the Acme problem, perform the following sensitivity analyses on the three prior probabilities and comment on the results.

    **a.** Vary the probability of a great national market in a one-way sensitivity analysis from 0 to 0.6 in increments of 0.1. Do this in such a way that the probabilities of the two other outcomes, fair and awful, stay in the same ratio as they are currently, 7 to 4.

    **b.** Vary the probabilities of a great and a fair national market independently in a two-way sensitivity analysis. You can choose the ranges over which these vary, but you must ensure that the three prior probabilities continue to be nonnegative and sum to 1. (For example, you couldn't choose ranges where the probabilities of great and fair are 0.6 and 0.5.)

**29.** In the Acme problem, perform a sensitivity analysis on the quantity sold from a great national market (the value in cell B11). Let this value vary over a range of values *greater than* the current value of 600, so that a great national market is even more attractive than before. Does this ever change the optimal strategy? If so, in what way?

**30.** Using trial and error on the prior probabilities in the Acme problem, find values of them that make EVSI equal to 0. These are values where Acme will make the same decision, regardless of the test-market results it observes. Comment on why the test market is worthless for your particular prior probabilities.

### Skill-Extending Problems

**31.** We related EVPI to the value of an envelope that contains the true ultimate outcome. This concept can be extended to "less than perfect" information. For example, in the Acme problem suppose that the company could purchase information that would indicate, with certainty, that one of the following two outcomes will occur: (1) the national market will be great, or (2) the national market will not be great. Note that outcome (2) doesn't say whether the national market will be fair or awful; it just says that it won't be great. How much should Acme be willing to pay for such information?

**32.** The concept behind EVPI is that you purchase perfect information (the envelope), then open the envelope to see which outcome occurs, and then make an easy decision. You do *not*, however, get to choose what information the envelope contains. In contrast, sometimes a company can pay, not to obtain information, but to influence the outcome. Consider the following version of the Acme problem. There is no possibility of a test market, so that Acme must decide right away whether to market nationally. However, suppose Acme can pay to change the probabilities of the national market outcomes from their current values, 0.45, 0.35, and 0.20, to the new values $p$, $(7/11)(1 - p)$, and $(4/11)(1 - p)$, for some $p$. (In this way, the probabilities of fair and awful stay in the same ratio as before,

7 to 4, but by making $p$ large, the probability of a great outcome increases.)
a. How much should Acme be willing to pay for the change if $p = 0.6$? If $p = 0.8$? If $p = 0.95$?
b. Are these types of changes realistic? Answer by speculating on the types of actions Acme might be able to take to make the probability of a great national market higher. Do you think such actions would cost more or less than what Acme should be willing to pay for them (from part a)?

## 9.6 INCORPORATING ATTITUDES TOWARD RISK

Rational decision makers are sometimes willing to violate the EMV maximization criterion when large amounts of money are at stake. These decision makers are willing to sacrifice some EMV to reduce risk. Are you ever willing to do so personally? Consider the following scenarios.

- You have a chance to enter a lottery where you will win $100,000 with probability 0.1 or win nothing with probability 0.9. Alternatively, you can receive $5000 for certain. How many of you—truthfully—would take the certain $5000, even though the EMV of the lottery is $10,000? Or change the $100,000 to $1,000,000 and the $5000 to $50,000 and ask yourself whether you'd prefer the sure $50,000.

- You can buy collision insurance on your expensive new car or not buy it. The insurance costs a certain premium and carries some deductible provision. If you decide to pay the premium, then you are essentially paying a certain amount to avoid a gamble: the possibility of wrecking your car and not having it insured. You can be sure that the premium is greater than the expected cost of damage; otherwise, the insurance company would not stay in business. Therefore, from an EMV standpoint you should not purchase the insurance. But how many of you drive without this type of insurance?

These examples, the second of which is certainly realistic, illustrate situations where rational people do not behave as EMV maximizers. Then how do they act? This question has been studied extensively by many researchers, both mathematically and behaviorally. Although there is still not perfect agreement, most researchers believe that if certain basic behavioral assumptions hold, people are **expected utility** maximizers—that is, they choose the alternative with the largest expected utility. Although we will not go deeply into the subject of expected utility maximization, the discussion in this section presents the main ideas.

### 9.6.1 Utility Functions

We begin by discussing an individual's **utility function**. This is a mathematical function that transforms monetary values—payoffs and costs—into *utility values*. Essentially, an individual's utility function specifies the individual's preferences for various monetary payoffs and costs and, in doing so, it automatically encodes the individual's attitudes toward risk. Most individuals are *risk averse*, which means intuitively that they are willing to sacrifice some EMV to avoid risky gambles. In terms of the utility function, this means that every extra dollar of payoff is worth slightly less to the individual than the previous dollar, and every extra dollar of cost is considered slightly more costly (in terms of utility) than the previous dollar. The resulting utility functions are shaped as shown in Figure 9.41. Mathematically, these functions are said to be *increasing* and *concave*. The increasing part means that they go uphill—everyone prefers more money to less money. The concave part means that they increase at a decreasing rate. This is the risk-averse behavior.

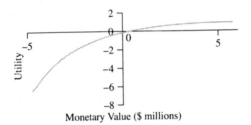

**Figure 9.41**

Risk-Averse Utility Function

There are two aspects of implementing **expected utility maximization** in a real decision analysis. First, an individual's (or company's) utility function must be assessed. This is a time-consuming task that typically involves many trade-offs. It is usually carried out by experts in the field, and we do not discuss the details of the process here. Second, the resulting utility function is used to find the best decision. This second step is relatively straightforward. You substitute utility values for monetary values in the decision tree and then fold back as usual. That is, you calculate expected *utilities* at probability branches and take maximums (of expected *utilities*) at decision branches. We will look at a numerical example later in this section.

### 9.6.2 Exponential Utility

As we have indicated, utility assessment is tedious. Even in the best of circumstances, when a trained consultant attempts to assess the utility function of a single person, the process requires the person to make a series of choices between hypothetical alternatives involving uncertain outcomes. Unless the person has some training in probability, these choices will probably be difficult to understand, let alone make, and it is unlikely that the person will answer *consistently* as the questioning proceeds. The process is even more difficult when a *company's* utility function is being assessed. Because different company executives typically have different attitudes toward risk, it can be difficult for these people to reach a consensus on a common utility function.

For these reasons, classes of ready-made utility functions have been developed. One important class is called *exponential utility* and has been used in many financial investment decisions. An exponential utility function has only one adjustable numerical parameter, called the *risk tolerance*, and there are straightforward ways to discover an appropriate value of this parameter for a particular individual or company. So the advantage of using an exponential utility function is that it is relatively easy to assess. The drawback is that exponential utility functions do not capture all types of attitudes toward risk. Nevertheless, their ease of use has made them popular.

An **exponential utility function** has the following form:

> *Exponential utility*
>
> $$U(x) = 1 - e^{-x/R} \qquad (9.6)$$

Here $x$ is a monetary value (a payoff if positive, a cost if negative), $U(x)$ is the utility of this value, and $R > 0$ is the risk tolerance. As the name suggests, the risk tolerance measures how much risk the decision maker will accept. The larger the value of $R$, the *less* risk averse the decision maker is. That is, a person with a large value of $R$ is more willing to take risks than a person with a small value of $R$. In the limit, a person with an extremely large value of $R$ is an EMV maximizer.

> The *risk tolerance* for an exponential utility function is a single number that specifies an individual's aversion to risk. The higher the risk tolerance, the less risk averse the individual is.

To assess a person's (or company's) exponential utility function, only one number, the value of $R$, needs to be assessed. There are a couple of tips for doing this. First, it has been shown that the risk tolerance is approximately equal to that dollar amount $R$ such that the decision maker is indifferent between the following two options:

* Option 1: Obtain no payoff at all.
* Option 2: Obtain a payoff of $R$ dollars or a loss of $R/2$ dollars, depending on the flip of a fair coin.

For example, if you are indifferent between a bet where you win $1000 or lose $500, with probability 0.5 each, and not betting at all, your $R$ is approximately $1000. From this criterion it certainly makes intuitive sense that a wealthier person (or company) ought to have a larger value of $R$. This has been found in practice.

A second tip for finding $R$ is based on empirical evidence found by Ronald Howard, a prominent decision analyst. Through his consulting experience with large companies, he discovered tentative relationships between risk tolerance and several financial variables: net sales, net income, and equity. [See Howard (1988).] Specifically, he found that $R$ was approximately 6.4% of net sales, 124% of net income, and 15.7% of equity for the companies he studied. For example, according to this prescription, a company with net sales of $30 million should have a risk tolerance of approximately $1.92 million. Howard admits that these percentages are only guidelines. However, they do indicate that larger and more profitable companies tend to have larger values of $R$, which means that they are more willing to take risks involving large dollar amounts.

We illustrate the use of the expected utility criterion, and exponential utility in particular, in the following example.

## EXAMPLE 9.5 DECIDING WHETHER TO ENTER RISKY VENTURES AT VENTURE LIMITED

Venture Limited is a company with net sales of $30 million. The company currently must decide whether to enter one of two risky ventures or invest in a sure thing. The gain from the latter is a sure $125,000. The possible outcomes for the less risky venture are a $0.5 million loss, a $0.1 million gain, and a $1 million gain. The probabilities of these outcomes are 0.25, 0.50, and 0.25, respectively. The possible outcomes of the more risky venture are a $1 million loss, a $1 million gain, and a $3 million gain. The probabilities of these outcomes are 0.35, 0.60, and 0.05, respectively. If Venture Limited must decide on exactly one of these alternatives, what should it do?

**Objective** To see how the company's risk averseness, determined by its risk tolerance in an exponential utility function, affects its decision.

## WHERE DO THE NUMBERS COME FROM?

The outcomes for each of the risky alternatives probably form a continuum of possible values. However, as in Example 9.4, the company has classified these into a few possibilities and made intelligent estimates of the monetary consequences and probabilities of these discrete possibilities.

## Solution

*Don't worry about the actual utility values (for example, whether they are positive or negative). Only the relative magnitudes matter in terms of decision making.*

We assume that Venture Limited has an exponential utility function. Also, based on Howard's guidelines, we assume that the company's risk tolerance is 6.4% of its net sales, or $1.92 million. (A sensitivity analysis on this parameter will be performed later on.) You can substitute into Equation (9.6) to find the utility of any monetary outcome. For example, the gain from the riskless alternative (in thousands of dollars) is 125, and its utility is

$$U(125) = 1 - e^{-125/1920} = 1 - 0.9370 = 0.0630$$

As another example, the utility of a $1 million loss is

$$U(-1000) = 1 - e^{-(-1000)/1920} = 1 - 1.6834 = -0.6834$$

These are the values we use (instead of monetary values) in the decision tree.

## DEVELOPING THE DECISION TREE MODEL

Fortunately, PrecisionTree takes care of the details. After building a decision tree and labeling it (with monetary values) in the usual way, click on the name of the tree (the box on the far left of the tree) to open the dialog box shown in Figure 9.42. Then fill in the information under the Utility Function tab as shown in the figure. This says to use an exponential utility function with risk tolerance 1920, the value in cell B5. (As indicated in the spreadsheet, all monetary values are measured in $1000s.) It also indicates that expected utilities (as opposed to EMVs) should appear in the decision tree.

*The tree is built and labeled (with monetary values) exactly as before. PrecisionTree then takes care of calculating the expected utilities.*

The completed tree for this example is shown in Figure 9.43. (See the file **Using Exponential Utility.xlsx**.) You build it in exactly the same way as usual and link probabilities and monetary values to its branches in the usual way. For example, there is a link in cell C22 to the monetary value in cell B12. However, the expected values shown in the tree (those shown in color on a computer screen) are expected *utilities*, and the optimal decision is the one with the largest expected utility. In this case the expected utilities for the riskless option, investing in the less risky venture, and investing in the more risky venture

Figure 9.42

Dialog Box for
Specifying the
Exponential Utility
Criterion

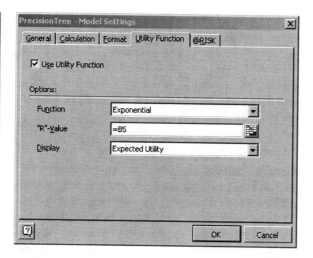

Figure 9.43

Decision Tree for
Risky Venture
Example

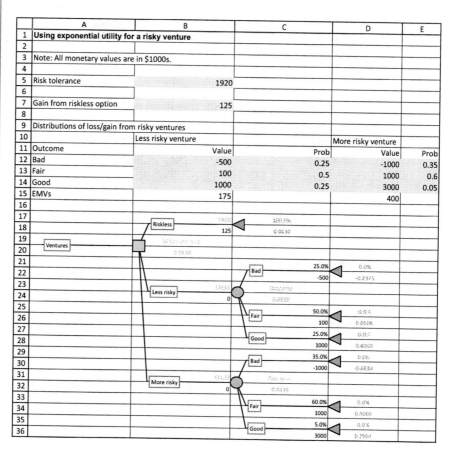

| | A | B | C | D | E |
|---|---|---|---|---|---|
| 1 | **Using exponential utility for a risky venture** | | | | |
| 2 | | | | | |
| 3 | Note: All monetary values are in $1000s. | | | | |
| 4 | | | | | |
| 5 | Risk tolerance | | 1920 | | |
| 6 | | | | | |
| 7 | Gain from riskless option | | 125 | | |
| 8 | | | | | |
| 9 | Distributions of loss/gain from risky ventures | | | | |
| 10 | | Less risky venture | | More risky venture | | |
| 11 | Outcome | Value | Prob | Value | Prob |
| 12 | Bad | -500 | 0.25 | -1000 | 0.35 |
| 13 | Fair | 100 | 0.5 | 1000 | 0.6 |
| 14 | Good | 1000 | 0.25 | 3000 | 0.05 |
| 15 | EMVs | 175 | | 400 | |

are 0.0630, 0.0525, and 0.0439, respectively. Therefore, the optimal decision is to take the riskless option.

## Discussion of the Solution

As indicated in the tree, the riskless option is best in terms of the expected utility criterion; it has the largest expected utility. However, note that the EMVs of the three

*A risk-averse decision maker typically gives up EMV to avoid risk—when the stakes are large enough.*

decisions are $125,000, $175,000, and $400,000. (The latter two of these are calculated in row 15 as the usual SUMPRODUCT of monetary values and probabilities.) So from an EMV point of view, the more risky venture is definitely best. In fact, the ordering of the three alternatives using the EMV criterion is exactly the *opposite* of the ordering using expected utility. But because Venture Limited is sufficiently risk averse and the monetary values are sufficiently large, the company is willing to sacrifice $275,000 of EMV to avoid risk.

### Sensitivity Analysis

How sensitive is the optimal decision to the key parameter, the risk tolerance? You can answer this by changing the risk tolerance and watching how the decision tree changes. You can check that when the company becomes *more* risk tolerant, the more risky venture eventually becomes optimal. In fact, this occurs when the risk tolerance increases to approximately $2.210 million. In the other direction, of course, when the company becomes *less* risk tolerant, the riskless decision continues to be optimal. (The "middle" decision, the less risky alternative, is evidently not optimal for *any* value of the risk tolerance.) The bottom line is that the decision considered optimal depends entirely on the attitudes toward risk of Venture Limited's top management. ▨

### 9.6.3 Certainty Equivalents

Now let's change the problem slightly so that Venture Limited has only two options. It can either enter the less risky venture or receive a *certain* dollar amount $x$ and avoid the gamble altogether. We want to find the dollar amount $x$ so that the company is indifferent between these two options. If it enters the risky venture, its expected utility is 0.0525, calculated earlier. If it receives $x$ dollars for certain, its utility is

$$U(x) = 1 - e^{-x/1920}$$

To find the value $x$ where the company is indifferent between the two options, set $1 - e^{-x/1920}$ equal to 0.0525, or $e^{-x/1920} = 0.9475$, and solve for $x$. Taking natural logarithms of both sides and multiplying by 1920, the result is

$$x = -1920 \ln(0.9475) = 104$$

(Because of the units of measure, this is really $104,000.) This value is called the **certainty equivalent** of the risky venture. The company is indifferent between entering the less risky venture and receiving $104,000 to avoid it. Although the EMV of the less risky venture is $175,000, the company acts as if it is equivalent to a sure $104,000. In this sense, the company is willing to give up the difference in EMV, $71,000, to avoid a gamble.

By a similar calculation, the certainty equivalent of the more risky venture is approximately $86,000. That is, the company acts as if this more risky venture is equivalent to a sure $86,000, when in fact its EMV is a hefty $400,000. In this case, the company is willing to give up the difference in EMV, $314,000, to avoid this particular gamble. Again, the reason is that the company wants to avoid risk. You can see these certainty equivalents in PrecisionTree by changing the Display box in Figure 9.42 to show Certainty Equivalent. The resulting tree is shown in Figure 9.44. The certainty equivalents we just discussed appear in cells C24 and C32. (Note that we rounded the values in the text to the nearest $1000. The values in the figure are more exact.)

Figure 9.44    Certainty Equivalents in Tree

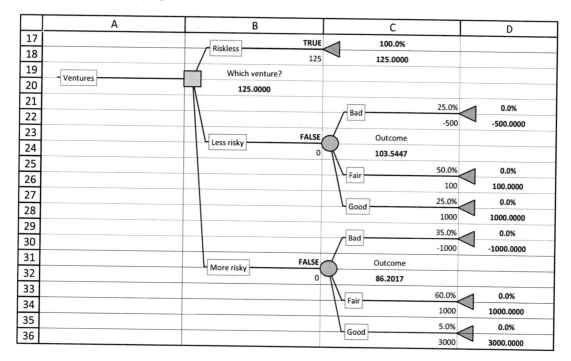

| | A | B | C | D |
|---|---|---|---|---|
| 17 | | Riskless | TRUE  ◀   100.0% | |
| 18 | | | 125    125.0000 | |
| 19 | Ventures | Which venture? | | |
| 20 | | 125.0000 | | |
| 21 | | | | |
| 22 | | | Bad   25.0% ◀   0.0% | |
| 23 | | Less risky |    -500    -500.0000 | |
| 24 | | FALSE  ◯ Outcome | | |
| 25 | | 0    103.5447 | | |
| 26 | | | Fair   50.0% ◀   0.0% | |
| 27 | | |    100    100.0000 | |
| 28 | | | Good   25.0% ◀   0.0% | |
| 29 | | |    1000    1000.0000 | |
| 30 | | | Bad   35.0% ◀   0.0% | |
| 31 | | More risky   FALSE ◯ |    -1000    -1000.0000 | |
| 32 | | 0    86.2017 | Outcome | |
| 33 | | | | |
| 34 | | | Fair   60.0% ◀   0.0% | |
| 35 | | |    1000    1000.0000 | |
| 36 | | | Good   5.0% ◀   0.0% | |
| | | |    3000    3000.0000 | |

## EXAMPLE   9.4 MARKETING A NEW PRODUCT AT ACME (CONTINUED)

Before concluding this section, we take a last look at the Acme marketing decision from the previous section. Suppose Acme decides to use expected utility as its criterion with an exponential utility function? Is the EMV-maximizing decision still optimal? Remember that this strategy first performed the test market and then marketed nationally only if the test-market results were great.

**Objective**   To see how risk aversion affects Acme's strategy.

### Solution

There is very little work to do. You first enter a risk tolerance value in a blank cell. Then, starting with the tree from Figure 9.32, fill out the dialog box in Figure 9.42, with a link to the risk tolerance cell. (See the finished version of the file Acme Marketing Decisions 2.xlsx for the details.) It is then interesting to perform a sensitivity analysis on the risk tolerance. We tried this, letting the risk tolerance vary from 1000 to 10,000 (remember that these are in thousands of dollars) and seeing whether the decision to run a test market changes. The results appear in Figure 9.45.

Do you understand why it is better to run the test market only if the risk tolerance is sufficiently large? It is not really because of the cost of the test market. When the risk tolerance is small, the company is so risk averse that it never markets nationally—on *any* of the "National market?" decision nodes. So information from the test market is worthless. However, as *R* increases, the company becomes less risk averse and in some scenarios, its

Figure 9.45    Sensitivity to Risk Tolerance for Acme Decision

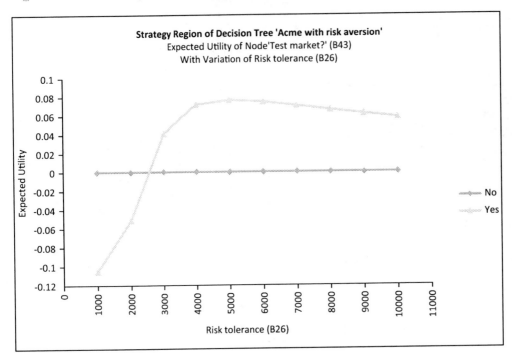

best decision is to market nationally. In these cases, the information from the test market can be worth its price. (If you don't follow this reasoning, open the finished version of the file, try large and small values of the risk tolerance, and see how the TRUEs and FALSEs on the decision tree change.) ▪

### 9.6.4 Is Expected Utility Maximization Used?

The previous discussion indicates that expected utility maximization is a fairly involved task. The question, then, is whether the effort is justified. Theoretically, expected utility maximization might be interesting to researchers, but is it really used in the business world? The answer appears to be: not very often. For example, one article on the practice of decision making [see Kirkwood (1992)] quotes Ronald Howard—the same person we quoted previously—as having found risk aversion to be of practical concern in only 5% to 10% of business decision analyses. This same article quotes the president of a Fortune 500 company as saying, "Most of the decisions we analyze are for a few million dollars. It is adequate to use expected value (EMV) for these."

## PROBLEMS

### Skill-Building Problems

**33.** For the risky venture example, create a line chart that includes three series—that is, three lines (or curves). Each line should show the expected utility of a particular decision for a sequence of possible risk tolerance values. This chart should make it clear when the more risky option becomes optimal and whether the less risky option is ever optimal.

**34.** In the risky venture example, the more risky alternative, in spite of its dominating EMV, is not preferred by a decision maker with a risk tolerance of $1.92 million. Now suppose everything stays the same except for the best monetary outcome of the more risky alternative (the value in cell D14). How much larger must this value be for the decision maker to prefer the more risky alternative? What is the corresponding EMV at that point?

35. In the risky venture example, suppose there is no riskless alternative; the only two possible decisions are the less risky venture and the more risky venture. Explore which of these is the preferred alternative for a range of risk tolerances. Can you find a cutoff point for the risk tolerance such that the less risky venture is preferred for risk tolerances below the cutoff and the more risky venture is preferred otherwise?

## Skill-Extending Problems

36. Do the absolute magnitudes of the monetary outcomes matter in the risky venture example? Consider the following two possibilities. In each case, multiply all monetary values in the example by a factor of A. (For example, double them if A = 2.) For each part, briefly explain your findings.

a. Currently, an EMV maximizer would choose the most risky venture. Would this continue to be the case for any factor A?

b. Currently, an expected utility maximizer with a risk tolerance of $1.92 million prefers the riskless alternative. Would this continue to be the case for any factor A greater than 1? What about when A is less than 1? You can answer by using trial and error on A.

c. Referring to the dialog box in Figure 9.42, there is a Display dropdown list with three options: expected value (EMV), expected utility, and certainty equivalent. The latter is defined for any gamble as the sure monetary amount a risk-averse person would take as a trade for the risky gamble. For example, you can check that the certainty equivalent for the more risky alternative is 86.2017 (in thousands of dollars). Explain what this really means by calculating the utility of 86.2017 manually and comparing it to the *expected* utility from the more risky venture (as shown on the tree). How does this explain why the decision maker prefers the riskless alternative to the more risky venture?

## 9.7 CONCLUSION

In this chapter we have discussed methods that can be used in decision-making problems where uncertainty is a key element. Perhaps the most important skill you can gain from this chapter is the ability to approach decision problems with uncertainty in a systematic manner. This systematic approach requires you to list all possible decisions or strategies, list all possible uncertain outcomes, assess the probabilities of these outcomes (possibly with the aid of Bayes' rule), calculate all necessary monetary values, and finally do the necessary calculations to obtain the best decision. If large dollar amounts are at stake, you might also need to perform a utility analysis, where the decision maker's attitudes toward risk are taken into account. Once the basic analysis has been completed, using best guesses for the various parameters of the problem, you should perform a sensitivity analysis to see whether the best decision continues to be best within a range of input parameters.

## Summary of Key Terms

| Term | Explanation | Excel | Page | Equation |
|------|-------------|-------|------|----------|
| Payoff (or cost) table | A table that lists the payoffs (or costs) for all combinations of decisions and uncertain outcomes | | 478 | |
| Maximin criterion | The pessimist's criterion; find the worst possible payoff for each decision, and choose the decision with the best of these | | 479 | |

*(continued)*

| Term | Explanation | Excel | Page | Equation |
|------|-------------|-------|------|----------|
| Maximax criterion | The optimist's criterion; find the best possible payoff for each decision, and choose the decision with the best of these | | 480 | |
| Expected monetary value (EMV) | The weighted average of the possible payoffs from a decision, weighted by their probabilities | | 480 | |
| EMV criterion | Choose the decision with the maximum EMV | | 480 | |
| Decision tree | A graphical device for illustrating all of the aspects of the decision problem and for finding the optimal decision (or decision strategy) | | 482 | |
| Folding-back procedure | Calculation method for decision tree; starting at the right, take EMVs at probability nodes, maximums of EMVs at decision nodes | | 484 | |
| Risk profile | Chart that represents the probability distribution of monetary outcomes for any decision | | 484 | |
| PrecisionTree | Useful Excel add-in developed by Palisade for building and analyzing decision trees in Excel | Has its own ribbon | 492 | |
| PrecisionTree strategy region chart | Useful for seeing how the optimal decision changes as selected inputs vary | Use PrecisionTree Sensitivity Analysis button | 501 | |
| PrecisionTree tornado and spider charts | Useful for seeing which inputs affect a selected EMV the most | Use PrecisionTree Sensitivity Analysis button | 501 | |
| Bayes' rule | Formula for updating probabilities as new information becomes available; *prior probabilities* are transformed into *posterior probabilities* | | 505 | 9.1 |
| Law of total probability | The denominator in Bayes' rule, for calculating the (unconditional) probability of an information outcome | | 505 | 9.2 |
| Expected value of sample information (EVSI) | The most the (imperfect) *sample information* (such as the results of a test market) would be worth | | 513 | 9.4 |
| Expected value of perfect information (EVPI) | The most *perfect information* on some uncertain outcome would be worth; represents an upper bound on *any* EVSI | | 513 | 9.5 |
| Contingency plan | A decision strategy where later decisions depend on earlier decisions and outcomes observed in the meantime | | 515 | |
| Expected utility maximization | Choosing the decision that maximizes the *expected utility;* typically sacrifices EMV to avoid risk when large monetary amounts are at stake | | 526 | |
| Utility function | A mathematical function that encodes an individual's (or company's) attitudes toward risk | | 526 | |

(*continued*)

| Term | Explanation | Excel | Page | Equation |
|------|-------------|-------|------|----------|
| Exponential utility function, risk tolerance | A popular class of utility functions, where only a single parameter, the *risk tolerance*, has to be specified | | 527 | 9.6 |
| Certainty equivalent | The sure dollar value equivalent to the expected utility of a gamble | | 530 | |

## PROBLEMS

### Skill-Building Problems

**37.** The SweetTooth Candy Company knows it will need 10 tons of sugar six months from now to implement its production plans. Jean Dobson, SweetTooth's purchasing manager, has essentially two options for acquiring the needed sugar. She can either buy the sugar at the going market price when she needs it, six months from now, or she can buy a futures contract now. The contract guarantees delivery of the sugar in six months but the cost of purchasing it will be based on today's market price. Assume that possible sugar futures contracts available for purchase are for five tons or ten tons only. No futures contracts can be purchased or sold in the intervening months. Thus, SweetTooth's possible decisions are to (1) purchase a futures contract for ten tons of sugar now, (2) purchase a futures contract for five tons of sugar now and purchase five tons of sugar in six months, or (3) purchase all ten tons of needed sugar in six months. The price of sugar bought now for delivery in six months is $0.0851 per pound. The transaction costs for five-ton and ten-ton futures contracts are $65 and $110, respectively. Finally, Ms. Dobson has assessed the probability distribution for the possible prices of sugar six months from now (in dollars per pound). The file P09_37.xlsx contains these possible prices and their corresponding probabilities.
   a. Given that SweetTooth wants to acquire the needed sugar in the least costly way, create a cost table that specifies the cost (in dollars) associated with each possible decision and possible sugar price in the future.
   b. Use PrecisionTree to identify the decision that minimizes SweetTooth's expected cost of meeting its sugar demand.
   c. Perform a sensitivity analysis on the optimal decision, letting each of the three currency inputs vary one at a time plus or minus 25% from its base value, and summarize your findings. In response to which of these inputs is the expected cost value most sensitive?

**38.** Carlisle Tire and Rubber, Inc., is considering expanding production to meet potential increases in the demand for one of its tire products. Carlisle's alternatives are to construct a new plant, expand the existing plant, or do nothing in the short run. The market for this particular tire product may expand, remain stable, or contract. Carlisle's marketing department estimates the probabilities of these market outcomes as 0.25, 0.35, and 0.40, respectively. The file P09_38.xlsx contains Carlisle's estimated payoff (in dollars) table.
   a. Use PrecisionTree to identify the strategy that maximizes this tire manufacturer's expected profit.
   b. Perform a sensitivity analysis on the optimal decision, letting each of the monetary inputs vary one at a time plus or minus 10% from its base value, and summarize your findings. In response to which monetary inputs is the expected profit value most sensitive?

**39.** A local energy provider offers a landowner $180,000 for the exploration rights to natural gas on a certain site and the option for future development. This option, if exercised, is worth an additional $1,800,000 to the landowner, but this will occur only if natural gas is discovered during the exploration phase. The landowner, believing that the energy company's interest in the site is a good indication that gas is present, is tempted to develop the field herself. To do so, she must contract with local experts in natural gas exploration and development. The initial cost for such a contract is $300,000, which is lost forever if no gas is found on the site. If gas is discovered, however, the landowner expects to earn a net profit of $6,000,000. The landowner estimates the probability of finding gas on this site to be 60%.
   a. Create a payoff table that specifies the landowner's payoff (in dollars) associated with each possible decision and each outcome with respect to finding natural gas on the site.
   b. Use PrecisionTree to identify the strategy that maximizes the landowner's expected net earnings from this opportunity.
   c. Perform a sensitivity analysis on the optimal decision, letting each of the inputs vary one at a time plus or minus 25% from its base value, and summarize your findings. In response to which model inputs is the expected profit value most sensitive?

**40.** Techware Incorporated is considering the introduction of two new software products to the market. In particular, the company has four options regarding these two proposed products: introduce neither product, introduce product 1 only, introduce product 2 only, or introduce both products. Research and development costs for products 1 and 2 are $180,000 and $150,000, respectively. Note that the first option entails no costs because research and development efforts have not yet begun. The success of these software products depends on the trend of the national economy in the coming year and on the consumers' reaction to these products. The company's revenues earned by introducing product 1 only, product 2 only, or both products in various states of the national economy are given in the file P09_40.xlsx. The probabilities of observing a strong, fair, or weak trend in the national economy in the coming year are assessed to be 0.30, 0.50, and 0.20, respectively.

a. Create a payoff table that specifies Techware's net revenue (in dollars) for each possible decision and each outcome with respect to the trend in the national economy.

b. Use PrecisionTree to identify the strategy that maximizes Techware's expected net revenue from the given marketing opportunities.

c. Perform a sensitivity analysis on the optimal decision, letting each of the inputs vary one at a time plus or minus 25% from its base value, and summarize your findings. In response to which model inputs is the expected net revenue value most sensitive?

**41.** Consider an investor with $10,000 available to invest. He has the following options regarding the allocation of his available funds: (1) he can invest in a risk-free savings account with a guaranteed 3% annual rate of return; (2) he can invest in a fairly safe stock, where the possible annual rates of return are 6%, 8%, or 10%; or (3) he can invest in a more risky stock, where the possible annual rates of return are 1%, 9%, or 17%. Note that the investor can place all of his available funds in any one of these options, or he can split his $10,000 into two $5000 investments in any two of these options. The joint probability distribution of the possible return rates for the two stocks is given in the file P09_41.xlsx.

a. Create a payoff table that specifies this investor's return (in dollars) in one year for each possible decision and each outcome with respect to the two stock returns.

b. Use PrecisionTree to identify the strategy that maximizes the investor's expected earnings in one year from the given investment opportunities.

c. Perform a sensitivity analysis on the optimal decision, letting the amount available to invest and the risk-free return both vary, one at a time, plus or minus 100% from their base values, and summarize your findings.

**42.** A buyer for a large department store chain must place orders with an athletic shoe manufacturer six months prior to the time the shoes will be sold in the department stores. In particular, the buyer must decide on November 1 how many pairs of the manufacturer's newest model of tennis shoes to order for sale during the coming summer season. Assume that each pair of this new brand of tennis shoes costs the department store chain $45 per pair. Furthermore, assume that each pair of these shoes can then be sold to the chain's customers for $70 per pair. Any pairs of these shoes remaining unsold at the end of the summer season will be sold in a closeout sale next fall for $35 each. The probability distribution of consumer demand for these tennis shoes during the coming summer season has been assessed by market research specialists and is provided in the file P09_42.xlsx. Finally, assume that the department store chain must purchase these tennis shoes from the manufacturer in lots of 100 pairs.

a. Create a payoff table that specifies the contribution to profit (in dollars) from the sale of the tennis shoes by this department store chain for each possible purchase decision and each outcome with respect to consumer demand.

b. Use PrecisionTree to identify the strategy that maximizes the department store chain's expected profit earned by purchasing and subsequently selling pairs of the new tennis shoes.

c. Perform a sensitivity analysis on the optimal decision, letting the three monetary inputs vary one at a time over reasonable ranges, and summarize your findings. In response to which model inputs is the expected earnings value most sensitive?

**43.** Each day the manager of a local bookstore must decide how many copies of the community newspaper to order for sale in her shop. She must pay the newspaper's publisher $0.40 for each copy, and she sells the newspapers to local residents for $0.75 each. Newspapers that are unsold at the end of day are considered worthless. The probability distribution of the number of copies of the newspaper purchased daily at her shop is provided in the file P09_43.xlsx. Create a payoff table that lists the profit from each order quantity (multiples of 1000 only) and each demand, and use it to find the order quantity that maximizes expected profit. Why is this an easier approach than a decision tree for this particular problem?

**44.** Two construction companies are bidding against one another for the right to construct a new community center building in Bloomington, Indiana. The first construction company, Fine Line Homes, believes that its competitor, Buffalo Valley Construction, will place a bid for this project according to the distribution shown in the file P09_44.xlsx. Furthermore, Fine Line Homes estimates that it will cost $160,000 for its own company to construct this building. Given its fine reputation and long-standing service within the local community, Fine Line Homes believes that it will likely be awarded the project in the event that it and Buffalo Valley Construction submit exactly the same bids. Create a payoff table that lists the profit from each Fine Line bid and each competing bid, and use it to find the bid that maximizes Fine Line's expected profit. Why is this an easier approach than a decision tree for this particular problem?

**45.** Suppose that you have sued your employer for damages suffered when you recently slipped and fell on an icy surface that should have been treated by your company's physical plant department. Specifically, your injury resulting from this accident was sufficiently serious that you, in consultation with your attorney, decided to sue your company for $500,000. Your company's insurance provider has offered to settle this suit with you out of court. If you decide to reject the settlement and go to court, your attorney is confident that you will win the case but is uncertain about the amount the court will award you in damages. He has provided his assessment of the probability distribution of the court's award to you in the file P09_45.xlsx. In addition, there are extra legal fees of $10,000 you will have to pay if you go to court. Let $S$ be the insurance provider's proposed out-of-court settlement (in dollars). For which values of $S$ will you decide to accept the settlement? For which values of $S$ will you choose to take your chances in court? Assume that you are seeking to maximize the expected net payoff from this litigation.

**46.** One of your colleagues has $2000 available to invest. Assume that all of this money must be placed in one of three investments: a particular money market fund, a stock, or gold. Each dollar your colleague invests in the money market fund earns a virtually guaranteed 3% annual return. Each dollar he invests in the stock earns an annual return characterized by the probability distribution provided in the file P09_46.xlsx. Finally, each dollar he invests in gold earns an annual return characterized by the probability distribution given in the same file.
   **a.** If your colleague must place all of his available funds in a single investment, which investment should he choose to maximize his expected earnings over the next year?
   **b.** Suppose now that your colleague can place all of his available funds in one of these three investments as before, or he can invest $1000 in one alternative and $1000 in another. Assuming that he seeks to maximize his expected total earnings in one year, how should he allocate his $2000?

**47.** Consider a population of 2000 individuals, 800 of whom are women. Assume that 300 of the women in this population earn at least $60,000 per year, and 200 of the men earn at least $60,000 per year.
   **a.** What is the probability that a randomly selected individual from this population earns less than $60,000 per year?
   **b.** If a randomly selected individual is observed to earn less than $60,000 per year, what is the probability that this person is a man?
   **c.** If a randomly selected individual is observed to earn at least $60,000 per year, what is the probability that this person is a woman?

**48.** Yearly automobile inspections are required for residents of the state of Pennsylvania. Suppose that 18% of all inspected cars in Pennsylvania have problems that need to be corrected. Unfortunately, Pennsylvania state inspections fail to detect these problems 12% of the time. On the other hand, assume that an inspection never detects a problem when there is no problem. Consider a car that is inspected and is found to be free of problems. What is the probability that there is indeed something wrong that the inspection has failed to uncover?

**49.** Consider again the landowner's decision problem described in Problem 39. Suppose now that, at a cost of $90,000, the landowner can request that a soundings test be performed on the site where natural gas is believed to be present. The company that conducts the soundings concedes that 30% of the time the test will indicate that no gas is present when it actually is. When natural gas is not present in a particular site, the soundings test is accurate 90% of the time.
   **a.** Given that the landowner pays for the soundings test and the test indicates that gas is present, what is the landowner's revised estimate of the probability of finding gas on this site?
   **b.** Given that the landowner pays for the soundings test and the test indicates that gas is not present, what is the landowner's revised estimate of the probability of not finding gas on this site?
   **c.** Should the landowner request the given soundings test at a cost of $90,000? Explain why or why not. If not, at what price (if any) would the landowner choose to obtain the soundings test?

**50.** The chief executive officer of a firm in a highly competitive industry believes that one of her key employees is providing confidential information to the competition. She is 90% certain that this informer is the vice president of finance, whose contacts have been extremely valuable in obtaining financing for the company. If she decides to fire this vice president and he is the informer, she estimates that the company will gain $500,000. If she decides to fire this vice president but he is not the informer, the company will lose his expertise and still have an informer within the staff; the CEO estimates that this outcome would cost her company about $2.5 million. If she decides not to fire this vice president, she estimates that the firm will lose $1.5 million regardless of whether he actually is the informer (because in either case the informer is still with the company). Before deciding whether to fire the vice president for finance, the CEO could order lie detector tests. To avoid possible lawsuits, the lie detector tests would have to be administered to all company employees, at a total cost of $150,000. Another problem she must consider is that the available lie detector tests are not perfectly reliable. In particular, if a person is lying, the test will reveal that the person is lying 95% of the time. Furthermore, if a person is not lying, the test will indicate that the person is not lying 85% of the time.

**a.** To minimize the expected total cost of managing this difficult situation, what strategy should the CEO adopt?

**b.** Should the CEO order the lie detector tests for all of her employees? Explain why or why not.

**c.** Determine the maximum amount of money that the CEO should be willing to pay to administer lie detector tests.

**d.** How sensitive are the results to the accuracy of the lie detector test? Are there any "reasonable" values of the error probabilities that change the optimal strategy?

**51.** A customer has approached a bank for a $100,000 one-year loan at a 12% interest rate. If the bank does not approve this loan application, the $100,000 will be invested in bonds that earn a 6% annual return. Without additional information, the bank believes that there is a 4% chance that this customer will default on the loan, assuming that the loan is approved. If the customer defaults on the loan, the bank will lose $100,000. At a cost of $1000, the bank can thoroughly investigate the customer's credit record and supply a favorable or unfavorable recommendation. Past experience indicates that in cases where the customer did not default on the approved loan, the probability of receiving a favorable recommendation on the basis of the credit investigation was 0.80. Furthermore, in cases where the customer defaulted on the approved loan, the probability of receiving a favorable recommendation on the basis of the credit investigation was 0.25.

**a.** What strategy should the bank follow to maximize its expected profit?

**b.** Calculate and interpret the expected value of sample information (EVSI) for this decision problem.

**c.** Calculate and interpret the expected value of perfect information (EVPI) for this decision problem.

**d.** How sensitive are the results to the accuracy of the credit record recommendations? Are there any

"reasonable" values of the error probabilities that change the optimal strategy?

**52.** A company is considering whether to market a new product. Assume, for simplicity, that if this product is marketed, there are only two possible outcomes: success or failure. The company assesses that the probabilities of these two outcomes are $p$ and $1 - p$, respectively. If the product is marketed and it proves to be a failure, the company will have a net loss of $450,000. If the product is marketed and it proves to be a success, the company will have a net gain of $750,000. If the company decides not to market the product, there is no gain or loss. The company is also considering whether to survey prospective buyers of this new product. The results of the consumer survey can be classified as favorable, neutral, or unfavorable. In similar cases where proposed products were eventually market successes, the fractions of cases where the survey results were favorable, neutral, or unfavorable were 0.6, 0.3, and 0.1, respectively. In similar cases where proposed products were eventually market failures, the fractions of cases where the survey results were favorable, neutral, or unfavorable were 0.1, 0.2, and 0.7, respectively. The total cost of administering this survey is $C$ dollars.

**a.** Let $p = 0.4$. For which values of $C$, if any, would this company choose to conduct the consumer survey?

**b.** Let $p = 0.4$. What is the largest amount that this company would be willing to pay for perfect information about the potential success or failure of the new product?

**c.** Let $p = 0.5$ and $C = \$15,000$. Find the strategy that maximizes the company's expected earnings in this situation. Does the optimal strategy involve conducting the consumer survey? Explain why or why not.

**53.** The U.S. government is attempting to determine whether immigrants should be tested for a contagious disease. Assume that the decision will be made on a financial basis. Furthermore, assume that each immigrant who is allowed to enter the United States and has the disease costs the country $100,000. Also, each immigrant who is allowed to enter the United States and does not have the disease will contribute $10,000 to the national economy. Finally, assume that $x$ percent of all potential immigrants have the disease. The U.S. government can choose to admit all immigrants, admit no immigrants, or test immigrants for the disease before determining whether they should be admitted. It costs $T$ dollars to test a person for the disease, and the test result is either positive or negative. A person who does not have the disease *always* tests negative. However, 10% of all people who *do* have the disease test negative. The government's goal is to maximize the expected net financial benefits per potential immigrant.

**a.** If $x = 10$, what is the largest value of $T$ at which the U.S. government will choose to test potential immigrants for the disease?

**b.** How does your answer to the question in part **a** change if $x$ increases to 15?

**c.** If $x = 5$ and $T = \$500$, what is the government's optimal strategy?

**d.** If $x = 5$, calculate and interpret the expected value of perfect information (EVPI) for this decision problem.

**54.** The senior executives of an oil company are trying to decide whether to drill for oil in a particular field in the Gulf of Mexico. It costs the company \$600,000 to drill in the selected field. Company executives believe that if oil is found in this field its estimated value will be \$3,400,000. At present, this oil company believes that there is a 45% chance that the selected field actually contains oil. Before drilling, the company can hire a geologist at a cost of \$55,000 to prepare a report that contains a recommendation regarding drilling in the selected field. In many similar situations in the past where this geologist has been hired, the geologist has predicted oil on 75% of all fields that have contained oil, and he has predicted no oil on 85% of all fields that have not contained oil.

**a.** Assuming that this oil company wants to maximize its expected net earnings, use a decision tree to determine its optimal strategy.

**b.** Calculate and interpret EVSI for this decision problem. Experiment with the accuracy probabilities of the geologist to see how EVSI changes as they change.

**c.** Calculate and interpret EVPI for this decision problem.

**55.** FineHair is developing a new product to promote hair growth in cases of male pattern baldness. If FineHair markets the new product and it is successful, the company will earn \$1,000,000 in additional profit. If the marketing of this new product proves to be unsuccessful, the company will lose \$350,000 in development and marketing costs. In the past, similar products have been successful 30% of the time. At a cost of \$50,000, the effectiveness of the new restoration product can be thoroughly tested. In past tests on similar products, the test predicted success on 70% of products that were ultimately successful, and it predicted failure on 75% of products that were ultimately failures.

**a.** Identify the strategy that maximizes FineHair's expected net earnings in this situation.

**b.** Calculate and interpret EVSI for this decision problem.

**c.** Calculate and interpret EVPI for this decision problem.

**56.** A product manager at Clean & Brite (C&B) wants to determine whether her company should market a new brand of toothpaste. If this new product succeeds in the marketplace, C&B estimates that it could earn \$1,800,000 in future profits from the sale of the new toothpaste. If this new product fails, however, the company expects that it could lose approximately \$750,000. If C&B chooses not to market this new brand, the product manager believes that there would be little, if any, impact on the profits earned through sales of C&B's other products. The manager has estimated that the new toothpaste brand will succeed with probability 0.50. Before making her decision regarding this toothpaste product, the manager can spend \$75,000 on a market research study. Based on similar studies with past products, C&B believes that the study will predict a successful product, given that product would actually be a success, with probability 0.75. It also believes that the study will predict a failure, given that the product would actually be a failure, with probability 0.65.

**a.** To maximize expected profit, what strategy should the C&B product manager follow?

**b.** Calculate and interpret EVSI for this decision problem.

**c.** Calculate and interpret EVPI for this decision problem.

**57.** Ford is going to produce a new vehicle, the Pioneer, and wants to determine the amount of annual capacity it should build. Ford's goal is to maximize the profit from this vehicle over the next 10 years. Each vehicle will sell for \$13,000 and incur a variable production cost of \$10,000. Building one unit of annual capacity will cost \$3000. Each unit of capacity will also cost \$1000 per year to maintain, even if the capacity is unused. Demand for the Pioneer is unknown but marketing estimates the distribution of annual demand to be as shown in the file P09_57.xlsx. Assume that the number of units sold during a year is the minimum of capacity and annual demand.

**a.** Explain why a capacity of 1,300,000 is not a good choice.

**b.** Which capacity level should Ford choose?

**58.** Pizza King (PK) and Noble Greek (NG) are competitive pizza chains. PK believes there is a 25% chance that NG will charge \$6 per pizza, a 50% chance NG will charge \$8 per pizza, and a 25% chance that NG will charge \$10 per pizza. If PK charges price $p_1$ and NG charges price $p_2$, PK will sell $100 + 25(p_2 - p_1)$ pizzas. It costs PK \$4 to make a pizza. PK is considering charging \$5, \$6, \$7, \$8, or \$9 per pizza. To maximize its expected profit, what price should PK charge for a pizza?

**59.** Many decision problems have the following simple structure. A decision maker has two possible decisions, 1 and 2. If decision 1 is made, a *sure* cost of $c$ is incurred. If decision 2 is made, there are two possible outcomes, with costs $c_1$ and $c_2$ and probabilities $p$ and $1 - p$. We assume that $c_1 < c < c_2$. The idea is that decision 1, the riskless decision, has a moderate cost, whereas decision 2, the risky decision, has a low cost $c_1$ or a high cost $c_2$.

   a. Find the decision maker's cost table, that is, the cost for each possible decision and each possible outcome.
   b. Calculate the expected cost from the risky decision.
   c. List as many scenarios as you can think of that have this structure. (Here's an example to get you started. Think of insurance, where you pay a sure premium to avoid a large possible loss.)

60. A nuclear power company is deciding whether to build a nuclear power plant at Diablo Canyon or at Roy Rogers City. The cost of building the power plant is $10 million at Diablo and $20 million at Roy Rogers City. If the company builds at Diablo, however, and an earthquake occurs at Diablo during the next five years, construction will be terminated and the company will lose $10 million (and will still have to build a power plant at Roy Rogers City). Without further expert information the company believes there is a 20% chance that an earthquake will occur at Diablo during the next five years. For $1 million, a geologist can be hired to analyze the fault structure at Diablo Canyon. She will predict either that an earthquake will occur or that an earthquake will not occur. The geologist's past record indicates that she will predict earthquake on 95% of the occasions for which an earthquake will occur and no earthquake on 90% of the occasions for which an earthquake will not occur. Should the power company hire the geologist? Also, calculate and interpret EVSI and EVPI.

61. Consider again Techware's decision problem described in Problem 40. Suppose now that Techware's utility function of net revenue $x$ (measured in dollars), earned from the given marketing opportunities, is $U(x) = 1 - e^{-x/350000}$.

   a. Find the decision that maximizes Techware's expected utility. How does this optimal decision compare to the optimal decision with an EMV criterion? Explain any difference between the two optimal decisions.
   b. Repeat part a when Techware's utility function is $U(x) = 1 - e^{-x/50000}$.

62. Consider again the bank's customer loan decision problem in Problem 51. Suppose now that the bank's utility function of profit $x$ (in dollars) is $U(x) = 1 - e^{-x/150000}$. Find the strategy that maximizes the bank's expected utility in this case. How does this optimal strategy compare to the optimal

decision with an EMV criterion? Explain any difference between the two optimal strategies.

63. The Indiana University basketball team trails by two points with eight seconds to go and has the ball. Should it attempt a two-point shot or a three-point shot? Assume that the Indiana shot will end the game and that no foul will occur on the shot. Assume that a three-point shot has a 30% chance of success, and a two-point shot has a 45% chance of success. Finally, assume that Indiana has a 50% chance of winning in overtime.

## Skill-Extending Problems

64. George Lindsey (1959) looked at box scores of more than 1000 baseball games and found the expected number of runs scored in an inning for each on-base and out situation to be as listed in the file P09_64.xlsx. For example, if a team has a man on first base with one out, it scores 0.5 run on average until the end of the inning. You can assume throughout this problem that the team batting wants to maximize the expected number of runs scored in the inning.

   a. Use this data to explain why, in most cases, bunting with a man on first base and no outs is a bad decision. In what situation might bunting with a man on first base and no outs be a good decision?
   b. Assume there is a man on first base with one out. What probability of stealing second makes an attempted steal a good idea?

65. One controversial topic in basketball (college or any other level) is whether to foul a player deliberately with only a few seconds left in the game. Specifically, consider the following scenario. With about 10 seconds left in the game, team A is ahead of team B by three points, and team B is just about to inbound the ball. Assume team A has committed enough fouls so that future fouls result in team B going to the free-throw line. If team A purposely commits a foul as soon as possible, team B will shoot two foul shots (a point apiece). The thinking is that this is better than letting team B shoot a three-point shot, which would be their best way to tie the game and send it into overtime. However, there is a downside to fouling. Team B could make the first free throw, purposely miss the second, get the rebound, and score a two-point shot to tie the game, or it even score a three-point shot to win the game. Examine this decision, using reasonable input parameters. It doesn't appear that this deliberate fouling strategy is used very often, but do you think it should be used?

66. The following situation actually occurred in a 2009 college football game between Washington and

Notre Dame. With about 3.5 minutes left in the game, Washington had fourth down and one yard to go for a touchdown, already leading by two points. Notre Dame had just had two successful goal-line stands from in close, so Washington's coach decided not to go for the touchdown and the virtually sure win. Instead, Washington kicked a field goal, and Notre Dame eventually won in overtime. Use a decision tree, with some reasonable inputs, to see whether Washington made a wise decision or should have gone for the touchdown. Note the only "monetary" values here are 1 and 0. You can think of Washington getting $1 if they win and $0 if they lose. Then the EMV is $1*P(Win) + 0*P(lose) = P(Win)$, so maximizing EMV is equivalent to maximizing the probability of winning.

**67.** Mr. Maloy has just bought a new $30,000 sport utility vehicle. As a reasonably safe driver, he believes that there is only about a 5% chance of being in an accident in the coming year. If he is involved in an accident, the damage to his new vehicle depends on the severity of the accident. The probability distribution for the range of possible accidents and the corresponding damage amounts (in dollars) are given in the file P09_67.xlsx. Mr. Maloy is trying to decide whether he is willing to pay $170 each year for collision insurance with a $300 deductible. Note that with this type of insurance, he pays the *first* $300 in damages if he causes an accident and the insurance company pays the remainder.
   **a.** Create a cost table that specifies the cost (in dollars) associated with each possible decision and type of accident.
   **b.** Use PrecisionTree to identify the strategy that minimizes Mr. Maloy's annual expected cost.
   **c.** Perform a sensitivity analysis on the optimal decision with respect to the probability of an accident, the premium, and the deductible amount, and summarize your findings. (You can choose the ranges to test.) In response to which of these three inputs is the expected cost most sensitive?

**68.** The purchasing agent for a PC manufacturer is currently negotiating a purchase agreement for a particular electronic component with a given supplier. This component is produced in lots of 1000, and the cost of purchasing a lot is $30,000. Unfortunately, past experience indicates that this supplier has occasionally shipped defective components to its customers. Specifically, the proportion of defective components supplied by this supplier has the probability distribution given in the file P09_68.xlsx. Although the PC manufacturer can repair a defective component at a cost of $20 each, the purchasing agent learns that this supplier will now assume the cost of replacing defective components in excess of the first 100 faulty items found in a given lot. This guarantee may be purchased by the PC manufacturer prior to the receipt of a given lot at a cost of $1000 per lot. The purchasing agent wants to determine whether it is worthwhile to purchase the supplier's guarantee policy.
   **a.** Create a cost table that specifies the PC manufacturer's total cost (in dollars) of purchasing and repairing (if necessary) a complete lot of components for each possible decision and each outcome with respect to the proportion of defective items.
   **b.** Use PrecisionTree to identify the strategy that minimizes the expected total cost of achieving a complete lot of satisfactory microcomputer components.
   **c.** Perform a sensitivity analysis on the optimal decision with respect to the number of components per lot and the three monetary inputs, and summarize your findings. (You can choose the ranges to test.) In response to which of these inputs is the expected cost most sensitive?

**69.** A home appliance company is interested in marketing an innovative new product. The company must decide whether to manufacture this product in house or employ a subcontractor to manufacture it. The file P09_69.xlsx contains the estimated probability distribution of the cost of manufacturing one unit of this new product (in dollars) if the home appliance company produces the product in house. This file also contains the estimated probability distribution of the cost of purchasing one unit of the product if from the subcontractor. There is also uncertainty about demand for the product in the coming year, as shown in the same file. The company plans to meet all demand, but there is a capacity issue. The subcontractor has unlimited capacity, but the home appliance company has capacity for only 5000 units per year. If it decides to make the product in house and demand is greater than capacity, it will have to purchase the excess demand from an external source at a premium: $225 per unit. Assuming that the company wants to minimize the expected cost of meeting demand in the coming year, should it make the new product in house or buy it from the subcontractor? Do you need a decision tree, or will a cost table with EMV calculations suffice? (You can assume that neither the company nor the subcontractor will ever produce *more* than demand.)

**70.** A grapefruit farmer in central Florida is trying to decide whether to take protective action to limit damage to his crop in the event that the overnight temperature falls to a level well below freezing. He is concerned that if the temperature falls sufficiently low and he fails to make an effort to protect his grapefruit trees, he runs the risk of losing his entire crop, which is worth approximately $75,000. Based on the latest forecast issued by the National Weather Service, the farmer estimates that there is a 60% chance that he will lose his entire crop if it is left unprotected. Alternatively, the farmer can insulate his fruit by spraying water on all of the trees in his orchards. This action, which would likely cost the farmer $C$ dollars, would prevent total devastation but might not completely protect the grapefruit trees from incurring some damage as a result of the unusually cold overnight temperatures. The file P09_70.xlsx contains the assessed distribution of possible damages (in dollars) to the insulated fruit in light of the cold weather forecast. The farmer wants to minimize the expected total cost of coping with the threatening weather.

a. Find the maximum value of $C$ below which the farmer should insulate his crop to limit the damage from the unusually cold weather.

b. Set $C$ equal to the value identified in part **a**. Perform sensitivity analysis to determine under what conditions, if any, the farmer would be better off not spraying his grapefruit trees and taking his chances in spite of the threat to his crop.

c. Suppose that $C$ equals $25,000, and in addition to this protection, the farmer can purchase insurance on the crop. Discuss possibilities for reasonable insurance policies and how much they would be worth to the farmer. You can assume that the insurance is relevant only if the farmer purchases the protection, and you can decide on the terms of the insurance policy.

71. A retired partner from a large brokerage firm has one million dollars available to invest in particular stocks or bonds. Each investment's annual rate of return depends on the state of the economy in the coming year. The file P09_71.xlsx contains the distribution of returns for these stocks and bonds as a function of the economy's state in the coming year. As this file indicates, the returns from stocks and bonds in a fair economy are listed as $X$ and $Y$. This investor wants to allocate her one million dollars to maximize her expected value of the portfolio one year from now.

a. If $X = Y = 15\%$, find the optimal investment strategy for this investor. (*Hint*: You could try a decision tree approach, but it would involve a massive tree. It is much easier to find an algebraic expression for the expected final value of the investment when a percentage $p$ is put in stocks and the remaining percentage is put in bonds. Given this expression, the best value of $p$ should be obvious.)

b. For which values of $X$ (where $10\% < X < 20\%$) and $Y$ (where $12.5\% < Y < 17.5\%$), if any, will this investor prefer to place all of her available funds in stocks? Use the same method as in part **a** for each combination of $X$ and $Y$.

72. A city in Ohio is considering replacing its fleet of gasoline-powered automobiles with electric cars. The manufacturer of the electric cars claims that this municipality will experience significant cost savings over the life of the fleet if it chooses to pursue the conversion. If the manufacturer is correct, the city will save about $1.5 million dollars. If the new technology employed within the electric cars is faulty, as some critics suggest, the conversion to electric cars will cost the city $675,000. A third possibility is that less serious problems will arise and the city will break even with the conversion. A consultant hired by the city estimates that the probabilities of these three outcomes are 0.30, 0.30, and 0.40, respectively. The city has an opportunity to implement a pilot program that would indicate the potential cost or savings resulting from a switch to electric cars. The pilot program involves renting a small number of electric cars for three months and running them under typical conditions. This program would cost the city $75,000. The city's consultant believes that the results of the pilot program would be significant but not conclusive; she submits the values in the file P09_72.xlsx, a compilation of probabilities based on the experience of other cities, to support her contention. For example, the first row of her table indicates that given that a conversion to electric cars actually results in a savings of $1.5 million, the conditional probabilities that the pilot program will indicate that the city saves money, loses money, and breaks even are 0.6, 0.1, and 0.3, respectively. What actions should the city take to maximize its expected savings? When should it run the pilot program, if ever? (Note: If you set up the input section of your spreadsheet in the right way, you will be able to perform all of the Bayes' rule calculations with a couple of *copyable* formulas.)

73. A manufacturer must decide whether to extend credit to a retailer who would like to open an account with the firm. Past experience with new accounts indicates that 45% are high-risk customers, 35% are moderate-risk customers, and 20% are low-risk customers. If credit is extended, the manufacturer can expect to lose $60,000 with a high-risk customer, make $50,000 with a moderate-risk customer, and make $100,000 with a low-risk customer. If the manufacturer decides not to extend credit to a customer, the manufacturer neither makes nor loses any money. Prior to making a credit extension decision, the manufacturer can obtain a credit rating report on the retailer at a cost of $2000. The credit agency concedes that its rating procedure is not completely reliable. In particular, the credit rating procedure will rate a low-risk customer as a moderate-risk customer with probability 0.10 and as a high-risk customer with probability 0.05. Similarly, the given rating procedure will rate a moderate-risk customer as a low-risk customer with probability 0.06

and as a high-risk customer with probability 0.07. Finally, the rating procedure will rate a high-risk customer as a low-risk customer with probability 0.01 and as a moderate-risk customer with probability 0.05. Find the strategy that maximizes the manufacturer's expected net earnings. (*Note:* If you set up the input section of your spreadsheet in the right way, you will be able to perform all of the Bayes' rule calculations with a couple of *copyable* formulas.)

74. A television network earns an average of $1.6 million each season from a hit program and loses an average of $400,000 each season on a program that turns out to be a flop. Of all programs picked up by this network in recent years, 25% turn out to be hits and 75% turn out to be flops. At a cost of $C$ dollars, a market research firm will analyze a pilot episode of a prospective program and issue a report predicting whether the given program will end up being a hit. If the program is actually going to be a hit, there is a 90% chance that the market researchers will predict the program to be a hit. If the program is actually going to be a flop, there is only a 20% chance that the market researchers will predict the program to be a hit.
   a. Assuming that $C = \$160{,}000$, find the strategy that maximizes the network's expected profit.
   b. What is the maximum value of $C$ that the network should be willing to pay the market research firm?
   c. Calculate and interpret EVPI for this decision problem.

75. A publishing company is trying to decide whether to publish a new business law textbook. Based on a careful reading of the latest draft of the manuscript, the publisher's senior editor in the business textbook division assesses the distribution of possible payoffs earned by publishing this new book. The file P09_75.xlsx contains this probability distribution. Before making a final decision regarding the publication of the book, the editor can learn more about the text's potential for success by thoroughly surveying business law instructors teaching at universities across the country. Historical frequencies based on similar surveys administered in the past are also provided in this file.
   a. Find the strategy that maximizes the publisher's expected payoff if the survey cost is $10,000.
   b. What is the most that the publisher would be willing to pay to conduct a new survey of business law instructors?
   c. Assuming that a survey could be constructed that provides perfect information to the publisher, how much would the company be willing to pay to acquire and implement such a survey?

76. Sharp Outfits is trying to decide whether to ship some customer orders now via UPS or wait until after the threat of another UPS strike is over. If Sharp Outfits

decides to ship the requested merchandise now and the UPS strike takes place, the company will incur $60,000 in delay and shipping costs. If Sharp Outfits decides to ship the customer orders via UPS and no strike occurs, the company will incur $4000 in shipping costs. If Sharp Outfits decides to postpone shipping its customer orders via UPS, the company will incur $10,000 in delay costs regardless of whether UPS goes on strike. Let $p$ represent the probability that UPS will go on strike and impact Sharp Outfits's shipments.
   a. For which values of $p$, if any, does Sharp Outfits minimize its expected total cost by choosing to postpone shipping its customer orders via UPS?
   b. Suppose now that, at a cost of $1000, Sharp Outfits can purchase information regarding the likelihood of a UPS strike in the near future. Based on similar strike threats in the past, the company assesses that if there will be a strike, the information will predict a strike with probability 0.75, and if there will not be a strike, the information will predict no strike with probability 0.85. Provided that $p = 0.15$, what strategy should Sharp Outfits pursue to minimize its expected total cost?
   c. Use the tree from part **b** to find the EVSI when $p = 0.15$. Then use a data table to find EVSI for $p$ from 0.05 to 0.30 in increments of 0.05, and chart EVSI versus $p$.
   d. Continuing part **b**, compute and interpret the EVPI when $p = 0.15$.

77. A homeowner wants to decide whether he should install an electronic heat pump in his home. Given that the cost of installing a new heat pump is fairly large, the homeowner wants to do so only if he can count on being able to recover the initial expense over *five* consecutive years of cold winter weather. After reviewing historical data on the operation of heat pumps in various kinds of winter weather, he computes the expected annual costs of heating his home during the winter months with and without a heat pump in operation. These cost figures are shown in the file P09_77.xlsx. The probabilities of experiencing a mild, normal, colder than normal, and severe winter are $0.2(1 - x), 0.5(1 - x), 0.3(1 - x)$, and $x$, respectively. In words, we let the last probability vary, we let the other three be in the ratio 2 to 5 to 3, and we force them to sum to 1.
   a. Given that $x = 0.1$, what is the most that the homeowner is willing to pay for the heat pump?
   b. If the heat pump costs $500, how large must $x$ be before the homeowner decides it is economically worthwhile to install the heat pump?
   c. Given that $x = 0.1$, calculate and interpret EVPI when the heat pump costs $500.
   d. Repeat part **c** when $x = 0.15$.

78. Sarah Chang is the owner of a small electronics company. In six months, a proposal is due for an

electronic timing system for the next Olympic Games. For several years, Chang's company has been developing a new microprocessor, a critical component in a timing system that would be superior to any product currently on the market. However, progress in research and development has been slow, and Chang is unsure whether her staff can produce the microprocessor in time. If they succeed in developing the microprocessor (probability $p_1$), there is an excellent chance (probability $p_2$) that Chang's company will win the $1 million Olympic contract. If they do not, there is a small chance (probability $p_3$) that she will still be able to win the same contract with an alternative but inferior timing system that has already been developed. If she continues the project, Chang must invest $200,000 in research and development. In addition, making a proposal (which she will decide whether to do after seeing whether the R&D is successful) requires developing a prototype timing system at an additional cost. This additional cost is $50,000 if R&D is successful (so that she can develop the new timing system), and it is $40,000 if R&D is unsuccessful (so that she needs to go with the older timing system). Finally, if Chang wins the contract, the finished product will cost an additional $150,000 to produce.

a. Develop a decision tree that can be used to solve Chang's problem. You can assume in this part of the problem that she is using EMV (of her net profit) as a decision criterion. Build the tree so that she can enter any values for $p_1$, $p_2$, and $p_3$ (in input cells) and automatically see her optimal EMV and optimal strategy from the tree.

b. If $p_2 = 0.8$ and $p_3 = 0.1$, what value of $p_1$ makes Chang indifferent between abandoning the project and going ahead with it?

c. How much would Chang benefit if she knew for certain that the Olympic organization would guarantee her the contract? (This guarantee would be in force only if she were successful in developing the product.) Assume $p_1 = 0.4$, $p_2 = 0.8$, and $p_3 = 0.1$.

d. Suppose now that this is a relatively big project for Chang. Therefore, she decides to use expected utility as her criterion, with an exponential utility function. Using some trial and error, see which risk tolerance changes her initial decision from "go ahead" to "abandon" when $p_1 = 0.4$, $p_2 = 0.8$, and $p_3 = 0.1$.

70. The Ventron Engineering Company has just been awarded a $2 million development contract by the U.S. Army Aviation Systems Command to develop a blade spar for its Heavy Lift Helicopter program. The blade spar is a metal tube that runs the length of and provides strength to the helicopter blade. Due to the unusual length and size of the Heavy Lift Helicopter

blade, Ventron is unable to produce a single-piece blade spar of the required dimensions using existing extrusion equipment and material. The engineering department has prepared two alternatives for developing the blade spar: (1) sectioning or (2) an improved extrusion process. Ventron must decide which process to use. (Backing out of the contract at any point is not an option.) The risk report has been prepared by the engineering department. The information from this report is explained next.

The sectioning option involves joining several shorter lengths of extruded metal into a blade spar of sufficient length. This work will require extensive testing and rework over a 12-month period at a total cost of $1.8 million. Although this process will definitely produce an adequate blade spar, it merely represents an extension of existing technology.

To improve the extrusion process, on the other hand, it will be necessary to perform two steps: (1) improve the material used, at a cost of $300,000, and (2) modify the extrusion press, at a cost of $960,000. The first step will require six months of work, and if this first step is successful, the second step will require another six months of work. If both steps are successful, the blade spar will be available at that time, that is, a year from now. The engineers estimate that the probabilities of succeeding in steps 1 and 2 are 0.9 and 0.75, respectively. However, if either step is unsuccessful (which will be known only in six months for step 1 and in a year for step 2), Ventron will have no alternative but to switch to the sectioning process—and incur the sectioning cost on top of any costs already incurred.

Development of the blade spar must be completed within 18 months to avoid holding up the rest of the contract. If necessary, the sectioning work can be done on an accelerated basis in a six-month period, but the cost of sectioning will then increase from $1.8 million to $2.4 million. The director of engineering, Dr. Smith, wants to try developing the improved extrusion process. He reasons that this is not only cheaper (if successful) for the current project, but its expected side benefits for future projects could be sizable. Although these side benefits are difficult to gauge, Dr. Smith's best guess is an additional $2 million. (These side benefits are obtained only if both steps of the modified extrusion process are completed successfully.)

a. Develop a decision tree to maximize Ventron's EMV. This includes the revenue from this project, the side benefits (if applicable) from an improved extrusion process, and relevant costs. You don't need to worry about the time value of money; that is, no discounting or net present values are required. Summarize your findings in words in the spreadsheet.

**b.** What value of side benefits would make Ventron indifferent between the two alternatives?

**c.** How much would Ventron be willing to pay, right now, for perfect information about both steps of the improved extrusion process? (This information would tell Ventron, right now, the ultimate success or failure outcomes of both steps.)

**80.** Suppose an investor has the opportunity to buy the following contract, a stock call option, on March 1. The contract allows him to buy 100 shares of ABC stock at the end of March, April, or May at a guaranteed price of $50 per share. He can exercise this option at most once. For example, if he purchases the stock at the end of March, he can't purchase more in April or May at the guaranteed price. The current price of the stock is $50. Each month, assume that the stock price either goes up by a dollar (with probability 0.55) or goes down by a dollar (with probability 0.45). If the investor buys the contract, he is hoping that the stock price will go up. The reasoning is that if he buys the contract, the price goes up to $51, and he buys the stock (that is, he exercises his option) for $50, he can then sell the stock for $51 and make a profit of $1 per share. On the other hand, if the stock price goes down, he doesn't have to exercise his option; he can just throw the contract away.

**a.** Use a decision tree to find the investor's optimal strategy (that is, when he should exercise the option), *assuming* he purchases the contract.

**b.** How much should he be willing to pay for such a contract?

**81.** [Based on Balson et al. (1992).] An electric utility company is trying to decide whether to replace its PCB transformer in a generating station with a new and safer transformer. To evaluate this decision, the utility needs information about the likelihood of an incident, such as a fire, the cost of such an incident, and the cost of replacing the unit. Suppose that the total cost of replacement as a present value is $75,000. If the transformer is replaced, there is virtually no chance of a fire. However, if the current transformer is retained, the probability of a fire is assessed to be 0.0025. If a fire occurs, the cleanup cost could be high ($80 million) or low ($20 million). The probability of a high cleanup cost, given that a fire occurs, is assessed at 0.2.

**a.** If the company uses EMV as its decision criterion, should it replace the transformer?

**b.** Perform a sensitivity analysis on the key parameters of the problem that are difficult to assess, namely, the probability of a fire, the probability of a high cleanup cost, and the high and low cleanup costs. Does the optimal decision from part **a** remain optimal for a wide range of these parameters?

**c.** Do you believe EMV is the correct criterion to use in this type of problem involving environmental accidents?

**82.** The ending of the game between the Indianapolis Colts and the New England Patriots (NFL teams) in Fall 2009 was quite controversial. With about two minutes left in the game, the Patriots were ahead 34 to 28 and had the ball on their *own* 28-yard line with fourth down and two yards to go. Their coach, Bill Belichick, decided to go for the first down rather than punt, contrary to conventional wisdom. They didn't make the first down, so that possession went to the Colts, who then scored a touchdown to win by a point. Belichick was harshly criticized by most of the media, but was his unorthodox decision really a bad one?

**a.** Use a decision tree to analyze the problem. You can make some simplifying decisions: (1) the game would essentially be over if the Patriots made a first down, and (2) at most one score would occur after a punt or a failed first down attempt. (Note that there are no monetary values. However, you can assume the Patriots receive $1 for a win and $0 for a loss, so that maximizing EMV is equivalent to maximizing the probability that the Patriots win.)

**b.** Show that the Patriots should go for the first down if $p > 1 - q/r$. Here, $p$ is the probability the Patriots make the first down, $q$ is the probability the Colts score a touchdown after a punt, and $r$ is the probability the Colts score a touchdown after the Patriots fail to make a first down. What are your best guesses for these three probabilities? Based on them, was Belichick's decision a good one?

**83.** Suppose you believe that the price of a particular stock goes up each day with probability $p$ and goes down with probability $1-p$. You also believe the daily price changes are independent of one another. However, you are not sure of the value of $p$. Based on your current information, you believe $p$ could be 0.40, 0.45, 0.50, or 0.55, with probabilities 0.15, 0.25, 0.35, and 0.25, respectively. Then you watch the stock price changes for 25 days and observe 12 ups and 13 downs. Use Bayes' rule to find the posterior distribution of $p$. Based on this posterior distribution, calculate the probability that there will be at least 15 ups in the *next* 30 price changes. (*Hint*: Think in terms of the binomial distribution.)

## Modeling Problems

**84.** Your company needs to make an important decision that involves large monetary consequences. You have listed all of the possible outcomes and the monetary payoffs and costs from all outcomes and all potential decisions. You want to use the EMV criterion, but you realize that this requires probabilities and you see no way to find the required probabilities. What can you do?

85. If your company makes a particular decision in the face of uncertainty, you estimate that it will either gain $10,000, gain $1000, or lose $5000, with probabilities 0.40, 0.30, and 0.30, respectively. You (correctly) calculate the EMV as $2800. However, you distrust the use of this EMV for decision-making purposes. After all, you reason that you will never receive $2800; you will receive $10,000, $1000, or lose $5000. Discuss this reasoning.

86. In the previous question, suppose you have the option of receiving a check for $2700 instead of making the risky decision described. Would you make the risky decision, where you *could* lose $5000, or would you take the sure $2700? What would influence your decision?

87. In a classic oil-drilling example, you are trying to decide whether to drill for oil on a field that might or might not contain any oil. Before making this decision, you have the option of hiring a geologist to perform some seismic tests and then predict whether there is any oil or not. You assess that if there is actually oil, the geologist will predict there is oil with probability 0.85. You also assess that if there is no oil, the geologist will predict there is no oil with probability 0.90. Why will these two probabilities *not* appear on the decision tree? Which probabilities *will* be on the decision tree?

88. Your company has signed a contract with a good customer to ship the customer an order no later than 20 days from now. The contract indicates that the customer will accept the order even if it is late, but instead of paying the full price of $10,000, it will be allowed to pay 10% less, $9000, due to lateness. You estimate that it will take anywhere from 17 to 22 days to ship the order, and each of these is equally likely. You believe you are in good shape, reasoning that the expected days to ship is the average of 17 through 22, or 19.5 days. Because this is less than 20, you will get your full $10,000. What is wrong with your reasoning?

89. You must make one of two decisions, each with possible gains and possible losses. One of these decisions is much riskier than the other, having much larger possible gains but also much larger possible

losses, and it has a larger EMV than the safer decision. Because you are risk averse and the monetary values are large relative to your wealth, you base your decision on expected utility, and it indicates that you should make the safer decision. It also indicates that the certainty equivalent for the risky decision is $210,000, whereas its EMV is $540,000. What do these two numbers mean? What do you know about the certainty equivalent of the safer decision?

90. A potentially huge hurricane is forming in the Caribbean, and there is some chance that it might make a direct hit on Hilton Head Island, South Carolina, where you are in charge of emergency preparedness. You have made plans for evacuating everyone from the island, but such an evacuation is obviously costly and upsetting for all involved, so the decision to evacuate shouldn't be made lightly. Discuss how you would make such a decision. Is EMV a relevant concept in this situation? How would you evaluate the consequences of uncertain outcomes?

91. It seems obvious that if you can purchase information before making an ultimate decision, this information should generally be worth something, but explain exactly why (and when) it is sometimes worth nothing.

92. Insurance companies wouldn't exist unless customers were willing to pay the price of the insurance and the insurance companies were making a profit. So explain how insurance is a win-win proposition for customers and the company.

93. You often hear about the trade-off between risk and reward. Is this trade-off part of decision making under uncertainty when the decision maker uses the EMV criterion? For example, how does this work in investment decisions?

94. Can you ever use the material in this chapter to help you make your own real-life decisions? Consider the following. You are about to take an important and difficult exam in one of your MBA courses, and you see an opportunity to cheat. Obviously, from an ethical point of view, you shouldn't cheat, but from a purely monetary point of view, could it also be the wrong decision? To model this, consider the long-term monetary consequences of all possible outcomes.

The Jogger Shoe Company is trying to decide whether to make a change in its most popular brand of running shoes. The new style would cost the same to produce and be priced the same, but it would incorporate a new kind of lacing system that (according to its marketing research people) would make it more popular.

There is a fixed cost of $300,000 for changing over to the new style. The unit contribution to before-tax profit for either style is $8. The tax rate is 35%. Also, because the fixed cost can be depreciated and will therefore affect the after-tax cash flow, a depreciation method is needed. You can assume it is straight-line depreciation.

The current demand for these shoes is 190,000 pairs annually. The company assumes this demand will continue for the next three years if the current style is retained. However, there is uncertainty about demand for the new style, if it is introduced. The company models this uncertainty by assuming a normal distribution in year 1, with mean 220,000 and standard deviation 20,000. The company also assumes that this demand, whatever it is, will remain constant for the next three years. However, if demand in year 1 for the new style is sufficiently low, the company can always switch back to the current style and realize an annual demand of 190,000. The company wants a strategy that will maximize the expected net present value (NPV) of total cash flow for the next three years, where a 15% interest rate is used for the purpose of calculating NPV. ▪

The Westhouser Paper Company in the state of Washington currently has an option to purchase a piece of land with good timber forest on it. It is now May 1, and the current price of the land is $2.2 million. Westhouser does not actually need the timber from this land until the beginning of July, but its top executives fear that another company might buy the land between now and the beginning of July. They assess that there is a 5% chance that a competitor will buy the land during May. If this does not occur, they assess that there is a 10% chance that the competitor will buy the land during June. If Westhouser does not take advantage of its current option, it can attempt to buy the land at the beginning of June or the beginning of July, provided that it is still available.

Westhouser's incentive for delaying the purchase is that its financial experts believe there is a good chance that the price of the land will fall significantly in one or both of the next two months. They assess the possible price decreases and their probabilities in Table 9.7 and Table 9.8. Table 9.7 shows the probabilities of the possible price decreases during May. Table 9.8 lists the *conditional* probabilities of the possible price decreases in June, *given* the price decrease in May. For example, it indicates that if the price decrease in May is $60,000, then the possible price decreases in June are $0, $30,000, and $60,000 with respective probabilities 0.6, 0.2, and 0.2.

If Westhouser purchases the land, it believes that it can gross $3 million. (This does not count the cost of purchasing the land.) But if it does not purchase the land, Westhouser believes that it can make $650,000 from alternative investments. What should the company do?

Table 9.7    Distribution of Price Decrease in May

| Price Decrease | Probability |
|---|---|
| $0 | 0.5 |
| $60,000 | 0.3 |
| $120,000 | 0.2 |

Table 9.8    Distribution of Price Decrease in June

| Price Decrease in May | | | | | |
|---|---|---|---|---|---|
| $0 | | $60,000 | | $120,000 | |
| June Decrease | Probability | June Decrease | Probability | June Decrease | Probability |
| $0 | 0.3 | $0 | 0.6 | $0 | 0.7 |
| $60,000 | 0.6 | $30,000 | 0.2 | $20,000 | 0.2 |
| $120,000 | 0.1 | $60,000 | 0.2 | $40,000 | 0.1 |

Biotechnical Engineering specializes in developing new chemicals for agricultural applications. The company is a pioneer in using the sterile-male procedure to control insect infestations. It operates several laboratories around the world that raise insects and expose them to extra-large doses of radiation, making them sterile. As an alternative to chlorinated hydrocarbon pesticides, such as DDT, the sterile-male procedure has been used frequently with a good track record of success, most notably with the Mediterranean fruit fly (or Medfly).

That pest was controlled in California through the release of treated flies on the premise that the sterile male flies would compete with fertile wild males for mating opportunities. Any female that has mated with a sterile fly will lay eggs that do not hatch. The California Medfly campaigns required about five successive releases of sterile males—at intervals timed to coincide with the time for newly hatched flies to reach adulthood—before the Medfly was virtually eliminated. (Only sterile flies were subsequently caught in survey traps.) The effectiveness of the sterile-male procedure was enhanced by the release of malathion poisonous bait just a few days before each release, cutting down on the number of viable wild adults.

More recently, Biotechnical Engineering has had particular success in using genetic engineering to duplicate various insect hormones and pheromones (scent attractants). Of particular interest is the application of such methods against the Gypsy Moth, a notorious pest that attacks trees. The company has developed synthetic versions of both hormones and pheromones for that moth. It has a synthetic sexual attractant that male moths can detect at great distances. Most promising is the synthetic juvenile hormone.

The juvenile hormone controls moth metamorphosis, determining the timing for the transformation of a caterpillar into a chrysalis and then into an adult. Too much juvenile hormone wreaks havoc with this process, causing caterpillars to turn into freak adults that cannot reproduce.

Biotechnical Engineering has received a government contract to test its new technology in an actual eradication campaign. The company will participate in a small-scale campaign against the Gypsy Moth in the state of Oregon. Because the pest is so damaging, Dr. June Scribner, the administrator in charge, is considering using DDT as an alternative procedure. Of course, that banned substance is only available for government emergency use because of the environmental damage it may cause. In addition to spraying with DDT, two other procedures may be employed: (1) using Biotechnical's scent lure, followed by the release of sterile males, and (2) spraying with the company's juvenile hormone to prevent larvae from developing into adults. Dr. Scribner wants to select the method that yields the best expected payoff, described below.

Although both of the newer procedures are known to work under laboratory conditions, there is some uncertainty about successful propagation of the chemicals in the wild and about the efficacy of the sterile-male procedure with moths.

If the scent-lure program is launched at a cost of $5 million, Biotechnical claims that it will have a fifty-fifty chance of leaving a low number of native males versus a high number. Once the results of that phase are known, a later choice must be made to spray with DDT or to release sterile males; the cost of the sterilization and delivery of the insects to the countrside is an additional $5 million. But if this two-phase program is successful, the net present value of the worth of trees saved is $30 million, including the benefit of avoiding all other forms of environmental damage. The indigenous moth population would be destroyed, and a new infestation could occur only from migrants. Biotechnical's experience with other eradication programs indicates that if the scent lure leaves a small native male population, there is a 90% chance for a successful eradication by using sterile males; otherwise, there is only a 10% chance for success by using sterile males. A failure results in no savings.

---

[9]This case was written by Lawrence L. Lapin, San Jose State University.

The cost of synthesizing enough juvenile hormone is $3 million. Biotechnical maintains that the probability that the hormone can be effectively disseminated is only 0.20. If it works, the worth of the trees saved and environmental damage avoided will be $50 million. This greater level of savings is possible because of the permanent nature of the solution because a successful juvenile hormone can then be applied wherever the moths are known to exist, virtually eliminating the pest from the environment. But if the hormone does not work, the DDT must still be used to save the trees.

DDT constitutes only a temporary solution, and the worth of its savings in trees is far less than the worth of either of the esoteric eradication procedures—if they prove successful. To compare alternatives, Dr. Scribner proposes using the net advantage (crop and environmental savings, minus cost) relative to where she would be were she to decide to use DDT at the outset or were she to be forced to spray with it later. (Regardless of the outcome, Biotechnical will be reimbursed for all expenditures. The decision is hers, not the company's.)

## Questions

1. Under Biotechnical's proposal, the selection of DDT without even trying the other procedures would lead to a neutral outcome for the government, having zero payoff. Discuss the benefits of Dr. Scribner's proposed payoff measure.

2. Construct Dr. Scribner's decision tree diagram, using the proposed payoff measure.

3. What action will maximize Dr. Scribner's expected payoff?

4. Dr. Scribner is concerned about the assumed fifty-fifty probability for the two levels of surviving native males following the scent-lure program.

   a. Redo the decision tree analysis to find what action will maximize Dr. Scribner's expected payoff when the probability of low native males is, successively, (1) 0.40 or (2) 0.60 instead.

   b. How is the optimal action affected by the probability level assumed for the low native male outcome?

5. Dr. Scribner is concerned about the assumed 0.20 probability for the dissemination success of the juvenile hormone.

   a. Keeping all other probabilities and cash flows at their original levels, redo the decision tree analysis to find what action will maximize Dr. Scribner's expected payoff when the probability of juvenile hormone success is, successively, (1) 0.15 or (2) 0.25 instead.

   b. How is the optimal action affected by the probability level assumed for the juvenile hormone's success?

6. Dr. Scribner is concerned about the assumed probability levels for the success of the sterile-male procedure.

   a. Keeping all other probabilities and cash flows at their original levels, redo the decision tree analysis to find what action will maximize Dr. Scribner's expected payoff when the sterile-male success probabilities are instead as follows:

   (1) 80% for a low number of native males and 5% for a high number of native males

   (2) 70% for a low number of native males and 15% for a high number of native males

   b. How is the optimal action affected by the probability level assumed for the success of the sterile-male procedure?

7. Dr. Scribner is concerned about the assumed levels for the net present value of the worth of trees saved and damage avoided. She believes these amounts are only accurate within a range of ±10%.

   a. Keeping all other probabilities and cash flows at their original levels, redo the decision tree analysis to find what action will maximize Dr. Scribner's expected payoff when the two net present values are instead, successively, (1) 10% lower or (2) 10% higher than originally assumed.

   b. How is the optimal action affected by the level assumed for the NPVs of the savings from using one of the two esoteric Gypsy Moth eradication procedures? ▪

Image Source/Jupiter Images

## DEVELOPING BOARDING STRATEGIES AT AMERICA WEST

Management science often attempts to solve problems that we all experience. One such problem is the boarding process for airline flights. As customers, we all hate to wait while travelers boarding ahead of us store their luggage and block the aisles. But this is also a big problem for the airlines. Airlines lose money when their airplanes are on the ground, so they have a real incentive to reduce the turnaround time from when a plane lands until it departs on its next flight. Of course, the turnaround time is influenced by several factors, including passenger deplaning, baggage unloading, fueling, cargo unloading, airplane maintenance, cargo loading, baggage loading, and passenger boarding. Airlines try to perform all of these tasks as efficiently as possible, but passenger boarding is particularly difficult to shorten. Although the airlines want passengers to board as quickly as possible, they don't want to use measures that might antagonize their passengers.

One study by van den Briel et al. (2005) indicates how a combination of management science methods, including simulation, was used to make passenger boarding more efficient at America West Airlines. America West (which merged with US Airways in 2006) was a major U.S. carrier based in Phoenix, Arizona. It served more destinations nonstop than any other airline.

The airline's fleet consisted of Airbus A320s, Airbus A319s, Boeing 757s, Boeing 737s, and Airbus A318s.

At the time of the study, airlines used a variety of boarding strategies, but the predominant strategy was the back-to-front (BF) strategy where, after boarding first-class passengers and passengers with special needs, the rest of the passengers are boarded in groups, starting with rows in the back of the plane. As the authors suspected (and most of us have experienced), this strategy still results in significant congestion. Within a given section of the plane (the back, say), passengers storing luggage in overhead compartments can block an aisle. Also, people in the aisle or middle seat often need to get back into the aisle to let window-seat passengers be seated. The authors developed an integer programming (IP) model to minimize the number of such aisle blockages. The decision variables determined which groups of seats should be boarded in which order. Of course, the BF strategy was one possible feasible solution, but it turned out to be a suboptimal solution. The IP model suggested that the best solution was an outside-in (OI) strategy, where groups of passengers in window seats board first, then groups in the middle seats, and finally groups in aisle seats, with all of these groups going essentially in a back-to-front order.

The authors recognized that their IP model was at best an idealized model of how passengers actually behave. Its biggest drawback is that it ignores the inherent randomness in passenger behavior. Therefore, they followed up their optimization model with a simulation model. As they state, "We used simulation to validate the analytical model and to obtain a finer level of detail." This validation of an approximate or idealized analytical model is a common use for simulation. To make the simulation as realistic as possible, they used two cameras, one inside the plane and one inside the bridge leading to the plane, to tape customer behavior. By analyzing the tapes, they were able to estimate the required inputs to their simulation model, such as the time between passengers, walking speed, blocking time, and time to store luggage in overhead compartments. After the basic simulation model was developed, it was used as a tool to evaluate various boarding strategies suggested by the IP model. It also allowed the authors to experiment with changes to the overall boarding process that might be beneficial. For example, reducing congestion *inside* the airplane is not very helpful if the gate agent at the entrance to the bridge processes passengers too slowly. Their final recommendation, based on a series of simulation experiments, was to add a second gate agent (there had been only one before) and to board passengers in six groups using an OI strategy. The simulation model suggested that this could reduce the boarding time by about 37%.

The authors' recommendations were implemented first as a pilot project and then systemwide. The pilot results were impressive, with a 39% reduction in boarding times. By September 2003, the new boarding strategies had been implemented in 80% of America West's airports, with a decrease in departure delays as much as 60.1%. Besides this obvious benefit to the airline, customers also appear to be happier. Now they can easily understand when to queue up for boarding, and they experience less blocking after they get inside the plane. ■

## 10.1 INTRODUCTION

A **simulation model** is a computer model that imitates a real-life situation. It is like other mathematical models, but it explicitly incorporates uncertainty in one or more input variables. When you run a simulation, you allow these random input variables to take on various values, and you keep track of any resulting output variables of interest. In this way, you are able to see how the outputs vary as a function of the varying inputs.

The fundamental advantage of a simulation model is that it provides an entire distribution of results, not simply a single bottom-line result. As an example, suppose an automobile manufacturer is planning to develop and market a new model car. The company is ultimately interested in the net present value (NPV) of the profits from this car over the next 10 years. However, there are many uncertainties surrounding this car, including the yearly customer demands for it, the cost of developing it, and others. The company could develop a spreadsheet model for the 10-year NPV, using its *best guesses* for these uncertain quantities. It could then report the NPV based on these best guesses. However, this analysis would be incomplete and probably misleading—there is no guarantee that the NPV based on best-guess inputs is representative of the NPV that will actually occur. It is much better to treat the uncertainty explicitly with a simulation model. This involves entering probability distributions for the uncertain quantities and seeing how the NPV varies as the uncertain quantities vary.

Each different set of values for the uncertain quantities can be considered a scenario. Simulation allows the company to generate many scenarios, each leading to a particular NPV. In the end, it sees a whole distribution of NPVs, not a single best guess. The company can see what the NPV will be on average, and it can also see worst-case and best-case results.

These approaches are summarized in Figures 10.1 and 10.2. Figure 10.1 indicates that the deterministic (non-simulation) approach, using best guesses for the uncertain inputs, is generally *not* the appropriate method. It leads to the "flaw of averages," as we will discuss later in the chapter. The problem is that the outputs from the deterministic model are often not representative of the true outputs. The appropriate method is shown in Figure 10.2. Here the uncertainty is modeled explicitly with random inputs, and the end result is a probability distribution for each of the important outputs.

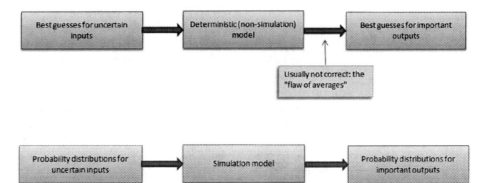

**Figure 10.1**

Inappropriate Deterministic Model

**Figure 10.2**

Appropriate Simulation Model

Simulation models are also useful for determining how sensitive a system is to changes in operating conditions. For example, the operations of a supermarket could be simulated. Once the simulation model has been developed, it could then be run (with suitable modifications) to ask a number of what-if questions. For example, if the supermarket experiences a 20% increase in business, what will happen to the average time customers must wait for service?

A huge benefit of computer simulation is that it enables managers to answer these types of what-if questions without actually changing (or building) a physical system. For example, the supermarket might want to experiment with the number of open registers to see the effect on customer waiting times. The only way it can *physically* experiment with more registers than it currently owns is to purchase more equipment. Then if it determines that this equipment is not a good investment—customer waiting times do not decrease appreciably—the company is stuck with expensive equipment it doesn't need. Computer simulation is a much less expensive alternative. It provides the company with an electronic replica of what would happen *if* the new equipment were purchased. Then, if the simulation indicates that the new equipment is worth the cost, the company can be confident that purchasing it is the right decision. Otherwise, it can abandon the idea of the new equipment *before* the equipment has been purchased.

Spreadsheet simulation modeling is quite similar to the other modeling applications in this book. You begin with input variables and then relate these with appropriate Excel formulas to produce output variables of interest. The main difference is that simulation uses *random* numbers to drive the whole process. These random numbers are generated with special functions that we will discuss in detail. Each time the spreadsheet recalculates, all of the random numbers change. This provides the ability to model the logical process once and then use Excel's recalculation ability to generate many different scenarios. By collecting the data from these scenarios, you can see the most likely values of the outputs and the best-case and worst-case values of the outputs.

In this chapter we begin by illustrating spreadsheet models that can be developed with built-in Excel functionality. However, because simulation is becoming such an important tool for analyzing real problems, add-ins to Excel have been developed to streamline the process of developing and analyzing simulation models. Therefore, we then introduce @RISK, one of the most popular simulation add-ins. This add-in not only augments the simulation capabilities of Excel, but it also enables you to analyze models much more quickly and easily.

The purpose of this chapter is to introduce basic simulation concepts, show how simulation models can be developed in Excel, and demonstrate the capabilities of the @RISK add-in. Then in the next chapter, armed with the necessary simulation tools, we will explore a number of interesting and useful simulation models.

Before proceeding, you might ask whether simulation is really used in the business world. The answer is a resounding yes. The chapter opener described an airline example, and many other examples can be found online. For example, if you visit www.palisade.com, you will see descriptions of interesting @RISK applications from companies that regularly use this add-in. Simulation has always been a powerful tool, but it had limited use for several reasons. It typically required specialized software that was either expensive or difficult to learn, or it required a lot of tedious computer programming. Fortunately, in the past two decades, spreadsheet simulation, together with Excel add-ins such as @RISK, has put this powerful methodology in the hands of the masses—people like you and the companies you are likely to work for. Many businesses now understand that there is no longer any reason to ignore uncertainty; they can model it directly with spreadsheet simulation.

## 10.2 PROBABILITY DISTRIBUTIONS FOR INPUT VARIABLES

*In spreadsheet simulation models, input cells can contain random numbers. Any output cells then vary as these random inputs change.*

In this section we discuss the building blocks of spreadsheet simulation models. All spreadsheet simulation models are similar to the spreadsheet models from previous chapters. They have a number of cells that contain values of input variables. The other cells then contain formulas that embed the logic of the model and eventually lead to the output variable(s) of interest. The primary difference between the spreadsheet models you have developed so far and simulation models is that at least one of the input variable cells in a simulation model contains *random* numbers. Each time the spreadsheet recalculates, the random numbers change, and the new random values of the inputs produce new values of the outputs. This is the essence of simulation—it enables you to see how outputs vary as random inputs change.

Excel Tip: **Recalculation Key**
*The easiest way to make a spreadsheet recalculate is to press the* **F9 key**. *This is often called the "recalc" key.*

Technically speaking, input cells do not contain random numbers; they contain *probability distributions*. In general, a probability distribution indicates the possible values of a variable and the probabilities of these values. As a very simple example, you might indicate by an appropriate formula (to be described later) that you want a probability distribution with possible values 50 and 100, and corresponding probabilities 0.7 and 0.3. If you force the sheet to recalculate repeatedly and watch this input cell, you will see the value 50 about 70% of the time and the value 100 about 30% of the time. No other values besides 50 and 100 will appear.

When you enter a given probability distribution in a random input cell, you are describing the possible values and the probabilities of these values that you believe mirror reality. There are many probability distributions to choose from, and you should always attempt to choose an *appropriate* distribution for each specific problem. This is not necessarily an easy task. Therefore, we address it in this section by answering several key questions:

▨ What types of probability distributions are available, and why do you choose one probability distribution rather than another in an actual simulation model?

▨ Which probability distributions can you use in simulation models, and how do you invoke them with Excel formulas?

In later sections we address one additional question: Does the choice of input probability distribution really matter—that is, are the *outputs* from the simulation sensitive to this choice?

---

## FUNDAMENTAL INSIGHT

### Basic Elements of Spreadsheet Simulation

A spreadsheet simulation model requires three elements: (1) a method for entering random quantities from specified probability distributions in input cells, (2) the usual types of Excel formulas for relating outputs to inputs, and (3) the ability to make the spreadsheet recalculate many times and capture the resulting outputs for statistical analysis. Excel has some capabilities for performing these steps, but Excel add-ins such as @RISK provide much better tools for automating the process.

---

## 10.2.1 Types of Probability Distributions

Imagine a toolbox that contains the probability distributions you know and understand. As you obtain more experience in simulation modeling, you will naturally add probability distributions to your toolbox that you can then use in future simulation models. We begin by adding a few useful probability distributions to this toolbox. However, before adding any specific distributions, it is useful to provide a brief review of some important general characteristics of probability distributions. These include the following distinctions:

▨ Discrete versus continuous
▨ Symmetric versus skewed

Choosing Probability Distributions
for Uncertain Inputs

In simulation models, it is important to choose *appropriate* probability distributions for all uncertain inputs. These choices can strongly affect the results. Unfortunately, there are no "right answers." You need to choose the probability distributions that best encode your uncertainty, and this is not necessarily easy. However, the properties discussed in this section provide you with useful guidelines for making reasonable choices.

- Bounded versus unbounded
- Nonnegative versus unrestricted.

### Discrete Versus Continuous

A probability distribution is *discrete* if it has a finite number of possible values.[1] For example, if you throw two dice and look at the sum of the faces showing, there are only 11 discrete possibilities: the integers 2 through 12. In contrast, a probability distribution is *continuous* if its possible values are essentially some continuum. An example is the amount of rain that falls during a month in Indiana. It could be any decimal value from 0 to, say, 15 inches.

The graph of a discrete distribution is a series of spikes, as shown in Figure 10.3.[2] The height of each spike is the probability of the corresponding value.

**Figure 10.3**

**A Typical Discrete Probability Distribution**

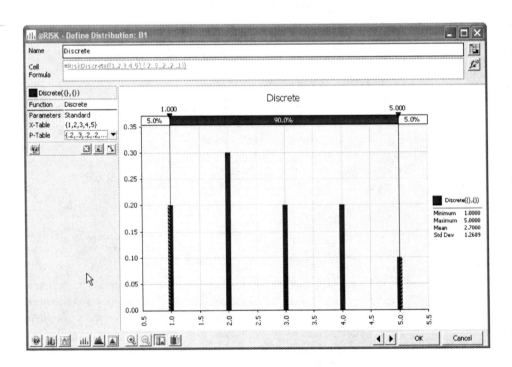

[1] Actually, it is possible for a discrete variable to have a *countably infinite* number of possible values, such as all the nonnegative integers 0, 1, 2, and so on. However, this is not an important distinction for practical applications.
[2] This figure and several later figures have been captured from Palisade's @RISK add-in.

In contrast, a continuous distribution is characterized by a *density function*, a smooth curve as shown in Figure 10.4. There are two important properties of density functions. First, the height of the density function above any value indicates the relative likelihood of that value, and second, probabilities can be calculated as areas under the curve.

**A Typical
Continuous
Probability
Distribution**

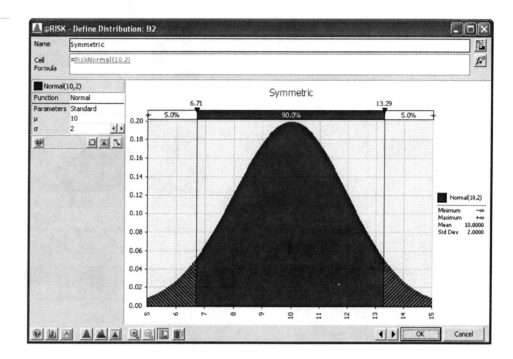

Sometimes it is convenient to treat a discrete probability distribution as continuous, and vice versa. For example, consider a student's random score on an exam that has 1000 possible points. If the grader scores each exam to the nearest integer, then even though the score is really discrete with many possible integer values, it is probably more convenient to model its distribution as a continuum. Continuous probability distributions are typically more intuitive and easier to work with than discrete distributions in cases such as this, where there are many possible values. In contrast, continuous distributions are sometimes *discretized* for simplicity.

### Symmetric Versus Skewed

A probability distribution can either be symmetric or skewed to the left or right. Figures 10.4, 10.5, 10.6 provide examples of each of these. You typically choose between a symmetric and skewed distribution on the basis of realism. For example, if you want to model a student's score on a 100-point exam, you will probably choose a left-skewed distribution. This is because a few poorly prepared students typically "pull down the curve." On the other hand, if you want to model the time it takes to serve a customer at a bank, you will probably choose a right-skewed distribution. This is because most customers take only a minute or two, but a few customers take a long time. Finally, if you want to model the monthly return on a stock, you might choose a distribution symmetric around zero, reasoning that the stock return is just as likely to be positive as negative and there is no obvious reason for skewness in either direction.

## Figure 10.5

A Positively Skewed
Probability
Distribution

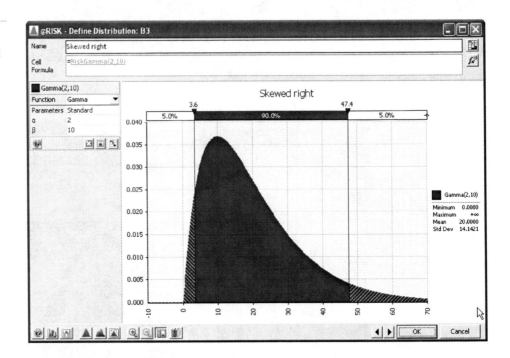

## Figure 10.6

A Negatively Skewed
Probability
Distribution

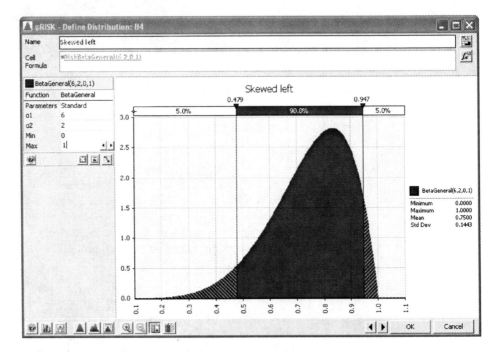

### Bounded Versus Unbounded

A probability distribution is *bounded* if there are values *A* and *B* such that no possible value
can be less than *A* or greater than *B*. The value *A* is then the *minimum* possible value, and
the value *B* is the *maximum* possible value. The distribution is *unbounded* if there are no
such bounds. Actually, it is possible for a distribution to be bounded in one direction but
not the other. As an example, the distribution of scores on a 100-point exam is bounded
between 0 and 100. In contrast, the distribution of the amount of damages Mr. Jones

submits to his insurance company in a year is bounded on the left by 0, but there is no natural upper bound. Therefore, you might model this amount with a distribution that is bounded by 0 on the left but is unbounded on the right. Alternatively, if you believe that no damage amount larger than $20,000 can occur, you could model this amount with a distribution that is bounded in both directions.

### Nonnegative Versus Unrestricted

One important special case of bounded distributions is when the only possible values are *nonnegative*. For example, if you want to model the random cost of manufacturing a new product, you know for sure that this cost must be nonnegative. There are many other such examples. In such cases, you should model the randomness with a probability distribution that is bounded below by 0. This rules out negative values that make no practical sense.

## 10.2.2 Common Probability Distributions

Now that you know the *types* of probability distributions available, you can add some common probability distributions to your toolbox. The file Probability Distributions.xlsx was developed to help you learn and explore these. Each sheet in this file illustrates a particular probability distribution. It describes the general characteristics of the distribution, indicates how you can generate random numbers from the distribution either with Excel's built-in functions or with @RISK functions, and it includes histograms of these distributions from simulated data to illustrate their shapes.[3]

It is important to realize that each of the following distributions is really a *family* of distributions. Each member of the family is specified by one or more parameters. For example, there is not a *single* normal distribution; there is a normal distribution for each possible mean and standard deviation you specify. Therefore, when you try to find an appropriate input probability distribution in a simulation model, you first have to choose an appropriate family, and then you have to select the appropriate parameters for that family.

### Uniform Distribution

The **uniform distribution** is the "flat" distribution illustrated in Figure 10.7. It is bounded by a minimum and a maximum, and all values between these two extremes are equally likely. You can think of this as the "I have no idea" distribution. For example, a manager might realize that a building cost is uncertain. If she can state only that, "I know the cost will be between $20,000 and $30,000, but other than this, I have no idea what the cost will be," then a uniform distribution from $20,000 to $30,000 is a natural choice. However, even though some people do use the uniform distribution in such cases, these situations are arguably not very common or realistic. If the manager really thinks about it, she can probably provide more information about the uncertain cost, such as, "The cost is more likely to be close to $25,000 than to either of the extremes." Then some distribution other than the uniform is more appropriate.

Regardless of whether the uniform distribution is an appropriate candidate as an input distribution, it is important for another reason. All simulation software packages, including Excel, are capable of generating random numbers uniformly distributed between 0 and 1. These are the building blocks of most simulated random numbers, in that random numbers from other probability distributions are generated from them.

---

[3]In later sections of this chapter, and all through the next chapter, we discuss much of @RISK's functionality. For this section, the only functionality we use is @RISK's collection of functions, such as RISKNORMAL and RISKTRIANG, for generating random numbers from various probability distributions. You can skim the details of these functions for now and refer back to them as necessary in later sections.

Figure 10.7

The Uniform
Distribution

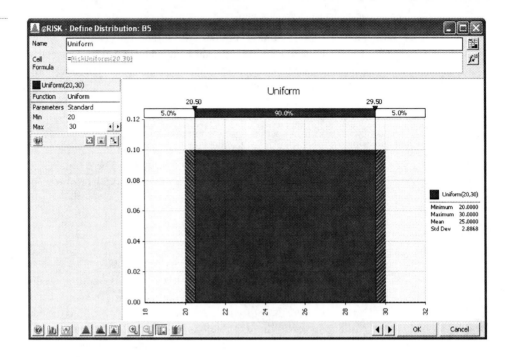

In Excel, you can generate a random number between 0 and 1 by entering the formula

=RAND()

in any cell. (The parentheses to the right of RAND indicate that this is an Excel function with no arguments. These parentheses must be included.)

**Excel Function: *RAND***

*To generate a random number equally likely to be anywhere between 0 and 1, enter the formula =**RAND**() into any cell. Press the F9 key, or recalculate in any other way, to make it change randomly.*

In addition to being between 0 and 1, the numbers created by this function have two properties that you would expect "random" numbers to have.

1. **Uniform property.** Each time you enter the RAND function in a cell, all numbers between 0 and 1 have the same chance of occurring. This means that approximately 10% of the numbers generated by the RAND function will be between 0.0 and 0.1; 10% of the numbers will be between 0.65 and 0.75; 60% of the numbers will be between 0.20 and 0.80; and so on. This property explains why the random numbers are said to be *uniformly distributed* between 0 and 1.

2. **Independence property.** Different random numbers generated by =**RAND**() formulas are *probabilistically independent*. This implies that when you generate a random number in cell A5, say, it has no effect on the values of any other random numbers generated in the spreadsheet. For example, if one call to the RAND function yields a large random number such as 0.98, there is no reason to suspect that the next call to RAND will yield an abnormally small (or large) random number; it is unaffected by the value of the first random number.

**Excel Tip:** *Besides the RAND function, there is one other function built into Excel that generates random numbers, the RANDBETWEEN function. It takes two integer arguments, as in =**RANDBETWEEN(1,6)**, and returns a random integer between these values* *(including the endpoints) so that all such integers are equally likely. The function was introduced in Excel 2007. (It was actually available in previous versions of Excel, but only if the Analysis Toolpak add-in was loaded.)*

To illustrate the RAND function, open a new workbook, enter the formula **=RAND()** in cell A4, and copy it to the range A4:A503. This generates 500 random numbers. Figure 10.8 displays a possible set of values. However, when you try this on your PC, you will undoubtedly obtain *different* random numbers. This is an inherent characteristic of simulation—no two answers are ever exactly alike. Now press the recalc (F9) key. All of the random numbers will change. In fact, each time you press the F9 key or do anything to make your spreadsheet recalculate, all of the cells containing the RAND function will change.

**Figure 10.8**

Uniformly Distributed Random Numbers Generated by the RAND Function

| | A | B | C | D |
|---|---|---|---|---|
| 1 | 500 random numbers from RAND function | | | |
| 2 | | | | |
| 3 | Random # | | | |
| 4 | 0.639741246 | | | |
| 5 | 0.977449085 | | | |
| 6 | 0.826336662 | | | |
| 7 | 0.794236038 | | | |
| 8 | 0.326052217 | | | |
| 9 | 0.540446013 | | | |
| 10 | 0.012582316 | | | |
| 501 | 0.868540879 | | | |
| 502 | 0.297930515 | | | |
| 503 | 0.960969187 | | | |

A histogram of the 500 random numbers appears in Figure 10.9. (Again, if you try this on your PC, the shape of your histogram will not be identical to the one shown in Figure 10.9, because it will be based on *different* random numbers.) From property 1, you would expect *equal* numbers of observations in the 10 categories. Obviously, the heights of the bars are *not* exactly equal, but the differences are due to chance—not to a faulty random number generator.

**Figure 10.9**

Histogram of the 500 Random Numbers Generated by the RAND Function

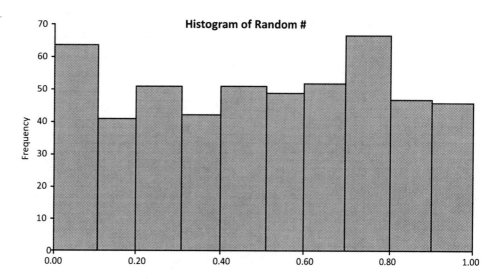

*The "random" numbers generated by the RAND function (or by the random number generator in any simulation software package) are not really random. They are sometimes called pseudo-random numbers. Each successive random number follows the previous random number by a complex arithmetic operation. If you happen to know the details of this arithmetic operation, you can predict ahead of time exactly which random numbers will be generated by the RAND function. This is quite different from using a "true" random mechanism, such as spinning a wheel, to get the next random number—a mechanism that would be impractical to implement on a computer. Mathematicians and computer scientists have studied many ways to produce random numbers that have the two properties we just discussed, and they have developed many competing random number generators such as the RAND function in Excel. The technical details need not concern you. The important point is that these random number generators produce numbers that appear to be random and are useful for simulation modeling.*

It is simple to generate a uniformly distributed random number with a minimum and maximum other than 0 and 1. For example, the formula

=200+100*RAND()

generates a number uniformly distributed between 200 and 300. (Make sure you see why.) Alternatively, you can use the @RISK formula[4]

=RISKUNIFORM(200,300)

You can take a look at this and other properties of the uniform distribution on the Uniform sheet in the Probability Distributions.xlsx file. (See Figure 10.10.)

**Figure 10.10**   Properties of Uniform Distribution

| | A | B | C | D | E | F | G | H |
|---|---|---|---|---|---|---|---|---|
| 1 | Uniform distribution | | | | | | | |
| 2 | | | | | | | | |
| 3 | Characteristics | | | This is a flat distribution between two values, | | | | |
| 4 | Continuous | | | labeled here MinVal and MaxVal. Note that if | | | | |
| 5 | Symmetric | | | MinVal=0 and MaxVal=1, then you can just use | | | | |
| 6 | Bounded in both directions | | | Excel's RAND function. | | | | |
| 7 | Not necessarily positive (depends on bounds) | | | | | | | |
| 8 | | | | | | | | |
| 9 | Parameters | | | | | | | |
| 10 | MinVal | 50 | | | | | | |
| 11 | MaxVal | 100 | | | | | | |
| 12 | | | | | | | | |
| 13 | Excel | | Example | | | | | |
| 14 | =MinVal + (MaxVal-MinVal)*RAND() | | 96.105704 | | | | | |
| 15 | | | | | | | | |
| 16 | @RISK | | | | | | | |
| 17 | =RISKUNIFORM(MinVal,MaxVal) | | 96.880610 | | | | | |

[4]As we have done with other Excel functions, we capitalize the @RISK functions, such as RISKUNIFORM, in the text. However, this is not necessary when you enter the formulas in Excel.

> **@RISK Function: *RISKUNIFORM***
>
> *To generate a random number from any uniform distribution, enter the formula* **=RISKUNIFORM(MinVal,MaxVal)** *in any cell. Here,* MinVal *and* MaxVal *are the minimum and maximum possible values. Note that if* MinVal *is 0 and* MaxVal *is 1, this function is equivalent to Excel's RAND function.*

### FREEZING RANDOM NUMBERS

The automatic recalculation of random numbers can be useful sometimes and annoying at other times. There are situations when you want the random numbers to stay fixed—that is, you want to *freeze* them at their current values. The following three-step method does this.

1. Select the range that you want to freeze, such as A4:A503 in Figure 10.8.
2. Press Ctrl+c to copy this range.

*Random numbers that have been frozen do not change when you press the F9 key.*

3. With the same range still selected, select the Paste Values option from the Paste dropdown menu on the Home ribbon. This procedure pastes a copy of the range onto itself, except that the entries are now numbers, not formulas. Therefore, whenever the spreadsheet recalculates, these numbers do not change.

Each sheet in the Probability Distributions.xlsx file has a list of 500 random numbers that have been frozen. The histograms in the sheets are based on the frozen random numbers. However, we encourage you to enter "live" random numbers in column B over the frozen ones and see how the histogram changes when you press F9.

## 10.2.3 Using @RISK to Explore Probability Distributions[5]

The Probability Distributions.xlsx file illustrates a few frequently used probability distributions, and it shows the formulas required to generate random numbers from these distributions. Another option is to use Palisade's @RISK add-in, which allows you to experiment with probability distributions. Essentially, it allows you to see the shapes of various distributions and to calculate probabilities for them, all in a user-friendly graphical interface.

To run @RISK, click on the Windows Start button, go to the Programs tab, locate the Palisades DecisionTools suite, and select @RISK. After a few seconds, you will see the welcome screen, which you can close. At this point, you should have an @RISK tab and corresponding ribbon. Select a blank cell in your worksheet, and then click on Define Distributions on left of the @RISK ribbon (see Figure 10.11). You will see one of several galleries of distributions, depending on the tab you select. For example, Figure 10.12

**Figure 10.11** @RISK Ribbon

[5]Palisade previously offered a stand-alone program called RISKview for exploring probability distributions, and we discussed it in the previous edition. However, Palisade discontinued RISKview and instead incorporates its functionality in @RISK.

Figure 10.12

Gallery of
Continuous
Distributions

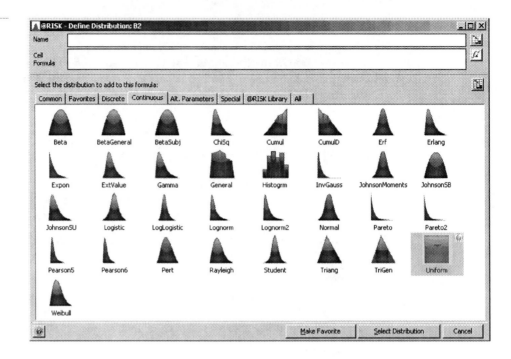

shows the gallery of continuous distributions. Highlight one of the distributions and click on Select Distribution. For example, choose the uniform distribution with minimum 75 and maximum 150. You will see the shape of the distribution and a few summary measures to the right, as shown in Figure 10.13. For example, it indicates that the mean and standard deviation of this uniform distribution are 112.5 and 21.65.

Everything in this window is interactive. Suppose you want to find the probability that a value from this distribution is less than 95. You can drag the left-hand "slider" in the diagram (the vertical line with the triangle at the top) to the position 95, as shown in Figure 10.13.

Figure 10.13

@RISK Illustration
of Uniform
Distribution

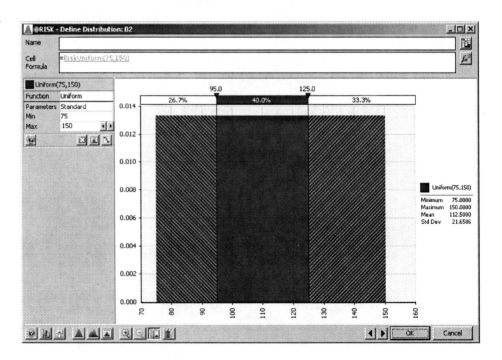

You see immediately that the left-hand probability is 0.267. Similarly, if you want the probability that a value from this distribution is greater than 125, you can drag the right-hand slider to the position 125 to see that the required probability is 0.3333. (Rather than sliding, you can enter the numbers, such as 95 and 125, directly into the areas above the sliders.)

You can also enter probabilities instead of values. For example, if you want the value such that there is probability 0.10 to the left of it—the 10th percentile—enter 10% in the left space above the chart. You will see that the corresponding value is 82.5. Similarly, if you want the value such that there is probability 0.10 to the right of it, enter 10% in the right space above the chart, and you will see that the corresponding value is 142.5.

The Define Distributions window in @RISK is quick and easy. We urge you to use it and experiment with some of its options. By the way, you can click on the third button from the left at the bottom of the window to copy the chart into an Excel worksheet. However, you then lose the interactive capabilities, such as moving the sliders.

### Discrete Distribution

A **discrete distribution** is useful for many situations, either when the uncertain quantity is not really continuous (the number of televisions demanded, for example) or when you want a discrete approximation to a continuous variable. All you need to specify are the possible values and their probabilities, making sure that the probabilities sum to 1. Because of this flexibility in specifying values and probabilities, discrete distributions can have practically any shape.

As an example, suppose a manager estimates that the demand for a particular brand of television during the coming month will be 10, 15, 20, or 25, with respective probabilities 0.1, 0.3, 0.4, and 0.2. This typical discrete distribution is illustrated in Figure 10.14.

The interactive capabilities of @RISK's Define Distributions window, with its sliders, make it perfect for finding probabilities or percentiles for any given distribution.

**Figure 10.14**

**Discrete Distribution (from @RISK)**

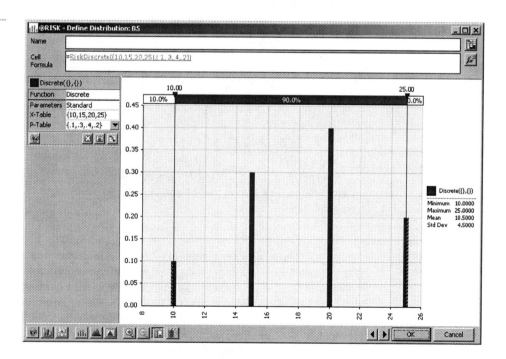

The Discrete sheet of the Probability Distributions.xlsx file indicates how to work with a discrete distribution. (See Figure 10.15.) As you can see, there are two quite different ways to generate a random number from this distribution. We discuss the Excel way in detail in section 10.4. For now, we simply mention that this is one case (of many) where it

Figure 10.15    Properties of a Discrete Distribution

| | A | B | C | D | E | F | G | H | I |
|---|---|---|---|---|---|---|---|---|---|
| 1 | General discrete distribution | | | | | | | | |
| 2 | | | | | | | | | |
| 3 | Characteristics | | | | | | | | |
| 4 | Discrete | | | | This can have any shape, depending | | | | |
| 5 | Can be symmetric or skewed (or bumpy, i.e., basically any shape) | | | | on the list of possible values and their | | | | |
| 6 | Bounded in both directions | | | | probabilities. | | | | |
| 7 | Not necessarily positive (depends on possible values) | | | | | | | | |
| 8 | | | | | | | | | |
| 9 | Parameters | | | | Lookup table required for Excel method | | | | |
| 10 | | Values | Probabilities | | CumProb | Value | | | |
| 11 | | 10 | 0.1 | | 0 | 10 | | | |
| 12 | | 15 | 0.3 | | 0.1 | 15 | | | |
| 13 | | 20 | 0.4 | | 0.4 | 20 | | | |
| 14 | | 25 | 0.2 | | 0.8 | 25 | | | |
| 15 | | | | | | | | | |
| 16 | Excel | | Example | | | | | | |
| 17 | =VLOOKUP(RAND(),LookupTable,2) | | 10 | | | | | | |
| 18 | | | | | | | | | |
| 19 | @RISK | | | | | | | | |
| 20 | =RISKDISCRETE(Values,Probs) | | 20 | | | | | | |

@RISK's way of generating a discrete random number is much simpler and more intuitive than Excel's method, which requires cumulative probabilities and a lookup function.

is much easier to generate random numbers with @RISK functions than with built-in Excel functions. Assuming that @RISK is loaded, all you need to do is enter the function RISKDISCRETE with two arguments, a list of possible values and a list of their probabilities, as in

=RISKDISCRETE(B11:B14,C11:C14)

The Excel way, which requires cumulative probabilities and a lookup table, takes more work and is harder to remember.

> @RISK Function:  *RISKDISCRETE*
> *To generate a random number from any discrete probability distribution, enter the formula =RISKDISCRETE(**valRange,probRange**) into any cell. Here* valRange *is the range where the possible values are stored, and* probRange *is the range where their probabilities are stored.*

The selected input distributions for any simulation model reflect historical data and an analyst's best judgment as to what will happen in the future.

At this point, a relevant question is why a manager would choose this particular discrete distribution. First, it is clearly an approximation. After all, if it is possible to have demands of 20 and 25, it should also be possible to have demands between these values. Here, the manager approximates a discrete distribution with *many* possible values—all integers from 0 to 50, say—with a discrete distribution with a few well-chosen values. This is common in simulation modeling. Second, where do the probabilities come from? They are probably a blend of historical data (perhaps demand was near 15 in 30% of previous months) and the manager's subjective feelings about demand *next* month.

### Normal Distribution

The *normal distribution* is the familiar bell-shaped curve that is the hallmark of much of statistical theory. (See Figure 10.16.) It is useful in simulation modeling as a continuous

Figure 10.16

Normal Distribution
(from @RISK)

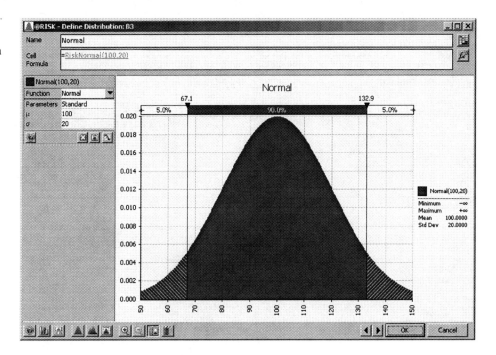

*Normally distributed
random numbers will
almost certainly be
within three standard
deviations of the mean.*

input distribution. However, it is *not* always the most appropriate distribution. It is symmetric, which can be a drawback when a skewed distribution is more realistic. Also, it allows negative values, which are not appropriate in many situations. For example, the demand for televisions cannot be negative. Fortunately, this possibility of negative values is often not a problem. Suppose you generate a normally distributed random number with mean 100 and standard deviation 20. Then, as you might remember from statistics, there is almost no chance of having values more than three standard deviations to the left of the mean, and this rules out negative values for all practical purposes.

A tip-off that a normal distribution might be an appropriate candidate for an input variable is a statement such as, "We believe the most likely value of demand is 100, and the chances are about 95% that demand will be no more than 40 units on either of side of this most likely value." Because a normally distributed value is within two standard deviations of its mean with probability 0.95, this statement translates easily to a mean of 100 and a standard deviation of 20. This does not imply that a normal distribution is the *only* candidate for the distribution of demand, but the statement naturally leads to this distribution.

The Normal sheet in the Probability Distributions.xlsx file indicates how you can generate normally distributed random numbers in Excel, either with or without @RISK. (See Figure 10.17.) This is one case where an add-in is not really necessary. The formula

=NORMINV(RAND(),*Mean,Stdev*)

always works. Still, this is not as easy to remember as @RISK's formula

=RISKNORMAL(*Mean,Stdev*)

---

@RISK Function: ***RISKNORMAL***

*To generate a normally distributed random number, enter the formula =RISKNOR-MAL(**Mean,Stdev**) in any cell. Here,* Mean *and* Stdev *are the mean and standard deviation of the normal distribution.*

---

Figure 10.17    Properties of the Normal Distribution

|    | A | B | C | D | E | F | G | H |
|----|---|---|---|---|---|---|---|---|
| 1 | **Normal distribution** | | | | | | | |
| 2 | | | | | | | | |
| 3 | **Characteristics** | | | | | | | |
| 4 | Continuous | | | This is the familiar bell-shaped curve, defined by two parameters: the mean and the standard deviation. | | | | |
| 5 | Symmetric (bell-shaped) | | | | | | | |
| 6 | Unbounded in both directions | | | | | | | |
| 7 | Is both positive and negative | | | | | | | |
| 8 | | | | | | | | |
| 9 | **Parameters** | | | | | | | |
| 10 | Mean | 100 | | | | | | |
| 11 | Stdev | 10 | | | | | | |
| 12 | | | | | | | | |
| 13 | **Excel** | | **Example** | | | | | |
| 14 | =NORMINV(RAND(),Mean,Stdev) | | 96.41946055 | | | | | |
| 15 | | | | | | | | |
| 16 | **@RISK** | | | | | | | |
| 17 | =RISKNORMAL(Mean,Stdev) | | 90.3093316 | | | | | |

## Triangular Distribution

The **triangular distribution** is somewhat similar to the normal distribution in that its density function rises to some point and then falls, but it is more flexible and intuitive than the normal distribution. Therefore, it is an excellent candidate for many continuous input variables. The shape of a triangular density function is literally a triangle, as shown in Figure 10.18. It is specified by three easy-to-understand parameters: the minimum possible value, the most likely value, and the maximum possible value. The high point of the triangle

Figure 10.18

Triangular
Distribution (from
@RISK)

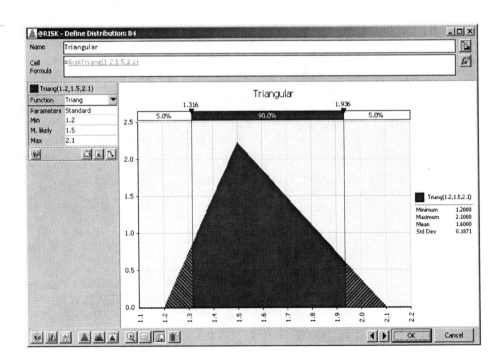

is above the most likely value. Therefore, if a manager states, "We believe the most likely development cost is $1.5 million, and we don't believe the development cost could possibly be less than $1.2 million or greater than $2.1 million," the triangular distribution with these three parameters is a natural choice. As in this numerical example, note that the triangular distribution can be skewed if the mostly likely value is closer to one extreme than another. Of course, it can also be symmetric if the most likely value is right in the middle.

The Triangular sheet of the Probability Distributions.xlsx file indicates how to generate random values from this distribution. (See Figure 10.19.) As you can see, there is no way to do it with native Excel (at least not without a macro). However, it is easy with @RISK, using the RISKTRIANG function, as in

=RISKTRIANG(B10,B11,B12)

This function takes three arguments: the minimum value, the most likely value, and the maximum value—in this order and separated by commas. You will see this function in many of our examples. Just remember that it has an abbreviated spelling: **RISKTRIANG**, not RISKTRIANGULAR.

**Figure 10.19** Properties of the Triangular Distribution

| | A | B | C | D | E | F | G | H | I | J |
|---|---|---|---|---|---|---|---|---|---|---|
| 1 | Triangular distribution | | | | | | | | | |
| 2 | | | | | | | | | | |
| 3 | Characteristics | | | The density of this distribution is literally a triangle. The "top" of the | | | | | | |
| 4 | Continuous | | | triangle is above the most likely value, and the base of the triangle | | | | | | |
| 5 | Can be symmetric or skewed in either direction | | | extends from the minimum value to the maximum value. It is | | | | | | |
| 6 | Bounded in both directions | | | intuitive for nontechnical people because the three parameters are | | | | | | |
| 7 | Not necessarily positive (depends on bounds) | | | meaningful. | | | | | | |
| 8 | | | | | | | | | | |
| 9 | Parameters | | | | | | | | | |
| 10 | Min | 50 | | | | | | | | |
| 11 | MostLikely | 85 | | | | | | | | |
| 12 | Max | 100 | | | | | | | | |
| 13 | | | | | | | | | | |
| 14 | Excel | | | | | | | | | |
| 15 | There is no easy way to do it except by writing a macro. | | | | | | | | | |
| 16 | | | | | | | | | | |
| 17 | @RISK | | Example | | | | | | | |
| 18 | =RISKTRIANG(Min,MostLikely,Max) | | 62.61066937 | | | | | | | |

@RISK Function: *RISKTRIANG*
*To generate a random number from a triangular distribution, enter the formula =RISK-TRIANG (**MinVal,MLVal,MaxVal**) in any cell. Here,* **MinVal** *is the minimum possible value,* MLVal *is the most likely value, and* MaxVal *is the maximum value.*

## Binomial Distribution

The *binomial distribution* is a discrete distribution that applies to a very specific situation: when a number of independent and identical trials occur, and each trial results in a *success* or *failure*. Then the binomial random number is the number of successes in these trials. The two parameters of this distribution, $n$ and $p$, are the number of trials and the probability of success on each trial.

A random number
from a binomial
distribution indicates
the number of
successes in a certain
number of identical
trials.

As an example, suppose an airline company sells 170 tickets for a flight and estimates that 80% of the people with tickets will actually show up for the flight. How many people will actually show up? It is tempting to state that *exactly* 80% of 170, or 136 people, will show up, but this neglects the inherent randomness. A more realistic way to model this situation is to say that each of the 170 people, independently of one another, will show up with probability 0.8. Then the number of people who actually show up is binomially distributed with $n = 170$ and $p = 0.8$. (This assumes independent behavior across passengers, which might not be the case, for example, if whole families either show up or don't.) This distribution is illustrated in Figure 10.20.

**Figure 10.20**

**Binomial Distribution (from @RISK)**

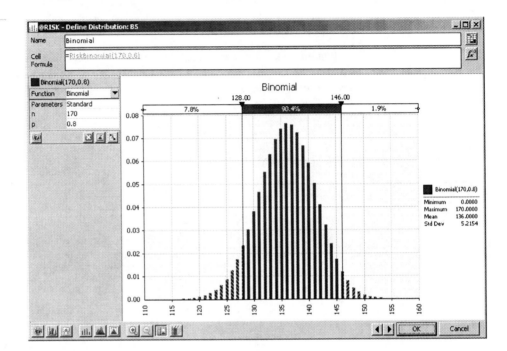

The Binomial sheet of the Probability Distributions.xlsx file indicates how to generate random numbers from this distribution. (See Figure 10.21.) Although it is possible to do this with Excel using the built-in CRITBINOM function and the RAND function, it is not very intuitive or easy to remember. Clearly, the @RISK way is preferable. In the airline example, you would generate the number who show up with the formula

=RISKBINOMIAL(170,0.8)

Note that the histogram in this figure is approximately bell-shaped. This is no accident. When the number of trials $n$ is reasonably large and $p$ isn't too close to 0 or 1, the binomial distribution can be well approximated by the normal distribution.

> **@RISK Function: *RISKBINOMIAL***
> *To generate a random number from a binomial distribution, enter the formula* **=RISKBINOMIAL(NTrials,PSuccess)** *in any cell. Here,* **NTrials** *is the number of trials, and* **PSuccess** *is the probability of a success on each trial.*

A common question asked by students is which distribution to use for a given uncertain quantity such as the price of oil, the demand for laptops, and so on. Admittedly, the

**Figure 10.21    Properties of the Binomial Distribution**

| | A | B | C | D | E | F | G | H |
|---|---|---|---|---|---|---|---|---|
| 1 | Binomial distribution | | | | | | | |
| 2 | | | | | | | | |
| 3 | Characteristics | | | | | | | |
| 4 | Discrete | | | This distribution is of the number of "successes" in a | | | | |
| 5 | Can be symmetric or skewed | | | given number of identical, independent trials, when the | | | | |
| 6 | Bounded below by 0, bounded above by Ntrials | | | probability of success is constant on each trial. | | | | |
| 7 | Nonnegative | | | | | | | |
| 8 | | | | | | | | |
| 9 | Parameters | | | | | | | |
| 10 | NTrials | 170 | | | | | | |
| 11 | PSuccess | 0.8 | | | | | | |
| 12 | | | | | | | | |
| 13 | Excel | | Example | | | | | |
| 14 | =CRITBINOM(NTrials,PSuccess,RAND()) | | 139 | | | | | |
| 15 | | | | | | | | |
| 16 | @RISK | | | | | | | |
| 17 | =RISKBINOMIAL(NTrials,PSuccess) | | 133 | | | | | |

choices we make in later examples are sometimes for convenience. However, in real business situations the choice is not always clear-cut, and it can make a difference in the results. Stanford professor Sam Savage and two of his colleagues discuss this choice in a series of two articles on "Probability Management." (These articles from February and April 2006 are available online at http://lionhrtpub.com/orms/ORMS-archive.html.) They argue that with the increasing importance of simulation models in today's business world, input distributions should not only be chosen carefully, but they should be kept and maintained as important corporate assets. They shouldn't just be chosen in some ad hoc fashion every time they are needed. For example, if the price of oil is an important input in many of a company's decisions, then experts within the company should assess an appropriate distribution for the price of oil and modify it as necessary when new information arises. The authors even suggest a new company position, Chief Probability Officer, to control access to the company's probability distributions.

So as you are reading these two simulation chapters, keep Savage's ideas in mind. The choice of probability distributions for inputs is not easy, yet neither is it arbitrary. The choice *can* make a difference in the results. This is the reason why you want as many families of probability distributions in your toolbox as possible. You then have more flexibility to choose a distribution that is appropriate for your situation.

## PROBLEMS

*Solutions for problems whose numbers appear within a colored box can be found in the Student Solutions Files. Refer to this book's preface for purchase information.*

### Skill-Building Problems

1. Use the RAND function and the Copy command to generate a set of 100 random numbers.
   a. What fraction of the random numbers are smaller than 0.5?
   b. What fraction of the time is a random number less than 0.5 followed by a random number greater than 0.5?
   c. What fraction of the random numbers are larger than 0.8?
   d. Freeze these random numbers. However, instead of pasting them over the original random numbers, paste them onto a new range. Then press the F9 recalculate key. The original random numbers should change, but the pasted copy should remain the same.

2. Use Excel's functions (not @RISK) to generate 1000 random numbers from a normal distribution with mean 100 and standard deviation 10. Then freeze these random numbers.
   a. Calculate the mean and standard deviation of these random numbers. Are they approximately what you would expect?
   b. What fraction of these random numbers are within $k$ standard deviations of the mean? Answer for $k = 1$; for $k = 2$; for $k = 3$. Are the answers close to what they should be (about 68% for $k = 1$, about 95% for $k = 2$, and over 99% for $k = 3$)?
   c. Create a histogram of the random numbers using 10 to 15 categories of your choice. Does this histogram have approximately the shape you would expect?

3. Use @RISK to draw a uniform distribution from 400 to 750. Then answer the following questions.
   a. What are the mean and standard deviation of this distribution?
   b. What are the 5th and 95th percentiles of this distribution?
   c. What is the probability that a random number from this distribution is less than 450?
   d. What is the probability that a random number from this distribution is greater than 650?
   e. What is the probability that a random number from this distribution is between 500 and 700?

4. Use @RISK to draw a normal distribution with mean 500 and standard deviation 100. Then answer the following questions.
   a. What is the probability that a random number from this distribution is less than 450?
   b. What is the probability that a random number from this distribution is greater than 650?
   c. What is the probability that a random number from this distribution is between 500 and 700?

5. Use @RISK to draw a triangular distribution with parameters 300, 500, and 900. Then answer the following questions.
   a. What are the mean and standard deviation of this distribution?
   b. What are the 5th and 95th percentiles of this distribution?
   c. What is the probability that a random number from this distribution is less than 450?
   d. What is the probability that a random number from this distribution is greater than 650?
   e. What is the probability that a random number from this distribution is between 500 and 700?

6. Use @RISK to draw a binomial distribution that results from 50 trials with probability of success 0.3 on each trial, and use it to answer the following questions.

   a. What are the mean and standard deviation of this distribution?
   b. You have to be more careful in interpreting @RISK probabilities with a discrete distribution such as this binomial. For example, if you move the left slider to 11, you find a probability of 0.139 to the left of it. But is this the probability of "less than 11" or "less than or equal to 11"? One way to check is to use Excel's BINOMDIST function. Use this function to interpret the 0.139 value from @RISK.
   c. Using part b to guide you, use @RISK to find the probability that a random number from this distribution will be greater than 17. Check your answer by using the BINOMDIST function appropriately in Excel.

7. Use @RISK to draw a triangular distribution with parameters 200, 300, and 600. Then superimpose a normal distribution on this drawing, choosing the mean and standard deviation to match those from the triangular distribution. (Click on the Add Overlay button and then choose the distribution to superimpose.)
   a. What are the 5th and 95th percentiles for these two distributions?
   b. What is the probability that a random number from the triangular distribution is less than 400? What is this probability for the normal distribution?
   c. Experiment with the sliders to answer questions similar to those in part b. Would you conclude that these two distributions differ most in the extremes (right or left) or in the middle? Explain.

8. We all hate to keep track of small change. By using random numbers, it is possible to eliminate the need for change and give the store and the customer a fair deal. This problem indicates how it could be done.
   a. Suppose that you buy something for $0.20. How could you use random numbers (built into the cash register system) to decide whether you should pay $1.00 or nothing?
   b. If you bought something for $9.60, how would you use random numbers to eliminate the need for change?
   c. In the long run, why is this method fair to both the store and the customers? Would you personally (as a customer) be willing to abide by such a system?

Skill-Extending Problems

9. A company is about to develop and then market a new product. It wants to build a simulation model for the entire process, and one key uncertain input is the development cost. For each of the following scenarios, choose an appropriate distribution together with its

parameters, justify your choice in words, and use @RISK to draw your chosen distribution.

a. Company experts have no idea what the distribution of the development cost is. All they can state is "we are 95% sure it will be at least $450,000, and we are 95% sure it will be no more than $650,000."

b. Company experts can still make the same statement as in part **a**, but now they can also state: "We believe the distribution is symmetric, reasonably bell-shaped, and its most likely value is about $550,000."

c. Company experts can still make the same statement as in part **a**, but now they can also state: "We believe the distribution is skewed to the right, and its most likely value is about $500,000."

10. Continuing the preceding problem, suppose that another key uncertain input is the development time, which is measured in an *integer* number of months.

For each of the following scenarios, choose an appropriate distribution together with its parameters, justify your choice in words, and use @RISK to draw your chosen distribution.

a. Company experts believe the development time will be from 6 to 10 months, but they have absolutely no idea which of these will result.

b. Company experts believe the development time will be from 6 to 10 months. They believe the probabilities of these five possible values will increase linearly to a most likely value at 8 months and will then decrease linearly.

c. Company experts believe the development time will be from 6 to 10 months. They believe that 8 months is twice as likely as either 7 months or 9 months and that either of these latter possibilities is three times as likely as either 6 months or 10 months.

## 10.3 SIMULATION AND THE FLAW OF AVERAGES

To help motivate simulation modeling in general, we present a simple example in this section. It will clearly show the distinction between Figure 10.1 (a deterministic model with best-guess inputs) and Figure 10.2 (an appropriate simulation model). In doing so, it will illustrate a pitfall called the "flaw of averages" that you should always try to avoid.[6]

---

**EXAMPLE** | **10.1 ORDERING CALENDARS AT WALTON BOOKSTORE**

In August, Walton Bookstore must decide how many of next year's nature calendars to order. Each calendar costs the bookstore $7.50 and sells for $10. After January 1, all unsold calendars will be returned to the publisher for a refund of $2.50 per calendar. Walton believes that the number of calendars it can sell by January 1 follows some probability distribution with mean 200. Walton believes that ordering to the average demand, that is, ordering 200 calendars, is a good decision. Is it?

**Objective** To illustrate the difference between a deterministic model with a best guess for uncertain inputs and a simulation model that incorporates uncertainty explicitly.

### WHERE DO THE NUMBERS COME FROM?

The monetary values are straightforward. The mean demand is probably an estimate based on historical demands for similar calendars.

### Solution

A deterministic model appears in Figure 10.22. (See the file Walton Bookstore 1.xlsx. Assuming the best guess for demand, Walton orders to this average value, and it appears

---

[6]As far as we know, the term "flaw of averages" was coined by Sam Savage, the same Stanford professor quoted earlier.

Figure 10.22

Deterministic Model

| | A | B | C | D | E | F |
|---|---|---|---|---|---|---|
| 1 | Walton's bookstore - deterministic model | | | | | |
| 2 | | | | | | |
| 3 | Cost data | | | | | |
| 4 | Unit cost | $7.50 | | | | |
| 5 | Unit price | $10.00 | | | | |
| 6 | Unit refund | $2.50 | | | | |
| 7 | | | | | | |
| 8 | Uncertain quantity | | | | | |
| 9 | Demand (average shown) | 200 | | | | |
| 10 | | | | | | |
| 11 | Decision variable | | | | | |
| 12 | Order quantity | 200 | | | | |
| 13 | | | | | | |
| 14 | Profit model | | | | | |
| 15 | | Demand | Revenue | Cost | Refund | Profit |
| 16 | | 200 | $2,000.00 | $1,500.00 | $0.00 | $500.00 |

that the company's best guess for profit is $500. (The formulas in cells B16:F16 are straightforward. Anticipating that the order quantity and demand will not always be equal, they are $=$B9, $=$B5*MIN(B9,B12), $=$B4*B12, $=$B6*MAX(B12-B9,0), and $=$C16-D16+E16.) Before reading further, do you believe that the *average* profit will be $500 when uncertainty in demand is introduced explicitly (and the company still orders 200 calendars)? Think what happens to profit when demand is less than 200 and when it is greater than 200. Are these two cases symmetric?

We now contrast this with a simulation model where the demand in cell B9 is replaced by a random number. For this example, we assume that demand is *normally* distributed with mean 200 and standard deviation 40, although these specific assumptions are not crucial for the qualitative aspects of the example. All you need to do is enter the formula $=$ROUND(RISKNORMAL(200,40),0) in cell B9, where the ROUND function has been used to round to the nearest integer. Now the model appears as in Figure 10.23.

The random demand in cell B9 is now live, as are its dependents in row 16, so each time you press the F9 key, you get a new demand and associated profit. Do you get about

Figure 10.23

Simulation Model

| | A | B | C | D | E | F |
|---|---|---|---|---|---|---|
| 1 | Walton's bookstore - simulation model | | | | | |
| 2 | | | | | | |
| 3 | Cost data | | | | | |
| 4 | Unit cost | $7.50 | | | | |
| 5 | Unit price | $10.00 | | | | |
| 6 | Unit refund | $2.50 | | | | |
| 7 | | | | | | |
| 8 | Uncertain quantity (assumed normal with mean 200, stdev 40) | | | | | |
| 9 | Demand (random) | 263 | | | | |
| 10 | | | | | | |
| 11 | Decision variable | | | | | |
| 12 | Order quantity | 200 | | | | |
| 13 | | | | | | |
| 14 | Profit model | | | | | |
| 15 | | Demand | Revenue | Cost | Refund | Profit |
| 16 | | 263 | $2,000.00 | $1,500.00 | $0.00 | $500.00 |

$500 in profit on average? Absolutely not! The situation isn't symmetric. The *largest* profit you can get is $500, which occurs about half the time, whenever demand is greater than 200. A typical such situation appears in the figure, where the excess demand of 63 is simply lost. However, when demand is less than 200, the profit is *less than* $500, and it keeps decreasing as demand decreases.

We ran @RISK with 1000 iterations (which will be explained in detail in section 10.5) and found the resulting histogram of 1000 simulated profits shown in Figure 10.24. The large spike on the right is due to the cases where demand is 200 or more and profit is $500. All the little spikes to the left are where demand is less than 200 and profit is less than $500, sometimes considerably less. You can see on the right that the *mean* profit, the average of the 1000 simulated profits, is only about $380, well less than the $500 suggested by the deterministic model.

Figure 10.24

Histogram of
Simulated Profits

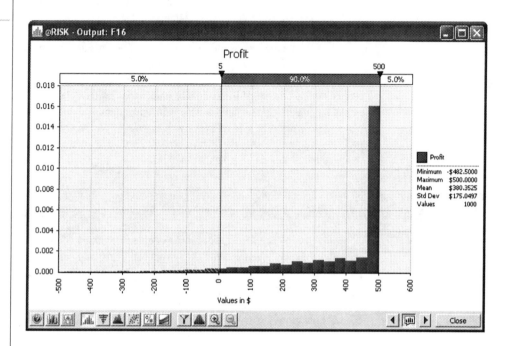

The point of this simple example is that a deterministic model can be very misleading. In particular, the output from a deterministic model that uses best guesses for uncertain inputs is *not* necessarily equal to, or even close to, the average of the output from a simulation. This is exactly what "the flaw of averages" means. ▪

In this section, we show how spreadsheet simulation models can be developed and analyzed with Excel's built-in tools without using add-ins. As you will see, this is certainly possible, but it presents two problems. First, the @RISK functions illustrated in the Probability Distributions.xlsx file are not available. You are able to use only Excel's RAND function and transformations of it to generate random numbers from various probability distributions. Second, there is a bookkeeping problem. Once you build an Excel model with output cells linked to appropriate random input cells, you can press the F9 key as often as you like to see how the outputs vary. However, there is no quick way to keep track of these output values and summarize them. This bookkeeping feature is the real strength of a simulation add-in such as @RISK. It can be done with Excel, usually with data tables, but the summarization of the resulting data is completely up to the user—you. Therefore, we strongly recommend that you use the "Excel-only" method described in this section only if you don't have an add-in such as @RISK.

To illustrate the Excel-only procedure, we continue analyzing the calendar problem from Example 10.1. This general problem occurs when a company (such as a news vendor) must make a one-time purchase of a product (such as a newspaper) to meet customer demands for a certain period of time. If the company orders too few newspapers, it will lose potential profit by not having enough on hand to satisfy its customers. If it orders too many, it will have newspapers left over at the end of the day that, at best, can be sold at a loss. More generally, the problem is to match supply to an uncertain demand, a very common problem in business. In much of the rest of this chapter, we will discuss variations of this problem.

EXAMPLE | **10.2 SIMULATING WITH EXCEL ONLY AT WALTON BOOKSTORE**

Recall that Walton Bookstore must decide how many of next year's nature calendars to order. Each calendar costs the bookstore $7.50 and sells for $10. After January 1, all unsold calendars will be returned to the publisher for a refund of $2.50 per calendar. In this version, we assume that demand for calendars (at the full price) is given by the probability distribution shown in Table 10.1. Walton wants to develop a simulation model to help it decide how many calendars to order.

Table 10.1    Probability Distribution of Demand for Walton Example

| Demand | Probability |
|--------|-------------|
| 100 | 0.30 |
| 150 | 0.20 |
| 200 | 0.30 |
| 250 | 0.15 |
| 300 | 0.05 |

**Objective**    To use built-in Excel tools—including the RAND function and data tables, but no add-ins—to simulate profit for several order quantities and ultimately choose the "best" order quantity.

WHERE DO THE NUMBERS COME FROM?

The numbers in Table 10.1 are the key to the simulation model. They are discussed in more detail next.

## Solution

We first discuss the probability distribution in Table 10.1. It is a discrete distribution with only five possible values: 100, 150, 200, 250, and 300. In reality, it is clear that other values of demand are possible. For example, there could be demand for exactly 187 calendars. In spite of its apparent lack of realism, we use this discrete distribution for two reasons. First, its simplicity is a nice feature to get you started with simulation modeling. Second, discrete distributions are often used in real business simulation models. Even though the discrete distribution is only an *approximation* to reality, it can still provide important insights into the actual problem.

As for the probabilities listed in Table 10.1, they are typically drawn from historical data or (if historical data are lacking) educated guesses. In this case, the manager of Walton Bookstore has presumably looked at demands for calendars in previous years, and he has used any information he has about the market for next year's calendars to estimate, for example, that the probability of a demand for 200 calendars is 0.30. The five probabilities in this table *must* sum to 1. Beyond this requirement, they should be as reasonable and consistent with reality as possible.

It is important to realize that this is really a decision problem under uncertainty. Walton must choose an order quantity *before* knowing the demand for calendars. Unfortunately, Solver cannot be used because of the uncertainty.[7] Therefore, we develop a simulation model for any *fixed* order quantity. Then we run this simulation model with various order quantities to see which one appears to be best.

### DEVELOPING THE SIMULATION MODEL

Now we discuss the ordering model. For any fixed order quantity, we show how Excel can be used to simulate 1000 replications (or any other number of replications). Each replication is an independent replay of the events that occur. To illustrate, suppose you want to simulate profit if Walton orders 200 calendars. Figure 10.25 illustrates the results obtained by simulating 1000 independent replications for this order quantity. (See the file Walton Bookstore 2.xlsx.) Note that there are many hidden rows in Figure 10.25. To develop this model, use the following steps.

**① Inputs.** Enter the cost data in the range B4:B6, the probability distribution of demand in the range E5:F9, and the proposed order quantity, 200, in cell B9. Pay particular attention to the way the probability distribution is entered (and compare to the Discrete sheet in the Probability Distributions.xlsx file). Columns E and F contain the possible demand values and the probabilities from Table 10.1. It is also necessary (see step 2 for the reasoning) to have the cumulative probabilities in column D. To obtain these, first enter the value 0 in cell D5. Then enter the formula

=F5+D5

in cell D6 and copy it to the range D7:D9.

**② Generate random demands.** The key to the simulation is the generation of the customer demands in the range B19:B1018 from the random numbers generated by the RAND function and the probability distribution of demand. Here is how it works. The interval from 0 to 1 is split into five segments: 0.0 to 0.3 (length 0.3), 0.3 to 0.5 (length 0.2), 0.5 to 0.8 (length 0.3), 0.8 to 0.95 (length 0.15), and 0.95 to 1.0 (length 0.05). Note that these lengths are the probabilities of the various demands. Then a demand is

---

[7]Palisade Corporation has another Excel add-in called RISKOptimizer that can be used for optimization in a simulation model. It is included in the suite that you own, but we will not discuss it here.

Figure 10.25    Walton Bookstore Simulation Model

| | A | B | C | D | E | F | G | H | I | J |
|---|---|---|---|---|---|---|---|---|---|---|
| 3 | Cost data | | | Demand distribution | | | | Range names used: | | |
| 4 | Unit cost | $7.50 | | Cum Prob | Demand | Probability | | LookupTable | =Model!$D$5:$F$9 | |
| 5 | Unit price | $10.00 | | 0.00 | 100 | 0.30 | | Order_quantity | =Model!$B$9 | |
| 6 | Unit refund | $2.50 | | 0.30 | 150 | 0.20 | | Unit_cost | =Model!$B$4 | |
| 7 | | | | 0.50 | 200 | 0.30 | | Unit_price | =Model!$B$5 | |
| 8 | Decision variable | | | 0.80 | 250 | 0.15 | | Unit_refund | =Model!$B$6 | |
| 9 | Order quantity | 200 | | 0.95 | 300 | 0.05 | | | | |
| 10 | | | | | | | | | | |
| 11 | Summary measures for simulation below | | | | | | | | | |
| 12 | Average profit | $193.63 | | 95% confidence interval for expected profit | | | | | | |
| 13 | Stdev of profit | $331.68 | | Lower limit | $173.07 | | | | | |
| 14 | Minimum profit | -$250.00 | | Upper limit | $214.18 | | | | | |
| 15 | Maximum profit | $500.00 | | | | | | | | |
| 16 | | | | | | | | | | |
| 17 | Simulation | | . | | | | | Distribution of profit | | |
| 18 | Replication | Demand | Revenue | Cost | Refund | Profit | | Value | Frequency | |
| 19 | 1 | 100 | $1,000 | $1,500 | $250 | -$250 | | -250 | 316 | |
| 20 | 2 | 150 | $1,500 | $1,500 | $125 | $125 | | 125 | 185 | |
| 21 | 3 | 200 | $2,000 | $1,500 | $0 | $500 | | 500 | 499 | |
| 22 | 4 | 100 | $1,000 | $1,500 | $250 | -$250 | | | | |
| 23 | 5 | 100 | $1,000 | $1,500 | $250 | -$250 | | | | |
| 1016 | 998 | 200 | $2,000 | $1,500 | $0 | $500 | | | | |
| 1017 | 999 | 200 | $2,000 | $1,500 | $0 | $500 | | | | |
| 1018 | 1000 | 200 | $2,000 | $1,500 | $0 | $500 | | | | |

associated with each random number, depending on which interval the random number falls in. For example, if a random number is 0.5279, this falls in the third interval, so it is associated with the third possible demand value, 200.

*This rather cumbersome procedure for generating a discrete random number is not necessary when you use @RISK.*

To implement this procedure, you use a VLOOKUP function based on the range D5:F9 (named LookupTable). This table has the cumulative probabilities in column D and the possible demand values in column E. In fact, the whole purpose of the cumulative probabilities in column D is to allow the use of the VLOOKUP function. To generate the simulated demands, enter the formula

=VLOOKUP(RAND(),LookupTable,2)

in cell B19 and copy it to the range B20:B1018. This formula compares any RAND value to the values in D5:D9 and returns the appropriate demand from E5:E9. (In the file, you will note that random cells are colored green. This coloring convention is not required, but we use it consistently to identify the random cells.)

This step is the key to the simulation, so make sure you understand exactly what it entails. The rest is bookkeeping, as indicated in the following steps.

**3** **Revenue.** Once the demand is known, the number of calendars sold is the smaller of the demand and the order quantity. For example, if 150 calendars are demanded, 150 will be sold. But if 250 are demanded, only 200 can be sold (because Walton orders only 200). Therefore, to calculate the revenue in cell C19, enter the formula

=Unit_price*MIN(B19,Order_quantity)

**4** **Ordering cost.** The cost of ordering the calendars does not depend on the demand; it is the unit cost multiplied by the number ordered. Calculate this cost in cell D19 with the formula

=Unit_cost*Order_quantity

**⑤ Refund.** If the order quantity is greater than the demand, there is a refund of $2.50 for each calendar left over; otherwise, there is no refund. Therefore, calculate the refund in cell E19 with the formula

`=Unit_refund*MAX(Order_quantity-B19,0)`

For example, if demand is 150, then 50 calendars are left over, and this MAX is 50, the larger of 50 and 0. However, if demand is 250, then no calendars are left over, and this MAX is 0, the larger of −50 and 0. (This calculation could also be accomplished with an IF function instead of a MAX function.)

**⑥ Profit.** Calculate the profit in cell F19 with the formula

`=C19+E19-D19`

**⑦ Copy to other rows.** This is a "one-line" simulation, where all of the logic is captured in a single row, row 19. For one-line simulations, you can replicate the logic with new random numbers very easily by copying down. Copy row 19 down to row 1018 to generate 1000 replications.

**⑧ Summary measures.** Each profit value in column F corresponds to one randomly generated demand. You usually want to see how these vary from one replication to another. First, calculate the average and standard deviation of the 1000 profits in cells B12 and B13 with the formulas

`=AVERAGE(F19:F1018)`

and

`=STDEV(F19:F1018)`

Similarly, calculate the smallest and largest of the 1000 profits in cells B14 and B15 with the MIN and MAX functions.

**⑨ Confidence interval for mean profit.** Calculate a 95% confidence interval for the mean profit in cells E13 and E14 with the formulas

`=B12-1.96*B13/SQRT(1000)`

and

`=B12+1.96*B13/SQRT(1000)`

(See the next section on confidence intervals for details.)

**⑩ Distribution of simulated profits.** There are only three possible profits, −$250, $125, or $500 (depending on whether demand is 100, 150, or at least 200—see the following discussion). You can use the COUNTIF function to count the number of times each of these possible profits is obtained. To do so, enter the formula

`=COUNTIF($F$19:$F$1018,H19)`

in cell I19 and copy it down to cell I21.

## Checking Logic with Deterministic Inputs

It can be difficult to check whether the logic in your model is correct, because of the random numbers. The reason is that you usually get different output values, depending on the particular random numbers generated. Therefore, it is sometimes useful to enter well-chosen *fixed* values for the random inputs, just to see whether your logic is correct. We call these *deterministic checks*. In the present example, you might try several fixed demands, at least one of which is *less than* the order quantity and at least one of which is *greater than* the order quantity. For example, if you enter a fixed demand of 150, the revenue, cost, refund, and profit should be $1500, $1500, $125, and $125, respectively. Or if you enter a fixed demand of 250, these outputs are $2000, $1500, $0, and $500. There is no randomness in these values; every correct model should get these same values. If your model doesn't get these values, there must be a logic error in your model that has nothing to do with random numbers or simulation. Of course, you should fix any such logical errors before reentering the *random* demand and running the simulation.

You can make a similar check by keeping the random demand, repeatedly pressing the F9 key, and watching the outputs for the different random demands. For example, if the refund is not $0 every time demand exceeds the order quantity, you know you have a logical error in at least one formula. The advantage of deterministic checks is that you can compare your results with those of other users, using *agreed-upon test values* of the random quantities. You should all get exactly the same outputs.

### Discussion of the Simulation Results

At this point, it is a good idea to stand back and see what you have accomplished. First, in the body of the simulation, rows 19 through 1018, you randomly generated 1000 possible demands and the corresponding profits. Because there are only five possible demand values (100, 150, 200, 250, and 300), there are only five possible profit values: $-$250$, $125, $500, $500, and $500. Also, note that for the order quantity 200, the profit is $500 regardless of whether demand is 200, 250, or 300. (Make sure you understand why.) A tally of the profit values in these rows, including the hidden rows, indicates that there are 316 rows with profit equal to $-$250$ (demand 100), 185 rows with profit equal to $125 (demand 150), and 499 rows with profit equal to $500 (demand 200, 250, or 300). The average of these 1000 profits is $193.63, and their standard deviation is $331.68. (Again, however, remember that your answers will probably differ from these because of different random numbers.)

Typically, a simulation model should capture one or more output variables, such as profit. These output variables depend on random inputs, such as demand. The goal is to estimate the probability distributions of the outputs. In the Walton simulation the estimated probability distribution of profit is

$$P(\text{Profit} = -\$250) = 316/1000 = 0.316$$

$$P(\text{Profit} = \$125) = 185/1000 = 0.185$$

$$P(\text{Profit} = \$500) = 499/1000 = 0.499$$

The estimated mean of this distribution is $193.63 and the estimated standard deviation is $331.68. It is important to realize that if the entire simulation is run again with *different* random numbers (such as the ones you might have generated on your PC), the answers will probably be slightly different. This is the primary reason for the confidence interval in cells E13 and E14. This interval expresses the remaining uncertainty about the *mean* of the profit distribution. Your best guess for this mean is the average of the 1000 profits you happened to observe. However, because the corresponding confidence interval is somewhat wide, from $173.07 to $214.18, you are not at all sure of the *true* mean of the profit distribution. You are only 95% confident that the true mean is within this interval. If you run this simulation again with different random numbers, the average profit might be somewhat different from the average profit you observed, $193.63, and the other summary statistics will probably also be different. (For illustration, we pressed the F9 key five times and got the following average profits: $213.88, $206.00, $212.75, $219.50, and $189.50. So this is truly a case of "answers will vary.")

## Notes about Confidence Intervals

*The confidence interval provides a measure of accuracy of the mean profit, as estimated from the simulation.*

It is common in computer simulations to estimate the mean of some distribution by the average of the simulated observations. The usual practice is then to accompany this estimate with a **confidence interval,** which indicates the accuracy of the estimate. You might recall from statistics that to obtain a confidence interval for the mean, you start with the estimated mean and then add and subtract a multiple of the *standard error* of the estimated mean. If the estimated mean (that is, the average) is $\overline{X}$, the confidence interval is given in the following formula.

> *Confidence Interval for the Mean*
>
> $$\overline{X} \pm (\text{Multiple} \times \text{Standard Error of } \overline{X})$$

The standard error of $\overline{X}$ is the standard deviation of the observations divided by the square root of *n*, the number of observations:

> *Standard Error of* $\overline{X}$
>
> $$s/\sqrt{n}$$

Here, *s* is the symbol for the standard deviation of the observations. You can obtain it with the STDEV function in Excel.

The *multiple* in the confidence interval formula depends on the confidence level and the number of observations. If the confidence level is 95%, for example, then the multiple is usually very close to 2, so a good guideline is to go out two standard errors on either side of the average to obtain an approximate 95% confidence interval for the mean.

> *Approximate 95% Confidence Interval for the Mean*
>
> $$\overline{X} \pm 2s/\sqrt{n}$$

To be more precise, if *n* is reasonably large, which is almost always the case in simulations, the central limit theorem implies that the correct multiple is the number from the standard normal distribution that cuts off probability 0.025 in each tail. This is a famous number in statistics: 1.96. Because 1.96 is very close to 2, it is acceptable for all practical purposes to use 2 instead of 1.96 in the confidence interval formula. (Note that you should use a different multiple if you want a 90% or a 99% confidence level rather than a 95% level.)

*The idea is to choose the number of iterations large enough so that the resulting confidence interval will be sufficiently narrow.*

Analysts often plan a simulation so that the confidence interval for the mean of some important output will be sufficiently narrow. The reasoning is that narrow confidence intervals imply more precision about the estimated mean of the output variable. If the confidence level is fixed at some value such as 95%, the only way to narrow the confidence interval is to simulate more replications. Assuming that the confidence level is 95%, the following value of *n* is required to ensure that the resulting confidence interval will have a half-length approximately equal to some specified value *B*:

> *Sample Size Determination*
>
> $$n = \frac{4 \times (\text{Estimated standard deviation})^2}{B^2}$$

This formula requires an estimate of the standard deviation of the output variable. For example, in the Walton simulation the 95% confidence interval with $n = 1000$ has half-length ($214.18 − $173.07)/2 = $20.56. Suppose that you want to reduce this half-length to $12.50—that is, you want $B = $12.50. You do not know the exact standard deviation of the profit distribution, but you can estimate it from the simulation as $331.68. Therefore, to obtain the required confidence interval half-length $B$, you need to simulate $n$ replications, where

$$n = \frac{4(328.04)^2}{12.50^2} \approx 2755$$

(When this formula produces a noninteger, it is common to round upward.) The claim, then, is that if you rerun the simulation with 2817 replications rather than 1000 replications, the half-length of the 95% confidence interval for the mean profit will be close to $12.50.

### Finding the Best Order Quantity

You are not yet finished with the Walton example. So far, the simulation has been run for only a single order quantity, 200. Walton's ultimate goal is to find the *best* order quantity. Even this statement must be clarified. What does "best" mean? As in Chapter 9, one possibility is to use the *expected* profit—that is, EMV—as the optimality criterion, but other characteristics of the profit distribution could influence the decision. You can obtain the required outputs with a data table. Specifically, you use a data table to rerun the simulation for other order quantities. This data table and a corresponding chart are shown in Figure 10.26. (This is still part of the finished version of the Walton Bookstore 2.xlsx file.)

Figure 10.26 Data Table for Walton Bookstore Simulation

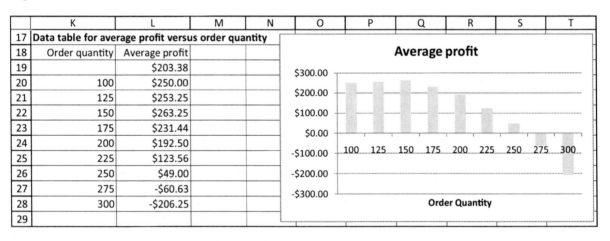

| | K | L | M | N | O | P | Q | R | S | T |
|---|---|---|---|---|---|---|---|---|---|---|
| 17 | Data table for average profit versus order quantity | | | | | | | | | |
| 18 | Order quantity | Average profit | | | | | | | | |
| 19 | | $203.38 | | | | | | | | |
| 20 | 100 | $250.00 | | | | | | | | |
| 21 | 125 | $253.25 | | | | | | | | |
| 22 | 150 | $263.25 | | | | | | | | |
| 23 | 175 | $231.44 | | | | | | | | |
| 24 | 200 | $192.50 | | | | | | | | |
| 25 | 225 | $123.56 | | | | | | | | |
| 26 | 250 | $49.00 | | | | | | | | |
| 27 | 275 | -$60.63 | | | | | | | | |
| 28 | 300 | -$206.25 | | | | | | | | |
| 29 | | | | | | | | | | |

To optimize in simulation models, try various values of the decision variable(s) and run the simulation for each of them.

To create this table, enter the trial order quantities shown in the range K20:K28, enter the link =B12 to the average profit in cell L19, and select the data table range K19:L28. Then select Data Table from the What-If Analysis dropdown list, specifying that the column input cell is B9. (See Figure 10.25.) Finally, construct a column chart of the average profits in the data table. Note that an order quantity of 150 appears to maximize the average profit. Its average profit of $263.25 is slightly higher than the average profits from nearby order quantities and much higher than the profit gained from an order of 200 or more calendars. However, again keep in mind that this is a simulation, so that all of these average profits depend on the particular random numbers generated. If you rerun the simulation with different random numbers, it is conceivable that some other order quantity could be best. (Did you notice in the data table that the average profits in cells L19 and L24 are both based on an order quantity of 200? They are different because they are based on different random numbers.)

Excel Tip: *Calculation Settings with Data Tables*
*Sometimes you will create a data table and the values will be constant the whole way down. This could mean you did something wrong, but more likely it is due to a calculation setting. To check, go to the Formulas ribbon and click on the Calculation Options dropdown arrow. If it isn't Automatic (the default setting), you need to click on the Calculate Now (or Calculate Sheet) button or press the F9 key to make the data table calculate correctly. (The Calculate Now and F9 key recalculate everything in your workbook. The Calculate Sheet option recalculates only the active sheet.) Note that the Automatic Except for Data Tables setting is there for a reason. Data tables, especially those based on complex simulations, can take a lot of time to recalculate, and with the default setting, this recalculation occurs every time anything changes in your workbook. So the Automatic Except for Data Tables setting is handy to prevent data tables from recalculating until you force them to by pressing the F9 key or clicking on one of the Calculate buttons.*

## Using a Data Table to Repeat Simulations

The Walton simulation is a particularly simple one-line simulation model. All of the logic—generating a demand and calculating the corresponding profit—can be captured in a single row. Then to replicate the simulation, you can simply copy this row down as far as you like. Many simulation models are significantly more complex and require more than one row to capture the logic. Nevertheless, they still result in one or more output quantities (such as profit) that you want to replicate. We now illustrate another method of replicating with Excel only that is more general (still using the Walton example). It uses a data table to generate the replications. Refer to Figure 10.27 and the file Walton Bookstore 3.xlsx.

Through row 19, this model is exactly like the previous model. That is, it uses the given data at the top of the spreadsheet to construct a typical "prototype" of the simulation in row 19. This time, however, do not copy row 19 down. Instead, form a data table in the range A23:B1023 to replicate the basic simulation 1000 times. In column A, list the replication numbers, 1 to 1000. Next, enter the formula **=F19** in cell B23. This forms a link to the profit from the prototype row for use in the data table. Then create a data table and enter *any blank cell* (such as C23) as the column input cell. (No row input cell is necessary, so its box should be left empty.) This tricks Excel into repeating the row 19 calculations 1000 times, each time with a new random number, and reporting the profits in column B of the data table. (If you wanted to see other simulated quantities, such as revenue, for each replication, you could add extra output columns to the data table.)

Excel Tip: *How Data Tables Work*
*To understand this procedure, you must understand exactly how data tables work. When you create a data table, Excel takes each value in the left column of the data table (here, column A), substitutes it into the cell designated as the column input cell, recalculates the spreadsheet, and returns the output value (or values) you have requested in the top row of the data table (such as profit). It might seem silly to substitute each replication number from column A into a blank cell such as cell C23, but this part is really irrelevant. The important part is the recalculation. Each recalculation leads to a new random demand and corresponding profit, and these profits are the quantities you want to keep track of.*

The key to simulating many replications in Excel (without an add-in) is to use a data table with any blank cell as the column input cell.

Figure 10.27   Using a Data Table to Simulate Replications

| | A | B | C | D | E | F | G | H | I | J |
|---|---|---|---|---|---|---|---|---|---|---|
| 1 | Simulation of Walton's bookstore | | | | | | | | | |
| 2 | | | | | | | | | | |
| 3 | Cost data | | | Demand distribution | | | | Range names used: | | |
| 4 | Unit cost | $7.50 | | CumProb | Demand | Probability | | LookupTable | =Model!$D$5:$F$9 | |
| 5 | Unit price | $10.00 | | 0.00 | 100 | 0.30 | | Order_quantity | =Model!$B$9 | |
| 6 | Unit refund | $2.50 | | 0.30 | 150 | 0.20 | | Unit_cost | =Model!$B$4 | |
| 7 | | | | 0.50 | 200 | 0.30 | | Unit_price | =Model!$B$5 | |
| 8 | Decision variable | | | 0.80 | 250 | 0.15 | | Unit_refund | =Model!$B$6 | |
| 9 | Order quantity | 200 | | 0.95 | 300 | 0.05 | | | | |
| 10 | | | | | | | | | | |
| 11 | Summary measures from simulation below | | | | | | | | | |
| 12 | Average | $189.13 | | 95% confidence interval for expected profit | | | | | | |
| 13 | StDev | $327.89 | | Lower limit | $168.81 | | | | | |
| 14 | Minimum | -$250.00 | | Upper limit | $209.45 | | | | | |
| 15 | Maximum | $500.00 | | | | | | | | |
| 16 | | | | | | | | | | |
| 17 | Simulation | | | | | | | | | |
| 18 | | Demand | Revenue | Cost | Refund | Profit | | | | |
| 19 | | 100 | $1,000 | $1,500 | $250 | -$250 | | | | |
| 20 | | | | | | | | | | |
| 21 | Data table for replications, each shows profit from that replication | | | | | | | | | |
| 22 | Replication | Profit | | | | | | | | |
| 23 | | -$250 | | | | | | | | |
| 24 | 1 | -$250 | | | | | | | | |
| 25 | 2 | $500 | | | | | | | | |
| 26 | 3 | $500 | | | | | | | | |
| 27 | 4 | -$250 | | | | | | | | |
| 1021 | 998 | $500 | | | | | | | | |
| 1022 | 999 | $500 | | | | | | | | |
| 1023 | 1000 | $500 | | | | | | | | |

*Of course, this means that you should not freeze the quantity in cell B19 before forming the data table. The whole point of the data table is to use a different random number for each replication, and this will occur only if the random demand in row 19 is "live."*

### Using a Two-Way Data Table

You can carry this method one step further to see how the profit depends on the order quantity. Here you use a two-way data table with the replication number along the side and possible order quantities along the top. See Figure 10.28 and the file Walton Bookstore 4.xlsx. Now the data table range is A23:J1023, and the driving formula in cell A23 is again the link =**F19**. The column input cell should again be *any blank cell*, and the row input cell should be B9 (the order quantity). Each cell in the body of the data table shows a simulated profit for a particular replication and a particular order quantity, and each is based on a *different* random demand.

By averaging the numbers in each column of the data table (see row 14), you can see that 150 again appears to be the best order quantity. It is also helpful to construct a column chart of these averages, as in Figure 10.29. Now, however, assuming you have not frozen anything, the data table and the corresponding chart will change each time you press the F9 key. To see whether 150 is always the best order quantity, you can press the F9 key and see whether the bar above 150 continues to be the highest.

**Figure 10.28** Using a Two-Way Data Table for the Simulation Model

| | A | B | C | D | E | F | G | H | I | J |
|---|---|---|---|---|---|---|---|---|---|---|
| 1 | Simulation of Walton's bookstore | | | | | | | | | |
| 2 | | | | | | | | | | |
| 3 | Cost data | | | Demand distribution | | | | Range names used: | | |
| 4 | Unit cost | $7.50 | | CumProb | Demand | Probability | | LookupTable | =Model!$D$5:$F$9 | |
| 5 | Unit price | $10.00 | | 0.00 | 100 | 0.30 | | Order_quantity | =Model!$B$9 | |
| 6 | Unit refund | $2.50 | | 0.30 | 150 | 0.20 | | Unit_cost | =Model!$B$4 | |
| 7 | | | | 0.50 | 200 | 0.30 | | Unit_price | =Model!$B$5 | |
| 8 | Decision variable | | | 0.80 | 250 | 0.15 | | Unit_refund | =Model!$B$6 | |
| 9 | Order quantity | 200 | | 0.95 | 300 | 0.05 | | | | |
| 10 | | | | | | | | | | |
| 11 | Summary measures of simulated profits for each order quantity | | | | | | | | | |
| 12 | | | | Order quantity | | | | | | |
| 13 | | 100 | 125 | 150 | 175 | 200 | 225 | 250 | 275 | 300 |
| 14 | Average profit | $250.00 | $261.13 | $267.75 | $237.44 | $206.38 | $118.69 | $16.75 | -$99.81 | -$209.63 |
| 15 | Stdev profit | $0.00 | $83.67 | $169.54 | $243.62 | $327.49 | $361.44 | $429.60 | $432.34 | $442.74 |
| 16 | | | | | | | | | | |
| 17 | Simulation | | | | | | | | | |
| 18 | | Demand | Revenue | Cost | Refund | Profit | | | | |
| 19 | | 100 | $1,000 | $1,500 | $250 | -$250 | | | | |
| 20 | | | | | | | | | | |
| 21 | Data table showing profit for replications with various order quantities | | | | | | | | | |
| 22 | Replication | | | Order quantity | | | | | | |
| 23 | ($250.00) | 100 | 125 | 150 | 175 | 200 | 225 | 250 | 275 | 300 |
| 24 | 1 | $250 | $313 | $0 | $250 | -$250 | 375 | 625 | 125 | 375 |
| 25 | 2 | $250 | $313 | $375 | -$125 | $125 | 0 | -500 | -250 | -375 |
| 26 | 3 | $250 | $125 | $375 | $438 | $500 | 375 | 250 | -250 | 0 |
| 27 | 4 | $250 | $313 | $0 | $438 | $500 | 375 | 250 | -625 | -750 |
| 1021 | 998 | $250 | $313 | $375 | $438 | $125 | 375 | 625 | -625 | -375 |
| 1022 | 999 | $250 | $313 | $0 | $438 | $500 | 375 | 250 | 500 | 375 |
| 1023 | 1000 | $250 | $313 | $375 | $438 | $500 | 562.5 | -500 | 500 | 375 |

**Figure 10.29**

Column Chart of Average Profits for Different Order Quantities

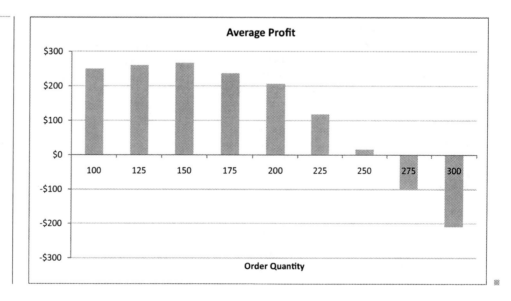

By now you should appreciate the usefulness of data tables in spreadsheet simulations. They allow you to take a prototype simulation and replicate its key results as often as you like. This method makes summary statistics (over the entire group of replications) and corresponding charts fairly easy to obtain. Nevertheless, it takes some work to create the data tables and charts. In the next section you will see how the @RISK add-in does a lot of this work for you.

## PROBLEMS

### Skill-Building Problems

**11.** Suppose you own an expensive car and purchase auto insurance. This insurance has a $1000 deductible, so that if you have an accident and the damage is less than $1000, you pay for it out of your pocket. However, if the damage is greater than $1000, you pay the first $1000 and the insurance pays the rest. In the current year there is probability 0.025 that you will have an accident. If you have an accident, the damage amount is normally distributed with mean $3000 and standard deviation $750.

   **a.** Use Excel to simulate the amount you have to pay for damages to your car. This should be a one-line simulation, so run 5000 iterations by copying it down. Then find the average amount you pay, the standard deviation of the amounts you pay, and a 95% confidence interval for the average amount you pay. (Note that many of the amounts you pay will be 0 because you have no accidents.)

   **b.** Continue the simulation in part **a** by creating a two-way data table, where the row input is the deductible amount, varied from $500 to $2000 in multiples of $500. Now find the average amount you pay, the standard deviation of the amounts you pay, and a 95% confidence interval for the average amount you pay for each deductible amount.

   **c.** Do you think it is reasonable to assume that damage amounts are *normally* distributed? What would you criticize about this assumption? What might you suggest instead?

**12.** In August of the current year, a car dealer is trying to determine how many cars of the next model year to order. Each car ordered in August costs $20,000. The demand for the dealer's next year models has the probability distribution shown in the file P10_12.xlsx. Each car sells for $25,000. If demand for next year's cars exceeds the number of cars ordered in August, the dealer must reorder at a cost of $22,000 per car. Excess cars can be disposed of at $17,000 per car.

Use simulation to determine how many cars to order in August. For your optimal order quantity, find a 95% confidence interval for the expected profit.

**13.** In the Walton Bookstore example, suppose that Walton receives no money for the first 50 excess calendars returned but receives $2.50 for every calendar after the first 50 returned. Does this change the optimal order quantity?

**14.** A sweatshirt supplier is trying to decide how many sweatshirts to print for the upcoming NCAA basketball championships. The final four teams have emerged from the quarterfinal round, and there is now a week left until the semifinals, which are then followed in a couple of days by the finals. Each sweatshirt costs $10 to produce and sells for $25. However, in three weeks, any leftover sweatshirts will be put on sale for half price, $12.50. The supplier assumes that the demand for his sweatshirts during the next three weeks (when interest in the tournament is at its highest) has the distribution shown in the file P10_14.xlsx. The residual demand, after the sweatshirts have been put on sale, has the distribution also shown in this file. The supplier, being a profit maximizer, realizes that every sweatshirt sold, even at the sale price, yields a profit. However, he also realizes that any sweatshirts produced but not sold (even at the sale price) must be thrown away, resulting in a $10 loss per sweatshirt. Analyze the supplier's problem with a simulation model.

### Skill-Extending Problems

**15.** In the Walton Bookstore example with a discrete demand distribution, explain why an order quantity other than one of the possible demands cannot maximize the expected profit. (*Hint:* Consider an order of 190 calendars, for example. If this maximizes expected profit, then it must yield a higher expected profit than an order of 150 or 100. But then an order of 200 calendars must also yield a larger expected profit than 190 calendars. Why?)

# 10.5 INTRODUCTION TO @RISK

Spreadsheet simulation modeling has become extremely popular in recent years, both in the academic and corporate communities. Much of the reason for this popularity is due to simulation add-ins such as **@RISK.** There are two primary advantages to using such an add-in. First, an add-in gives you easy access to many probability distributions you might want to use in your simulation models. You already saw in section 10.2 how the RISKDIS-CRETE, RISKNORMAL, and RISKTRIANG functions, among others, are easy to use and remember. Second, an add-in allows you to perform simulations much more easily than is possible with Excel alone. To replicate a simulation in Excel, you typically need to build a data table. Then you have to calculate summary statistics, such as averages, standard deviations, and percentiles, with built-in Excel functions. If you want graphs to enhance the analysis, you have to create them. In short, you have to perform a number of time-consuming steps for each simulation. Simulation add-ins such as @RISK perform much of this work automatically.

*@RISK provides a number of functions for simulating from various distributions, and it takes care of all the bookkeeping in spreadsheet simulations. Excel simulations without @RISK require much more work for the user.*

Although we will focus only on @RISK in this book, it is not the only simulation add-in available for Excel. Two worthy competitors are Crystal Ball, developed by Decisioneering (www.decisioneering.com) and Risk Solver Platform, developed by Frontline Systems, the developer of Solver (www.frontsys.com). Both Crystal Ball and Risk Solver Platform have much of the same functionality as @RISK. However, the authors have a natural bias for @RISK—we have been permitted by its developer, Palisade Corporation (www.palisade.com), to provide the academic version free with this book. If it were not included, you would have to purchase it from Palisade at a fairly steep price. Indeed, Microsoft Office does not include @RISK, Crystal Ball, Risk Solver Platform, or any other simulation add-in—you must purchase them separately.

## 10.5.1 @RISK Features

Here is an overview of some of @RISK's features. We will discuss all of these in more detail in this section.

1. @RISK contains a number of functions such as RISKNORMAL and RISKDIS-CRETE that make it easy to generate observations from a wide variety of probability distributions. You saw some of these in section 10.2.

2. You can designate any cell or range of cells in your simulation model as *output cells*. When you run the simulation, @RISK automatically keeps summary measures (averages, standard deviations, percentiles, and others) from the values generated in these output cells across the replications. It also creates graphs such as histograms based on these values. In other words, @RISK takes care of tedious bookkeeping operations for you.

3. @RISK has a special function, **RISKSIMTABLE**, that allows you to run the same simulation several times, using a different value of some key input variable each time. This input variable is often a decision variable. For example, suppose that you would like to simulate an inventory ordering policy (as in the Walton Bookstore example). Your ultimate purpose is to compare simulation outputs across a number of possible order quantities such as 100, 150, 200, 250, and 300. If you use an appropriate formula involving the RISKSIMTABLE function, the entire simulation is performed for each of these order quantities separately—with one click of a button. You can then compare the outputs to choose the best order quantity.

### 10.5.2 Loading @RISK

To build simulation models with @RISK, you need to have Excel open with @RISK added in. The first step, if you have not already done so, is to install the Palisade DecisionTools suite with the Setup program. Then you can load @RISK by clicking on the Windows Start button, selecting the Programs group, selecting the Palisade DecisionTools group, and finally selecting the @RISK item. If Excel is already open, this loads @RISK inside Excel. If Excel is not yet open, this launches Excel and @RISK simultaneously.[8] After @RISK is loaded, you see an @RISK tab and the corresponding @RISK ribbon in Figure 10.30.[9]

**Figure 10.30**   @RISK Ribbon

### 10.5.3 @RISK Models with a Single Random Input Variable

*The majority of the work (and thinking) goes into developing the model. Setting up @RISK and then running it are relatively easy.*

In the remainder of this section we illustrate some of @RISK's functionality by revisiting the Walton Bookstore example. The next chapter demonstrates the use of @RISK in a number of interesting simulation models. Throughout our discussion, you should keep one very important idea in mind. The development of a simulation model is basically a two-step procedure. The first step is to build the model itself. This step requires you to enter all of the logic that transforms inputs (including @RISK functions such as RISKDISCRETE) into outputs (such as profit). This is where most of the work and thinking go, exactly as in models from previous chapters, and @RISK cannot do this for you. It is *your* job to enter the formulas that link inputs to outputs appropriately. However, once this logic has been incorporated, @RISK takes over in the second step. It automatically replicates your model, with different random numbers on each replication, and it reports any summary measures that you request in tabular or graphical form. Therefore, @RISK greatly decreases the amount of busy work you need to do, but it is not a magic bullet.

We begin by analyzing an example with a single random input variable.

---

**EXAMPLE** | **10.3 USING @RISK AT WALTON BOOKSTORE**

Recall that Walton Bookstore buys calendars for $7.50, sells them at the regular price of $10, and gets a refund of $2.50 for all calendars that cannot be sold. In contrast to Example 10.2, assume now that Walton estimates a triangular probability distribution for demand, where the minimum, most likely, and maximum values of demand are 100, 175, and 300, respectively. The company wants to use this probability distribution, together with @RISK, to simulate the profit for any particular order quantity, with the ultimate goal of finding the best order quantity.

*This is the same Walton Bookstore model as before, except that a triangular distribution for demand is used.*

**Objective**   To learn about @RISK's basic functionality by revisiting the Walton Bookstore problem.

---

[8]We have had the best luck when we (1) close other applications we are not currently using, and (2) launch Excel and @RISK together by starting @RISK. However, it is also possible to start @RISK *after* Excel is already running.
[9]If you have been using version 5.0 of @RISK, you will see only minor changes in the newer versions (5.5.1 or 5.7) now available. However, if you have been using version 4.5, you will see *major* changes in the user interface.

The monetary values are the same as before. The parameters of the triangular distribution of demand are probably Walton's best subjective estimates, possibly guided by its experience with previous calendars. As in many simulation examples, the triangular distribution has been chosen for simplicity. In this case, the manager would need to estimate only three quantities: the minimum possible demand, the maximum possible demand, and the most likely demand.

## Solution

We use this example to illustrate important features of @RISK. We first show how it helps you to implement an appropriate input probability distribution for demand. Then we show how it can be used to build a simulation model for a specific order quantity and generate outputs from this model. Finally, we show how the RISKSIMTABLE function enables you to simultaneously generate outputs from several order quantities so that you can choose the optimal order quantity.

### DEVELOPING THE SIMULATION MODEL

The spreadsheet model for profit is essentially the same model developed previously *without* @RISK, as shown in Figure 10.31. (See the file Walton Bookstore 5.xlsx.) There are only a few new things to be aware of.

Figure 10.31   Simulation Model with a Fixed Order Quantity

| | A | B | C | D | E | F | G | H | I | J |
|---|---|---|---|---|---|---|---|---|---|---|
| 1 | Simulation of Walton's Bookstore using @RISK | | | | | | | Range names used: | | |
| 2 | | | | | | | | Order_quantity | =Model!$B$9 | |
| 3 | Cost data | | | Demand distribution - triangular | | | | Unit_cost | =Model!$B$4 | |
| 4 | Unit cost | $7.50 | | Minimum | 100 | | | Unit_price | =Model!$B$5 | |
| 5 | Unit price | $10.00 | | Most likely | 175 | | | Unit_refund | =Model!$B$6 | |
| 6 | Unit refund | $2.50 | | Maximum | 300 | | | | | |
| 7 | | | | | | | | | | |
| 8 | Decision variable | | | | | | | | | |
| 9 | Order quantity | 200 | | | | | | | | |
| 10 | | | | | | | | | | |
| 11 | Simulation | | | | | | | | | |
| 12 | | Demand | Revenue | Cost | Refund | Profit | | | | |
| 13 | | 187 | $1,870 | $1,500 | $33 | $403 | | | | |
| 14 | | | | | | | | | | |
| 15 | Summary measures of profit from @RISK - based on 1000 iterations | | | | | | | | | |
| 16 | Minimum | -$235.00 | | | | | | | | |
| 17 | Maximum | $500.00 | | | | | | | | |
| 18 | Average | $337.50 | | | | | | | | |
| 19 | Standard deviation | $189.05 | | | | | | | | |
| 20 | 5th percentile | -$47.50 | | | | | | | | |
| 21 | 95th percentile | $500.00 | | | | | | | | |
| 22 | P(profit <= 300) | 0.360 | | | | | | | | |
| 23 | P(profit > 400) | 0.515 | | | | | | | | |

**①  Input distribution.** To generate a random demand, enter the formula

`=ROUND(RISKTRIANG(E4,E5,E6),0)`

in cell B13 for the random demand. This uses the RISKTRIANG function to generate a demand from the triangular distribution. (As before, our convention is to color random input cells green.) Excel's ROUND function is used to round demand to the nearest integer. Recall from the discussion in section 10.3 that Excel has no built-in functions to generate random numbers from a triangular distribution, but this is easy with @RISK.

**2** **Output cell.** When the simulation runs, you want @RISK to keep track of profit. In @RISK's terminology, you need to designate the Profit cell, F13, as an *output cell*. To do this, select cell F13 and then click on the Add Output button on the @RISK ribbon. (See Figure 10.30.) This adds **RISKOUTPUT("*label*")+** to the cell's formula. (Here, "label" is a label that @RISK uses for its reports. In this case it makes sense to use "Profit" as the label.) The formula in cell F13 changes from

=C13+E13-D13

to

=RISKOUTPUT("Profit")+C13+E13-D13

The RISKOUTPUT function indicates that a cell is an output cell, so that @RISK will keep track of its values throughout the simulation.

The plus sign following RISKOUTPUT does *not* indicate addition. It is simply @RISK's way of indicating that you want to keep track of the value in this cell (for reporting reasons) as the simulation progresses. Any number of cells can be designated in this way as output cells. They are typically the "bottom line" values of primary interest. Our convention is to color such cells gray for emphasis.

**3** **Summary functions.** There are several places where you can store @RISK results. One of these is to use @RISK statistical functions to place results in your model worksheet. @RISK provides several functions for summarizing output values. Some of these are illustrated in the range B16:B23 of Figure 10.31. They contain the formulas

These @RISK summary functions allow you to show simulation results on the same sheet as the model. However, they are totally optional.

=RISKMIN(F13)

=RISKMAX(F3)

=RISKMEAN(F13)

=RISKSTDDEV(F13)

=RISKPERCENTILE(F13,0.05)

=RISKPERCENTILE(F13,0.95)

=RISKTARGET(F13,300)

and

=1-RISKTARGET(F13,400)

The values in these cells are not meaningful until you run the simulation (so do not be alarmed if they contain error symbols when you open the file). However, once the simulation runs, these formulas capture summary statistics of profit. For example, RISKMEAN calculates the average of the 1000 simulated profits, RISKPERCENTILE finds the value such that the specified percentage of simulated profits are less than or equal to this value, and RISKTARGET finds the percentage of simulated profits less than or equal to the specified value. Although these same summary statistics also appear in other @RISK reports, it is handy to have them in the same worksheet as the model.

### Running the Simulation

After you develop the model, the rest is straightforward. The procedure is always the same: (1) specify simulation settings, (2) run the simulation, and (3) examine the results.

**1** **Simulation settings.** You must first choose some simulation settings. To do so, the buttons on the left in the Simulation group (see Figure 10.32) are useful. We typically do the following:

- Set Iterations to a number such as 1000. (@RISK calls replications "iterations.") Any number can be used, but because the academic version of @RISK allows only 1000 uninterrupted iterations, we typically choose 1000.

- Set Simulations to 1. In a later section, we will explain why you might want to request multiple simulations.

- Click on the "dice" button so that it becomes orange. This button is actually a toggle for what appears in your worksheet. If it is orange, the setting is called "Monte Carlo" and all random cells appear random (they change when you press the F9 key). If it is blue, only the *means* appear in random input cells and the F9 key has no effect. We prefer the Monte Carlo setting, but both settings have exactly the same effect when you run the simulation.

- Many more settings are available by clicking on the button to the left of the "dice" button, but the ones we mentioned should suffice. In addition, more permanent settings can be chosen from Application Settings under Utilities on the @RISK ribbon. You can experiment with these, but the only one we like to change is the Place Reports In setting. The default is to place reports in a new workbook. If you like the reports to be in the same workbook as your model, you can change this setting to Active Workbook.

**Figure 10.32**

**Simulation Group on @RISK Ribbon**

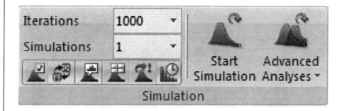

*Leave Latin Hypercube sampling on. It produces more accurate results.*

**@RISK TECHNICAL ISSUES:** *Latin Hypercube Sampling and Mersenne Twister Generator*

*Two settings you shouldn't change are the Sampling Type and Generator settings (available from the button to the left of the "dice" button and then the Sampling tab). They should remain at the default Latin Hypercube and Mersenne Twister settings. The Mersenne Twister is one algorithm, of many, for generating random numbers, and it has been shown to have very good statistical properties. (Not all random number generators do.) **Latin Hypercube sampling** is a more efficient way of sampling than the other option (Monte Carlo) because it produces a more accurate estimate of the output distribution. In fact, we were surprised how accurate it is. In repeated runs of this model, always using different random numbers, we virtually always got a mean profit within a few pennies of $337.50. It turns out that this is the true mean profit for this input distribution of demand. Amazingly, simulation estimates it correctly—almost exactly—on virtually every run. Unfortunately, this means that a confidence interval for the mean, based on @RISK's outputs and the usual confidence interval formula (which assumes Monte Carlo sampling), is much wider (more pessimistic) than it should be. Therefore, we do not even calculate such confidence intervals from here on.*

**2** **Run the simulation.** To run the simulation, simply click on the Start Simulation on the @RISK ribbon. When you do so, @RISK repeatedly generates a random number for each random input cell, recalculates the worksheet, and keeps track of all output cell values. You can watch the progress at the bottom left of the screen.

**3** **Examine the results.** The big questions are (1) which results you want and (2) where you want them. @RISK provides a lot of possibilities, and we mention only our favorites.

- You can ask for summary measures in your model worksheet by using the @RISK statistical functions, such as RISKMEAN, discussed earlier.

- The quickest way to get results is to select an input or output cell (we chose the profit cell, F13) and then click on the Browse Results button on the @RISK ribbon. (See Figure 10.33.) This provides an interactive histogram of the selected value, as shown in Figure 10.34. You can move the sliders on this histogram to see probabilities of various outcomes. Note that the window you see from Browse Results is temporary—it goes away when you click on Close. You can make a permanent copy of the chart by clicking on the third button from the left (see the bottom of Figure 10.34) and choosing one of the copy options.

*For a quick histogram of an output or input, select the output or input cell and click on @RISK's Browse Results button.*

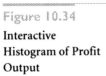
**Figure 10.33**

**Results and Tools Groups on @RISK Ribbon**

**Figure 10.34**

**Interactive Histogram of Profit Output**

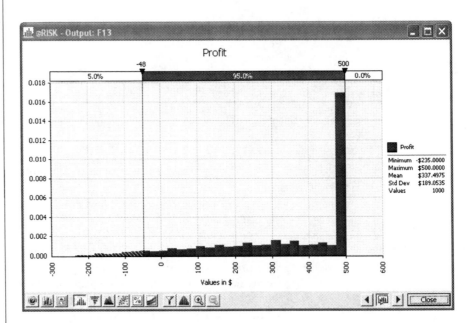

**@RISK Tip:** *Percentiles Displayed on Charts*

*When we displayed the chart in Figure 10.34 the first time, it had the right slider on 500 but showed 5% to the right of it. By default, @RISK puts the sliders at the 5th and 95th percentiles, so that 5% is on either side of them. For this example, 500 is indeed the 95th percentile (why?), but the picture is a bit misleading because there is no chance of a profit greater than 500. When we manually moved the right slider away from 500 and back again, it displayed as in Figure 10.34, correctly indicating that there is no probability to the right of 500.*

*For a quick (and customizable) report of the results, click on @RISK's Summary button.*

■ You can click on the Summary button (again, see Figure 10.33) to see the temporary window in Figure 10.35 with the summary measures for Profit. In general, this report shows the summary for *all* designated inputs and outputs. By default, this Results Summary window shows a mini histogram for each output and a number of numerical summary measures. However, it is easy to customize. If you right-click on this table and choose Columns for Table, you can check or uncheck any of the options. For most of the later screenshots in this book, we elected *not* to show the Graph and Errors columns, but instead to show median and standard deviation columns.

**Figure 10.35** Summary Table of Profit Output

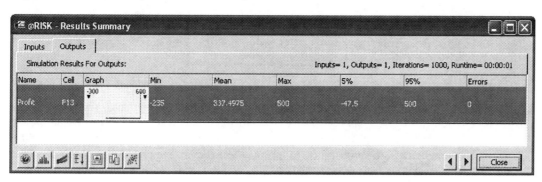

*If you want permanent copies of the simulation results, click on @RISK's Excel Reports buttons and check the reports you want. They will be placed in new worksheets.*

■ You can click on the Excel Reports button (again, see Figure 10.33) to choose from a number of reports that are placed on new worksheets. This is a good option if you want permanent (but non-interactive) copies of reports in your workbook. As an example, Figure 10.36 shows (part of) the Detailed Statistics report you can request. It has the same information as the summary report in Figure 10.35, plus a lot more.

### Discussion of the Simulation Results

The strength of @RISK is that it keeps track of any outputs you designate and then allows you to show the corresponding results as graphs or tables, in temporary windows or in permanent worksheets. As you have seen, @RISK provides several options for displaying results, and we encourage you to explore the possibilities. However, don't lose sight of the overall goal: to see how outputs vary as random inputs vary, and to generate reports that tell the story most effectively. For this particular example, the results in Figures 10.31, 10.34, 10.35, and 10.36 allow you to conclude the following:

■ The smallest simulated profit (out of 1000) was −$235, the largest was $500, the average was $337.50, and the standard deviation of the 1000 profits was $189.05. Of all simulated profits, 5% were −$47.50 or below, 95% were $500 or above, 36% were less than or equal to $300, and 51.5% were larger than $400. (See Figure 10.31. These results are also available from the summary table in Figure 10.35 or the detailed statistics report in Figure 10.36. In particular, the bottom of the detailed statistics report, not shown in the figure, allows you to ask for any percentiles or target values.)

Figure 10.36

@RISK Detailed
Statistics Report

| | B | C | D |
|---|---|---|---|
| 1 | **@RISK Detailed Statistics** | | |
| 2 | **Performed By:** Chris Albright | | |
| 3 | **Date:** Tuesday, September 29, 2009 11:54:02 AM | | |
| 4 | | | |
| 5 | | | |
| 6 | Name | Profit | Demand |
| 7 | Description | Output | RiskTriang(E4,E5,E6) |
| 8 | Cell | Model!F13 | Model!B13 |
| 9 | Minimum | -$235 | 102 |
| 10 | Maximum | $500 | 295 |
| 11 | Mean | $337 | 192 |
| 12 | Std Deviation | $189 | 41 |
| 13 | Variance | 35741.22 | 1702.818 |
| 14 | Skewness | -0.9485486 | 0.2346369 |
| 15 | Kurtosis | 2.796431 | 2.401627 |
| 16 | Errors | 0 | 0 |
| 17 | Mode | $500 | 175 |
| 18 | 5% Perc | -$48 | 127 |
| 19 | 10% Perc | $43 | 139 |
| 20 | 15% Perc | $103 | 147 |
| 21 | 20% Perc | $163 | 155 |
| 22 | 25% Perc | $208 | 161 |
| 23 | 30% Perc | $253 | 167 |
| 24 | 35% Perc | $290 | 172 |

- The profit distribution for this particular order quantity is extremely skewed to the left, with a large bar at $500. (See Figure 10.34.) Do you see why? It is because profit is exactly $500 if demand is greater than or equal to the order quantity, 200. In other words, the probability that profit is $500 equals the probability that demand is at least 200. (This probability is 0.4.) Lower demands result in decreasing profits, which explains the gradual decline in the histogram from right to left.

## Using RISKSIMTABLE

Walton's ultimate goal is to choose an order quantity that provides a large average profit. You could rerun the simulation model several times, each time with a different order quantity in the order quantity cell, and compare the results. However, this has two drawbacks. First, it takes a lot of time and work. The second drawback is more subtle. Each time you run the simulation, you get a *different* set of random demands. Therefore, one of the order quantities could win the contest just by luck. For a fairer comparison, it is better to test each order quantity on the *same* set of random demands.

The RISKSIMTABLE function in @RISK enables you to obtain a fair comparison quickly and easily. This function is illustrated in Figure 10.37. (See the file Walton Bookstore 6.xlsx.) There are two modifications to the previous model. First, the order quantities to test are listed in row 9. (We chose these as representative order quantities. You could change, or add to, this list.) Second, instead of entering a *number* in cell B9, you enter the *formula*

=RISKSIMTABLE(D9:I9)

Note that the list does not need to be entered in the spreadsheet (although it is a good idea to do so). You could instead enter the formula

=RISKSIMTABLE({150,175,200,225,250})

*The RISKSIMTABLE function allows you to run several simulations at once—one for each value of some variable (often a decision variable).*

Figure 10.37    Model with a RISKSIMTABLE Function

| | A | B | C | D | E | F | G | H | I | J | K |
|---|---|---|---|---|---|---|---|---|---|---|---|
| 1 | Simulation of Walton's Bookstore using @RISK | | | | | | | | Range names used: | | |
| 2 | | | | | | | | | Order_quantity | =Model!$B$9 | |
| 3 | Cost data | | | Demand distribution - triangular | | | | | Unit_cost | =Model!$B$4 | |
| 4 | Unit cost | $7.50 | | Minimum | 100 | | | | Unit_price | =Model!$B$5 | |
| 5 | Unit price | $10.00 | | Most likely | 175 | | | | Unit_refund | =Model!$B$6 | |
| 6 | Unit refund | $2.50 | | Maximum | 300 | | | | | | |
| 7 | | | | | | | | | | | |
| 8 | Decision variable | | | Order quantities to try | | | | | | | |
| 9 | Order quantity | 150 | | 150 | 175 | 200 | 225 | 250 | | | |
| 10 | | | | | | | | | | | |
| 11 | Simulated quantities | | | | | | | | | | |
| 12 | | Demand | Revenue | Cost | Refund | Profit | | | | | |
| 13 | | 253 | $1,500 | $1,125 | $0 | $375 | | | | | |
| 14 | | | | | | | | | | | |
| 15 | Summary measures of profit from @RISK - based on 1000 iterations for each simulation | | | | | | | | | | |
| 16 | Simulation | 1 | 2 | 3 | 4 | 5 | | | | | |
| 17 | Order quantity | 150 | 175 | 200 | 225 | 250 | | | | | |
| 18 | Minimum | -$235.00 | -$110.00 | -$235.00 | -$360.00 | -$485.00 | | | | | |
| 19 | Maximum | $500.00 | $437.50 | $500.00 | $562.50 | $625.00 | | | | | |
| 20 | Average | $337.50 | $367.20 | $337.51 | $270.32 | $175.00 | | | | | |
| 21 | Standard deviation | $189.05 | $121.86 | $189.05 | $247.05 | $286.96 | | | | | |
| 22 | 5th percentile | -$47.50 | $77.50 | -$47.50 | -$172.50 | -$297.50 | | | | | |
| 23 | 95th percentile | $500.00 | $437.50 | $500.00 | $562.50 | $625.00 | | | | | |

where the list of numbers must be enclosed in curly brackets. In either case, the worksheet displays the first member of the list, 150, and the corresponding calculations for this first order quantity. However, the model is now set up to run the simulation for *all* order quantities in the list.

To implement this, only one setting needs to be changed. As before, enter 1000 for the number of iterations, but also enter 5 for the number of simulations. @RISK then runs five simulations of 1000 iterations each, one simulation for each order quantity in the list, and it uses the *same* 1000 random demands for each simulation. This provides a fair comparison.

> @RISK Function: **RISKSIMTABLE**
>
> *To run several simulations all at once, enter the formula* **=RISKSIMTABLE (InputRange)** *in any cell. Here,* InputRange *refers to a list of the values to be simulated, such as various order quantities. Before running the simulation, make sure the number of simulations is set to the number of values in the* InputRange *list.*

You can again get results from the simulation in various ways. Here are some possibilities.

▧  You can enter the same @RISK statistical functions in cells in the model worksheet, as shown in rows 18–23 of Figure 10.37. The trick is to realize that each such function has an optional last argument that specifies the simulation number. For example, the formulas in cells C20 and C22 are

=RISKMEAN($F$13,C16)

and

=RISKPERCENTILE($F$13,0.05,C16)

Remember that the results in these cells are meaningless (or show up as errors) until you run the simulation.

- You can select the profit cell and click on Browse Results to see a histogram of profits, as shown in Figure 10.38. By default, the histogram shown is for the *first* simulation, where the order quantity is 150. However, if you click on the red histogram button with the pound sign, you can select any of the simulations. As an example, Figure 10.39 shows the histogram of profits for the fifth simulation, where the order quantity is 250. (Do you see why these two histograms are so different? When the order quantity is 150, there is a high probability of selling out; hence the spike on the right is large. But the probability of selling out with an order quantity of 250 is much lower; hence its spike on the right is much less dominant.)

Figure 10.38

Histogram of Profit with Order Quantity 150

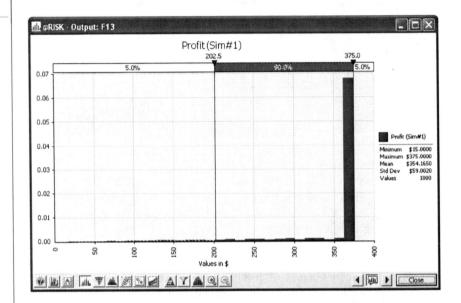

Figure 10.39

Histogram of Profit with Order Quantity 250

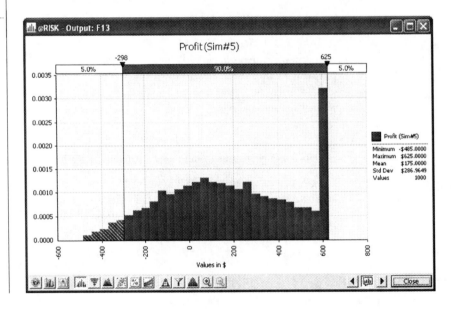

Figure 10.40   Summary Report for All Five Simulations

| Name | Cell | Sim# | Min | Mean | Max | Median | Std Dev | 5% | 95% |
|------|------|------|-----|------|-----|--------|---------|-----|-----|
| Profit | F13 | 1 | 15 | 354.165 | 375 | 375 | 59.00198 | 202.5 | 375 |
| Profit | F13 | 2 | -110 | 367.2025 | 437.5 | 437.5 | 121.8619 | 77.5 | 437.5 |
| Profit | F13 | 3 | -235 | 337.505 | 500 | 410 | 189.0538 | -47.5 | 500 |
| Profit | F13 | 4 | -360 | 270.3225 | 562.5 | 285 | 247.0473 | -172.5 | 562.5 |
| Profit | F13 | 5 | -485 | 175 | 625 | 160 | 286.9649 | -297.5 | 625 |

- You can click on the Summary button to get the results from all simulations shown in Figure 10.40. (These results match those in Figure 10.37.)
- You can click on Excel Reports to get any of a number of reports on permanent worksheets. Specifically, Quick Reports is a good choice. This produces several graphs and summary measures for each simulation, each on a different worksheet. This provides a lot of information with almost no work!

For this particular example, the results in Figures 10.37–10.40 are illuminating. You can see that an order quantity of 175 provides the largest *mean* profit. However, is this necessarily the optimal order quantity? This depends on the company's attitude toward risk. Certainly, larger order quantities incur more risk (their histograms are more spread out, their 5th and 95th percentiles are more extreme), but they also have more upside potential. On the other hand, a smaller order quantity, while having a somewhat smaller mean, might be preferable because of less variability. It is *not* an easy choice, but at least the simulation results provide plenty of information for making the decision. ▪

### 10.5.4 Some Limitations of @RISK

The academic version of @RISK has some limitations you should be aware of. (The commercial version of @RISK doesn't have these limitations. Also, the exact limitations could change as newer academic versions become available.)

- The simulation model must be contained in a single workbook with at most four worksheets, and each worksheet is limited to 300 rows and 100 columns.
- The number of @RISK input probability distribution functions, such as RISKNORMAL, is limited to 100.
- The number of unattended iterations is limited to 1000. You can request more than 1000, but you have to click a button after each 1000 iterations.
- All @RISK graphs contain a watermark.
- The Distribution Fitting tool can handle only 150 observations.

The first limitation shouldn't cause problems, at least not for the fairly small models discussed in this book. However, we strongly urge you to close all other workbooks when you are running an @RISK simulation model, *especially* if they also contain @RISK functions. @RISK does a lot of recalculation, both in your active worksheet and in all other worksheets or workbooks that are open. So if you are experiencing extremely slow simulations, this is probably the reason.

The second limitation can be a problem, especially in multiperiod problems. For example, if you are simulating 52 weeks of a year, and each week requires two random inputs, you are already over the 100-function limit. One way to get around this is to use built-in Excel functions for random inputs rather than @RISK functions whenever possible. For example, if you want to simulate the flip of a fair coin, the formula **=IF(RAND()<0.5,"Heads","Tails")** works just as well as the formula **=IF(RISKUNIFORM(0,1)<0.5,"Heads","Tails")**, but the former doesn't count against the 100-function limit.

### 10.5.5 @RISK Models with Several Random Input Variables

We conclude this section with another modification of the Walton Bookstore example. To this point, there has been a single random variable, demand. Often there are several random variables, each reflecting some uncertainty, and you want to include each of these in the simulation model. The following example illustrates how this can be done, and it also illustrates a very useful feature of @RISK, its sensitivity analysis.

---

**EXAMPLE** | **10.4 ADDITIONAL UNCERTAINTY AT WALTON BOOKSTORE**

As in the previous Walton Bookstore example, Walton needs to place an order for next year's calendar. We continue to assume that the calendars sell for $10 and customer demand for the calendars at this price is triangularly distributed with minimum value, most likely value, and maximum value equal to 100, 175, and 300. However, there are now two other sources of uncertainty. First, the maximum number of calendars Walton's supplier can supply is uncertain and is modeled with a triangular distribution. Its parameters are 125 (minimum), 200 (most likely), and 250 (maximum). Once Walton places an order, the supplier will charge $7.50 per calendar *if* he can supply the entire Walton order. Otherwise, he will charge only $7.25 per calendar. Second, unsold calendars can no longer be returned to the supplier for a refund. Instead, Walton will put them on sale for $5 apiece after January 1. At that price, Walton believes the demand for leftover calendars is triangularly distributed with parameters 0, 50, and 75. Any calendars *still* left over, say, after March 1, will be thrown away. Walton again wants to use simulation to analyze the resulting profit for various order quantities.

**Objective**    To develop and analyze a simulation model with multiple sources of uncertainty using @RISK, and to introduce @RISK's sensitivity analysis features.

#### WHERE DO THE NUMBERS COME FROM?

As in Example 10.3, the monetary values are straightforward, and the parameters of the triangular distributions are probably educated guesses, possibly based on experience with previous calendars.

#### Solution

As always, the first step is to develop the model. Then you can run the simulation with @RISK and examine the results.

## DEVELOPING THE SIMULATION MODEL

The completed model is shown in Figure 10.41. (See the file Walton Bookstore 7.xlsx.) The model itself requires a bit more logic than the previous Walton model. It can be developed with the following steps.

**Figure 10.41**    @RISK Simulation Model with Three Random Inputs

| | A | B | C | D | E | F | G | H | I | J | K | L | M |
|---|---|---|---|---|---|---|---|---|---|---|---|---|---|
| 1 | Simulation of Walton's Bookstore using @RISK | | | | | | | | | | Range names used: | | |
| 2 | | | | | | | | | | | Order_quantity | =Model!$B$10 | |
| 3 | Cost data | | | Demand distribution: triangular | | | | | | | Regular_price | =Model!$B$6 | |
| 4 | Unit cost 1 | $7.50 | | | Regular price | Sale price | | Supply distribution: triangular | | | Sale_price | =Model!$B$7 | |
| 5 | Unit cost 2 | $7.25 | | Minimum | 100 | 0 | | Minimum | 125 | | Unit_cost_1 | =Model!$B$4 | |
| 6 | Regular price | $10.00 | | Most likely | 175 | 50 | | Most likely | 200 | | Unit_cost_2 | =Model!$B$5 | |
| 7 | Sale price | $5.00 | | Maximum | 300 | 75 | | Maximum | 250 | | | | |
| 8 | | | | | | | | | | | | | |
| 9 | Decision variable | | | Order quantities to try | | | | | | | | | |
| 10 | Order quantity | 150 | | | 150 | 175 | 200 | 225 | 250 | | | | |
| 11 | | | | | | | | | | | | | |
| 12 | Simulated quantities | | | | At regular price | | | At sale price | | | | | |
| 13 | | Maximum supply | Actual supply | Cost | Demand | Revenue | Left over | Demand | Revenue | Profit | | | |
| 14 | | 179 | 150 | $1,125 | 164 | $1,500 | 0 | 45 | $0 | $375 | | | |
| 15 | | | | | | | | | | | | | |
| 16 | Summary measures of profit from @RISK - based on 1000 iterations for each simulation | | | | | | | | | | | | |
| 17 | Simulation | 1 | 2 | 3 | 4 | 5 | | | | | | | |
| 18 | Order quantity | 150 | 175 | 200 | 225 | 250 | | | | | | | |
| 19 | Minimum | $50.00 | -$137.50 | -$325.00 | -$421.75 | -$421.75 | | | | | | | |
| 20 | Maximum | $409.75 | $478.50 | $547.25 | $616.00 | $662.75 | | | | | | | |
| 21 | Average | $361.37 | $390.82 | $395.94 | $396.29 | $398.96 | | | | | | | |
| 22 | Standard deviation | $43.84 | $92.83 | $145.33 | $176.12 | $178.16 | | | | | | | |
| 23 | 5th percentile | $265.00 | $178.00 | $57.25 | $13.00 | $15.75 | | | | | | | |
| 24 | 95th percentile | $375.00 | $459.25 | $525.25 | $577.50 | $588.50 | | | | | | | |

**1**   **Random inputs.** There are three random inputs in this model: the maximum supply the supplier can provide Walton, the customer demand when the selling price is $10, and the customer demand for sale-price calendars. Generate these in cells B14, E14, and H14 (using the ROUND function to obtain integers) with the RISKTRIANG function. Specifically, the formulas in cells B14, E14, and H14 are

=ROUND(RISKTRIANG(I5,I6,I7),0)

=ROUND(RISKTRIANG(E5,E6,E7),0)

and

=ROUND(RISKTRIANG(F5,F6,F7),0)

Note that the formula in cell H14 generates the random *potential* demand for calendars at the sale price, even though there might not be any calendars left to put on sale.

**2**   **Actual supply.** The number of calendars supplied to Walton is the smaller of the number ordered and the maximum the supplier is able to supply. Calculate this value in cell C14 with the formula

=MIN(B14,Order_quantity)

**3**   **Order cost.** Walton gets the reduced price, $7.25, if the supplier cannot supply the entire order. Otherwise, Walton must pay $7.50 per calendar. Therefore, calculate the total order cost in cell D14 with the formula (using the obvious range names)

=IF(B14>=Order_quantity,Unit_cost_1,Unit_cost_2)*C14

④ **Other quantities.** The rest of the model is straightforward. Calculate the revenue from regular-price sales in cell F14 with the formula

=Regular_price*MIN(C14,E14)

Calculate the number left over after regular-price sales in cell G14 with the formula

=MAX(C14-E14,0)

Calculate the revenue from sale-price sales in cell I14 with the formula

=Sale_price*MIN(G14,H14)

Finally, calculate profit and designate it as an output cell for @RISK in cell J14 with the formula

=RISKOUTPUT("Profit")+F14+I14-D14

You could also designate other cells (the revenue cells, for example) as output cells.

⑤ **Order quantities.** As before, enter a RISKSIMTABLE function in cell B10 so that Walton can try different order quantities. Specifically, enter the formula

=RISKSIMTABLE(D10:H10)

in cell B10.

### Running the Simulation

On each iteration, @RISK generates a new set of random inputs and calculates the corresponding output(s).

As usual, the next steps are to specify the simulation settings (we chose 1000 iterations and five simulations), and run the simulation. It is important to realize what @RISK does when it runs a simulation when there are several random input cells. In each iteration, @RISK generates a random value for each input variable *independently*. In this example, it generates a maximum supply in cell B14 from one triangular distribution, it generates a regular-price demand in cell E14 from another triangular distribution, and it generates a sale-price demand in cell H14 from a third triangular distribution. With these input values, it then calculates profit. For each order quantity, it then iterates this procedure 1000 times and keeps track of the corresponding profits.[10]

### Discussion of the Simulation Results

Selected results are listed in Figure 10.41 (at the bottom), and the profit histogram for an order quantity of 200 is shown in Figure 10.42. (The histograms for the other order quantities are similar to what you have seen before, with more skewness to the left and a larger spike to the right as the order quantity decreases.) For this particular order quantity, the results indicate an average profit of about $396, a 5th percentile of $57, a 95th percentile of $525, and a distribution of profits that is again skewed to the left.

### Sensitivity Analysis

We now demonstrate a feature of @RISK that is particularly useful when there are several random input cells. This feature lets you see which of these inputs is most related to, or *correlated* with, an output cell. To perform this analysis, select the profit cell, J14, and click on the Browse Results button. You will see a histogram of profit in a temporary window, as we have already discussed, with a number of buttons at the bottom of the window. Click on the red button with the pound sign to select a simulation. We chose #3, where the order quantity is 200. Then click on the "tornado" button (the fifth button from

---

[10]It is also possible to *correlate* the inputs, as we demonstrate in the next section.

Figure 10.42

Histogram of
Simulated Profits for
Order Quantity 200

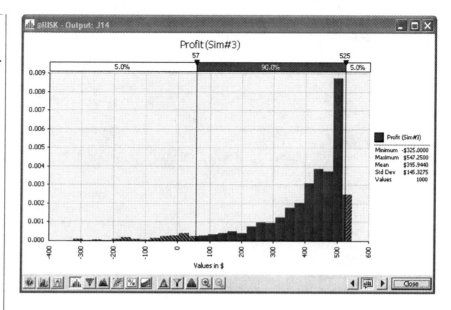

Figure 10.43

Tornado Graph for
Sensitivity Analysis

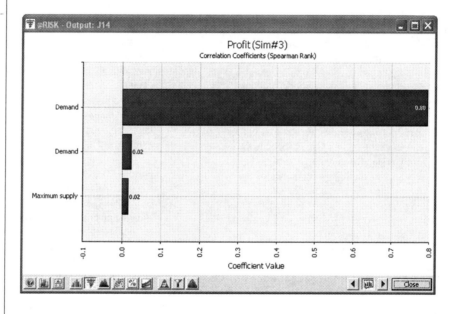

the left) and choose Correlation Coefficients. This produces the chart in Figure 10.43. (The Regression option produces similar results, but we believe the Correlation option is easier to understand.)

*A tornado chart indicates which of the random inputs have large effects on an output.*

This figure shows graphically and numerically how each of the random inputs correlates with profit: the higher the magnitude of the correlation, the stronger the relationship between that input and profit. In this sense, you can see that the regular-price demand has by far the largest effect on profit. The other two inputs, maximum supply and sale-price demand, are nearly uncorrelated with profit, so they are much less important. Identifying important input variables is important for real applications. If a random input is highly correlated with an important output, then it is probably worth the time and money to learn more about this input and possibly reduce the amount of uncertainty involving it. ▨

**16.** If you add several normally distributed random numbers, the result is normally distributed, where the mean of the sum is the sum of the individual means, and the variance of the sum is the sum of the individual variances. (Remember that variance is the square of standard deviation.) This is a difficult result to prove mathematically, but it is easy to demonstrate with simulation. To do so, run a simulation where you add three normally distributed random numbers, each with mean 100 and standard deviation 10. Your single output variable should be the sum of these three numbers. Verify with @RISK that the distribution of this output is approximately normal with mean 300 and variance 300 (hence, standard deviation $\sqrt{300} = 17.32$).

**17.** In Problem 11 from the previous section, we stated that the damage amount is normally distributed. Suppose instead that the damage amount is triangularly distributed with parameters 500, 1500, and 7000. That is, the damage in an accident can be as low as $500 or as high as $7000, the most likely value is $1500, and there is definite skewness to the right. (It turns out, as you can verify in @RISK, that the mean of this distribution is $3000, the same as in Problem 11.) Use @RISK to simulate the amount you pay for damage. Run 5000 iterations. Then answer the following questions. In each case, explain how the indicated event would occur.
   **a.** What is the probability that you pay a positive amount but less than $750?
   **b.** What is the probability that you pay more than $600?
   **c.** What is the probability that you pay exactly $1000 (the deductible)?

**18.** Continuing the previous problem, assume, as in Problem 11, that the damage amount is *normally* distributed with mean $3000 and standard deviation $750. Run @RISK with 5000 iterations to simulate the amount you pay for damage. Compare your results with those in the previous problem. Does it appear to matter whether you assume a triangular distribution or a normal distribution for damage amounts? Why isn't this a totally fair comparison? (*Hint*: Use @RISK's Define Distributions tool to find the standard deviation for the triangular distribution.)

**19.** In Problem 12 of the previous section, suppose that the demand for cars is normally distributed with mean 100 and standard deviation 15. Use @RISK to determine the "best" order quantity—in this case, the one with the largest mean profit. Using the statistics and/or graphs from @RISK, discuss whether this order quantity would be considered best by the car dealer. (The point is that a decision maker can use more than just *mean* profit in making a decision.)

**20.** Use @RISK to analyze the sweatshirt situation in Problem 14 of the previous section. Do this for the discrete distributions given in the problem. Then do it for normal distributions. For the normal case, assume that the regular demand is normally distributed with mean 9800 and standard deviation 1300 and that the demand at the reduced price is normally distributed with mean 3800 and standard deviation 1400.

**21.** Although the normal distribution is a reasonable input distribution in many situations, it does have two potential drawbacks: (1) it allows negative values, even though they may be extremely improbable, and (2) it is a symmetric distribution. Many situations are modeled better with a distribution that allows only positive values and is skewed to the right. Two of these that have been used in many real applications are the gamma and lognormal distributions. @RISK enables you to generate observations from each of these distributions. The @RISK function for the gamma distribution is RISKGAMMA, and it takes two arguments, as in **=RISKGAMMA(3,10)**. The first argument, which must be positive, determines the shape. The smaller it is, the more skewed the distribution is to the right; the larger it is, the more symmetric the distribution is. The second argument determines the scale, in the sense that the product of it and the first argument equals the mean of the distribution. (The mean in this example is 30.) Also, the product of the second argument and the square root of the first argument is the standard deviation of the distribution. (In this example, it is $\sqrt{3}(10) = 17.32$.) The @RISK function for the lognormal distribution is RISKLOGNORM. It has two arguments, as in **=RISKLOGNORM(40,10)**. These arguments are the mean and standard deviation of the distribution. Rework Example 10.2 for the following demand distributions. Do the simulated outputs have any different qualitative properties with these skewed distributions than with the triangular distribution used in the example?
   **a.** Gamma distribution with parameters 2 and 85
   **b.** Gamma distribution with parameters 5 and 35
   **c.** Lognormal distribution with mean 170 and standard deviation 60

In section 10.2, we discussed input distributions. The randomness in input variables causes the variability in the output variables. We now briefly explore whether the choice of input distribution(s) makes much difference in the distribution of an output variable such as profit. This is an important question. If the choice of input distributions doesn't matter much, then you do not need to agonize over this choice. However, if it *does* make a difference, then you have to be more careful about choosing the most appropriate input distribution for any particular situation. Unfortunately, it is impossible to answer the question definitively. The best we can say in general is, "It depends." Some models are more sensitive to changes in the shape or parameters of input distributions than others. Still, the issue is worth exploring.

We discuss two types of sensitivity analysis in this section. First, we check whether the shape of the input distribution matters. In the Walton Bookstore example, we assumed a triangularly distributed demand with some skewness. Are the results basically the same if a symmetric distribution such as the normal distribution is used instead? Second, we check whether the *independence* of input variables that have been assumed implicitly to this point is crucial to the output results. Many random quantities in real situations are *not* independent; they are positively or negatively correlated. Fortunately, @RISK enables you to build correlation into a model. We analyze the effect of this correlation.

### 10.6.1 Effect of the Shape of the Input Distribution(s)

We first explore the effect of the shape of the input distribution(s). As the following example indicates, if parameters that allow for a fair comparison are used, the shape can have a relatively minor effect.

---

**EXAMPLE**   **10.5 EFFECT OF DEMAND DISTRIBUTION AT WALTON'S**

We continue to explore the demand for calendars at Walton Bookstore. We keep the same unit cost, unit price, and unit refund for leftovers as in Example 10.3. However, in that example we assumed a triangular distribution for demand with parameters 100, 175, and 300. Assuming that Walton orders 200 calendars, is the distribution of profit affected if a *normal* distribution of demand is used instead?

**Objective**   To see whether a triangular distribution with some skewness gives the same profit distribution as a normal distribution for demand.

### WHERE DO THE NUMBERS COME FROM?

The numbers here are the same as in Example 10.3. However, as discussed next, the parameters of the normal distribution are chosen to provide a fair comparison with the triangular distribution used earlier.

### Solution

*For a fair comparison of alternative input distributions, the distributions should have (at least approximately) equal means and standard deviations.*

It is important in this type of analysis to make a fair comparison. When you select a normal distribution for demand, you must choose a mean and standard deviation for this distribution. Which values should you choose? It seems only fair to choose the *same* mean and standard deviation that the triangular distribution has. To find the mean and standard deviation for a triangular distribution with given minimum, most likely, and maximum values, you can take advantage of @RISK's Define Distributions tool. Select any blank cell, click on the Define Distributions button, select the triangular distribution, and enter the parameters 100, 175, and 300. You will see that the mean and standard deviation are 191.67 and 41.248, respectively. Therefore, for a fair comparison you should use a normal distribution with mean 191.67 and standard deviation 41.248. In fact, @RISK allows you to see a comparison of these two distributions, as in Figure 10.44. To get this chart, click on the Add Overlay button, select the normal distribution from the gallery, and enter 191.67 and 41.248 as its mean and standard deviation.

Figure 10.44

**Triangular and Normal Distributions for Demand**

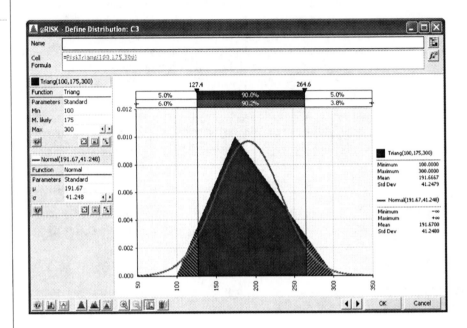

### DEVELOPING THE SIMULATION MODEL

The logic in this model is almost exactly the same as before. (See Figure 10.45 and the file Walton Bookstore 8.xlsx.) However, a clever use of the RISKSIMTABLE function allows you to run two simulations at once, one for the triangular distribution and one for the corresponding normal distribution. The following two steps are required.

**1** **RISKSIMTABLE function.** It is useful to index the two distributions as 1 and 2. To indicate that you want to run the simulation with both of them, enter the formula

=RISKSIMTABLE({1,2})

in cell B11. Note that when you enter actual numbers in this function, rather than cell references, you must put curly brackets around the list.

**2** **Demand.** When the value in cell B11 is 1, the demand distribution is triangular. When it is 2, the distribution is normal. Therefore, enter the formula

=ROUND(IF(B11=1,RISKTRIANG(E4,E5,E6),RISKNORMAL(H4,H5)),0)

in cell B15. The effect is that the first simulation will use the triangular distribution, and the second will use the normal distribution.

Look for ways to use the RISKSIMTABLE function. It can really improve efficiency because it runs several simulations at once.

Figure 10.45    @RISK Model for Comparing Two Input Distributions

| | A | B | C | D | E | F | G | H | I | J | K | L | M |
|---|---|---|---|---|---|---|---|---|---|---|---|---|---|
| 1 | Simulation of Walton's Bookstore using @RISK - two possible demand distributions | | | | | | | | | | Range names used: | | |
| 2 | | | | | | | | | | | Order_quantity | =Model!$B$9 | |
| 3 | Cost data | | | Demand distribution 1 - triangular | | | Demand distribution 2 - normal | | | | Unit_cost | =Model!$B$4 | |
| 4 | Unit cost | $7.50 | | Minimum | 100 | | Mean | 191.67 | | | Unit_price | =Model!$B$5 | |
| 5 | Unit price | $10.00 | | Most likely | 175 | | Stdev | 41.248 | | | Unit_refund | =Model!$B$6 | |
| 6 | Unit refund | $2.50 | | Maximum | 300 | | | | | | | | |
| 7 | | | | | | | | | | | | | |
| 8 | Decision variable | | | | | | | | | | | | |
| 9 | Order quantity | 200 | | | | | | | | | | | |
| 10 | | | | | | | | | | | | | |
| 11 | Demand distribution to use | 1 | ← | Formula is =RiskSimtable({1,2}) | | | | | | | | | |
| 12 | | | | | | | | | | | | | |
| 13 | Simulated quantities | | | | | | | | | | | | |
| 14 | | Demand | Revenue | Cost | Refund | Profit | | | | | | | |
| 15 | | 179 | $1,790 | $1,500 | $53 | $343 | | | | | | | |
| 16 | | | | | | | | | | | | | |
| 17 | Summary measures of profit from @RISK - based on 1000 iterations for each simulation | | | | | | | | | | | | |
| 18 | Simulation | 1 | 2 | | | | | | | | | | |
| 19 | Distribution | Triangular | Normal | | | | | | | | | | |
| 20 | Minimum | -$235.00 | -$595.00 | | | | | | | | | | |
| 21 | Maximum | $500.00 | $500.00 | | | | | | | | | | |
| 22 | Average | $337.48 | $342.82 | | | | | | | | | | |
| 23 | Standard devia on | $189.10 | $201.77 | | | | | | | | | | |
| 24 | 5th percentile | -$47.50 | -$70.00 | | | | | | | | | | |
| 25 | 95th percentile | $500.00 | $500.00 | | | | | | | | | | |

## Running the Simulation

The only @RISK setting to change is the number of simulations. It should now be set to 2, the number of values in the RISKSIMTABLE formula. Other than this, you run the simulation exactly as before.

## Discussion of the Simulation Results

The comparison is shown numerically in Figure 10.46 and graphically in Figure 10.47. As you can see, there is more chance of really low profits when the demand distribution is normal, but each simulation results in the same maximum profit. Both of these statements make sense. The normal distribution, being unbounded on the left, allows for very low demands, and these occasional low demands result in very low profits. On the other side, Walton's maximum profit is $500 regardless of the input distribution (provided that it allows demands greater than the order quantity). This occurs when Walton's sells all it orders, in which case excess demand has no effect on profit. Note that the mean profits for the two distributions differ by only about $5.

Figure 10.46    Summary Results for Comparison Model

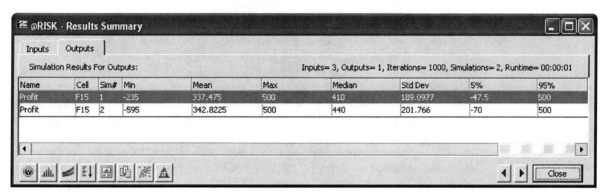

Figure 10.47   Graphical Results for Comparison Model

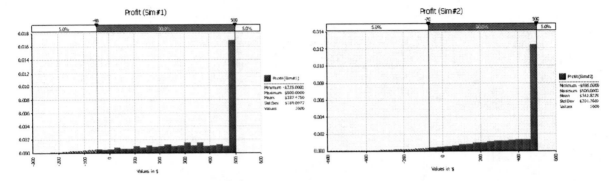

It is probably safe to conclude that the profit distribution in this model is not greatly affected by the choice of demand distribution, at least not when (1) the candidate input distributions have the same mean and standard deviation, and (2) their shapes are not *too* dissimilar. We would venture to guess that this general conclusion about insensitivity of output distributions to shapes of input distributions can be made in many simulation models. However, it is always worth checking, as we have done here, especially when there is a lot of money at stake. ▨

---

### FUNDAMENTAL INSIGHT

### Shape of the Output Distribution

Predicting the shape of the output distribution from the shape(s) of the input distribution(s) is difficult. For example, normally distributed inputs don't necessarily produce normally distributed outputs. It is also difficult to predict how sensitive the shape of the output distribution is to the shape(s) of the input distribution(s).

For example, normally and triangularly distributed inputs (with the same means and standard deviations) are likely to lead to similar output distributions, but there could be differences, say, in the tails of the output distributions. In any case, you should examine the *entire* output distribution carefully, not just a few of its summary measures.

---

### 10.6.2 Effect of Correlated Input Variables

*Input variables in real-world problems are often correlated, which makes the material in this section particularly important.*

Until now, all of the random numbers generated with @RISK functions have been probabilistically independent. This means, for example, that if a random value in one cell is much larger than its mean, the random values in other cells are completely unaffected. They are no more likely to be abnormally large or small than if the first value had been average or below average. Sometimes, however, independence is unrealistic. In such cases, the random numbers should be correlated in some way. If they are positively correlated, then large numbers will tend to go with large numbers, and small with small. If they are negatively correlated, then large will tend to go with small and small with large. As an example, you might expect daily stock price changes for two companies in the same industry to be positively correlated. If the price of one oil company increases, you might expect the price of another oil company to increase as well. @RISK enables you to build in this correlated behavior with the RISKCORRMAT function, as we illustrate in the following continuation of the Walton example.

# 10.6 CORRELATED DEMANDS FOR TWO CALENDARS AT WALTON'S

Suppose that Walton Bookstore must order two different calendars. To simplify the example, we assume that the calendars each have the same unit cost, unit selling price, and unit refund value as in previous examples. Also, we assume that each has a triangularly distributed demand with parameters 100, 175, and 300. However, we now assume they are "substitute" products, so that their demands are negatively correlated. This simply means that if a customer buys one, the customer is not likely to buy the other. Specifically, we assume a correlation of −0.9 between the two demands. How do these correlated inputs affect the distribution of profit, as compared to the situation where the demands are uncorrelated (correlation 0) or very *positively* correlated (correlation 0.9)?

**Objective**    To see how @RISK enables us to simulate correlated demands, and to see the effect of correlated demands on profit.

## WHERE DO THE NUMBERS COME FROM?

The only new input here is the correlation. It is probably negative because the calendars are substitute products, but it is a difficult number to estimate accurately. This is a good candidate for a sensitivity analysis.

## Solution

The key to building in correlation is @RISK's **RISKCORRMAT** (correlation matrix) function. To use this function, you must include a correlation matrix in the model, as shown in the range J5:K6 of Figure 10.48. (See the file Walton Bookstore 9.xlsx.)

Figure 10.48    Simulation Model with Correlations

| | A | B | C | D | E | F | G | H | I | J | K |
|---|---|---|---|---|---|---|---|---|---|---|---|
| 1 | Simulation of Walton's Bookstore using @RISK - correlated demands | | | | | | | | | | |
| 2 | | | | | | | | | | | |
| 3 | Cost data - same for each product | | | | Demand distribution for each product- triangular | | | | Correlation matrix between demands | | |
| 4 | Unit cost | $7.50 | | | Minimum | 100 | | | | Product 1 | Product 2 |
| 5 | Unit price | $10.00 | | | Most likely | 175 | | | Product 1 | 1 | -0.9 |
| 6 | Unit refund | $2.50 | | | Maximum | 300 | | | Product 2 | -0.9 | 1 |
| 7 | | | | | | | | | | | |
| 8 | Decision variables | | | | | | Note RISKSIMTABLE function in cell J6. | | Possible correlations to try | | |
| 9 | Order quantity 1 | 200 | | | | | | | | -0.9 | 0 | 0.9 |
| 10 | Order quantity 2 | 200 | | | | | | | | | |
| 11 | | | | | | | | | Range names used: | | |
| 12 | Simulated quantities | | | | | | | | Order_quantity_1 | =Model!$B$9 | |
| 13 | | Demand | Revenue | Cost | Refund | Profit | | | Order_quantity_2 | =Model!$B$10 | |
| 14 | Product 1 | 190 | $1,900 | $1,500 | $25 | $425 | | | Unit_cost | =Model!$B$4 | |
| 15 | Product 2 | 177 | $1,770 | $1,500 | $58 | $328 | | | Unit_price | =Model!$B$5 | |
| 16 | Totals | 367 | $3,670 | $3,000 | $83 | $753 | | | Unit_refund | =Model!$B$6 | |
| 17 | | | | | | | | | | | |
| 18 | Summary measures of profit from @RISK - based on 1000 iterations | | | | | | | | | | |
| 19 | Simulation | 1 | 2 | 3 | | | | | | | |
| 20 | Correlation | -0.9 | 0 | 0.9 | | | | | | | |
| 21 | Minimum | $272.50 | -$245.00 | -$425.00 | | | | | | | |
| 22 | Maximum | $1,000.00 | $1,000.00 | $1,000.00 | | | | | | | |
| 23 | Average | $675.04 | $675.04 | $675.04 | | | | | | | |
| 24 | Standard deviation | $157.59 | $262.33 | $365.23 | | | | | | | |
| 25 | 5th percentile | $392.50 | $205.00 | -$80.00 | | | | | | | |
| 26 | 95th percentile | $925.00 | $1,000.00 | $1,000.00 | | | | | | | |

A correlation matrix must always have 1s along its diagonal (because a variable is always perfectly correlated with itself) and the correlations between variables elsewhere. Also, the matrix must be symmetric, so that the correlations above the diagonal are a mirror image of those below it. (You can enforce this by entering the *formula* =**J6** in cell K5. Alternatively, @RISK allows you to enter the correlations only below the diagonal, or only above the diagonal, and it then infers the mirror images.)

The RISKCORRMAT function is "tacked on" as an extra argument to a typical random @RISK function.

To enter random values in any cells that are correlated, you start with a typical @RISK formula, such as

=RISKTRIANG(E4,E5,E6)

Then you add an extra argument, the RISKCORRMAT function, as follows:

=RISKTRIANG(E4,E5,E6,RISKCORRMAT(J5:K6,1))

The first argument of the RISKCORRMAT function is the correlation matrix range. The second is an index of the variable. In this example, the first calendar demand has index 1 and the second has index 2.

### @RISK Function: *RISKCORRMAT*

*This function enables you to correlate two or more input variables in an @RISK model. The function has the form RISKCORRMAT(CorrMat,Index), where CorrMat is a matrix of correlations and Index is an index of the variable being correlated to others. For example, if there are three correlated variables, Index is 1 for the first variable, 2 for the second, and 3 for the third. The RISKCORRMAT function is not entered by itself. Rather, it is entered as the last argument of a random @RISK function, such as =RISKTRIANG(10,15,30,RISKCORRMAT(CorrMat,2)).*

### DEVELOPING THE SIMULATION MODEL

Armed with this knowledge, the simulation model in Figure 10.48 is straightforward and can be developed as follows.

**1** **Inputs.** Enter the inputs in the blue ranges in columns B and E.

**2** **Correlation matrix.** For the correlation matrix in the range J5:H6, enter 1s on the diagonal, and enter the formula

=J6

in cell K5 (or leave cell K5 blank). Then enter the formula

=RISKSIMTABLE(I9:K9)

in cell J6. This allows you to simultaneously simulate negatively correlated demands, uncorrelated demands, and positively correlated demands.

**3** **Order quantities.** Assume for now that the company orders the *same* number of each calendar, 200, so enter this value in cells B9 and B10. However, the simulation is set up so that you can experiment with any order quantities in these cells, including unequal values.

**4** **Correlated demands.** Generate correlated demands by entering the formula

=ROUND(RISKTRIANG(E4,E5,E6,RISKCORRMAT(J5:K6,1)),0)

in cell B14 for demand 1 and the formula

=ROUND(RISKTRIANG(E4,E5,E6, RISKCORRMAT(J5:K6,2)),0)

in cell B15 for demand 2. The only difference between these is the index of the variable being generated. The first has index 1; the second has index 2.

**⑤ Other formulas.** The other formulas in rows 14 and 15 are identical to ones developed in previous examples, so they aren't presented again here. The quantities in row 16 are simply sums of rows 14 and 15. Also, the only @RISK output we designated is the total profit in cell F16, but you can designate others as output cells if you like.

### Running the Simulation

You should set up and run @RISK exactly as before. For this example, set the number of iterations to 1000 and the number of simulations to 3 (because three different correlations are being tested).

### Discussion of the Simulation Results

Selected numerical and graphical results are shown in Figures 10.49 and 10.50. You will probably be surprised to see that the *mean* total profit is the same, regardless of the correlation. This is no coincidence. In each of the three simulations, @RISK uses the *same* random numbers but "shuffles" them in different orders to get the correct correlations. This means that averages are unaffected. (The idea is that the average of the numbers 30, 26, and 48 is the same as the average of the numbers 48, 30, and 26.)

Figure 10.49 **Summary Results for Correlated Model**

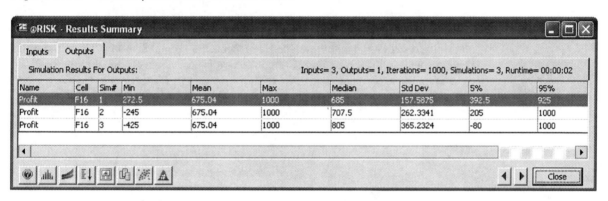

Figure 10.50 **Graphical Results for Correlated Model**

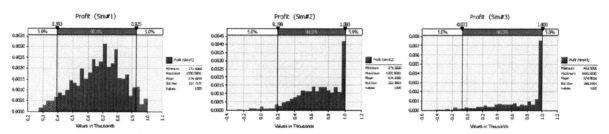

However, the correlation has a definite effect on the *distribution* of total profit. You can see this in Figure 10.49, for example, where the standard deviation of total profit increases as the correlation goes from negative to zero to positive. This same increase in variability is apparent in the histograms in Figure 10.50. Do you see intuitively why this increase in variability occurs? It is basically the "Don't put all of your eggs in one basket" effect. When the correlation is negative, high demands for one product tend to cancel low demands for the other product, so extremes in profit are rare. However, when the correlation is positive, high demands for the two products tend to go together, as do low demands. These make extreme profits on either end much more likely.

This same phenomenon would occur if you simulated an investment portfolio containing two stocks. When the stocks are positively correlated, the portfolio is much riskier (more variability) than when they are negatively correlated. Of course, this is the reason for diversifying a portfolio. ▪

## MODELING ISSUES

With the RISKCORRMAT function, you can correlate random numbers from any distributions.

We illustrated the RISKCORRMAT function for triangularly distributed values. However, it can be used with any of @RISK's distributions by tacking on RISKCORRMAT as a last argument. You can even mix them. For example, assuming CMat is the range name for a $2 \times 2$ correlation matrix, you could enter the formulas

=RISKNORMAL(10,2,RISKCORRMAT(CMat,1))

and

=RISKUNIFORM(100,200,RISKCORRMAT(CMat,2))

into any two cells. When you run the simulation, @RISK generates a sequence of normally distributed random numbers based on the first formula and another sequence of uniformly distributed random numbers based on the second formula. Then it shuffles them in some complex way until their correlation is approximately equal to the specified correlation in the correlation matrix. ▪

## FUNDAMENTAL INSIGHT

### Correlated Inputs

When you enter random inputs in an @RISK simulation model and then run the simulation, each iteration generates *independent* values for the random inputs. If you know or suspect that some of the inputs are positively or negatively correlated, you should build this correlation structure into the model explicitly with the RISKCORRMAT function. This function might not change the mean of an output, but it can definitely affect the variability and shape of the output distribution.

## PROBLEMS

### Skill-Building Problems

22. The Fizzy Company produces six-packs of soda cans. Each can is supposed to contain at least 12 ounces of soda. If the total weight in a six-pack is less than 72 ounces, Fizzy is fined $100 and receives no sales revenue for the six-pack. Each six-pack sells for $3.00. It costs Fizzy $0.02 per ounce of soda put in the cans. Fizzy can control the mean fill rate of its soda-filling machines. The amount put in each can by a machine is normally distributed with standard deviation 0.10 ounce.

a. Assume that the weight of each can in a six-pack has a 0.8 correlation with the weight of the other cans in the six-pack. What mean fill quantity maximizes expected profit per six-pack? Try mean fill rates from 12.00 to 12.35 in increments of 0.05.

b. If the weights of the cans in the six-pack are probabilistically independent, what mean fill quantity maximizes expected profit per six-pack? Try the same mean fill rates as in part **a**.

c. How can you explain the difference in the answers to parts **a** and **b**?

**23.** When you use @RISK's correlation feature to generate correlated random numbers, how can you verify that they are correlated? Try the following. Use the RISKCORRMAT function to generate two normally distributed random numbers, each with mean 100 and standard deviation 10, and with correlation 0.7. To run a simulation, you need an output variable, so sum these two numbers and designate the sum as an output variable. Now run @RISK with 500 iterations. Click on @RISK's Excel Reports button and check the Simulation Data option to see the actual simulated data.

a. Use Excel's CORREL function to calculate the correlation between the two input variables. It should be close to 0.7. Then create a scatterplot of these two input variables. The plot should indicate a definite positive relationship.

b. Are the two input variables correlated with the output? Use Excel's CORREL function to find out. Interpret your results intuitively.

**24.** Repeat the previous problem, but make the correlation between the two inputs equal to –0.7. Explain how the results change.

**25.** Repeat Problem 23, but now make the second input variable triangularly distributed with parameters 50, 100, and 500. This time, verify not only that the correlation between the two inputs is approximately 0.7, but also that the shapes of the two input distributions are approximately what they should be: normal for the first and triangular for the second. Do this by creating histograms in Excel. The point is that you can use @RISK's RISKCORRMAT function to correlate random numbers from *different* distributions.

**26.** Suppose you are going to invest equal amounts in three stocks. The annual return from each stock is normally distributed with mean 0.01 (1%) and standard deviation 0.06. The annual return on your portfolio, the output variable of interest, is the average of the three stock returns. Run @RISK, using 1000 iterations, on each of the following scenarios.

a. The three stock returns are highly correlated. The correlation between each pair is 0.9.

b. The three stock returns are practically independent. The correlation between each pair is 0.1.

c. The first two stocks are moderately correlated. The correlation between their returns is 0.4. The third stock's return is negatively correlated with the other two. The correlation between its return and each of the first two is −0.8.

d. Compare the portfolio distributions from @RISK for these three scenarios. What do you conclude?

e. You might think of a fourth scenario, where the correlation between each *pair* of returns is a large negative number such as −0.8. But explain intuitively why this makes no sense. Try to run the simulation with these negative correlations and see what happens.

**27.** The effect of the shapes of input distributions on the distribution of an output can depend on the output function. For this problem, assume there are 10 input variables. The goal is to compare the case where these 10 inputs each have a normal distribution with mean 1000 and standard deviation 250 to the case where they each have a triangular distribution with parameters 600, 700, and 1700. (You can check with @RISK's Define Distributions window that even though this triangular distribution is very skewed, it has the same mean and approximately the same standard deviation as the normal distribution.) For each of the following outputs, run two @RISK simulations, one with the normally distributed inputs and one with the triangularly distributed inputs, and comment on the differences between the resulting output distributions. For each simulation run 10,000 iterations.

a. Let the output be the *average* of the inputs.

b. Let the output be the *maximum* of the inputs.

c. Calculate the average of the inputs. Then the output is the minimum of the inputs if this average is less than 1000; otherwise, the output is the maximum of the inputs.

## Skill-Extending Problems

**28.** The Business School at State University currently has three parking lots, each containing 155 spaces. Two hundred faculty members have been assigned to each lot. On a peak day, an average of 70% of all lot 1 parking sticker holders show up, an average of 72% of all lot 2 parking sticker holders show up, and an average of 74% of all lot 3 parking sticker holders show up.

a. Given the current situation, estimate the probability that on a peak day, at least one faculty member with a sticker will be unable to find a spot. Assume that the number who show up at each lot is independent of the number who show up at the other two lots. Compare two situations: (1) each person can park only in the lot assigned to him or her, and (2) each person can park in any of the lots (pooling). (*Hint*: Use the RISKBINOMIAL function.)

b. Now suppose the numbers of people who show up at the three lots are highly correlated (correlation 0.9). How are the results different from those in part **a**?

# 10.7 CONCLUSION

Simulation has traditionally not received the attention it deserves in management science courses. The primary reason for this has been the lack of easy-to-use simulation software. Now, with Excel's built-in simulation capabilities, plus powerful and affordable add-ins such as @RISK, simulation is receiving its rightful emphasis. The world is full of uncertainty, which is what makes simulation so valuable. Simulation models provide important insights that are missing in models that do not incorporate uncertainty explicitly. In addition, simulation models are relatively easy to understand and develop. Therefore, we suspect that simulation models (together with optimization models) will soon be the primary emphasis of many management science courses—if they are not already. In this chapter we have illustrated the basic ideas of simulation, how to perform simulation with Excel built-in tools, and how @RISK greatly enhances Excel's basic capabilities. In the next chapter we will build on this knowledge to develop and analyze simulation models in a variety of business areas.

## Summary of Key Management Science Terms

| Term | Explanation | Excel | Pages |
|------|-------------|-------|-------|
| Simulation model | Model with random inputs that affect one or more outputs, where the randomness is modeled explicitly | | 552 |
| Probability distributions for input variables | Specification of the possible values and their probabilities for random input variables; these distributions must be specified in any simulation model | | 555 |
| Uniform distribution | The flat distribution, where all values in a bounded continuum are equally likely | | 559 |
| Discrete distribution | A general distribution where a discrete number of possible values and their probabilities are specified | | 565 |
| Triangular distribution | Literally a triangle-shaped distribution, specified by a minimum value, a most likely value, and a maximum value | | 568 |
| Latin hypercube sampling | An efficient way of simulating random numbers for a simulation model, where the results are more accurate than with other sampling methods | | 591 |
| Correlated inputs | Random quantities, such as returns from stocks in the same industry, that tend to go together (or possibly go in opposite directions from one another) | | 610 |

## Key Excel Terms

| Term | Explanation | Excel | Pages |
|------|-------------|-------|-------|
| F9 key | The "recalc" key, used to make a spreadsheet recalculate | Press the F9 key | 555 |
| RAND function | Excel's built-in random number generator; generates uniformly distributed random numbers between 0 and 1 | =RAND() | 560 |
| RANDBETWEEN function | Excel's built-in function for generating equally likely random integers over an indicated range | =RANDBETWEEN (*min,max*) | 560 |
| Freezing random numbers | Changing "volatile" random numbers into "fixed" numbers | Copy range, paste it onto itself with the Paste Values option | 563 |

*(continued)*

| Term | Explanation | Excel | Pages |
|------|-------------|-------|-------|
| @RISK random functions | A set of functions, including RISKNORMAL and RISKTRIANG, for generating random numbers from various distributions | =RISKNORMAL (*mean,stdev*) or =RISKTRIANG (*min,mostlikely,max*), for example | 563–570 |
| Replicating with Excel only | Useful when an add-in such as @RISK is not available | Develop simulation model, use a data table with any blank column input cell to replicate one or more outputs | 583 |
| @RISK | A useful simulation add-in developed by Palisade | @RISK ribbon | 587 |
| RISKSIMTABLE function | Used to run an @RISK simulation model for several values of some variable, often a decision variable | =RISKSIMTABLE (*list*) | 587 |
| RISKOUTPUT function | Used to indicate that a cell contains an output that will be tracked by @RISK | =RISKOUTPUT ("Profit") +Revenue-Cost, for example | 590 |
| RISKCORRMAT function | Used in @RISK to correlate two or more random input variables | =RISKNORMAL (100,10, RISKCORRMAT (*CorrMat,2*)), for example | 610 |

## PROBLEMS

### Skill-Building Problems

**29.** Six months before its annual convention, the American Medical Association must determine how many rooms to reserve. At this time, the AMA can reserve rooms at a cost of $150 per room. The AMA believes the number of doctors attending the convention will be normally distributed with a mean of 5000 and a standard deviation of 1000. If the number of people attending the convention exceeds the number of rooms reserved, extra rooms must be reserved at a cost of $250 per room.

    **a.** Use simulation with @RISK to determine the number of rooms that should be reserved to minimize the expected cost to the AMA. Try possible values from 4100 to 4900 in increments of 100.

    **b.** Redo part **a** for the case where the number attending has a triangular distribution with minimum value 2000, maximum value 7000, and most likely value 5000. Does this change the substantive results from part **a**?

**30.** You have made it to the final round of the show *Let's Make a Deal*. You know that there is a $1 million prize behind either door 1, door 2, or door 3. It is equally likely that the prize is behind any of the three doors. The two doors without a prize have nothing behind

them. You randomly choose door 2. Before you see whether the prize is behind door 2, host Monty Hall opens a door that has no prize behind it. Specifically, suppose that before door 2 is opened, Monty reveals that there is no prize behind door 3. You now have the opportunity to switch and choose door 1. Should you switch? Simulate this situation 1000 times. For each replication use an @RISK function to generate the door that leads to the prize. Then use another @RISK function to generate the door that Monty will open. Assume that Monty plays as follows: Monty knows where the prize is and will open an empty door, but he cannot open door 2. If the prize is really behind door 2, Monty is equally likely to open door 1 or door 3. If the prize is really behind door 1, Monty must open door 3. If the prize is really behind door 3, Monty must open door 1.

**31.** A new edition of a very popular textbook will be published a year from now. The publisher currently has 2000 copies on hand and is deciding whether to do another printing before the new edition comes out. The publisher estimates that demand for the book during the next year is governed by the probability distribution in the file P10_31.xlsx. A production run incurs a fixed cost of $10,000 plus a variable cost of $15 per book printed. Books are sold for $130 per book. Any demand that cannot be met incurs a penalty cost of $20 per book, due to loss of goodwill. Up to 500 of any leftover books can be sold to Barnes and Noble for $35 per book. The publisher is interested in maximizing expected profit. The following print-run sizes are under consideration: 0 (no production run) to 16,000 in increments of 2000. What decision would you recommend? Use simulation with 1000 replications. For your optimal decision, the publisher can be 90% certain that the actual profit associated with remaining sales of the current edition will be between what two values?

32. A hardware company sells a lot of low-cost, high-volume products. For one such product, it is equally likely that annual unit sales will be low or high. If sales are low (60,000), the company can sell the product for $10 per unit. If sales are high (100,000), a competitor will enter and the company will be able to sell the product for only $8 per unit. The variable cost per unit has a 25% chance of being $6, a 50% chance of being $7.50, and a 25% chance of being $9. Annual fixed costs are $30,000.
   a. Use simulation to estimate the company's expected annual profit.
   b. Find a 95% interval for the company's annual profit, that is, an interval such that about 95% of the actual profits are inside it.
   c. Now suppose that annual unit sales, variable cost, and unit price are equal to their respective *expected* values—that is, there is no uncertainty. Determine the company's annual profit for this scenario.
   d. Can you conclude from the results in parts **a** and **c** that the expected profit from a simulation is equal to the profit from the scenario where each input assumes its expected value? Explain.

33. W. L. Brown, a direct marketer of women's clothing, must determine how many telephone operators to schedule during each part of the day. W. L. Brown estimates that the number of phone calls received each hour of a typical eight-hour shift can be described by the probability distribution in the file P10_33.xlsx. Each operator can handle 15 calls per hour and costs the company $20 per hour. Each phone call that is not handled is assumed to cost the company $6 in lost profit. Considering the options of employing 6, 8, 10, 12, 14, or 16 operators, use simulation to determine the number of operators that minimizes the expected hourly cost (labor costs plus lost profits).

34. Assume that all of a company's job applicants must take a test, and that the scores on this test are normally distributed. The *selection ratio* is the cutoff point used by the company in its hiring process. For example, a selection ratio of 20% means that the company will accept applicants for jobs who rank in the top 20% of all applicants. If the company chooses a selection ratio

of 20%, the average test score of those selected will be 1.40 standard deviations above average. Use simulation to verify this fact, proceeding as follows.
   a. Show that if the company wants to accept only the top 20% of all applicants, it should accept applicants whose test scores are at least 0.842 standard deviation above average. (No simulation is required here. Just use the appropriate Excel normal function.)
   b. Now generate 1000 test scores from a normal distribution with mean 0 and standard deviation 1. The average test score of those selected is the average of the scores that are at least 0.842. To determine this, use Excel's DAVERAGE function. To do so, put the heading Score in cell A3, generate the 1000 test scores in the range A4:A1003, and name the range A3:A1003 Data. In cells C3 and C4, enter the *labels* Score and >0.842. (The range C3:C4 is called the *criterion range*.) Then calculate the average of all applicants who will be hired by entering the formula **=DAVERAGE(Data, "Score", C3:C4)** in any cell. This average should be close to the theoretical average, 1.40. This formula works as follows. Excel finds all observations in the Data range that satisfy the criterion described in the range C3:C4 (Score>0.842). Then it averages the values in the Score column (the second argument of DAVERAGE) corresponding to these entries. See online help for more about Excel's database "D" functions.
   c. What information would the company need to determine an optimal selection ratio? How could it determine the optimal selection ratio?

35. Lemington's is trying to determine how many Jean Hudson dresses to order for the spring season. Demand for the dresses is assumed to follow a normal distribution with mean 400 and standard deviation 100. The contract between Jean Hudson and Lemington's works as follows. At the beginning of the season, Lemington's reserves $x$ units of capacity. Lemington's must take delivery for at least $0.8x$ dresses and can, if desired, take delivery on up to $x$ dresses. Each dress sells for $160 and Hudson charges $50 per dress. If Lemington's does not take delivery on all $x$ dresses, it owes Hudson a $5 penalty for each unit of reserved capacity that is unused. For example, if Lemington's orders 450 dresses and demand is for 400 dresses, Lemington's will receive 400 dresses and owe Jean 400($50) + 50($5). How many units of capacity should Lemington's reserve to maximize its expected profit?

36. Dilbert's Department Store is trying to determine how many Hanson T-shirts to order. Currently the shirts are sold for $21, but at later dates the shirts will be offered at a 10% discount, then a 20% discount, then a 40% discount, then a 50% discount, and finally a

60% discount. Demand at the full price of $21 is believed to be normally distributed with mean 1800 and standard deviation 360. Demand at various discounts is assumed to be a multiple of full-price demand. These multiples, for discounts of 10%, 20%, 40%, 50%, and 60% are, respectively, 0.4, 0.7, 1.1, 2, and 50. For example, if full-price demand is 2500, then at a 10% discount customers would be willing to buy 1000 T-shirts. The unit cost of purchasing T-shirts depends on the number of T-shirts ordered, as shown in the file P10_36.xlsx. Use simulation to determine how many T-shirts the company should order. Model the problem so that the company first orders some quantity of T-shirts, then discounts deeper and deeper, as necessary, to sell all of the shirts.

## Skill-Extending Problems

**37.** The annual return on each of four stocks for each of the next five years is assumed to follow a normal distribution, with the mean and standard deviation for each stock, as well as the correlations between stocks, listed in the file P10_37.xlsx. You believe that the stock returns for these stocks in a given year are correlated, according to the correlation matrix given, but you believe the returns in different years are uncorrelated. For example, the returns for stocks 1 and 2 in year 1 have correlation 0.55, but the correlation between the return of stock 1 in year 1 and the return of stock 1 in year 2 is 0, and the correlation between the return of stock 1 in year 1 and the return of stock 2 in year 2 is also 0. The file has the formulas you might expect for this situation in the range C20:G23. You can check how the RISKCORRMAT function has been used in these formulas. Just so that there is an @RISK output cell, calculate the average of all returns in cell B25 and designate it as an @RISK output. (This cell is not really important for the problem, but it is included because @RISK requires at least one output cell.)

   **a.** Using the model exactly as it stands, run @RISK with 1000 iterations. The question is whether the correlations in the simulated data are close to what they should be. To check this, go to @RISK's Report Settings and check the Input Data option before you run the simulation. This gives you all of the simulated returns on a new sheet. Then calculate correlations for all pairs of columns in the resulting Inputs Data Report sheet. (StatTools can be used to create a matrix of all correlations for the simulated data.) Comment on whether the correlations are different from what they should be.

   **b.** Recognizing that this is a common situation (correlation within years, no correlation across years), @RISK allows you to model it by adding

a *third* argument to the RISKCORRMAT function: the year index in row 19 of the P10_37.xlsx file. For example, the RISKCORRMAT part of the formula in cell C20 becomes **=RISKNORMAL ($B$5,$C$5, RISKCORRMAT($B$12:$E$15, $B20,C$19))**. Make this change to the formulas in the range C20:G23, rerun the simulation, and redo the correlation analysis in part **a**. Verify that the correlations between inputs are now more in line with what they should be.

**38.** It is surprising (but true) that if 23 people are in the same room, there is about a 50% chance that at least two people will have the same birthday. Suppose you want to estimate the probability that if 30 people are in the same room, at least two of them will have the same birthday. You can proceed as follows.

   **a.** Generate random birthdays for 30 different people. Ignoring the possibility of a leap year, each person has a 1/365 chance of having a given birthday (label the days of the year 1 to 365). You can use the RANDBETWEEN function to generate birthdays.

   **b.** Once you have generated 30 people's birthdays, how can you tell whether at least two people have the same birthday? One way is to use Excel's RANK function. (You can learn how to use this function in Excel's online help.) This function returns the rank of a number relative to a given group of numbers. In the case of a tie, two numbers are given the same rank. For example, if the set of numbers is 4, 3, 2, 5, the RANK function returns 2, 3, 4, 1. (By default, RANK gives 1 to the *largest* number.) If the set of numbers is 4, 3, 2, 4, the RANK function returns 1, 3, 4, 1.

   **c.** After using the RANK function, you should be able to determine whether at least two of the 30 people have the same birthday. What is the (estimated) probability that this occurs?

**39.** United Electric (UE) sells refrigerators for $400 with a one-year warranty. The warranty works as follows. If any part of the refrigerator fails during the first year after purchase, UE replaces the refrigerator for an average cost of $100. As soon as a replacement is made, another one-year warranty period begins for the customer. If a refrigerator fails outside the warranty period, we assume that the customer immediately purchases another UE refrigerator. Suppose that the amount of time a refrigerator lasts follows a normal distribution with a mean of 1.8 years and a standard deviation of 0.3 year.

   **a.** Estimate the average profit per year UE earns from a customer.

   **b.** How could the approach of this problem be used to determine the optimal warranty period?

**40.** A Flexible Savings Account (FSA) plan allows you to put money into an account at the beginning of the calendar year that can be used for medical expenses. This amount is not subject to federal tax. As you pay medical expenses during the year, you are reimbursed by the administrator of the FSA until the money is exhausted. From that point on, you must pay your medical expenses out of your own pocket. On the other hand, if you put more money into your FSA than the medical expenses you incur, this extra money is lost to you. Your annual salary is $80,000 and your federal income tax rate is 30%.

a. Assume that your medical expenses in a year are normally distributed with mean $2000 and standard deviation $500. Build an @RISK model in which the output is the amount of money left to you after paying taxes, putting money in an FSA, and paying any extra medical expenses. Experiment with the amount of money put in the FSA, using a RISKSIMTABLE function.

b. Rework part a, but this time assume a gamma distribution for your annual medical expenses. Use 16 and 125 as the two parameters of this distribution. These imply the same mean and standard deviation as in part a, but the distribution of medical expenses is now skewed to the right, which is probably more realistic. Using simulation, see whether you should now put more or less money in an FSA than in the symmetric case in part a.

**41.** At the beginning of each week, a machine is in one of four conditions: 1 = excellent; 2 = good; 3 = average; 4 = bad. The weekly revenue earned by a machine in state 1, 2, 3, or 4 is $100, $90, $50, or $10, respectively. After observing the condition of the machine at the beginning of the week, the company has the option, for a cost of $200, of instantaneously replacing the machine with an excellent machine. The quality of the machine deteriorates over time, as shown in the file P10_41.xlsx. Four maintenance policies are under consideration:

- Policy 1: Never replace a machine.
- Policy 2: Immediately replace a bad machine.
- Policy 3: Immediately replace a bad or average machine.
- Policy 4: Immediately replace a bad, average, or good machine.

Simulate each of these policies for 50 weeks (using at least 250 iterations each) to determine the policy that maximizes expected weekly profit. Assume that the machine at the beginning of week 1 is excellent.

**42.** Simulation can be used to illustrate a number of results from statistics that are difficult to understand with nonsimulation arguments. One is the famous *central limit theorem*, which says that if you sample enough values from *any* population distribution and then average these values, the resulting average will be approximately normally distributed. Confirm this by using @RISK with the following population distributions (run a separate simulation for each): (a) discrete with possible values 1 and 2 and probabilities 0.2 and 0.8; (b) exponential with mean 1 (use the RISKEXPON function with the single argument 1); (c) triangular with minimum, most likely, and maximum values equal to 1, 9, and 10. (Note that each of these distributions is very skewed.) Run each simulation with 10 values in each average, and run 1000 iterations to simulate 1000 averages. Create a histogram of the averages to see whether it is indeed bell-shaped. Then repeat, using 30 values in each average. Are the histograms based on 10 values qualitatively different from those based on 30?

**43.** In statistics we often use observed data to test a hypothesis about a population or populations. The basic method uses the observed data to calculate a test statistic (a single number). If the magnitude of this test statistic is sufficiently large, the null hypothesis is rejected in favor of the research hypothesis. As an example, consider a researcher who believes teenage girls sleep longer than teenage boys on average. She collects observations on $n = 40$ randomly selected girls and $n = 40$ randomly selected boys. (Each observation is the average sleep time over several nights for a given person.) The averages are $\overline{X}_1 = 7.9$ hours for the girls and $\overline{X}_2 = 7.6$ hours for the boys. The standard deviation of the 40 observations for girls is $s_1 = 0.5$ hour; for the boys it is $s_2 = 0.7$ hour. The researcher, consulting a statistics textbook, then calculates the test statistic

$$\frac{\overline{X}_1 - \overline{X}_2}{\sqrt{s_1^2/40 + s_2^2/40}} = \frac{7.9 - 7.6}{\sqrt{0.25/40 + 0.49/40}} = 2.206$$

Based on the fact that 2.206 is "large," she claims that her research hypothesis is confirmed—girls do sleep longer than boys.

You are skeptical of this claim, so you check it out by running a simulation. In your simulation you assume that girls and boys have the *same* mean and standard deviation of sleep times in the entire population, say, 7.7 and 0.6. You also assume that the distribution of sleep times is normal. Then you repeatedly simulate observations of 40 girls and 40 boys from this distribution and calculate the test statistic. The question is whether the observed test statistic, 2.206, is "extreme." If it is larger than most or all of the test statistics you simulate, then the researcher is justified in her claim; otherwise, this large a statistic could have happened easily by chance, even if the girls and boys have identical population means. Use @RISK to see which of these possibilities occurs.

**44.** A technical note in the discussion of @RISK indicated that Latin Hypercube sampling is more efficient than Monte Carlo sampling. This problem allows you to see what this means. The file P10_44.xlsx gets you started. There is a single output cell, B5. You can enter any random value in this cell, such as **RISKNORMAL(500,100)**. There are already @RISK statistical formulas in rows 9–12 to calculate summary measures of the output for each of 10 simulations. On the @RISK ribbon, click on the button to the left of the "dice" button to bring up the Simulation Settings dialog box, click on the Sampling tab, and make sure the Sampling Type is Latin Hypercube. Run 10 simulations with at least 1000 iterations each, and then paste the results in rows 9–12 as *values* in rows 17–20. Next, get back in Simulations Settings and change the Sampling Type to Monte Carlo, run the 10 simulations again, and paste the results in rows 9–12 as values into rows 23–26. For each row, 17–20 and 23–26, summarize the 10 numbers in that row with AVERAGE and STDEV. What do you find? Why do we say that Latin Hypercube sampling is more efficient? (Thanks to Harvey Wagner at University of North Carolina for suggesting this problem.)

45. We are continually hearing reports on the nightly news about natural disasters—droughts in Texas, hurricanes in Florida, floods in California, and so on. We often hear that one of these was the "worst in over 30 years," or some such statement. Are natural disasters getting worse these days, or does it just appear so? How might you use simulation to answer this question? Here is one possible approach. Imagine that there are *N* areas of the country (or the world) that tend to have, to some extent, various types of weather phenomena each year. For example, hurricanes are always a potential problem for Florida, and fires are always a potential problem in southern California. You might model the severity of the problem for any area in any year by a normally distributed random number with mean 0 and standard deviation 1, where negative values are interpreted as good years and positive values are interpreted as bad years. (We suggest the normal distribution, but there is no reason other distributions couldn't be used instead.) Then you could simulate such values for all areas over a period of several years and keep track, say, of whether any of the areas have worse conditions in the current year than they have had in the past several years, where "several" could be 10, 20, 30, or any other number of years you want to test. What might you keep track of? How might you interpret your results?

## Modeling Problems

46. You are making several runs of a simulation model, each with a different value of some decision variable (such as the order quantity in the Walton calendar model), to see which decision value achieves the largest mean profit. Is it possible that one value beats another simply by random luck? What can you do to minimize the chance of a "better" value losing out to a "poorer" value?

47. If you want to replicate the results of a simulation model with Excel functions only, not @RISK, you can build a data table and let the column input cell be any blank cell. Explain why this works.

48. Suppose you simulate a gambling situation where you place many bets. On each bet, the distribution of your net winnings (loss if negative) is highly skewed to the left because there are some possibilities of really large losses but not much upside potential. Your only simulation output is the *average* of the results of all the bets. If you run @RISK with many iterations and look at the resulting histogram of this output, what will it look like? Why?

49. You plan to simulate a portfolio of investments over a multiyear period, so for each investment (which could be a particular stock or bond, for example), you need to simulate the change in its value for each of the years. How would you simulate these changes in a realistic way? Would you base it on historical data? What about correlations? Do you think the changes for different investments in a particular year would be correlated? Do you think changes for a particular investment in different years would be correlated? Do you think correlations would play a significant role in your simulation in terms of realism?

50. Big Hit Video must determine how many copies of a new video to purchase. Assume that the company's goal is to purchase a number of copies that maximizes its expected profit from the video during the next year. Describe how you would use simulation to shed light on this problem. Assume that each time a video is rented, it is rented for one day.

51. Many people who are involved in a small auto accident do not file a claim because they are afraid their insurance premiums will be raised. Suppose that City Farm Insurance has three rates. If you file a claim, you are moved to the next higher rate. How might you use simulation to determine whether a particular claim should be filed?

52. A building contains 1000 lightbulbs. Each bulb lasts at most five months. The company maintaining the building is trying to decide whether it is worthwhile to practice a "group replacement" policy. Under a group replacement policy, all bulbs are replaced every *T* months (where *T* is to be determined). Also, bulbs are replaced when they burn out. Assume that it costs $0.05 to replace each bulb during a group replacement and $0.20 to replace each burned-out bulb if it is replaced individually. How would you use simulation to determine whether a group replacement policy is worthwhile?

53. Why is the RISKCORRMAT function necessary? How does @RISK generate random inputs by default, that is, when RISKCORRMAT is not used?

54. Consider the claim that normally distributed inputs in a simulation model are bound to lead to normally distributed outputs. Do you agree or disagree with this claim? Defend your answer.

55. It is very possible that when you use a correlation matrix as input to the RISKCORRMAT function in an @RISK model, the program will inform you that this is an invalid correlation matrix. Provide an example of an obviously invalid correlation matrix involving at least three variables, and explain why it is invalid.

56. When you use a RISKSIMTABLE function for a decision variable, such as the order quantity in the Walton model, explain how this provides a "fair" comparison across the different values tested.

57. Consider a situation where there is a cost that is either incurred or not. It is incurred only if the value of some random input is less than a specified cutoff value. Why might a simulation of this situation give a very different average value of the cost incurred than a deterministic model that treats the random input as *fixed* at its mean? What does this have to do with the "flaw of averages"?

Egress, Inc., is a small company that designs, produces, and sells ski jackets and other coats. The creative design team has labored for weeks over its new design for the coming winter season. It is now time to decide how many ski jackets to produce in this production run. Because of the lead times involved, no other production runs will be possible during the season. Predicting ski jacket sales months in advance of the selling season can be quite tricky. Egress has been in operation for only three years, and its ski jacket designs were quite successful in two of those years. Based on realized sales from the last three years, current economic conditions, and professional judgment, 12 Egress employees have independently estimated demand for their new design for the upcoming season. Their estimates are listed in Table 10.2.

### Table 10.2  Estimated Demands

| | |
|--------|--------|
| 14,000 | 16,000 |
| 13,000 |  8000 |
| 14,000 |  5000 |
| 14,000 | 11,000 |
| 15,500 |  8000 |
| 10,500 | 15,000 |

To assist in the decision on the number of units for the production run, management has gathered the data in Table 10.3. Note that S is the price Egress charges retailers. Any ski jackets that do not sell during the season can be sold by Egress to discounters for V per jacket. The fixed cost of plant and

### Table 10.3  Monetary Values

| | |
|---|---|
| Variable production cost per unit ($C$): | $80 |
| Selling price per unit ($S$): | $100 |
| Salvage value per unit ($V$): | $30 |
| Fixed production cost ($F$): | $100,000 |

equipment is $F$. This cost is incurred regardless of the size of the production run.

### Questions

1. Egress management believes that a normal distribution is a reasonable model for the unknown demand in the coming year. What mean and standard deviation should Egress use for the demand distribution?

2. Use a spreadsheet model to simulate 1000 possible outcomes for demand in the coming year. Based on these scenarios, what is the expected profit if Egress produces $Q = 7800$ ski jackets? What is the expected profit if Egress produces $Q = 12,000$ ski jackets? What is the standard deviation of profit in these two cases?

3. Based on the same 1000 scenarios, how many ski jackets should Egress produce to maximize expected profit? Call this quantity $Q$.

4. Should $Q$ equal mean demand or not? Explain.

5. Create a histogram of profit at the production level $Q$. Create a histogram of profit when the production level $Q$ equals mean demand. What is the probability of a loss greater than $100,000 in each case? ▪

Management of Ebony, a leading manufacturer of bath soap, is trying to control its inventory costs. The weekly cost of holding one unit of soap in inventory is $30 (one unit is 1000 cases of soap). The marketing department estimates that weekly demand averages 120 units, with a standard deviation of 15 units, and is reasonably well modeled by a normal distribution. If demand exceeds the amount of soap on hand, those sales are *lost*—that is, there is no backlogging of demand. The production department can produce at one of three levels: 110, 120, or 130 units per week. The cost of changing the production level from one week to the next is $3000.

Management would like to evaluate the following production policy. If the current inventory is less than $L = 30$ units, they will produce 130 units in the next week. If the current inventory is greater than $U = 80$ units, they will produce 110 units in the next week. Otherwise, Ebony will continue at the previous week's production level.

Ebony currently has 60 units of inventory on hand. Last week's production level was 120.

## Questions

1. Develop a simulation model for 52 weeks of operation at Ebony. Graph the inventory of soap over time. What is the total cost (inventory cost plus production change cost) for the 52 weeks?

2. Run the simulation for 500 iterations to estimate the average 52-week cost with values of $U$ ranging from 30 to 80 in increments of 10. Keep $L = 30$ throughout.

3. Report the sample mean and standard deviation of the 52-week cost under each policy. Using the simulated results, is it possible to construct *valid* 95% confidence intervals for the average 52-week cost for each value of $U$? In any case, graph the average 52-week cost versus $U$. What is the best value of $U$ for $L = 30$?

4. What other production policies might be useful to investigate? ▪